NOTES
FROM THE
BURNING
AGE

NOTES
FROM THE
BURNING
AGE

CLAIRE NORTH

orbit

orbitbooks.net

ORBIT

First published in Great Britain in 2021 by Orbit

1 3 5 7 9 10 8 6 4 2

Copyright © 2021 by Claire North

The moral right of the author has been asserted.

A CIP catalogue record for this book
is available from the British Library.

HB ISBN 978-0-356-51475-8
C format 978-0-356-51474-1

Typeset in Bembo by M Rules
Printed and bound in Great Britain by
Clays Ltd, Elcograf S.p.A

Papers used by Orbit are from well-managed forests
and other responsible sources.

Orbit
An imprint of
Little, Brown Book Group
Carmelite House
50 Victoria Embankment
London EC4Y 0DZ

An Hachette UK Company
www.hachette.co.uk

www.orbitbooks.net

For Zara

Chapter 1

Yue was twelve when she saw the kakuy of the forest, but later she lied and said she saw only flame.

"Keep an eye on Vae!" hollered her aunty from her workshop door. "Are you listening to me?"

It was the long, hot summer when children paddled barefoot in the river through the centre of Tinics, a time for chasing butterflies and sleeping beneath the stars. School was out, and every class had found the thing that was demonstrably the best, most impressive thing to do. For the tenth grades about to take their aptitudes, it was cycling down the path from the wind farm head first, until they either lost their courage or their bikes flipped and they cartwheeled with bloody knees and grazed elbows. For the seventh, it was preparing their kites for the fighting season; the ninth were learning how to kiss in the hidden grove behind the compression batteries, and to survive the first heartbreak of a sixty-second romance betrayed.

Yue should have been sitting on grassy roofs with her class, making important pronouncements about grown-up things, now that she was twelve and thus basically a philosopher-queen. Instead, on that day, she was tucked beneath the spider tree reading on her inkstone. She had made it at school out of parts pulled from the recycling tubs, painted it orange and doodled relentlessly on the back. It was slower than most and struggled to do much more than plain text, but she refused to use any other. Sometimes she pretended that the stories she read on it were tracts on meaningful matters that younger children could not possibly comprehend, but mostly she read apocalyptic adventures, tales of teenagers who conquered all through grit, inventive use of grappling hooks and the power of love.

In a world on fire, Kendra and Winn must journey across the bitter European desert to find the last fresh water for their tribe . . .

. . . but all is not as it seems . . .

. . . only friendship can save them!

When we recount the stories of ourselves, we gloss over the acne and hormonal angst, the sloppy first steps into sexuality, the wild pouts and pompous self-declarations. Yue was coming into all these things, but that day even puberty could not disperse the universal cheer brought by sun and wind through velvet leaves.

Aunty Ram, however, could.

"Don't let Vae climb the kakuy tree! And be back in time for supper!"

Like a sleepy lion roused by the cackling of hyenas, Yue lifted her eyes from the inkstone in her lap to behold the sight of her displeasure – her sister. Three years younger, and therefore, in childhood terms, a squalling babe to Yue's majestic maturity, Vae was the perfect age for her wild enthusiasm to charm a naive stranger and infuriate anyone who knew her for more than fifteen minutes. Though they shared the same blue-black hair, squished nose and thumb-pinched chin, the same peanut skin and disturbingly triple-jointed thumbs, they had taken upon themselves the respective roles of older and younger sister with varying glee and earnestness. Whether her hearth-kin had intended to spend so much time congratulating Yue on how mature she was, I do not know. Whether they had meant to encourage Vae's giddy disobedience, I'm not sure either, for I was merely a guest. But the outcome was predictable – a reserved older child who felt constantly underappreciated, and a younger who cried petulantly whenever she was not indulged.

Did they love each other?

Of course they did.

But learning what that truly means would take time, and

though that summer felt as broad as the sky, time was running away like leaves in the river.

"And don't let her eat all the apples!"

Vae already stood in the little wooden gate, hopping from one foot to the other, ready to run. She wore beige shorts that hung a little lower than the knees, hand-me-downs from Yue handed down a little too soon, and her favourite t-shirt, faded green with pale blue zig-zags around the sleeves. She had stuffed her pockets with apples and tied her hair so loosely it was already starting to fall around her ears. What was worse, she had brought a friend – a boy, only a few months older than she, in russet shorts and a plain grey shirt, who shuffled and swayed, uneasy in the porch, as confused by Vae's energy as the snail by the swift.

The boy's name was Ven.

He was me, though I struggle now to remember ever being anything other than an observer to childhood, rather than a participant.

From the soft grass beneath the tree, Yue eyed her sister and myself, imparting, I felt, a clear declaration in her gaze that if we so much as sneezed out of place she would snitch to the first adult we saw, and that should Vae make herself sick gorging on fruit or spinning so fast she became herself dizzy, it was no one's problem but her own. I understood this; Vae was studied in the art of selective ignorance.

"Come on, Yue, we'll miss everything!" Vae shrilled, though quite what "everything" was, no one could fathom. Then she was running up the rubber road towards the server office on the corner, swinging past the egg-like kakuy stone that guarded the forest path without so much as a bow to its guardian form, and shrilling up the muddy track towards the ridge above. I followed, checking over my shoulder to see that our escort was coming, and reluctantly, at last, with studied slowness, Yue folded her inkstone down, slipped it into her pocket, shuffled bare feet into brown sandals and followed at a determinedly sluggish pace.

Yue's hearth was near the top of the hill, with a view down

the zig-zag street to the town below. The cables that ran to the server office came straight in across the valley, draped like a giant's clothes line above the river, too high for vines to tangle but the perfect height for flocks of fat wood pigeons and white-headed crows to congregate at dawn and dusk. When the wind blew right, the sound of running water and bicycle bells swept up the slopes into the forest above, along with every argument, shriek of laughter, out-of-tune melody and yap of barking dog. On second and fifth days, the electric truck came with supplies for the general store; on first, fourth and sixth, the postman came with packages and datasticks loaded with the latest books, newspapers, articles, magazines, animations and games, deposited at the server office to the delight of every bored child in winter. In the bathhouse at the upstream end of town, people gossiped about the price of resin, the quality of the newest strains of myce-lium, the latest soap opera downloaded to inkstone and what the neighbours said. Always what the neighbours said. Tinics was too small a town for any drama except our own.

Our temple straddled the river, raised up above a little water-fall of hollowed pools and smoothly etched rocks. Away from the spinning of the wind farms and the tick-tick-tick of the town's compression batteries, the priests offered up incense to the kakuy of wind and water, the living heart of the mountain and the blessed voices of the trees. They also frequently bored the children by talking about truth, love, harmony and awe, and occasionally delighted them by talking about fire, tornado, famine and fury – all the good stuff we actually wanted to hear.

The kakuy had blessed us, the Medj of the temple intoned. In autumn, the west wind powered inkstone, stove and bulb, and in spring the ice melted and the river flowed strong enough to keep the sewage plant pumping and the biowells bubbling. Life was a circle, in which all things served each other. The people of Tinics took this to heart, and the path through the forest to the wind farm was guarded by stone lanterns lit by bowing devotees with muttered thanks to the kakuy of leaf and soil for sheltering us within their bounds.

Up this same pebble-pocked track Vae now bounded, followed by myself and, behind, Yue. Vae had no time for ritual ablations before sacred stone or carved sign, for there was a destination she had to reach immediately, urgently, just in case the whole universe were to shift and dissolve in this instant, taking it away from her.

"Come on!" she hollered at her trailing entourage. "Come *on*!"

At the top of the carefully cut steps through the trees, the path forked, right to the batteries gently cranking up to capacity as the wind and sun charged them for the night, and left down a narrower, goat-cut wiggle through ever thicker shadow into the forest.

"Vae, you . . . " Yue began to gasp, but all too late, for down the narrower path her sister plunged without pause. Oak and pine, spruce and beech, the smell of wet, fresh bark in spring, hot sap seeping in summer, and mulching scarlet in autumn. In some places you could swing from the soft silver trunk of the alder as if you were dancing between prayer-wheels at the temple; in others the poplar had bent to create the perfect ladder to the sky. But Vae was interested in none of these – not when the best tree in the forest was waiting just down the path.

I followed as the way curled tight round the strict black stone of the hill, caught my grip on flaking branches that protruded from the rock itself, life jutting out to catch the afternoon sunlight drifting through the leaves. Streams trickled and danced below, heading for the river that fed the town, while above twigs brushed and chattered against each other in the breeze. Soon even the hissing of the batteries and the wind farm had faded, and though I knew Tinics was just a few hundred metres away, any stranger walking through the wood would have been astonished to stumble on humanity hidden behind so much green. The path faded to almost nothing, but this didn't stop Vae, who started scrambling up a fern-crowned slope of iron-flecked stone and daffodil lichen, moving like a spider, limb pushing limb.

"Heaven and earth, Vae!" Yue fumed, but Vae pretended she couldn't hear, because if she could hear she would have to admit that she was being naughty. Better by far to have missed her sister's complaints and apologise later, one foot twisting coyly in the dirt, hands behind her back, chin down, eyes up, a puppy in a muddy skirt.

Crows were cawing above, the busy, bickering racket that they usually reserved for evening squabbles, and for a moment I wondered if the hour was later than I thought and sunset was coming, and realised I'd come without a torch; but glancing at the watch on my wrist I saw it was far too early in the day for the crows to be complaining. Perhaps they too were disturbed by Vae's squealing delight and now bickered to make their displeasure known.

At the top of the highest ridge of the tallest hill, Vae finally stopped before the best tree in the wood. The kakuy tree was a hornbeam, older, the priests said, than even the great burning. As the old countries perished when the seas rose and the desert grew, as the peoples of the world mingled and fought for fresh water and fertile land, the hornbeam had grown, spinning towards the sun above and soil below, its roots entangling with its neighbour like children holding hands. Where humans walked, each tree seemed a separate, swaying thing; but below the forest their roots were one, perfect symbiosis. Truly a great spirit lived in the hornbeam, the people said, a mighty kakuy, so at its base they left their offerings and prayers, and every night before lighting the stone lanterns the Medj of the temple would come to give thanks to leaf and branch.

Vae had no interest in such things, though she was at least well trained enough to sprint round the four-metre girth of the trunk and bow once before the mossy base. Then, like the gleeful heretic she was, she was climbing, scurrying up, one foot in the first V-split of the trunk, a hand swinging for a snowy-lichen-crowned branch, off which she briefly dangled like a monkey.

Yue sighed and tutted, but was far too mature to argue with infants. Instead she circled the tree once, fingers brushing the valleys and peaks of moss-softened bark, bowed, pulled her ink-stone from her pocket and settled in against the base of the nearest non-theological tree to read. Above, Vae had already made it into the spluttering crown of the low trunk, where dozens of thick branches shot up like the frightened hair of a porcupine, and was bracing her feet for another push higher.

I performed my prayers without thinking, distracted, then picked around the base of the tree to see what offerings had been left here by priest and wanderer. The Temple liked to keep things neat, even in the heart of coiling nature, and someone had ordered the items around the trunk to create a pleasing palette of old and new, large and small. Here, a few links of ancient bicycle chain were welded into a bracelet, carefully framing a bunch of wilted lilac flowers. Next to that, the classical offering of grain, fading and spiky on the stem. A flask of home-brewed wine pressed in blood-red clay, probably toxic if more than sipped; a collection of the blackest stones pulled from the river bed; some shards of chitin scraped from the bottom of the resin well; and a little woven hat in blue, spun from the same bio-engineered silk that Mama Taaq grew on her spider tree. I circled the hornbeam, wondered if I should leave an offering and what I might ask for in return, when a glimmer of metal caught my eye. It was a tiny thing that I could pinch between thumb and forefinger like the wing of a butterfly. Someone had polished it up, the track marks of their effort still glistening in oily white. Any ink or pigments on the surface had long since flaked away, but characters were still visible, embossed by a great machine a long time ago. I recognised an archaic script, long since fallen out of use, but taught tediously in school by Uncle Mue through songs and games. Much of the lettering was unreadable, flattened by whatever force had carved out this tiny piece of history and offered it up to the forest gods. A few words I could just about read, picking them out from months of study. I mouthed them silently to myself as I shaped the syllables, dancing over some of the stranger shapes until I had the sound: *Product of China.*

Then Vae called out: "Are you coming?" and she was already halfway to the sky, dangling over a branch with one leg swinging back and forth under its own weight for the mere joy of feeling like she might fall. I returned my shard carefully to the bed of moss where I had found it, gave an awkward, quick half-bow to the tree, then started to climb. I was slower than Vae, but confident. The forest was my home, and my hearth did not teach its children how to dread the world that nourished us. Halfway up, I paused, drooping over a branch, stomach pressed to timber and arms flopping free.

"If you scratch your knees, Mama will be so angry," warned Yue from below, not looking up from her reading.

Vae stuck her tongue out; familiar with the habit, Yue returned the expression, still not lifting her gaze, above and below all such things.

"Yue's boring," Vae hissed. She was disappointed to realise that even in her most dramatic voice her elder sister either hadn't heard her or didn't care. With a haughty twist of her chin skywards, she turned away from the argument that she had most clearly won and resumed climbing. I paused a moment below her as a red-bellied beetle head-butted my curled hand, considered this obstruction to its journey, then climbed onto my skin and resumed its ambling, king of the world.

If you listen for the legs of a beetle over a child's skin, you will not hear it. But listen – now listen. And as well as hearing nothing from my crimson friend, I heard a greater nothing too. The crows had fallen silent. So had the songbirds and white-bellied thrushes, the leg-scratching insects and the little cooing creatures of the underbrush. Only the sound of Vae calling, "Ven! Higher!" broke through the hissing of the leaves.

The beetle reached the other end of my hand and wobbled for a moment on the edge, surprised, it seemed, by a steepness which on the way up had caused it no difficulty.

Now listen.

Listen.

Close your eyes and listen.

Leaf on leaf is the brush of something leathery, dry, living and dying. Below, Yue reads, one finger tapping against her elbow as she cradles the inkstone in her arms, eyes tracking across the words on its screen.

Listen.

And here it is. The crackling snap-snap-snap through the forest. Gases, popping apart, breaking something solid into pieces. A groaning of fibres under pressure and then giving way in a single tear, gushing out smoke and steam. The slow grinding creak of the oldest, weakest trunks finally giving way, the smack as they slash into a neighbour while they fall, the sudden updraught of ash and spark into the sky as the impact throws more flames out, caught in the wind.

The beetle, which had been searching for a way down and found none, reared up, opened a pair of bloody wings and buzzed away, bouncing under its own ungainly airborne weight.

And here it is, the tickle at the end of your nose, the taste of it on the tip of your tongue, the taste of black, a stinging in your eyes, and I realised what it was just as Vae shrilled: "Fire!"

The great forest was burning.

Vae was already halfway down the tree before I started moving, not a child any more but a creature entirely of the wood, of speed and limb slithering from foot to hand to foot. I tried to peer through the leaves, to see how close or how far it was, but Yue was on her feet shouting, gesturing furiously at us to get down, and how quickly the world changed! The sunlight, which had been pools of gold and silver pushing through the trees, was now a million broken shafts in the air, given form and dimensionality by the smoke drifting in with the wind. The noise of flame, which began in bits and pieces, was already an all-consuming roar, a sucking in of wind and an exhalation of fire that left no room to pick out the details of trees falling and earth turning to soot.

I reached the ground a few moments after Vae and immediately regretted it, the smoke now tumbling in thick and black, biting my eyes and prickling my throat. Yue pulled her shirt up across her face, and we copied her, scrambling, blinking, tears running down our cheeks, towards the path. Now I could look back, and see the orange glow beginning to drown out the day, and look below, and see it there too, pushing along the banks of the stream beneath the waterfall, moving so fast, like deer before the wolf.

"Stay close to me," Yue commanded, and for almost the first time since Vae was old enough to say "sister", she nodded and obeyed.

The path down, so easy to climb, familiar to us, was now slow, agonising anguish, every step unsteady, every breath a minute's tick on a spinning clock. Vae slipped and got back up without complaint; Yue grunted as her footing gave way and she caught herself on a root, her face curled in a snarl as if to dare the forest to betray her one more time, and she kept on going. I tumbled after them, on my bum as often as my feet, nettles prickling my fingers and stabbing through my shorts, until we reached the path above the river. Here the smoke was a broiling fog, and I blinked and could barely keep my eyes open, put my hands over my face to try and block it out, peered through splayed fingers and could hardly see a foot ahead of me. The noise of the fire was deafening, and I could feel its heat at my back, moving so fast, a warmth that began as the pleasant glow of the stove on an autumn day and now rose and blistered into a relentless, inescapable grapple that squeezed the life from my skin and the breath from my lungs. I called out for Vae, and thought I heard her answer; called out for Yue and couldn't see her, began to panic, then felt a hand catch mine and pull me along.

I don't know when we got turned around, when we lost our footing. I heard the compression batteries explode on the ridge overhead, a thunder as the overheated gas inside finally ruptured the buried tanks to shower what little of the forest wasn't blazing with mud and torn fibre and metal.

We briefly outran the flames into a little gully, a bowl of untouched elder thorns and purple flowers into which the smoke hadn't seeped. Then we crouched low, our faces crimson smeared with ash, and knew that we were lost. Vae started to cry, silently, and I knew I was mere moments behind, when Yue shook her head and hissed, "Down!"

10

I thought she meant down deeper into this gully, perhaps burying ourselves in soil and hoping the fire would pass by, but she rose to her feet and instead followed the land down, no path, no easy route, just swinging from tree to tree like a drunken squirrel, propelled by her own headlong momentum towards the bottom of the valley. If we had done this dance by daylight, it would have been ridiculously dangerous; by the light of the fire it felt entirely natural, and we flung ourselves after her, tripping on our own feet and tumbling for the darkness below.

I didn't hear the river over the fire, which now domed above us. Looking up for the first time, I could see actual flames withering the edges of the leaves on the trees in orange worms, spitting and spilling up the branches in fluorescent crimson. Then my feet hit water and sank almost immediately into the grit below. I caught myself for a second, lost my balance, fell onto my hands and knees and crawled after Yue, who was already knee-deep and wading deeper. I followed, catching at rocks and feet slipping, banging on stone as I slithered into the stream. The current caught sudden and hard a little before halfway, flowing freely round grey mottled boulders that had obscured its path. It pushed me to the side, and I pushed back, submerged my face briefly to wash away the burning around my eyes, looked up and for a second through the smoke saw Yue, now up to her waist, reaching out for Vae to my left and behind me. I was half-walking, half-swimming, arms flapping against the current as my feet buckled and slipped on stone, coughing black spit with every breath, ducking my head below as long as I dared only to surface and cough some more in the toxic blackness that raged through the valley. All around was ablaze, too bright to look at, my hair starting to curl from the heat of it pressing down against the river. When I was shoulder-deep, I turned my whole body against the current like a kite against the wind, straining as it tried to snatch me away. I reached for Yue, hoping to steady myself on her, and for an instant our fingers caught before the weight of water pushed us apart. Then she looked past me and her eyes went wide.

11

And there, on the edge of the water, was the kakuy of the forest.

I had seen in temple many different depictions of the kakuy who guarded this valley. In some he was a great wolf; in others a woman shrouded in a cloak of leaves. In some she was a great crow, the same size as the tree he perched on. In others they were little more than an oval stone, with one eye open as if to say, "Who disturbs my rest?" The Medj, when questioned about the true form of the kakuy, always shrugged and said: "How do you describe the colour green, or the taste of water?" The Medj have always had a good line in saying very little the nicest way.

The day the forest burned, he was eight feet tall, with a white belly of warm, wet fur and a back of crimson feathers that billowed and moulted from him as he bent towards the river's edge. His eyes were the yellow of the eagle, his snout was a ginger fox, his teeth were sharp, the claws on his hands and feet were black and curled. He rose up on two legs like a bucking horse, then fell down onto all fours and raised his huge head above a flabby neck as if he would howl at the flames; perhaps he did, but I could not hear him.

At his movement, the whole forest seemed to shudder and shake, and for the briefest moment the flames spun backwards as if the wind would change. The kakuy raised his head and howled again, and I felt the river turn icy cold where it held me and a roar of water surge momentarily higher than my head, pushing me under in breathless thunder before I gasped and thrust upwards and surfaced again.

The kakuy looked at us and seemed to see us for the very first time, and though I know very little of gods and the great spirits of the earth that holds us, I thought I saw in his eyes a sadness deeper than any I had ever known.

Then he too caught ablaze. First a feather, then a tuft of fur. He didn't move, didn't lurch into the water, but his mouth opened and closed as if he were screaming. His eyes rolled huge in his skull, and he spat and foamed and rippled from his hind legs to the tip of his nose as if about to vomit up black smoke from the

12

internal fire of his roasting organs. Like the crisp edge of an autumn leaf, he curled in on himself as the fire boiled from his toes to his top, front legs buckling first, then rear, snout hitting the ground last as he flopped down to his belly, then rolled to his side, black tongue out and lolling, lungs heaving and panting with burning breath until, at last, his eyes settled again on us. They stayed wide as the kakuy died.

Temple histories are judiciously vague as to which came first. Were the kakuy earth's punishment for man's disobedience? Did they wake when the sky rained acid and the forests were blasted pits, to punish humanity for its arrogance, to wipe away the men who had sullied this world? Or did the kakuy wake as the world burned by man's own design, to heal and salve what little remained, rolling back the desert and the salty sea? Ambiguity is often an ally to theology, as Old Lah would say.

I saw the kakuy fall, and when his blackened face hit the ground the whole forest groaned. Even through the fire and the burning, I heard it; the deep-timbered roaring of the trees bending against their roots, the cracking of stone and the rattling of the white-scarred branches, an earthquake that made the fire itself twist and recoil as if in shame at what it had done. Or perhaps I didn't. Perhaps in the delirium of heat and smoke and fear, I imagined it all.

I saw the kakuy fall, and when the last breath left his lungs, the wind whipped across the water as if blasted from the hurricane, and the river lurched and buckled as though the spirits of the deep were wailing for the death of their beloved kin, and I screamed and held Yue's hand tight, and she held mine and we slipped and slid together backwards against the turning of the current.

I saw the kakuy fall, and in that moment my flailing left hand caught another's. Vae's fingers brushed the palm of my hand, scrambling like the dancing feet of the spider for purchase. I snatched after her, caught her wrist, don't let go, don't let go, but the river was stronger than a child's grasp. Her fingers slipped a little further down my hand.

Her fingers have always been slipping down my hand.

13

Caught, in a final hook, joint-to-joint.

Don't let go, I begged, or maybe she did, it was hard to tell.

Then the river snatched her away.

I saw her go under, feet tipping up as her head fell back. I did not see her hands claw at the burning air. I did not hear her scream. I did not see her rise again to breathe, as the great forest burned.

Chapter 2

This is the history of the Burning Age, as taught by Temple scripture.

There came a time when humankind had dominion over all the earth. With their might, they tore down the mountains and built cities there. With their wisdom, they conquered the seas and skies. Great medicine there was in abundance, and even their gods called humanity special, the chosen creature raised up above all things. For their children, they laboured, to make a better world, and that world would be of man's making.

Yet their children did not give thanks for the labours of their elders, and lo: the skies turned yellow, the air too dark to breathe from the workings of their industry. The cracked earth bled poisons. The sea rose and salted the land, and no wall of man could restrain it. In winter, the ice melted; in summer, the world burned.

"What shall we do?" asked the wisest of the burning ones, but: "Mankind is stronger than mother earth and father sky," was the answer, "and we do not flinch before the fire."

And so the forests were felled and the rain burned the flesh of babes and the rivers ran with lead, and still mankind did not turn from its course, not even when the deserts consumed the fertile plains and the children themselves cried out for change.

"We are stronger than the storm," railed the greatest of the burning ones. "Weakness is the child's error."

It was about the time of the great migrations, when all the nations began to splinter like the burning bough and the wars of water and grain came upon the lands, that the kakuy woke. First they rose from the skeletons of the ocean reefs, glistening bone and acid breath. Then they climbed from the shattered mines, and their eyes were embers of coal and their feet broke the towns beneath their feet. Then they came from the sky itself, upon thunder and lightning they blazed, tearing down the monuments of man and bidding the earth swallow whole the sacrileges of the Burning Age.

The arrogant tried to fight back, as if their weapons were not forged of the same earth which now they sought to harm. They perished beneath the kakuy as the mouse in the eagle's claws. Those who survived fled to the last of the forests and the sacred hidden places, their thousand tongues blending into new language, their ancient ways changing as does the scudding sky.

From their prayers, Temple was born. The scattered people raised their hands to the falling rain and said: "No more will we confront sky and earth as enemy; henceforth, we shall give thanks to she that carries us. The sun will rise and the sun will set, and we will walk within this changing life as creatures of this world, born within her womb."

And at last, hearing their prayers, the kakuy turned their wrathful eyes from the remnants of humanity and left the tribes in peace. Where the great spirits walked, the land grew anew; where they laid their heads, fresh springs rose from the barren mountain. And as the forests grew, so in time the peoples of the world grew again, venturing forth as once their ancestors had, to carve a new world from the ashes of the old. We spread across the land and gave thanks for the harvest and the kakuy, who, their work complete, returned to the hidden places of this world to rest once more between sky and earth.

Let not your hands fell the tree but that another is planted.

Let not your ears hear the rain and think it falls for you.

Let not your tongue speak of conquering the mountain, for it will not shiver when winter comes.

And if your eyes should see the kakuy slumbering in their sacred caves, gentle in rest, remember to bow in prayer, for should they wake again, no tears shall douse the flames.

This is the teaching of the Temple on the history of the Burning Age. In deference to the scholars and priests who penned it, most of its lies stem from ignorance and omission, and the rest are at least well-intentioned, all things considered.

Chapter 3

After a great fire, rain.

Water evaporates, the heat pushing it higher and higher until suddenly it is too high, condensing around particles of soot and ash billowed into the heavens by the blaze.

When it falls, a lake tumbles down on you; there are no gentle drops, no merry dancing puddles. You are caught in a nightmare again, blinded by liquid where a moment before you were blinded by smoke. It is enough to turn the crimson world grey in moments, to bring hypothermia after heat exhaustion, until even your burns are shivering. Here too there is a cycle in all things – water from fire.

As the forest turned to white flaking ash that fluttered like butterfly wings, Yue did not believe that Vae was dead. We clung onto each other and slippery stones, hauling ourselves belly-first onto a little island of lichen and ash, choking on smoke and spluttering in the rain, and could see neither the carcass of the kakuy nor Vae.

We lay there all night, she and I, while the river buckled and roared around us. We didn't speak, didn't dare wriggle from our nested nook together. The forest was a glaring, bitter thing, threads of shimmering orange still peeking through the downpour like scars on the back of a writhing snake. I thought it was angry, thought perhaps the kakuy who'd died was some minor spirit of a lesser tree, and any second now we would look up and in the sky would be two eyes of lightning, talons of flame. The

18

creaking of the burnt-out husks of the doused trees falling went on all night, a deafening eulogy sometimes so near we flinched together, buried our heads in each other so we wouldn't have to see the branches crashing down around us. At other times, it was a faraway chorus, the funeral song of the wood.

In the morning, the first rescue team found us, calling our names, scrambling through the river – take our hands, take our hands. The men and women wore orange, coated in grey, waded through slurry and sludge knee-deep, a soup of rain, river and ash.

"Ambulance!" hollered someone. "Fetch the ambulance!"

The ambulance came as close as it could, where the river met the village. Tinics had survived the blaze with little more than a few sooty scars; fire was a part of forest life, and every hearth was set back a little from the trees, shelters built into the hill itself. But the power was out, the windfarm locked down and blackened, the compression batteries popped from the inside out, and the whole valley lay beneath a snowfall of ash, a hollow of soot and carbon.

"You have to find Vae," Yue muttered as we lay on the stretchers, batting away her oxygen mask. "I was looking after her."

As children, we look to adults to be perfect and say the right thing. Mama Taaq, face streaked grey from dust and tears, should have replied to her shivering, shuddering child: "You did everything right, my darling. You did everything you could and none of this is your fault."

Later she would say those words, but later was too late, because that night all she did was cry and turn away from her still-living daughter to try and find her dead one. These things are entirely natural and understandable – just not to a child.

We were still in the hospital in Tseonom when they found Vae's body, washed nearly seven kilometres downstream. They told the children she looked very peaceful, and when alone in the bathhouse I slipped beneath the water and held my breath until my throat spasmed and my face burned and my chest was a cavity swallowing me from the inside out, and then surfaced, and realised I would never believe anything an adult said ever again. I ran to my hearth and hid behind the rainwater butts and was angry, sullen, resentful, whimsical, manic, full of laughter and profoundly sad, until at last my mother grabbed me by the shoulders as I ran down the path shaded with hanging vines and managed to hold me still long enough to say: "My child lived!"

In a strange way, it had not occurred to me that night that, though one family had lost their daughter, another's son had been saved. It had not occurred to me to be grateful that I was still alive. The next day, we climbed the burnt hill to the plot of earth where Vae's body had been laid for the forest to take her, and my mother spoke of the cycle of all things, as the Medj do, of change as truth and death as inevitable, of there being no life where there was not its ending, and then said the one thing that the Medj always seemed to forget to add at the end of their sermons: "And it is all right to be sad about that."

Yue vanished into her room for the rest of the summer, and neither family nor friends could coax her out. They did not try very hard. People are rarely skilled at dealing with other people's pain. Do you carry on as if nothing had happened, or do you find yourself guilty that you were caught smiling, that you played a game a week after the funeral, or laughed at a joke a month after Vae's body was given to the sky and earth, or did your homework and made a meal because life continues? Grief never leaves, but life layers itself on top of the pain, time forming fresh scabs over bleeding wounds, no matter how much we wish we had stayed in the burning forest.

So summer ended, and life went on, and Yue went back to school. And sometimes she cried. And sometimes she laughed. And the teachers said she should talk to a counsellor, and she did, and the counsellor told her parents afterwards that there was nothing remarkable here, nothing extraordinary or strange. There was a child grieving; that was all there was to it. You do not fix grief; there is no pill. You only wait, and be there, and let time pass.

So we waited, and let time pass, and Yue's grief did not become a performance, did not become an all-consuming thing that defined her. There was too much life to be lived for that to be the sole quality of her nature. Instead, her thirteenth birthday came and went with some merriment and a little quiet, and then her fourteenth, and sometimes she caught my eye in the street and looked away, and I was still a child, still ashamed, so I turned my face from her too and went about my business as if neither she nor Vae had ever played with me in the forest.

Two years after the forest burned, the Medj of the town, bundled in patched beige robes, led the village up to the stump of the kakuy tree to plant fresh ferns in the ash-soil. The summer festival of Tinics had always been one of dancing, of games and competitive music-making, in which the most beautiful ballads had competed with those less tuneful souls who understood that an entertained audience was more likely than a moved one to crown you with a garland of flowers. After the fire, the festival had moved into the temple grounds, and we washed our hands in the little pools of water between the pebble rows and gave thanks to the food gifted us by the nearby towns that understood our loss. The priests spoke of the cycle of all things, and of how all things came back to life, and there had not been any dancing.

The next year, the elders of the village took hands with the youngest ones and circled the remnants of the hornbeam four times one way, then four times the other, then we all spread out to plant our offerings to the forest, and the soil was black as night and parted beneath my fingers at the lightest touch, eager to be fed.

That same night, when the adults were in the town making merry by precious citronella candlelight, Yue returned to the forest. With headtorch on her head and a water bottle in her hand, she set off up the blackened path through the scrubby, chin-high trunks and drooping, soot-scared monuments, heading for the highest ridge. The new trees pushing up from the corpses of the old, arm-thin and pale-skinned, were not yet so tall that she couldn't see her destination nor so frail that she couldn't use them to climb, hand-over-hand, towards the rising moon. She was becoming the woman I would one day meet in the winter wood; an oblong of tight mouth and stern eyes beneath a winding braid of hair. Hers were features most suited for a laughing grandmother's smile, and they would not fit easy with her until she reached that age.

Beneath the earth, roots tangled like lovers, one atop another, feeding the new green, and as the ferns uncoiled their fresh leaves and the ants nibbled at the fallen black trunks of yesteryear, the forest grew. Life had returned faster than anyone had expected. Not the old life; not the crows or the great rumbling bears, but the smaller, faster life that thrived in bracken and fern, that fed on the insects which thrived in sooty soil and loved to lick at dribbling nectar from freshly rising sap. For a few years, blooms of flowers had spread like rain, colours I had never seen before, yellows and oranges, pinks and lavenders, gaudy magenta and potassium blues verging on black. As the trees started to open their canopies again, the shadows would drive the flowers into smaller clumps of colour peeking at the light, the birds would return with their cackling and caws, and the wind would move the leaves in an old, familiar song. Perhaps then, the Medj said, the kakuy would bless us once again with their presence, and the fruit would grow ripe on the branches, and the wind would power our farms again, and our offerings would be rewarded with their grace, now that the hard years were over.

"When my tree carries fruit again," Mama Taaq would say, standing beneath the grey branches of her spider tree, "then I will know the kakuy have returned."

Her tree would not bear fruit for another four years, when the old hornbeam on the ridge finally flowered in spring. Within every living thing there is a kakuy; the soul of the stone polished by the sea, the spirit of the leaf turning crimson as it falls. All that lives must die, but death is not the end of living, and so the forest grew, and life found its path, and one day the great kakuy of the forest would walk again.

That night, Yue climbed up to an ebony monument to all that had been, a squatting shadow on the horizon. Even in death, the kakuy tree fed life: beetles and ants, fungus and moss creeping into every nook and corner, burrowing past the char to sup on the sap that had supped on the earth. Though the forest had crumbled, people still climbed to offer their tributes to the kakuy burned in fire. An apple, rotting, busily consumed by bugs. A fresh pink rose, propped up against the ravaged trunk where once Vae had climbed. A poem, folded, written in an archaic style and asking for romantic fortune and future wealth. A broken mask from some children's play, left in gratitude for who knew what blessing. And there, still glinting through the blackened soot and thick grains of dirt that shrouded it, a little metal shard.

Yue turned her headtorch on to see it more clearly, held it up to the light, ran her fingers over the ridged, ancient words.

Product of China.

She considered it quite a while before laying it down on a scarred old stone and turning her attention to me. I had not been invited to this place, but I also knew what anniversary this was, and Vae had been my friend. I had found my path to the burnt kakuy tree before Yue and stood next to it now, briefly defiant, for this was *my* night and *my* remembrance beneath the stars, and if Yue wanted to interrupt she should have come a year ago, when I first climbed through the dark of the ashen forest to mourn.

That defiance flickered out almost as soon as it had arisen, and for a moment there were just the two of us above the growing trees, fed by star and moon.

Now we stood, the pair of us, blinking in the dark, the light of her torch dazzling me as I flinched away from its glare. It took a moment for her to realise what the grimace on my face meant, and she turned off the beam and shuffled on the spot, momentarily dull as her eyes adjusted to the changing light.

Then we stood again a while, listening beneath the moonlight, as the forest grew.

She held out her hand, and I took it, and together we circled the fat, black stump of the kakuy tree once one way, once the other, and bowed together, hinging from the hips, and straightened up, hands finding each other again.

She did not look at me, nor I at her.

The forest grew, and the birds did not squabble in the sky, and after a little while Yue let go of my hand and walked away without a word.

That was twenty years ago.

Chapter 4

There is a cellar beneath an old block in the city of Vien that smells of malt and the sweat of men. One night there – or rather, one very early morning – I found myself sprawled along the long, sticky top of a bar as one man held down the back of my head and my bent left arm, pinning it against me with his own body weight, while another attempted to get a decent grip on my jerking, bucking right hand in order to cut my thumb off.

"No please please I can explain please it's a mistake you don't have to please . . . "

The cellar itself was a historical monument, reclaimed from the silt and crumble-down collapse of an ancient city, restored with stones plucked from the ruins of former monuments, buttressed with timber harvested by the Medj, who bowed to each tree in turn and made libations to the kakuy whose gift they were receiving. Dim yellow lanterns hung across the ceiling, powered by the solar batteries high above, and in each padded booth of low couch and table, a hollow was cut for the communal soup bowl, a heavy wooden board laid for the breaking of bread.

"Help, somebody help me!" I shrieked and gibbered, knowing perfectly well that I was the last in the bar, the keys to the front door in my pocket, the back door sealed. "Somebody help!"

During the day, the cellar hosted activities ranging from a meeting hall for monotheists, calling prayers to the old gods, to a twice-weekly knitting group, some of whose efforts were immortalised on the wall nearest the small stage where a dubious range of musical talent was occasionally demonstrated. Who knew you could knit a lobster? Not me.

At night, it had become a haven, first unofficially and then with a semi-official regularity, for members of Vien's Justice and Equality Brotherhood, two of whom were now attempting to remove my digits with a blunt flick knife.

"Whatever you want I can do whatever you need I'm sorry I'm sorry I'm sorry . . ."

Working in the bar had not been my first choice. The hours were long, the pay merely adequate, and any naive notion I had of doing something with my daylight hours was usually lost to restless sleep as sunlight streamed through the shutters of the hearth I called home. My manager had recognised something desperate in me and, faced with the choice between offering me help or exploiting my vulnerability, had chosen the latter. He was now noticeably absent, and I couldn't help but wonder if I would be berated for getting blood on the counter or not tidying up my own severed digits before locking up for the night.

The two gentlemen involved in the business of mutilation were learning on the job. The one who was holding me cheek-first against the countertop focused with a calm, almost bored, nonchalance on keeping my whole body pressed beneath the steady weight of his own, my wrist twisted in his grip. Meanwhile, his colleague tried to turn my right hand up, so that my thumb faced away from the rack of alcohol on the wall, locking my elbow to reduce any writhing to a limp fish's flipper-flap. He was succeeding too, one twisted fibre at a time, so I fell back on screaming, wailing and pleas for mercy, laced with more than a bit of self-pity as I contemplated the poor life choices that had brought me to this place.

Then a voice said, "What's your name?" and the third party to this escapade – a presence I'd barely noted until now – entered the conversation. His authority was enough to make his colleague pause in his work, the knife biting paper-cut thin into my joint.

"What?" I stammered. "I'm Kadri Tarrad, Kadri Tarrad, I live on Katalinastrasse, I'll do anything, please!"

26

"Your name is not Kadri Tarrad," tutted the voice, and perhaps there was a nod or an indication of displeasure at this conclusion, because the knife bit hard enough that I screamed:

"Ven Marzouki! My name is Ven Marzouki!"

The blade relaxed. I could feel blood running down my skin, spilling onto the bar, seeping through the thick, gloopy varnish into the wood.

"Where are you from, Ven Marzouki?"

"Lyvodia," I whimpered. I was surprised to find that though I had some control of my breath and voice, there was salt in my eyes and a capillary pulsed in the side of my cheek with such power I felt sure anyone looking at me would see a relentless, pounding twitch.

"You're far from home. Why did you lie?"

"I ..." I tried to turn my head away from the sight of my own blood, couldn't, closed my eyes and received a shaking of my skull for my efforts. "Whatever I've done to offend you, I'm sorry. You'll never see me again."

Another movement; another little signal somewhere outside my line of sight. The weight on my back relaxed long enough for hands to flip me round, now bending me concave, spine digging into wood, knife moving from my hand towards my throat. I caught a glimpse of face and eye, of assailants who were not in the mood for wit, then their boss rose from his chair, stepped around a small, round table, adjusted the collar of his coat and mused: "Are you a spy, Ven?"

"What? No. Please." I was still struggling to steady my breathing. "Please just let me go. You'll never see me again, I swear."

"Why are you here?"

"I work here! I just work here, *please*."

"Why *here*?"

"I don't know! Because they gave me a job, they gave me a job! It's not even a good job, please, whatever you think I've done I'll make it right. I'll leave, I swear by river and road."

The man shook his head, disappointed. The lights in the bar were turned down for the evening, a slick yellow pooling like acid, but I knew his face from the endless Brotherhood meetings in the hall. He was a picture of archival masculinity: 190 centimetres of subtle muscle beneath an orange-brown winter coat; shoulders that ran in a well-defined V up through his neck to a square jaw, chin with a nook in it that seemed moments away from becoming another mouth with its own scowls and grins; eyes the colour of autumn; straight, pulled-back oak hair inclining to grey. His order at meetings was always the same – a glass of pricey white wine grown from the vineyards on the coast, followed by endless chasers of water and the occasional cold floral tea. When party members passed out drunk or vomited in the corner, he would apologise, gesture to others in the assembly, and have the offending drunkard removed and the mess mopped up while we staff looked on in silence, grateful to have clients who looked after themselves. That, until this moment, had been the limit of our interaction.

"You swear like a priest."

I licked my lips, swallowed hard, tried to speak, fluffed the first few words, tried again. "I'll leave Vien. I promise. You'll never hear from me again."

"But I want to hear from you. I want to hear all sorts of things from you. I want to hear about your past, your present, your future. I would like you and I to have a conversation."

His enforcers were built to a different physical spec than his. Whereas his muscle was a careful construct of motion and control, theirs was the heavy wallop of gorged meat and slapping pain. His strength was merely one of many attributes he was proud of; theirs was the one thing in the world that gave them confidence.

"Are you going to turn me over to the guardia?" I wheezed, tongue an inelegant tool in a swelling mouth.

"Why would we do that?"

"I don't know. Because you can?"

"Yes. I can." He sounded almost kind; a disappointed uncle hoping that the vagrant child will have the guts to confess before the truth is dragged out with irons. "But perhaps there is another way."

In the temple, as a child, the Medj told me that everything

has a kakuy inside it, from the smallest pebble in the stream to the rolling black clouds that break on the tip of the mountain. I wondered what it would be like to be a kakuy of some small, thorny shrub, or the spirit of the cavern, and decided it would probably be better than this. Instead my very human form was deposited at a table in the corner of the cellar with the man who was to destroy everything, cradling a bloody thumb and a pounding skull, while he poured me a glass.

"Tell me about yourself, Ven. Kadri Tarrad. Whoever you pretend to be."

"Why?"

"I hold your life in my hand. Isn't that enough? "

I took the offered glass, drained it down. It was the good stuff, the stuff my manager would be angry to find missing. "I used to be a priest. I was training to take the vows."

"How did you go from chanting and waving incense around to tending bar here?"

"I wasn't good at the pastoral stuff. I was a linguist. My expertise was archaic scripts. I served on the academic review board, studying Burning Age heretical material. My job was to go through recovered servers and translate items for assessment as useful, heretical or somewhere in between."

The man poured another glass, barely looking at where the liquid fell. "Where was this?"

"Lyvodia."

"What kind of material did you study?"

I gripped the glass tight, and this time did not drink. My thumb was leaving little bloody marks on the glass, odd droplets and smears on the tabletop. "Whatever came in. We're finding archives and hard drives all the time. Most of the data is irrecoverable, but sometimes you get a lucky hit; a complex that was sealed against the worst, or something in the landfill mines that still carries data. Most of it is of purely anthropological interest – messages between people in offices, pictures of cats, pornography, and so on. You get a lot of porn. But sometimes you get something good, engineering data or a fiction archive, user manuals or location-tagged images we can compare to archaeological digs. My job was to translate the more challenging material for discussion and classification."

"How 'challenging'?" he asked, and there seemed almost a genuine curiosity in him, an academic fascination that did not tally with my present experience of blood and pain.

"Usually bigotry – social media hatred, violence against other humans on an ideological basis – ethnicity, religion, wealth, gender, sexual preference, and so on. Socially endorsed violence makes up more than 97% of heretical materials, in one form or another. It's unusual to stumble across a practical heresy."

"Define 'practical' heresy."

"Why?"

"Because I'm asking."

I rolled the glass between my hands, enjoying the brightness of the fresh blood that stayed behind. "Nerve agents. Ballistic missiles. Chemical warheads. Fossil-fuel fracking, tar sands, deep-sea extraction. Nuclear fission, depending on its use. Things like that. Most of the records left behind are of people justifying their use, rather than actual construction guides. Sometimes you'd be lucky and get a server from an old university or something. Medical information, water purification, materials science, geography, geology, aeronautics – you'd find the occasional wonder."

"Did you ever find anything?"

"Once or twice. Stem cells, quantum computing. Ancient tracts on economic models, demographic analysis, and so on."

"What did you think about it? Classifying the world into the sacred or the profane?"

I stared into the still surface of the glass between my fingers, realised I didn't even like the good stuff, drained it down anyway, felt a glimmer of spite and satisfaction. "I . . . it wasn't my job to think about it. I was just a translator."

The man in the tan coat smiled briefly, slipped a little deeper into his chair, one leg crossed over the other. He had tiny teeth in his chiselled face – a strange, baby-like anomaly in what was otherwise a textbook portrait of classic Burning Age masculinity.

"So how did you get from sitting in a dusty library to here, Medj of the Temple of the Lake?"

I looked up quickly, then away again lest he see something in my face that he disliked. "Why do you care?"

"Because if you are still a priest, you could be a spy. And if you are a spy, tonight will be full of regrets."

I licked my lips, pushed the empty glass away. "I stole information from the archives. Classified, heretical information. Sold it."

"What kind of information?"

"Anything. Didn't matter. Anything I could find. I downloaded it to datasticks and sold it to anyone who wanted to buy."

"Why did you do that?"

I didn't answer.

"I know you ran, Ven. I know the guardia are looking for you. I'm a good citizen. I should report you."

"If tonight is going to be full of regrets, I'd rather listening to bullshit wasn't one of them."

To my surprise, he smiled. A little smile – the twitching of lips that are enjoying their control, the flicker of delight in the game – that never left his features. But for a moment there was something human behind his eyes, a hint of someone real. "All right. I'm a bad citizen. I am much worse than the guardia. Is that enough?"

I looked round the room. The two thugs were still leaning against the bar, one now with a drink in his hand, bored, professionally paid not to give a damn, not to listen to things which didn't bother him. I looked down at my fingers, bloody and still bleeding in a crimson tangle. "It wasn't fair," I said.

"I beg your pardon?"

"It wasn't fair," I repeated. "I'm ... I worked hard. I could read nearly half a dozen archaic languages fluently and recognise a dozen more. I studied technical languages, coding languages, so I could piece together information from damaged drives or systems we didn't have an operating platform for. I worked while others slept, or ate, or prayed. I was good. I was better than the rest of them."

31

"If that's the case, why are you here? Shouldn't you be chanting scripture in some wealthy monastery?"

"They said I was worldly. Too concerned with human things. There was this man in the archives, working with me – 'working'. He didn't do anything. He just talked and talked as if he knew things, talking to hide how ignorant he was, and I did everything and then he talked and took the credit. And when I complained, they said no tree envies another the light. They said it like it mattered, like there was some great meaning in it. Platitudes. Little sayings, said in a certain way, to disguise the fact that they don't believe, they don't care, they don't ask questions. This is the way it is because that's how we do it. Honour the stones, they said. Each stone lives, and we lay them down and walk upon them, so give thanks to the stone beneath your feet. What does that even mean? I just wanted . . . I just wanted them to make people do their jobs, not treat their laziness like it was interesting or okay. I just wanted them to acknowledge that I was better."

"Some people are better."

"Temple says that it is pointless to argue if a shark is better than a bat. A shark cannot fly; a bat cannot swim. Why would we call something 'better' when it is incomparable?"

"What do you think?"

"I think it's shit. I think people who can't do their jobs wrote shit like that to make it okay that someone else is doing their work."

"That sounds a lot like heresy."

"I studied heresy. Heresy is forced sterilisation. Heresy is racial profiling, stock buybacks, election tampering. This wasn't heresy. It was the foundation of the Temple itself. I wanted more. And the only way I could . . . the best way I could see . . . I wanted money."

"Why?"

"Because I *earned* it."

"Monasteries have wealth. You could have left the archives and become some fat Medj living off the donations of ignorant people."

"Not in Lyvodia. The accumulation of wealth is a worldly affair. Wealth begets wealth, not justice or equality. We lived at the mercy of the laity, and what we had that was beyond what we needed, we gave away. Not like here – not like in Maze."

"You could have left. Gone to a university. Taught. Studied. The Medj release far more archaic data than they hoard. You could have had a good life, with your stem cells and your . . . little victories. Why sell the data?"

"It shouldn't be hidden. Our ancestors died discovering this. It belongs to us."

"That's very noble. I don't believe it."

"Greed is impure," I snapped. "It is one of the impurities. We take only what we need; the rest returns to the earth. That is what the Medj say. Endless anecdotes about . . . happy deer or motherly owls. They said I wasn't ideologically sound. That I did not understand the kakuy."

"Were they right?"

"I honour the kakuy," I barked. "I have always honoured them."

"Why?"

"What do you mean, 'why'? Because it's right. It's what has to be done. They woke when the earth was on fire, they can return us to the flames any time they please, burn the forests, raise the rivers, they can . . . " I stopped dead, breathing harder than I expected, gripping my bleeding thumb so tight the arteries of my arm pulsed all the way up to my shoulder.

"That isn't honouring," he murmured. "That's fear. You fear the kakuy."

"Don't you?" I retorted. "They are the world's judgement on our ancestors. They are . . . they are prison guards."

"I'm not sure you're right." He unfolded his legs, stretched out long, like a cat, folded his fingers behind the back of his head, arched his back, relaxed again, smiled. "But please – carry on."

"There's nothing more to say. They didn't listen to me. They said I was suffering from humanist delusions, putting the benefit of a select number of people above the welfare of the whole. They said I'd spent too much time in the archives, read too many

33

journals about ownership, about fantastical social distinctions, about ... conquering the earth. Taming it. Geoengineering. Solar mirrors. Cloud seeding. Lime in the oceans, artificial eruptions, carbon dumping, land reclamation. Our ancestors were so clever, so *powerful*. They were not afraid of fire."

"But they burned," he replied. A gentle nudge, a casual correction. "They all burned."

"The kakuy burned them. If the kakuy hadn't risen, maybe they could have tamed the world. Maybe they could."

He sucked in his teeth, long and slow. "Now that does sound like heresy."

I stared at the dirty wooden floor, resin and wood pounded tight by decades of stamping feet. "What are you going to do with me? I'll leave Vien. I swear, by ... I swear."

The man nodded, but it did not seem that he nodded at me. He considered the ceiling, stretched again, his body locking into a line from head to toe like the bracing of a bridge, before relaxing back into his seat. "No," he said at last. "No, I don't think so. You will stay here. You will continue to work here. My people will check your story. If it is a lie, you'll die, wherever you go. If not, I will occasionally call on you. That is all."

So saying, he rose at once, brushed the front of his coat with the palms of his hands in a single, slow, smooth motion, nodded at his men and headed for the door. I stood, wobbling after him, blathered, "No, wait, but ... what?"

"Good luck to you, Ven Marzouki. Kadri Tarrad." A half-wave, back turned to me now as he pushed the door open, letting in the cold Vien air.

"Wait, I—"

He was already gone with his guards, leaving me alone in the cellar, blood on the floor, keys in my pocket, nowhere else to go.

Chapter 5

Of the seven Provinces that send their Voices to the great Council in Budapesht, Maze is categorically the worst.

Though it is rich in land and blessed with great rivers and mountains, sweeping fertile plains and tall, noble forests, it has nothing of the cosmopolitan charm of Anatalia or the breath-catching richness of Lyvodia. To the north, it borders the endless black forests where live the nomadic Rus, who shunned the city and the hearth as heresies against the kakuy and returned instead to the horse and the steppe, leaving only scattered offerings of milk and blood upon the earth. To the west, it borders the shrouded lands that run all the way to the isles of the Anglaes, who hide behind their sea wall, maintaining a purity of race and culture that they claim survived even the great migrations of the burning, when all the peoples became one. When the ships of the Anglaes enter the southern seas for diplomacy or trade, or their convoys appear at the mouth of the Rhene River, their ambassadors wash their hands three times before greeting any of the peoples of the Provinces, then three times upon conclud-ing their business, lest the impure touch of the mongrel races corrupt them.

"Let there be peace between us," the Medj always say as they greet the shamans and the priests of these distant lands, "lest the kakuy wake."

However barbaric the peoples of the north may be, on that point at least we could agree. Until, perhaps, now.

Walk through Vien, capital of Maze, and smell the rot setting in.

It is a place of half-remembered monuments, of toppled temples to an ancient god, of the armless statues of forgotten heroes plucked from the mud and set in clusters around the garden parks. Wander past the benches where the lovers sit, beneath bowers of green, paths of scented roses and boxes of carrots and cabbages laid between the lawns, and see here – this figure of time-mottled stone might once have been a great general, or here – he might have been some forgotten king. Now they gaze down at the shrines of timber and mycelium brick grown from the fallen walls of their broken palaces, as though their marble eyes might weep the acid that erased them.

On the west side of the Ube River, great efforts are underway to rebuild some of the former grandeur. The cathedral spire had tumbled when the world burned, but the fallen stones have been painstakingly excavated, and now a new spire rises, and music washes from the open doors. Tourists flood in from Praha and Bukarest to hear the reconstructed ballads of Mozert, Beatless and Beyondsee, performed on the traditional instruments of the time to the booming halls, and several times a year the various monotheist denominations gather for prayers to their one God, calling out in archaic tongues for ancient prophecies to show them the newest way.

By the fat, sluggish river, the great temple of the city flies paper streamers from its wooden porch in spring and rings a booming gong for the dawn of winter, its priests clad in muddy brown bowing to the sun and moon between the high branches of the mottled plane trees. Yet at my first winter festival in Vien, while I had knelt in the snow and given thanks for the ice that keeps the mosquito at bay, for the white that glistens on black, for the fire that drives back the dark, for sunset red and cold dawn light, a novice came to me and exclaimed brightly: "Blessing to keep the flu away? For a small donation, we can offer you the protection of the kakuy for the next three months!"

My jaw nearly hit the floor, for here was the unthinkable: a

Medj offering magic, peddling false miracles for cash. In Lyvodia, such a thing would have been outrageous, with both the local priests and, perhaps more relevantly, the local clinics up in arms. As each Province was its own state, sharing those laws in common with its neighbour that were passed by Council, so each Temple of every Province had its own ceremonies and rituals – yet surely none could claim that this was one?

Shuffle from door to door in the bloody winter, and know that beneath your feet the foundations of the city are crumbling like the chalky cliff into the raging sea.

At the spring equinox, when the streets lit up with a thousand lanterns hung from every window and carried by children bouncing on their parents' backs, the puritans came, rallied from the Delta and Damasc, from Anatalia and the eastern lands by rumours of Maze's corruption. They paraded between the dancing crowds banging their drums and proclaiming heresy, heresy, heresy! You who shave your beards, who take medicines for your disease, who feast on milk and meat – heretics all! We are of the earth and from the earth comes all our qualities, so why would you try to alter your flesh or fight nature's course? The cycle is all; you cannot escape it. Heresy!

I followed at a distance until they reached the lines of local Medj in robes of brown and blue, who wound through the streets singing their songs and proclaiming that the path to basically all things – wealth, happiness, romantic fulfilment and good dentistry – came from giving generously to Temple. Come, come, they said. Make your offerings and be free. The bigger the offering, the freer you'll be.

These two factions, each heretical to the other, faced off on the corner of Leostrad and Altkirchweg, trying to outdo the other in chanting, banging of drums and displays of piety, egging each other on to more dramatic protestations of devotion, up to and including banging their heads against the walls until they bled, crying, "Our blood feeds the kakuy!" or "The kakuy will guarantee an easy pregnancy!"

Eventually the guardia had to split them up, and the pundits on the radio could not keep the contempt from their voices. The next day, Brotherhood members painted crimson murals of the fat Medj of the city and the fanatic, emaciated hermit of the south screaming at each other, spit flying from their grotesque, curling lips. The motto beneath simply said "Pray For Us", and people tutted and muttered that really, it wasn't right for those who claimed to be holy to behave that way – not right at all.

Walk through the city, blood pooling in your hand, and sense the thunder that comes before the storm.

The struts of an ancient bridge still stick up from the river, a sign beside their stubby fingers explaining the great engineering of the past, the mighty skills of our ancestors. A dome covered in tall grass where the spotted starlings bicker has been built on a base of marble and steel, and people come from all around to touch the white-polished walls and oooh and aahh and say that truly the builders of the past achieved remarkable things. The Provincial Assembly sits in a former palace, one side tumbled down and replaced with columns of pulped hemp and lime to support the solar glass ceilings where they meld into ancient stone, like the hermit crab nestling its way into the shell of the abandoned snail. On its walls are new reconstructions of ancient paintings – men with hands resting upon the globe they wished to conquer, swords at their sides, moustaches primed and chins high. At the feet of some, the sextant and the lead weight, for these are men who have mastered the earth as well as each other, and thought themselves greater than the fury of the skies.

"Our past was glorious – why should we hide?" demand the Assemblymen, and they have a point, for shame was never as comforting as lies.

In the winding streets far from the river, the hearths are pressed in tight and tall, feeding off each other's warmth in winter and bathing in each other's summer shade. Here are slung lines of laundry when the warm wind blows, and beneath them the shady swag of grape, sweet pea and ivy laced from one door to another. Outside every window run tresses of herbs and fragrant flowers, all the way to the roofs of the packed-in houses, where you may pluck some savoury treat to sprinkle on a hot dish from the stove, or whose scent in spring drives back the freshly spawned insects from the river. Shutters are thrown open so neighbours may call to each other in the morning, and behind each cluster of timber-framed housing is a courtyard where the elders tend the biovats that keep the pipes warm and play cards and argue over who is right about a point of forgotten memory.

The smell of fresh bread greets the dawn, though a new fad seems to emerge every few months as the historian-bakers of the city try to outdo each other recreating some ancient recipe – a sweet treat of cherries and rare, precious cocoa or coffee bean, or a folded pastry of extortionate, crumbling butter. Even the food in Vien looks to the past, with countless festivals where people gorge on milk and venison and sing songs from a time when all men were heroes.

And here a sight unforgivable, for in the doorways of the station sit the homeless men and women, abandoned by their own city. They huddle together on beds of card, until the guardia chase them away. Where should they go? Temple should take them in, but their doors are locked – go away, go away, you are no good here! The Assembly should fund refuges, places of safety, there should be hearths with open doors to give them shelter, but no.

Not any more.

"Maze is not here to empower laziness," proclaims the Chief Minister. "It is upon you to seize opportunity."

The Council has laws about this, enacted across all the Provinces – laws that Maze itself helped draft and ratify, in a gentler time. Inequality breeds contempt, Council says. Did we not learn from the great burning how the richest considered their lives more valuable, their moral worth and social deserts superior to those of the poorest? Did we not watch them build walls to keep out their fellow humans, proclaiming, "He who is rich is better to keep alive than the poorest teacher, doctor, nurse, builder, mother, father or child?"

The sea tore down even their walls, when all was said and done. But we should not wait for the ocean to settle our accounts.

39

"The Council is supposed to be advisory, a source of unification!" proclaims Antti Col, the Brotherhood banner flying at his back. "Instead they are tyrants seeking to tell us how to live!"

As timber falls to build ever bigger and more extravagant homes, where are the libations, the freshly planted saplings and the careful copses to nourish the life of the woods? All gone, all neglected. We take more than we give, and the leaves wither and the river rises; we tip our sewage straight into the fresh water that rises from beneath fertile mud, and the clouds boil and the wind blows icy from the north, and people wonder: are we poisoning ourselves, or will the kakuy do it for us?

What will we do if the kakuy wake?

The kakuy never slept, warns the pious Medj of the south. The wind and the ocean never cease, and the earth is patient. Tread lightly, my brethren. Do not shake the world too particularly when you pass.

No one I met in Vien had ever seen the kakuy.

Some said they weren't even real.

Dawn breaks across the city as I shuffle home through the rising light.

On the east bank of the Ube River, the streets are clean, broad and practical. Bicycle paths weave between the courtyard-shrouding hearths, old brick mixed with new mycelium and solar cell, creating a jigsaw of beige, white, crimson and grey. From the bathhouses and communal halls the morning smell of pine, yeast and tea brewed long enough to turn your insides brown mingled with polite chatter and discreet silences between courteous people. No one had the same burning interest in gossiping about their neighbours as we had in Tinics; to be caught griping about someone's plants dribbling onto your laundry was considered thoroughly unsophisticated, and the people of the west so very much wanted to be sophisticated.

I lived in a hearth like any other, thirteen of us to the tall, winding building. I ate alone, slept alone, declined offers of friendship when given, and rebutted even cordial inquiry with

40

monosyllabic grunts or a shaking of my head. If anyone tried to engage me on questions of politics or faith, I avoided it with a shrug and an "It's not really my business, is it?"

Strangely, this answer seemed to be accepted, though I could hardly imagine anything that might be more my business than the running of the world I lived in.

"Where are you from, with your accent?" a neighbour asked, and: "Lyvodia," I replied.

"Oh, Lyvodia! Lovely place. I go on holiday sometimes there. The people are so . . . so gentle, aren't they?"

By "gentle" he meant "lazy", for there was nothing quite as fashionable at this time as mocking the peoples of another Province. We were all meant to be one, and yet on the radio the Brotherhood howled and wailed against injustice, injustice – the gross injustice of being wedded by Council to Provinces who were lesser than our own!

"Ever going to go back?" my neighbour inquired, voice light as the butterfly, not meeting my eye.

"Not if I can help it."

He smiled and nodded and said nothing more, and after that didn't bother to greet me on the stairs.

So all things in Vien were rotten, including me.

Then, two months after the Brotherhood nearly cut my thumb off in a bar, they came back.

Chapter 6

In the heat of the moment, I had not taken much time to note the features of my assailants. When one of them came up to the counter and ordered a cup of hot rice wine, my stomach recognised him while my mind rebelled. His skin was much like mine, the deep olive that had emerged in those peoples who survived the great migrations, when the old tribal boundaries broke down, but he had dyed his dark hair a streaky crimson and pulled it back into a knot that seemed to elongate his high forehead into a cliff. I poured the drink with clammy hands, took his money, left the flask by his side and went about my business with the small of my back suddenly exposed, every hair on my arms standing tall, fingers clumsy and tongue dull in my mouth.

He watched me, that was all. The cellar was hot and crowded, filled mostly with the laughter of men and a few cross-legged women pressed into time-crumbling walls. The talk was of crop failures and discontent, of political change and social revolution, mixed with the usual hearth gossip and romantic misadventures. The man who'd tried to cut my thumb off did not participate in such things, but neither was he unknown. People who approached the bar nodded at him and turned away; respect without friendship.

I did my best to stay away from his end of the counter, but couldn't for ever. He finished his flask of wine, raised one hand, caught my eye. I approached, fumbled a few words, tried again. "Can I get you something else?"

"You read this?"

He pushed a slip of thin yellow paper over the counter. On it, written in archaic German, was a time and a place. The handwriting was stiff, clumsy — as if each unfamiliar character were copied one line at a time from a dictionary, rather than a familiar, flowing thing. I nodded, swallowed. "Anything else?"

He shook his head, tapped his empty cup three times on the wooden bar as if completing some ritual, rose and pushed his way through the crowd.

Four hours later, I stood in the doorway of an old-town mansion as the evening rain sang down the water pipes and made the reclaimed cobbles shimmer like the sea. I closed my eyes against the night and stamped my feet and puffed into my cupped hands and wondered whether I'd leave with my fingers still attached.

A few streets away, I heard a door slam, laughter, the clattering of a bike pushed along a slippery pavement. Someone tried to sing a few verses of a song — a Temple devotional, slurred and out of tune — before someone else louder and differently inebriated cut in with a Brotherhood anthem, a chorus of mankind's strength and dominion.

A cat meowed and a flock of pigeons darted away from their warm perches in the grassy roof above. Steam trickled from a vent by my feet, laced with the smell of pine.

I checked my watch, wound it, checked it again, found barely thirty seconds had passed, pulled my coat tighter, listened. Behind a shutter, a light turned on, then off again, then back on. A figure moved, looking for something in the dark, disturbed by restless dreams or aching bones. They found it; moved back towards a bed. The light turned off again. At the end of the street, the low whine of an electric truck as it passed by, the splash of sheets of water spilling up from a blocked drain in the reclaimed rubber road, the gentle whoosh of a cooling fan from the server office on the corner. Voices raised in the dark, passing by, fading away.

After fifteen minutes, I thought of going. Even the heartiest of revellers were headed to bed, leaving only the long-night novices about their sleepy prayers, if they bothered to pray at all.

I was half snoozing, swaying where I stood, when the car came. I had seen only a few private cars in my life. In Tseonom, the local clinic had one shared between whichever doctors were on call for the area, and in Bukarest the guardia and a few senior Assembly officials had possessed such things, but that was about the limit of it. Most farming hearths had their trucks and tractors, solar panels pressed to cabin roofs for an emergency recharge should they get stuck in the mud, battery packs swung in the middle of their chassis, but in a city like Vien these things were unusual status symbols, as vulgar as they were secretly, quietly envied.

This car pulled up a few feet in front of me, headlights low, engine silent, and as I approached I had to bend almost double to peer at the reflective windows. Before I could get a good look inside, the door opened, pushing me back, and a voice said: "Oh – he's wet."

I leant down to see the interior of the car. Three grey padded seats lined the back, the middle far smaller than the two either side. In the front were two more seats, both occupied, one by the man who had accosted me at the bar. In the back there was a man, a chiselled slab of human in a high-collared black jacket with translucent seashell buttons down the front and at his wrists.

"Are you getting in?" he asked, when I didn't move.

"Are you going to cut my thumb off?"

"Only if you don't get in. Come on, I have an early meeting and would like to shower first."

If sleep was also on his list of things to do, he did not say. I got into the car, pulled the door shut awkwardly, clung to the seat in front of me, heard his little snort of derision. "Put your seatbelt on."

I fumbled with the belt he indicated, struggled with where my arms were meant to go in relation to the strap. He didn't seem interested in my escapades, eyes fixed on the gently glowing inkstone in his lap. On this occasion he wore a ring, bearing the crossed axe and spade of the Brotherhood, oversized on a little finger. At the clip of my seatbelt locking shut, he looked up as if the sound were an alarm and passed me his inkstone.

"Read this."

It nearly slipped from my grasp, but I held tight, tried to focus on the words through the strange movement of the car. It was written in archaic English and was largely a preamble about following health and safety guidelines as laid out in legislation, and the importance of ear defenders. In the top right corner was a string of numbers and letters, a serial number that made my heart sink. I flipped to the next page, and when this audacity didn't elicit violence, kept reading. Soon the generic business gave way to more meaty topics, including guidelines on angles of ascension and declension, and the necessity of having a good wind sock.

"Well?" asked the man at last.

"What do you want to know?"

"What do you make of it?"

"It's a training manual."

"I was looking for a little more insight."

"It's a training manual for an armament. A mortar. This one is small, transported by one or two people. The explosive can fly over obstacles and be launched while in cover."

"What else?"

"It's a very dull read."

"Is it authentic?"

"I don't know, this is just a transcript, not the original. I'd have to see—"

For the first time since I'd got in the car, the man turned his head to look me straight in the eye. "Is it authentic?" He repeated the question as if confused by my stupidity, baffled that I could still be talking when, clearly, there was nothing else to say.

His eyes were blue, framed by the dark. The low white lights of the city pushed and pulled the shadows across his features as we sped down empty roads.

I looked away, swallowed, kept on reading. "The syntax is right, and the grammar's not bad," I mumbled. "But archaic

English was prone to breaking its own rules. Illustrations are wire-frame renderings, which isn't unusual in technical guides of this time. There's no data degradation I can see, although this is a transcript. But you'd expect something to have been lost, a few areas of missing or corrupted text from the original file, unless you were lucky and the hard drive was kept in natural cold storage that minimised contamination until unsealed. It's also noticeable that there isn't an exploded view of parts. Most manuals of this sort are designed to allow the operator to maintain their equipment in the field. That's . . . curious. Do you have any cross-referencing material?"

"Not yet."

"Then I can't definitively say."

"That's disappointing."

I shrugged. "You'd rather I lie? You don't need much to fake data from the burning; there's still a thriving black market in snake oil and material sciences. Anyone who says this is authentic without cross-checking is an idiot."

I tossed the inkstone onto the empty seat between us, not quite having the guts to throw it in his face. We drove in silence a while, rain running in little sideways-stretched dribbles down the windows, the man from the bar watching me in the driver's mirror from the front of the car. I found my reflection in the moving light across the glass fascinating, a hollow plucked-out version of how I imagined myself. My frizzy dark hair had grown out around my ears, making the face it framed seem smaller by comparison, green-grey eyes sinking into the sockets. The lines on my skin were deep enough to make my features appear crudely plugged together – a modular chin that didn't match the modular eyebrows that someone had glued to a second-hand skull. I tried to see the man behind me in the reflection in the glass, but the shadows of the car were too deep, so it was to nothing much and no one in particular that I said: "The serial number at the top." He didn't move, hands laced across one folded leg, so I went on. "That's a Temple librarian's code. I don't know the database it's from, but I recognise the prefix. Highly classified – heretical. The

46

kind of material that gets locked in an archive in some obscure mountain shrine. I don't know if it's real, and I absolutely don't want to know where or how you got it, but if it's fake, someone's tried very hard to replicate Temple codes."

I turned back to examine my companion, who said nothing. Then he leant across, picked up his inkstone, turned it off, slipped it into a pouch on the side of his seat, smiled at nothing much, nodded at no one in particular and said: "Thank you. We'll be in touch."

The car slowed. I didn't move. He half-turned his head, seemed to look straight through me, waiting. I thought about opening my mouth to ask a question and instead fumbled with the handle of the door and let myself out, shaking and shivering, into the sodden night.

Chapter 7

During the spring festival in Tinics, we would walk into the forest to find the first purple flowers, and it was considered good luck to be the first to spot the buzzing bee or hear the call of the common cuckoo. Even after the forest burned, the Medj took us into its ruins and we would find lesser gifts from the growing land; new green shoots arising from the split-open trunks, or fresh moss on the stone within which lived insect upon insect, so that as your eye adjusted to their tiny wiggling bodies of vanilla, white and grey, you saw more again, and more, zooming down into the heart of the thing as a telescope may look up into the darkness and see nothing but stars.

At the spring festival in Vien, people went to the temples to give offerings of money in exchange for good harvest, and many more protested outside saying it wasn't fair that the priests grew fat on their living while citizens suffered, and Antti Col and his Brotherhood cronies made indignant speeches outside the Assembly about the harvest being man's work, man's toil, the land being carved by our will, not fickle, faithless nature.

And in Tinics — in the place that had been my home — the forest grew.

Between winter and spring, I was contacted four more times by the men from the bar. Each time was the same — a late-night pick-up, an archaic document scraped from ancient servers. Two were definitively false. One was almost certainly the genuine article, which I was ordered to translate in full. All of them were heresy.

On my fifth encounter, I was summoned at 4 a.m. to a hearth near the old palace gardens. It was one of the few fully restored buildings of the old world, complete with tiny blue and green tiles woven into a zig-zag pattern across the floor, banisters of twisted iron, high windows of pure, not even solar, glass, and no more than two or three people living in it. I struggled to imagine inhabiting such a place, uncertain if I should walk on veined white stone or thick red carpet – or how many offerings had been made to the kakuy of earth and sky in thanks for the precious goods that built such a place. Not enough, I suspected. The mind that crafted such things did not have much capacity for humility before the sleepy spirit of the mountain.

Dawn was a thin greyness on the horizon, and beneath the bending branches of the springtime trees the Medj were beginning their morning prayers, the sound of half-hearted chanting carried by a cold, damp breeze to the cracked-open windows of the first floor. Soon the lights would be turned off for the silver day, and the streets would clatter with bicycles and cargo carriers, and the server offices would power up their networks as the bathhouses filled with steam. Facing it all, back to the door and eyes to the window, there he was: my sometimes-master and unknown blackmailer, dressed now in an old-fashioned silver waistcoat, a glass held in one hand, the contents hidden from my sight by the broad curve of his fingers. A long desk of black wood stood between us, its top adorned with red leather – real leather, perhaps, the real skin of an actual animal, kept supple and buffed by I knew not what magic. On it was his inkstone, the words already turned towards me as if conversation were an inconvenience best left for daylight hours. I approached beneath hanging bulbs in resin-crystal fittings, noted the private server and computer on the desk, the pictures on the wall of long-faded heroes' valiant deeds, the abstract illustrations and even one crackling, deep-dark work of monotheism that could well have been genuine, depicting a Christian saint with hands upturned towards a trumpeting angel. I had seen no sign that this man believed in anything at all, and the picture seemed to hang as part of a cultural history, a landmark in the journey of how the world came from there to here.

My observations had taken too long, for now he half-turned from the window to glance at me. "Well?"

I picked up the inkstone, read the first page, flipped to the second, stopped, read again, went back a page, forward a page, stopped. Put the inkstone down and, for the first time since I had met this man, held his gaze.

If this surprised him, he did not show it. Not an eyelash quivered in contemplation. "Yes?"

"It is a military paper on the use of radioactive substances in assassination."

"Is it genuine?"

My lips curled against my teeth, and I did not answer.

Now he turned fully, his shoulders following the angle of his neck as if a rod pinned him to the ground, around which he spun in sections.

"Is it genuine?"

"Probably. I am familiar with at least one of the cases it cites."

"Good. You will provide a full translation by sixth day."

"No."

Not an eye twitched, not a capillary flushed, but the corner of his mouth curled, almost as if he would smile. "No?"

"No. You have an inside source feeding you the kind of heresies that would make Temple inquisition bleed from the eyes, but you need me to verify and translate it. Fine. Pay me."

"Why would I do that?"

"Because my service is valuable to you."

"I think you forget the nature of our relationship."

"I don't. Hurting me doesn't do anything for you. It destroys a resource you want to use. When we met, you called me 'Medj of the Temple of the Lake'. I never said which temple I was from. You knew about me long before you brought the knives out, knew I wasn't Kadri Tarrad. You left me alone until I was useful. You have use of me. I'm not greedy; it won't be too expensive. But I want more. Pay me."

Slowly, he sat down, put the glass to one side, splayed his hands out across the desk one finger at a time. "I can see why you found the limited ambitions of your colleagues so frustrating. How much do you want?"

"Two hundred bi for every translation of fifty pages or less. More to be calculated on a per-page rate based on this figure thereafter. Illustrations still count as pages. And a retainer of one hundred bi a month."

"That is, of course, absurd."

"Any other translator would charge you twice as much and report you for heresy. It's a bargain and you know it."

"Do not overestimate your value."

"I think I have estimated it accurately, based on the current market."

The fingers on his left hand rippled, a motion picked up by his right, little finger to little finger across the desk. For a moment, his eyes looked past me, and I wondered if his thugs were waiting for a cue, knives ready, cracked knuckles and dark eyes. It took a physical clenching of my belly, a tightening of my fists, not to turn to check. Then he appeared to relax, nodded once and said: "Very well. But you will increase your output for us, and if we require other services you will comply quickly and without question – fully paid, of course. Agreed?"

"Agreed."

"Excellent. Take the translation. You will deliver it on fifth day."

He gestured loosely at the inkstone. I picked it up, swiped the files to my own, returned it to the desk, made to leave, found no monsters standing behind me, no cudgels raised to bash in my skull, stopped, looked back.

"What's your name?" I asked.

"You may call me Georg," he replied, and turned to contemplate the rising sun.

So began my involvement with the Brotherhood, heresy and the war.

Chapter 8

When I joined the Temple as a layman of the academic review board, my professor, Lah of the Temple of the Lake, sat me down in their little office above the courtyard of pine and pebble and said:

"In the basement of this temple we have a shelf of hard drives recovered and transcribed from the burning. They contain information on medical experiments conducted on prisoners of war and civilian populations across conflicts down the eras. Nerve gas, bacterial warfare, chemical bombs. Weaponised viruses that turned a body's immune system against itself, killing the young before killing the old. Compounds that sent a person blind, blistering the skin, the lungs; people drowning in their own fluids. Many were tortured; many died. People were experimented on based on their race and sexual orientation, or allowed to suffer with treatable conditions so that physicians could learn how death progressed. They have been declared heretical, abhorrent, but the academic review board has a duty to review heresies on an ongoing basis with one question in mind: Who are we now? Before the burning, it was considered heretical for women to behave in a manner considered male. Then these words changed – 'female', 'male'. They have changed again since that time. What is our new morality? What is our new heresy? What would you do with this information, kin of sky and earth? What would you do for those who lived, and those who died?"

"I don't know," I replied.

"Someone must decide. The burden falls on us. Three thousand words on these points by tomorrow afternoon, please."

That was when I was Ven Marzouki, before I became Kadri Tarrad, before Nadira came to me and said, "If you can stick your thumb in your assailant's windpipe, it really is very effective."

That was before I saw Yue again.

The Temple of the Lake in Bukarest was close to the local Assembly. Every winter and summer, the Chief Minister of Lyvodia would come and make offerings and drink hot tea with the priests and walk the grounds around the wide waters and discuss matters both theological and political. When I was a novice, Ull had only just been elected Chief Minister and felt it important to be seen nodding and paying polite attention to the words of the Medj who prayed beneath the spider-silk tree.

Sometimes, protesters came too, a dozen or so men and women with placards waved outside the temple doors. I was sent to offer them tea, and sometimes they took it, and sometimes they threw the cups on the floor, smashing the thin worked clay, which I swept up and used as ballast at the bottom of potted plants.

"Separation of church and state!" one man screamed in my face, when I asked him if he wanted a biscuit. "The Temple keeps us down!"

"Did you know," I asked politely, "that the idea of 'separation of church and state' is from an era known as the Enlightenment? It was an age in which humankind attempted to redefine its internal relationship with itself – with power and tyranny and justice – and its external relationship with the world, i.e. God, and through God, the planet."

The man just kept on chanting, his spittle flying in my face, which seemed a terrible waste of good tea.

After, as we watched Ull cycle away with his entourage back to the Assembly of Bukarest, Lah stood beside me in the half-open sliding door of their little room by the turned vegetable patch, sighed and said: "It is our own fault that the protesters are here. No one else is to blame."

I was silent. It was usually best to be silent when Lah was about to speak of things that troubled them.

"Before the Provinces united – when we were simply Lyvodia and Maze and Damasc and the Delta, and so on – Temple sent missionaries out across the lands in an attempt to convince each nation that we were one, humble beneath mother earth and father sky. Yet our most convincing argument was not one of universal fellowship, of compassion and justice and the beauty of this shared, sacred earth. Our most convincing argument was simply this: do not go to war, lest you wake the kakuy. The kakuy are hardly seen any more, but the memory of the creatures that crushed the cities and scoured humanity from the plains takes a long time to fade, even from the fickle memories of humanity. Fear brought the Provinces together in alliance. Fear created the Council to represent all of us as one; fear created the common laws of Assembly, democracy and peace. But fear is exhausting. Effective, but exhausting. And to the eyes of those who see Council as a tool of oppression, as a mouthpiece for the Temple that helped create it, there is nothing in our prayers that is not poison. They say that Temple inquisitors have infiltrated every corner of the Provinces – that our spies manipulate Assembly and government. When we say no, no, inquisitors are meant to stop the spread of nerve agents and automatic weaponry, all they hear is fear. Fear of the past. Fear of change. Fear of what humanity could be. The kakuy teach us that every breath of air is a gift, that the first shoot of spring green is a wonder to behold. But it is easier to be big and loud in your terror than to be tiny in your gratitude. We are to blame."

"What are we going to do about it?" I asked, young and naïve as I was.

Lah laughed, a single bark in the settling gloom. "I have no idea. Like the peoples of the Burning Age, I fear we see our ending come – and cannot imagine that we ourselves can prevent it. More tea, novice?"

In the years between then and now, only one thing has been consistent: as humankind squabbled and bickered, fought for power, prestige and status, back in Tinics the forest grew.

Chapter 9

This is how I became part of the Brotherhood, sworn to justice, humanism and the triumph of the human race.

From translating texts, I was one night summoned to receive some stolen data myself.

"My usual courier is indisposed," Georg sighed. "You'll have to make the drop."

"Fine. You'll pay me double."

He grinned, less at my cheek and more, I felt, because he had predicted that I would be cheeky and was glad at the accuracy of his guess. "You'll be paid by the hour. It should take you less than two."

A Medj, face hidden in hood and shadow, whispered to me through the side gate of the Temple of the River: "It's worth at least five times that!" but I had orders to only pay nine hundred bi for the datastick they slipped me, and they didn't stay to argue the point.

I knew how it felt to be that scuttling priest, slipping back into their dormitory in temple grounds, and felt neither sympathy nor fear that night.

"Well?" Georg asked.

"It's a collection of books on the theme of self-empowerment through wealth accumulation. 'Visualise yourself rich. Then make it happen. No university will teach you this secret. Belief unlocks your human potential and—'"

Georg waved me to silence. "What a shame," he sighed. "Another waste of time."

From receiving stolen data, I graduated to attending occasional meetings with not only Georg but also Kun Mi, Brika and Tanacha, introduced to me as senior policy figures within the Brotherhood's political wing. They rarely wanted my opinion on their ideas – tightening abortion laws to encourage births, changing laws on inheritance, re-writing press codes to force journalists to merely report what they said rather than comment on its factuality – but occasionally Georg would turn to me and say: "Did they do this in the burning?" and I would answer yay or nay, and very little more was needed from me.

One night, after another such meeting, Georg turned to me and said: "What do you think of those three?"

"I think they're so blinded by their own personal desire to get rich and get respect that they wouldn't recognise a good idea if it punched them in the face."

He beamed, nodded, brisk and bright, and proclaimed: "Yes. That's precisely how I feel on the matter."

And every month or so Georg passed me another document to translate or verify, and there it was at the top of every page, that little line of numbers and letters that marked the text below as classified, heretical, profane in Temple eyes. He never said where these documents were coming from, and I knew better than to ask.

Then one day towards the end of summer, he marched up to where I sat huddled over a stolen text and proclaimed: "You are now making the same wage as a medium-salaried assistant within my office. You will start here full-time next first day."

"Will I?"

"Yes."

"Why?"

"Because you will be quickly promoted, you will be safe, you will be part of one of the greatest movements in human history, and you'll no longer have to mop up vomit from the front step of the bar. Yes?"

"May I have a day to think about it?"

"If you really think it's necessary. I do not."

I quit the bar that very night and was moved to a side office in the same magnificent restored building which Georg had made his home. My work evolved again, from collecting data, performing mildly illicit acts and translating heresy to secretarial work for the Brotherhood itself, planning rallies and editing addresses by its elected Voices in the Assembly, researching talking points for debates, and cataloguing a never-ending stream of spreadsheets and databases of members, assets, resources and the occasional enemy.

"That is Ayodele," Georg murmured in my ear one day as we listened to a female voice on the radio proclaiming the need for urgent Temple reform and social dialogue. "She is trouble."

Four weeks later, a file with her name crossed my desk, sealed tight. I steamed it open in the local bathhouse, read it by torchlight, closed it up before passing it on to Georg. A week after that, Ayodele stood down from the Assembly, citing personal reasons, and in the by-election that followed her seat fell to the Brotherhood, and Georg invited me to his office for a toast.

"The good stuff," he explained, as I filled the glasses on the table. "Seeing how far we've come."

In the evening, I still translated archaic texts, ranging from the banal to the petrifying.

hey why arnt u ansring my calls? just call me back ok. I ddnt mean the thing i said. your being a child.

So many ancient servers were full of noise, noise, noise. Broken images of pets, babies and food. Messages from lovers and enemies long since dead, their passions recorded in stiff fonts and binary numbers.

babe i luv u wat u want 4 food? u seen what M said?

Even in the best-kept archives, you had to wade through the voices of the burning, peel back their lives to find the good stuff, the proper heresy for an ancient age.

People believe what they want to believe. Tell them what they want to hear. Social media moves faster than fact-checkers, so as long as you . . .

Improve your Spanish! Tres tristes tigres tragaban trigo en un trigal en tres tristes trastos. En tres tristes trastos tragaban trigo tres tristes tigres.

As the number of neutrons increase in the atom, it becomes unstable . . .

Six months after Georg started paying me for my work, I moved into a Brotherhood hearth built around the columns of what had once been a raised road just for cars. Segments had collapsed down the centuries, leaving only odd standing pillars of the past, on the top of which flocks of sparrows had made their homes, startling in black clouds at the shadow of a predator overhead.

Though this new place was more like the hearths I knew, with shared food at a shared table, there were no women in it, and chores were enforced as icy discipline rather than familial cooperation. The hydroponic walls were untended; the fish tanks empty. Conversation was the same litany of complaints every evening – of men who felt disappointed with their lot, held back from advancement, punished for failing to conform, unable to make something more. Men trapped within a system where the respect of your hearth was considered more valuable than your material possessions; where money did not pass to your children and the generation of wealth was not considered an accurate reflection of your contribution to society.

"I want to be a man," muttered a Brotherhood devotee called Sohrab as we bathed together in the hot tubs below the apartments, the light through the skylight above playing sunset orange and gold across his skin. "There was a time when that meant something. There was a time when it wasn't heresy to be strong."

There were other hearths where the women lived, and perhaps the conversation there was much the same. I had never lived with just one sex before.

When the rain broke, washing away the last heat of sticky summer, Georg stood with the windows of the office wide open, smelling the city open beneath the deluge, hands out to catch the fat drops as they pooled in his palm, and said: "How did air conditioning work?"

"A similar principle to artificial refrigeration," I answered. The sky blistered purple and yellow, ocean grey and midnight blue, as though the heavens had held their breath and could gasp no more.

"When a liquid converts to a gas, it absorbs heat. Compounds flowing through a closed system would constantly evaporate and condense. When they evaporated, they cooled the pipes they flowed through. When they condensed, they released the heat to the outside world."

"Why don't we do that now?"

"Temple declared it heresy. They said that the chemicals were dangerous, and that making heat in order to move heat away from you just made more heat, and that if you heated up the world in order to keep your parlour cool, you were not living by the ways of the kakuy."

"What do you think?"

"I think that trying to stay cool on a hot planet by heating up the planet more . . . in the long run isn't a winning idea. It would, as the Medj say, displease the kakuy."

"But if only a few had air conditioning? Only the select? Assuming equality seems the mistake here, not the technology itself." I shrugged, and he nodded at nothing much, contemplating the rain. "Must be damned hot in those priest robes."

"Most Medj like to preach from the shade," I replied, watching the water tumble in sheets from the gutter across the street, a miniature waterfall of reflected light. Tiny rivers bounced and wriggled towards the drains, carrying fallen leaves and the settled dust of summer away.

"Memorise these," Georg said, pushing a datastick into my hand.

Loaded into my inkstone, it revealed a series of names and faces, some posed, others caught on an angle. I studied every feature, lay at night trying to imagine them alive, breathing and laughing, returned to work the next day to find a new suit of finest linen and spider silk on the back of my chair.

"It's a loan," Georg said, with a smile in the corner of his mouth, as I stroked the translucent beetle-black of the sleeve. "Try not to spill wine on it."

That evening we attended a party in a restored villa a few blocks from the Assembly. Every detail had been paid to the recreation, from the wood-panelled walls to the paper books – with actual words printed in them – lining the walls. I ran my finger along the shelf, mouthing the ancient names of Hemmingveg, Jelinek, Attwood, Chang and Koates. I doubted the spines had ever been cracked, smelt the fresh glue in the bindings, wondered how much it had cost to have such extraordinary things made and who had translated them from their ancient texts. Double doors with handles of polished brass opened to reveal a long white table laden with duck, chicken, pork, beef, fish eggs and delicate slices of pink salmon on beds of ice, glasses of bubbling wine and fresh red lobster. I stared in amazement as people went to fill their plates, tried to work out the cost of getting such goods, of transporting so much refrigerated flesh from so far away. Then Georg was by my side and murmured, "Mind yourself," and I closed my mouth and wondered what else he had seen in my eyes.

"Her." A tilt of his chin towards a woman, crystal glass spinning in a gloved hand.

"Minister for Energy, Lerna Binks," I replied.

A half-nod; perhaps thanks for information he did not know, perhaps acknowledgement of a test completed.

"Him."

"Head of northern section railways, Chiwocha Ckahad."

"What do you think of him?"

"That he's never eaten lobster before."

"Have you?"

"No. I've never seen one."

"Then how can you judge?"

I bit my lip, bowed my head. He raised his glass to salute someone of minimal importance who'd saluted him, breathed: "Stay close, always behind, and do not speak until spoken to."

I nodded and followed him deeper into the crowd.

" . . . I mean the Assembly in Damasc is hardly functioning at all these days, it's all just talk talk talk . . . "

"Council laws, always just more Council laws, don't do this, do do that, do you know I spend more time these days learning Council laws than I actually do running my business?"

"Who do they even think they . . . "

"What do you mean, 'crack the shell'? Oh gosh that's terribly . . . I mean, isn't it . . . ?"

"Do we even need Council? Do we even need the other Provinces? Georg, help us out here, help me explain this to him, he's so . . . "

"Georg Mestri. I see you still know how to throw a party."

"Pav. I didn't expect you to attend."

A moment of panic – I didn't recognise this man with a shock of snow-white hair above a tiny almond face. His eyes were huge compared to his tiny hook nose and tight little smile, and though he was nearly a foot shorter than Georg, he managed to hold the little space he inhabited as though every other person in the room were some distant grandchild and he the progenitor of it all. He smiled at Georg and tipped his glass, which he held between his fingertips with his little finger out, as if trying to counter-balance all that weight of crystal, then glanced at me, eyebrow raised. "And this is . . . "

"Kadri Tarrad, my assistant."

"That's a very nice suit, Kadri."

"Thank you. It's not mine."

Another flash of a smile, and then his attention was back where it belonged, burning straight into Georg's eyes, and though the smile remained it was the grin of the shark that knows no other way to show its teeth. Georg adjusted his weight a little more evenly, a tiny tic in his body that prefaced battle, and I briefly felt relieved – he was as surprised to see this man called Pav as I was. "And how long are you gracing Vien with your presence?"

"Not long. Back to see the old hearth, a few friends – you know how it is."

"Of course. I imagine Council keeps you busy."

"Even on Council we have the occasional holiday."

"Do you? I thought all the pronouncements, the new laws, the 'don't-do-this, don't-do-thats' that you people seem to endlessly impose on the Provinces would keep you up every day and every night."

61

"Our output is only proportional to your imagination. I had no idea how creative the Assembly of Maze could be in coming up with new ways to undermine their own democracy."

"A democracy controlled by Temple is hardly democracy, wouldn't you agree?"

"When I last checked, it seemed to me that the Vien Assembly had more influence over Temple than any Medj over a Minister. Didn't I read that Antti Col managed to get a priest to bless his car?" Pav's laugh was sharp as the glass he held, a tinkle of playing light, a flash of pointed teeth. It was gone so abruptly, listeners might have wondered if it was there at all. "How is Antti doing, Georg?"

"Looking forward to the elections."

"Of course he is. I'm sure he'll do very well."

"Tell me – do you still pray every morning for forgiveness, Pav? I heard you dress in a special gown and brush your teeth with charcoal – a malicious rumour, I'm sure."

"I pray every morning and every night, just to be safe, but alas, my favourite penitent robes don't always fit in the travel bag. You know I respect you, don't you?"

"You have always been very clear about your sentiment."

"Council cannot stop the people of Maze electing Antti to the Assembly, if that's what they want. But the Provinces were united with one purpose at their heart – that the kakuy must sleep. You can march up and down and throw these delightful parties and make all the noise you want. But if you wake the kakuy . . . "

"Have you ever seen a kakuy?" Georg cut in, a little louder, eyes fixed on some different place. "No. Of course you haven't. Neither has Jia, or any of her Council. Neither has anyone in Vien, except in paintings at Temple. So while it is absolutely lovely to see you here, of course – always welcome, please do try the lobster – let's not base our discussions on a hypothetical, shall we?"

Pav's smile curled in tight for just a moment – just a moment – before he relaxed again, tipped the lip of his glass towards Georg in salute, drained the liquid down and turned away.

*

"Who was that?" I asked in the soft, low-lit aftermath of the party. The cleaners were moving across the room, shoving half-chewed meat and bits of bone into compost bags for the biowells, the heat of bodies still sticky in the room.

"Hum?" Georg stood by the window, sipping water, watching the night.

"The man called Pav."

"Ah, yes. He was not invited."

"Who is he?"

"Pav Krillovko. He used to be an Assembly member here, many years ago. A servant of Maze. Now he works in Budapesht as chief of staff for the Voice of Council herself, passing down pronouncements to all the Provinces as if he wasn't once one of us. A waste. He was a good man, before Temple got to him."

"He appeared to threaten you without having the power to act on it."

A snort of laughter. "Quite. That is the Council's way, isn't it? Their power rests on habit. We are habituated to obeying what they say without question, but if a Province chooses not to, to resist, then it turns out the Council is quite incapable of enforcing its pronouncements. Pav knows that. Interesting that he came here in person."

I opened my mouth to ask something more, to blurt out words, questions, and stopped myself. Georg rolled the glass between the palms of his hands as plates of wasted food were thrown into stinking bags for the biopits, and in the world outside even the prowling cats slumbered.

"Good night, Georg," I said.

"Good night, Kadri," he replied, without looking back.

Chapter 10

At the autumn festival, I went out of habit to the temple to give thanks for the gifts of the earth, for the heat of the sun and the cold of the rain. I bowed my head to the wind and was grateful for its touch, but other members of the Brotherhood tutted and shook their heads and said it was rank superstition. Human is the superior species, they intoned. Whether by accident or design, we had only ourselves to thank for our thriving.

Later, I was invited to dine with some of the women of the party. I had almost never seen these mysterious figures, dressed primly in knee-length skirts and tight buttoned shirts. But even the Brotherhood felt it necessary for its members to rest on occasion, so I found myself kneeling at a long, low table decked with beans and lentils, fresh forest mushrooms and apple stew, next to a woman called Rilka. Her short black hair was cut to a line across her shoulders, and she sliced all her food into perfect, tiny morsels, before eating one at a time as if waiting for bitterness.

"We are mothers," she proclaimed. "We have forgotten what it was to be proud of that. You cannot be a real woman unless you give birth. Only then, real."

I did not think she had any children, and she did not look at her food as she nibbled it down.

One night, returning to my room, I encountered on the stairs the self-same gentleman who had been so enthusiastic about removing my thumb from my hand. He saw me, recognised me,

64

smiled. I moved my hands together automatically to bow as he passed by, but instead he held out his right hand, an archaic gesture from another era. I shook his hand awkwardly. He gripped far longer than the archives said he should, squeezed tight until my bones scraped and squelched against each other above my palm, grinned, patted me on the shoulder and let me go.

The next day, I realised he had moved into the room next to mine. In the bathhouse, the others called him Klem, and he was an excellent gardener, tending to each leaf like a tailor to a regal gown. We sometimes smiled at each other in passing and never had a conversation.

Chapter 11

In my ninth month working for the Brotherhood, I met Antti Col. The leader of the Brotherhood should have been a charismatic demagogue, a handsome, striking man able to express the frustration of everyone who felt they wanted more, more, more. Instead, as he strode into Georg's office in a flutter of evening blue and golden lapel pin, he was a diminutive weed next to Georg's spring tree, with teeth like yellow fungi and a foul, ranting mouth.

"Fuck the Assembly," he proclaimed, flinging himself sideways across Georg's winter-green couch. "Fuck the Provinces."

Georg poured him a drink as he ranted, decrying Jia, Voice of the Council, as a stupid little whore. The temples were run by ancient toads, outdated dens for paedophiles, and anyway the streets loved him, and had Georg read the latest reports from Budapesht?

"I have," murmured Georg. "Encouraging."

"Is that what you call it? Fucking cowards."

He drained the proffered drink, didn't seem to enjoy it, waved his glass for a refill, which Georg provided. That too was guzzled, and as he laid the glass down, the angle of his arm drifted towards where I stood, silent in my corner, and for the first time his eyes met mine. "Who's that?" he barked, sober and cold.

"That is Kadri, my assistant."

"Why's he just standing there?"

"He's waiting for instructions."

"Fuck off – there you go."

My eyes flickered to Georg, who half-nodded in confirmation. I gave a tiny bow from the waist and closed the double doors behind me on my way out.

On the last day of autumn, I cycle up to the forest's edge where the lumber merchants have sliced away the trees. All has been torn down and spat into machines – even the youngest saplings, the freshest growth. It was a pointless destruction, out of balance with the bargain we once struck with the kakuy. There is low thunder in the distance; tonight there will be lightning bright enough to punch through shutter, window, eyelid and sleep, a gasping awake as the heavens grumble in the fading heat.

The Assembly voted to harvest more timber, more from the forests in the hills above, to fish the rivers harder, deeper, to let the factories drain poisons into the downstream gullies and inlets. At my little desk outside Georg's office, I read the letters of protest from the other Provinces, the Assemblies of Bukarest and Budapesht, and from the Council itself.

"Are they going to do anything about it?" Georg would ask.

"Not that I can tell," I replied.

"Then it's just a waste of words. They will want to buy the things we sell, sooner or later. They'll come round. Temple won't be able to stop them – it doesn't know how."

"I was Temple. They will fight you."

He shrugged. "I don't fear the inquisitors."

At the edge of the devastation is a black line where the still-living forest waits for its fate, leaves brushing together like lovers' skin, roots tangled like claws into black, crawling soil. I watch the darkness and it watches back, and though I do not see the kakuy, I think that tonight he prowls beneath the moon in the form of the great black wolf, and I hear his voice howling and know that in this place nothing new will grow, as if the land were sown with salt.

Three months later, I see Yue.

Chapter 12

And where has Yue been, these twenty-odd years?

Why, she has been in Bukarest, studying, learning, working to become the best.

And then?

She has gone to Budapesht, to work for the Council, bringing the Provinces together in one Grand Assembly, doing so well, our Yue, doing so well.

Sometimes she returns to Tinics, at the spring and harvest festivals.

Then she only came back for spring.

Then she did not come back at all.

Mama Taaq spun spider silk from her tree and stirred the fish tanks at the top of the stream and said well, well. She's doing . . . so well. In time, even the nosiest of neighbours stopped asking about it.

And now?

Why, she is walking in Jia's delegation as it arrives at Vien's central station, a few people behind the Voice of Council herself. She is deputy to Krima vaMiyani, who everyone knows is a spy who pretends she's got an interest in culture and telecommunications. She is smiling politely to Antoni Witt, who is already eyeing up the heresies of Maze and muttering about extraordinary actions and desperate times – comments Antti Col has been quick to pick up on as provocative, dangerous. Council serves the Provinces, he snaps; it does not command them.

She is grown up, and having grown up there is nothing of the fire in her any more. She burned from the inside out, and now there are only cool palms pressed together in polite bow; ice smile and stone gaze. She does not see me – or if she does, she does not make the connection between my face, pressed into the shadows, and the boy who once stood with her by the kakuy tree.

She arrives two weeks after Assembly elections in which the Brotherhood wins the majority of seats in the Vien Assembly. She is here, officially, as part of the Council's overall responsibility to visit the Provinces and engage with the cities, Assemblies and temples.

They are here, unofficially, because the election put Antti Col in the Chief Minister's seat, and Antti Col is a humanist and a heretic.

"Fair reward for fair work!" he chants from the podium in the square. "Recognition of human difference, of the power of our diversity – that there are those born with talent, intelligence, strength, that men and women not the same, that we have our own unique parts to play in the balance of the world! A human balance! A human world!"

Georg does not stand on the podium. It is not his place.

When the speech is done, everyone applauds, except Jia, her followers and Yue.

Antti met Jia at the Assembly building, a vast converted pre-burning-era palace that had at one time held princes and kings, then dinosaurs and skeletons of great beasts. It now held restored statues of ancient gods and nude boys holding spears, and cases boasting a range of anthropological specimens from the history of Maze, from the first clay figures carved in mud to the gold cigarette bowls and restored combustion engines of the Burning Age, each adorned with little plaques explaining the traditions and beliefs of the time.

Antti brought Jia there as a power play, the Council forced to come and pay homage at the upstart's place of work, forced to climb the steps up to the great doors beneath the domed roof and flying flags, forced to wait her turn to see the newly appointed master of the Province, forced to smile when finally let in by a pasty demagogue.

I had never seen Jia in person before. I had voted for her in Council elections several times, and the general view of the Lyvodian Assembly was that she was a decent administrator, keeping the Provinces vaguely united through a mixture of tact and legalism. She was older than I expected, her straight black hair turning grey and swept up into a high, stiff topknot. She walked slow and stiff-backed through the halls, but when she sat, her spine would curve down in a little arch, as if the effort of erection were too much to be sustained. Her eyes were tiny in the almond folds of her long, pinched face, but whenever a camera was near she'd tilt her chin up to force her gaze down, creating the impression of a wider, more trustworthy stare. She bowed a little to any stranger who bowed to her, hands pressed together; bowed more to Assembly members, and noted but did not respond when delegates from the Brotherhood barely bowed at her in reply, their disrespect and disdain visible in every curl of their lips or sideways remark.

I kept out of her line of sight, positioning myself in corners and behind inkstone and briefcase, little more than portable furniture in human form. From here, I watched Yue. She walked some three metres behind Jia, buried in the older woman's entourage. Where Jia's stick-like straightness bespoke a harsh dignity, Yue was a metal string pulled between two rods, humming with a tension ready to snap. Her hair was braided either side, close to her skull; her tunic was crow-black, her hands encased in thin grey gloves. She carried her inkstone like a weapon, ready to draw and smash against her opponents, and her eyes scanned left and right, up and down, taking in everything like a cat who is unsure if it sees prey or a trap.

Everything except me.

For a moment, I thought of calling out to her, stepping out and catching her hand.

I did not.

70

Somewhere, hundreds of miles away, the forest was coming back to life. Vae never would.

"The mining – strip mining! When the kakuy wake ..."

"When the kakuy wake, when the kakuy wake, when the hell did the kakuy last wake?"

Voices half-heard through the door, arguments about politics, war, a glimpse of Yue at the back, in the room but not of it, stiff and straight as the winter pine.

"The kakuy don't care about borders; what happens in Maze will affect us all!"

Georg sticks his head out of the room to murmur: "More alcohol. This will be a delight."

I nod and go to fetch another bottle. The door closes tight behind Georg, blocking out the little trickle of sound I had been so attentively noting from the gloom.

I find Krima vaMiyani sat on a long balcony round the side of the room where Jia and her cohorts argued and raged, booted feet up on the railing, a drink of something fruity and full of seeds by her side, hat pulled across her eyes to block out the hard winter sun. Seeing her, I immediately move to retreat, but before I can she says: "Kadri Tarrad, isn't it?"

I freeze, turn, wait.

"Georg's assistant. I've seen you scurrying around in his wake. Do you love him?"

"What?" I blurt.

She tilts the hat a little back from her eyes, revealing eyebrows like razorblades, cobalt-black skin and lips painted shocking crimson, so bright on her face it is almost impossible to see anything but her thin, polite smile. "Do you love him?"

"No. I don't love him."

"Do you believe him?"

"Depends what you mean."

"That's a no, then. Are you greedy? I know you used to steal secrets from Temple."

71

From behind the door to her left, I hear voices raised in a sudden gale, then subsiding again. Her eyes don't leave my face as mine flicker to door, to sky, to my shoes and finally back to her. "It occurs to me," I say at last, "if you could convince me to spy for you between now and the time it takes for someone to miss you, that would probably be one of the fastest recruitments in the history of espionage."

She tuts and shakes her head. "On the contrary. The only way I could recruit you in the few charming seconds we have would be if I had spent months researching you to establish precisely how to leverage my approach. You may experience this moment as an instant, but I know how much work has gone into it. I know that there are gaps in your story, Kadri. Things even Georg doesn't know."

"Perhaps — but I'm not convinced you know them either. All you can see are the empty places, not what should fill them."

"I am chief of security for Council itself. I can find out."

"You can threaten me, of course. But you have to consider how scared I am of Georg. And I am. I am scared of him."

She sighs, shakes her head. The moment is gone. She has lost interest, returned to lounging in the last dredges of sun. Did this encounter even happen? Who's to say.

"Too bad," she muses, soft as autumn rain. "Too bad."

Two days later, Jia was gone, and Yue with her, riding the train back to Bukarest.

"That's enough for now," Georg mused, as I closed the shutters across the study windows. "That's enough."

I nodded, picked up my things, turned to leave, my standard dismissal.

"Will you drink?"

I stopped in the door, turned slowly, looked at him, found myself wanting to look away — a habit I thought I had broken in our months of association. He had turned from his customary position by the window to gaze directly at me, and when I didn't immediately answer he nodded towards the decanter on

72

the cabinet by the wall. I put my bag down, walked numbly to the vessel, poured – one for him, one for me – returned to where he stood, handed his drink over, stood dumb as he held it up.

"You are supposed to chink your glass," he explained. "It is a tradition of the Burning Age."

I knocked my glass against his, surprised at the heaviness of it, the depth of its ring. He drained his drink down in a single gulp, so I followed suit. The alcohol burned all the way to my stomach, a sickly-sweet taste of plum and syrup lingering on my tongue. Georg gestured at his couch. I sat, knees together, hands wrapped round my empty glass, and waited. He slipped into his desk chair, rolling back a little into its tanned depths, watched me, said at last: "What do you believe, Kadri Tarrad?"

I thought about the question a long, long time. I had learned that it was always better to stop and think, where Georg was concerned.

"Nothing," I said at last. "But there are things I know to be true, which you might call beliefs. I know that humanity was once master of this world. I know that there was a time when everyone had a car, and big houses, and … well, maybe not everyone. But it was the aspiration. We aspired. We made our choices."

"You're just quoting Antti's speeches – my speeches," he chided. "I asked what you believe."

"I told you. Nothing. None of this makes a difference to me. None of this changes a damn about who I am, or what I do."

"That seems … disappointing. For you, I mean. On a personal level."

I blinked, swallowed every other flutter of feeling that threatened to run across my face. In my time knowing him, I had never heard Georg express anything to do with sorrow, or joy, or any shred of human experience beyond the turning of the sun and the march of an idea. I thought I should say something, claw back the moment to some time before he had found a place in his heart to judge me, couldn't find anything worth saying.

He spared me the effort. "You come from Lyvodia, yes?"

I nodded.

"Where in Lyvodia?"

"Tseonom."

"So you would have been a child when the forest burned?"

In the place where the red leaves fall above a roaring river, the kakuy dies. Close my eyes and the forest is in me, burning still. I understand now that it will burn until the day I die.

"Yes."

"Did you see it?"

"Yes."

"What did it look like?"

"It . . . there was a lot of smoke. I saw blackness, but heard the fire. They took the children away. They kept us safe."

In the ashes of the night, Mama Taaq does not comfort her daughter who sits in the back of the ambulance. Tomorrow she will. Tonight Vae has died, and even the adults are human when the rain falls.

"Did they tell you why the fire started?"

I shook my head.

"Do you know?"

"I found out later. The old Chief Minister, he wanted a new . . . something . . . a road . . . but the Medj told him it would damage too much. They said the forest protected the land, and cutting down so much would bring harm and the anger of the kakuy. So he burned it all, because he could, and the kakuy did not stop him."

"No. They didn't."

"Neither did he build his road," I added, a little sharper than I meant, and he replied with a knife-edge look, a cutting into my soul, an inquiry that ripped through my bones and out the other side. "These things have always been . . . obscure," I stumbled. "When the forest burned, the land suffered. Mudslides and floods, crop failures, wild beasts attacking, stinking summers and freezing nights. Was this because the kakuy were wrathful? Or was it because trees have roots that bind the soil together in heavy rain? Temple says that these things are one and the same."

"What do you think?"

I half-closed my eyes. "I don't, any more."

Georg's lips drew in thin, a tiny motion I had learned to recognise over many years. Not exactly displeasure, but a sign of something to come, a change in the air. Then he barked: "Come with me."

I followed, scuttling to keep up as he marched down through the building, to a small triangular door set in the wall beneath a staircase, then down again. The cellar was cold and dry, the walls lined with inactive hard drives, boxed-up files and spare batteries, some large enough to boost a car, some tiny enough to slip into an inkstone. At the back was a low white door, with bolts at top and bottom. I had never been through it, never seen it unlocked, but now it opened with a juddering, time-warped scrape along the earth. Beyond was a smaller room, adapted for storage and then abandoned again, the remnants of fans and coolers still visible hanging from the walls, a shocking waste of valuable resources. In the middle, beneath a long white strip of lights, was a stool, and sitting on the stool was a man.

His nose was broken, the blood across his face so smeared by beating it was hard to tell the source of each splattered bleed. Spit, snot, tears and the broken liquids of shattered bones all mixed together to create rivers through the crimson, and he held one hand close to his chest – a hand from which two fingers and a thumb had already been removed. Klem, my next-door neighbour from the cold, stern hearth, sat against the back wall, reading. Sohrab doodled on his inkstone.

Georg pulled the door behind us closed, shutting in the cold and stink of iron. The bloody man looked up slowly, struggled to find focus, looked away. I huddled against the wall, trying to vanish into it as I had when Yue walked by. Georg said: "He's a spy. Sent by the Council. One of Krima's, meant to undermine us. Council says it doesn't interfere in Provincial democracy, and here he is."

The man shook his head but didn't speak, as if this were an ancient argument between old friends – no point continuing it now. Georg patted him on the shoulder, a gesture he'd performed on me a hundred thoughtless times, a habit that had seemed paternal and now would never be the same again. "Jia thinks Maze is going to split from the Provinces. They think we have fallen to humanism."

I looked from Georg to the man in the chair and back again. The childishness of it struck me suddenly, so hard I nearly laughed, and I had to squeeze my arms around my chest to hold in the bizarre hysteria.

"Would you?" Georg asked, and he had a knife in his hand. I had not seen him pick it up from a shelf or be handed it by my digit-clipping neighbour. It had a wooden handle, a folding steel blade. I took it, resting the tip on my left hand, like a royal sceptre. Georg gestured towards the man in the chair, who coughed on what might have been a whimper, a cry for mercy. I stepped towards him. He started to cry, not loudly, but with hiccupping gasps of breath. Somewhere through the stink of blood there was the high acid of urine and the severed fibres of the butcher's yard.

I shook my head, stepped away.

"No." I turned the blade, offered the handle back to Georg. He didn't take it, one eyebrow raised – another familiar gesture, the mountain buckling before the volcano bursts. "Get him to organise your spreadsheets," I snapped, tilting my chin towards Sohrab, who barely lifted his eyes from his inkstone. "Get him to run your errands or translate archaic text. When these two" – I indicated Sohrab and Klem – "can tell the difference between data corruption from degraded hard drives and random letters thrown in by a greedy forger, then come back to me and I'll do your dirty work."

"You're sacked," Georg replied.

I shrugged, and as no one seemed willing to take the knife, I folded the blade, walked to the door, laid it down. Perhaps the bloody man might make a run for it, have a chance; I doubted it, but he eyed that weapon with a sudden alertness that could be his doom.

"Pack your belongings and leave the hearth," added Georg as I jostled with the warped door, my exit somewhat undermined by its slow drag across the floor.

I nodded, hesitated, put my hands together in front of my heart, and bowed.

Then I turned and walked away from the killing room, leaving behind my boss, two murderers and a living corpse.

Chapter 13

Here I am.

Packing up my life.

The room in the hearth is small and grey. I have not filled it with possessions. Temple teaches us that the valuing of material things is how the Burning Age fell. We do not need to buy pretty things to prove our worth. From the earth we come, to the earth we shall return, and no gold or silver will change the crumbling of our bones.

Here, whispers Lah in my ear – here is the fellowship of your kin.

Here, proclaims Nadira as she stands upon the hill – here is the wind and there is the road. Travel it, and see where it will take you.

Here, calls out Vae in her child's sing-song. Here is the forest! Come into the forest, come play!

Here, tuts Georg. Here. Here are men who dream bigger than all that.

There is a telephone in the kitchen. Spin the dialler and listen to it clickety-clack, a sprung shudder as it waits for the next number. I could call the guardia. I could call someone. I do not. Winter has turned the world monochrome. The yellow lights of the hearth are the only colour in a world drained to grey. Even the street-lamps are the white of snow, picking out stardust in the ice below.

I think I feel hungry, but it is not hunger. The idea of eating enthrals and terrifies me.

I fold my clothes, smoothing out the creases, sleeve over chest, taking up the smallest, neatest place in the bag. The first train to Bukarest won't leave for another three hours. The journey will take approximately seventeen hours, with a change in Budapesht. Usually I'd take the night train, setting off just after supper and arriving in time for a brunch of hot bread, fresh tomato and cheese. I wonder what I will say when I go home. I wonder if the lake around the temple has frozen again, and if the novices go skating when their chores are done.

Downstairs, the telephone is silent above the kitchen sink. No one calls, and neither do I.

Most of what I own is on an inkstone. My clothes fit in a bag across my shoulder. I took no memorabilia with me nor made anything here that was worth remembering. The burning is over, but on the surface of the moon there is a portrait of a man's family, left by an astronaut hundreds of years ago who was allowed to carry no more than that little weight with him into space. I have no pictures of my past, nothing worth remembering in my present.

I pull my sleeves down over my wrists, adjust my bag over my shoulder, head for the door. There are a couple of floorboards which squeak loudly; I avoid them on automatic, glance into the courtyard below as I pass the window, see the turned-over mud which in spring will be a lettuce patch and stems of garlic, carrot and potato, the winding tendrils of the sweet pea. There had been days when I was almost happy in the garden, helping tie fresh growth to the trellis wall, nibbling on the first pods of the harvest. My feet carry me away.

The gate is timber coated with the slick resin from the algae vats. I push it open just wide enough to let myself out into the dark, trying to keep the screeching to a minimum. Outside, sitting on the bonnet of his car, Klem is waiting for me. There is still some blood on the side of his neck, fresh from his work in the cellar. I stop and stare at him. He does not smile. Nods once. Puts a hand on my arm, guides me into the open passenger door and slams it shut behind me.

Chapter 14

There is a shrine a few miles outside the city, built on stilts above the wet earth. When the Ube floods, the water rises up beneath it until it appears to float in an inland sea. At such times, you must reach it by boat, the slippery green steps vanished beneath the river's skin. It boasts no resident Medj nor lay acolytes; it stands so the fishermen may stop when reeling in the nets and give thanks to the kakuy of the river and the blessings that the water gave and the life that will feed them until they perish. Not many people visit these days.

The wooden structure is little more than a platform with a small roofed shed at one end, where the liquid form of the kakuy of the Ube is represented in ancient fused glass pulled from the landfill mines. Offerings of bits of net and the occasional hook are left before it, along with the more traditional incense and alcohol. Unlike the larger temples, these offerings are not regularly cleaned out by the novices, and the wax candles have spilt rivers of white and yellow down the altar like a frozen waterfall. The Medj in Maze long ago grew neglectful of their tasks, and on that night of waning moon, the river stank of something chemical, and white foam bubbled and shifted on the surface like oil on silt, cracking the thin sheet of ice that was trying to form.

It was a strange place for an execution, I thought, but so be it. The tide was low enough that I could see the stairs to the single hanging lantern above the wooden gateway to the shrine, and towards these I was waved, Klem waiting below as if the idea of setting foot on sanctified ground displeased him.

I climbed the steps, clinging to the rail as my feet skidded on decades of tide-washed grime that never fully dried, that was too alive to freeze. One candle burned in the altar; three more hung in lanterns round the high-beamed timber frame of this little floating pavilion, peeking through fat-coned icicles. There was no electricity, nor any attempt to generate it, just the creaking timbers of the floor and the smell of mud. A small wooden bench was set to the side of the shrine for the older fishermen to sit on after a long day's contemplation. Here, bent over and ankles crossed, was Georg. He looked smaller than I had ever seen him, older, as if the presence of the kakuy took something from him. Or perhaps he was going to sleep – perhaps this night was the one night of the year when he actually closed his eyes and snored like a hibernating bear. His breath puffed in clouds captured by yellow candlelight, rolling up towards the moon. He didn't look at me as I approached. Georg never looked at much that wasn't inside his own head. I stood before the shrine for a moment, contemplating my next move. Then I put my hands together and bowed. Here, now, seemed as good a time as any.

Then Georg said: "Temple sends spies too."

I nodded, staring into the flame of the single flickering candle. Brilliant colour against the blue of night, its spilling illumination catching the otherwise smothered reds and umbers of the painted shrine.

"Once Antti has enough support in the Assembly, we are going to declare independence from Council. Throw out Temple. Live as people should."

I said nothing. There didn't seem anything worth saying.

He straightened up, unwinding the curl of his back like a fern uncoiling its leaf. My lack of feedback seemed briefly annoying for him, which is perhaps why his next words were: "When I was fifteen, I saw the kakuy of the mountain."

A freezing terror twisted in my belly. I tasted it in my mouth and didn't know why, couldn't put my finger on what it was in

81

this moment that robbed me of my training, my common sense. Without thinking, I reached out to cup the flame in my right hand, feeling its warmth push a little too close to burning, half-closed my eyes to enjoy the sensation.

"My father and I were not welcome at a hearth," he continued, turning his head as if telling an old story to an uninterested moon. "My father was a brilliant man. Difficult, angry, brilliant. He saw things that other people did not see, questioned everything. The Medj smiled their little smiles and said oh yes, how interesting, you should think about that more. But after a while they stopped smiling and said no, no, you've got it wrong, this is dangerous. We would try to negotiate a bed, and they'd give us a week, a month at most, then send us on our way. They couldn't accept him because he was smarter than them, and didn't hide it. He didn't pretend to be happy when he was sad, or that he was content with just ... dust and water. He wanted more, and if the world was run in any meaningfully intelligent way he would have had it. More than anyone else living. But he didn't. He hit me, sometimes. The hearths were outraged. It made me a stronger man; it gave me discipline, focus, but all they saw was a grown man striking a child. He was not wrong to do it. He had a constant pain in his shoulder, all the time. We went to the clinics and they did their tests and couldn't find anything wrong, prescribed painkillers, but they do things to your brain, make you slow. He never took them. Pain does not make a man kind. It is part of who we are, and we are scared of it.

"We lived on charity, and when times were good the hearths said of course, of course, come in. And when times were bad they told us to wait in the door and brought us soup, said the fires were low and the batteries were empty, and perhaps we'd have better comfort if we begged at Temple. 'Begging'. My father despised the word. It is not a word for men, he said. But we were beggars for a while – I have outgrown his dishonesty. Then, one winter, he went to the black mountains and got work in the forest, harvesting timber, but he cut down more than his pitiful share. The kakuy will be angry, they said – the kakuy knows we have taken more trees than will re-grow here, and it will be displeased at our greediness. For fear of the mountain, they punished the man – can you imagine it?

"My father was always proud. He swore he would kill the kakuy, said they died as easily as any other living thing, that we should not fear the avalanche or the fire, that we could surpass our cowardly natures. He told me to stay behind, but I did not, and he knew he couldn't stop me. I followed a hundred paces behind, as we climbed through the thickening snow and fading moonlight. That night it was as if the sky itself were trying to throw us back, as if the kakuy knew we were coming and what he intended. No more gods, he said. Man must decide for himself. He should have died fighting a god; should have run it through, red on white. Instead, he fell. The wind caught him and tripped him up; he lost his footing in the dark and fell into a ravine hidden beneath snow. No defiance or rage, just eaten by the darkness. They say the mountain killed him, but I lay belly-down on the edge of that cliff and called for my father, lay there until the first light of dawn and the snowstorm had passed, until my lips were white and I was starting to feel warm again inside.

"That was when I saw it: the wolf of the mountains, taller than any man, blood in its eyes and on its jaw, tail twitching through the snow, fur of crystal ice. It watched me from the last shadows of the night, until the rising light drew a line across the snow that seemed to strike it like fire. Then it reared up, turned away, galloped back into the mist, so heavy I could feel every strike of its paws upon the earth, until suddenly it stopped mid-stride as if it had flown into the air. A few minutes later, I heard the sounds of people from the hearth below, calling out for us, climbing up the mountain in search of me and my father. I didn't call back, but they found us anyway, led upwards as if pulled by the rising sun towards the summit. They wrapped me in blankets and put me on the back of a sledge and said it must have been the kakuy's blessing that saved my life, must have been a miracle. Humans are hard-wired to find the worst in a situation, did you know that? It was how our ancestors survived, expecting tigers when

83

there were none, expecting disaster so that when disaster finally came, they were prepared. So we have always blamed ourselves for the very worst that the world must offer – blamed our sin, our wickedness, our evil ways. But when there is good in this world – when our hearts keep beating because they are strong, when our limbs return to life because we are young and vibrant and want to live – we say it is a blessing. We thank anyone but ourselves and dismiss pride as arrogance, ability as hubris. We even know this about ourselves, can recognise our own genetic traits. And yet knowledge, it seems, does not yet triumph over instinct."

He grunted, an almost-laugh, and lapsed back into silence, head turning towards the floor, hands pressed together in his lap. I pulled my fingers back from the flame, turned to examine him, felt for the very first time like his equal and wondered how the forest grew.

He let out a breath, half-shook his head, rose to his feet. I stepped away instinctively, then hesitated, stepped forward again, holding my ground. He was taller than me, broader across the chest and back, but I had options which were unbecoming of a temple-trained renegade. "Council sends spies. Temple too," he said.

I shrugged. "If you think I'm a spy, you should probably have killed me a while ago."

"I have spent several nights thinking the same thing."

"Why don't you just torture me, like the other guy?"

"Torture makes people say what you want to hear."

"Is he a spy?"

"Oh, absolutely. That is certain."

"How can you be so sure?" He didn't answer, eyes bright in reflected candlelight. I sighed, leaned back on the altar, feeling suddenly old, cold. "Council sends spies against you – I under-stand that. You send spies back. You have always enjoyed the game. Winning is how you know you're better, yes?"

"Yes."

"But you didn't bring me here to kill me."

"No."

"Then why am I here? You aren't one for indecision. Sack me or kill me; if not, I've got a train to catch."

"The kakuy of the river is dying." He gestured loosely towards the water, towards the guttering light and slithering mud. "The fishermen's offerings are rotten, we take what we need, the kakuy dies but the river flows. The river will still flow, as long as people need it to. Do you understand?"

I shrugged. "Am I dead? Am I at least sacked?"

He shook his head.

"Then why bother with all this?"

"Because a spy, embedded for as long as you have been, would not simply have walked away. Maybe you wouldn't have killed another agent; maybe you would have tried to talk your way out of it. Maybe you would have killed him too, or called your handler, or the guardia – done something. You should have done something, to protect your cover or your colleague. Otherwise, all this would have been for nothing. But you walked away."

I felt sickness in my belly, warmth on my face, heard the sea in my ears. I reached out again for the candle, spun my fingers round the flame like a spider weaving a web, listened to the slow sludgy groan of the dying river, to the steady breathing of Georg beside me, then pinched the candle out.

"There's a spare room above my office," he said. "You will move in there tonight."

"I want a pay rise."

"Of course you do."

"No more bullshit. If you want to kill people in your cellar, that's your business. But I don't know if your little revolution is going to succeed, so I need plausible deniability. I'm not some hired killer. You've got Klem for that, or Sohrab. They can deal with it."

"I agree." He held out his hand. "Settled, then?"

I shook it, his fingers hot against my frozen skin.

Chapter 15

From that day forth, I became Georg's shadow. As the Brotherhood cemented its control of the Assembly, as heresy clawed deeper into the very fabric of the state and the kakuy of the river died, I was there, foam tossed in Georg's wake. I translated profanity, ran errands, organised his laundry, met forgers, spies and generals at his behest, made sure there was always the good stuff to drink in the cabinet. I learned his taste, his moods, his inclination. When he got a cold, resentful and furious at nature for slowing him down when there was so much to do, so so much, I made him lemon tea and stood over him until it was drained, tutting at his faces and his snarls. When he went to the bathhouse, I read to him out loud from the edge of the tub, so that even when scrubbing soap into his hair he could still be thinking on the day's events.

I did all this as the kakuy stirred in the mountains and the Provinces slipped ever closer to war. I did it, because I was a traitor.

Three weeks after the blood had been cleaned from the cellar floor, Georg and the Brotherhood leaders retired to a mountain chalet of timber and fresh fire above the snow. The easiest way up the mountain was by cable car: the first up a steep slope of a sheer black cliff which in the sunset turned bloody scarlet; the second a string between two peaks, which clunked and rattled on its spinning cogs and swayed in the high, whistling breeze. It was a good place to plot heresy, far from prying eyes. I wondered

86

if in these mountains Georg had seen his wolf, and if his habit of walking barefoot upon the snow reminded him of that kakuy darting from the light.

While the great and the good settled in for a night of drinking and planning the overthrow of the old order of things, I was left with fetching and carrying baggage. There was more than could fit into a single cable car up the mountain with their guests, and so up and down again I went alone, peering out over the whistling void from the gloom of the swaying compartment.

It was while struggling to load a moving car with these goods at the bottom of the mountain that Nadira approached. She wore a knitted red hat and thick brown mittens, black boots and a padded blue coat that made her look significantly rounder than her build. She sidled up to me as I worked my way round the arc of belongings I had piled up at the base of the cable car's turning red wheel, bowed politely and said: "Is there room for another, sky-kin?"

"The chalet at the top has been reserved for a private function."

"I didn't realise you could reserve mountains for yourself."

"Members of the Assembly are there."

"Ah – men of influence."

"Brotherhood," I replied with a little smile. "They like having things to themselves."

"How very strange," she mused. "But what if I just stay on the car and do not get off? I would love the ride."

"I'm sure that is fine. There is an interchange at the top, and as no one is helping me— Ah, quickly, step on board!"

She slipped into the approaching car as it swung round the clunking wheel on its rolled carbon cable, pulling her knees up to avoid the cases I slung in behind her. "This is a lot to carry," she mused, as I hopped unevenly in over the welt of luggage I had created, slamming the door shut as we began to ascend.

"It's a working vacation," I muttered, the words sour in my mouth as I considered the amount of work this had given me, relative to how little vacation. We picked up speed as we transitioned from the slower cable of the station to the long line heading skywards, lurching as we shifted tracks. "You know all about those, Nadira."

She grinned, tiny teeth in a plum face. Her hat was pulled low over bushy black eyebrows, her lips were almost the same soft pinky-beige as her cheeks, and her age had always been hard to deduce through the tight, sun-baked impermeability of her skin. "How do the Brotherhood feel about holiday pay?" she asked.

"Is this a professional question, or are you just curious?"

"Curiosity; holidays are not as heretical as strip mining or cluster munitions or jet fuel."

"You read my reports."

"Devoured them."

"Then what in the name of fire and ash are you doing about it?" I snarled. "I have given the inquisition *everything*. Every theft, every assault, every bribe and blackmail, every *murder* the Brotherhood has committed. They have information on oil rigs. They have information about machine guns. Where in the name of sun and moon are they getting it? How are they getting it? Classified Temple reports, sealed heresies on my desk! Last week I got a document on forced sterilisation with a hand-written note from a damn inquisitor on it. 'Bad stuff, send to anthropology.' They are stripping the forests, they are building *tanks*. They talk about ... about 'social engineering' and the rights of wealth, about free market and geoengineering. They are ... *What the hell are you doing about it?*"

My hands were shaking, my throat suddenly so tight I wondered if I'd swallowed down too much of the cold, if the wolf of the mountains would find my blood turned to ice, my heart a stone in my chest. I pressed my head against the walls of the car as we swayed upwards, and she watched, eyebrows drawn, hands relaxed.

Finally Nadira said: "The inquisition does not have the same powers as a Council operation. Temple is not meant to interfere politically – our remit is tracking and cataloguing heretical material."

"Fuck that. This *is* political."

"Do you need out? We can get you out, Ven."

The words – the first time I had heard these words in so long – sank into my gut like tar. I sat down on a rickety wall of luggage, pressed one hand against the wall to stop myself slipping, stared into her eyes and realised that, a lot like Georg, I couldn't tell when she was lying.

"They killed a man," I mumbled, surprised to find the words coming from my lips. "They said he was a spy."

"I know."

"Was he?"

"Almost certainly. A Council agent – one of Krima's."

"The last few weeks they've rolled up whole networks."

"I know. Krima came to us."

"What did she say?"

"She wanted to know if Temple had any assets in Vien. She knows the Brotherhood would be an inquisition target. She was as close to desperate as I've ever seen her."

I nodded dully, curling up tight against the thin cold of the mountain. "She tried to recruit me, when Jia was in town. It was ... it seemed a somewhat reckless play. Nadira – how does Georg have access to so much heresy? How did he find the Council spy?"

Nadira half-closed her eyes, and there was for an instant a hint of the Medj she had been before she joined the inquisition, a drawing in of breath and a settling into the frosty air that did not recoil from cold but rather gave thanks for it, thanks for the heat of her body. I wondered if I did that – if Georg sometimes saw my gratitude for the touch of rain.

"Georg has a spy in the Council," she said, eyes still a little closed, fingers uncurling in her lap as if she might cradle these words, uttered in the shaking cabin of our ride. "The inquisition is almost certain of it."

"How?"

"The connection between Temple and Council has always been ... complicated. The one has always supported the other, but so very much of the heresy we uncover is political. And

89

there have always been accusations that the inquisition oversteps the mark. 'Dabbling', as they say. Every Province has a secular review board to oversee Temple classification of heresies, to ensure that we are not, as they put it, keeping humankind in the dark. In Damasc, the secular boards are if anything even harsher in their censorship than Temple inquisitors. In Maze, the board has long ceased being anything other than an oppositional body determined to unclassify as much material as possible. Council also has a review board, to oversee the most dangerous, most sensitive material in Temple archives – the kind of material no one Province should have access to. Over time the relationship has become ... more than strictly academic. The kakuy must sleep. Council must keep the peace, no matter what the Provinces do. To aid this, the Temple sometimes shares intelligence of ... political relevance, you might say."

In Bukarest, there are still protesters chanting at the gates of the temple, calling out for freedom from the chains of the Medj. I wondered if Lah still served them tea. "That sounds profoundly illegal – and unethical."

Nadira smiled. "I think perhaps it is. It is also sometimes necessary. Lah has written a great deal of highly classified and stunningly tedious philosophical tracts on the subject. You should read them some day." I didn't answer, and finally her eyes opened again, head tilted to one side, a curious bird. Softly in the hush of the passing sky: "There must be peace, Ven. Can you imagine what would happen if war wakes the kakuy?"

I curled tighter in my coat, the cold heart-deep. "They knew who he was, but they tortured him anyway. The Council spy. They knew. And I walked away."

"You protected your mission. Not too hot, not too cold. Georg Mestri only trusts people he thinks he can own. Do you want out?"

The first time I met Nadira, it was at the Temple of the Lake, two months after Lah recruited me to the inquisition. She sang the evening prayers before a congregation of laypeople and novices, a solo voice without drum or bell, and after there was honey cake and camomile tea and people asked her how her little book of poems was going and if she'd had any luck finding a publisher, and I saw only a devout civilian, a little frumpy and a little loud, and couldn't quite believe she was inquisition until Lah swore by moon and star she was. It took me weeks to ask her how she did it – how she played so well the part of the affable neighbour writing barely competent poetry. "By being it," she replied primly. "And I'll thank you to call my poetry average at least."

Now the snow moves upon the mountain, a skin-sharp biting of silver in the dark, and I say: "Antti is going to pass a motion granting the Brotherhood access to all temple servers in Maze – even the classified ones. As soon as the bill gets out of committee, they're going to send militia. The Medj won't have time to erase the data; every archive in the Province will be seized."

"Council can oppose it in court. Tie it up for months."

"They're hoping Council will. Further proof of the interference of outside forces on Provincial independence. Doesn't matter – the militia will occupy the temples the moment the bill is read. They're calling it a 'day of people's action'. The temple in Grazt has nuclear fission on its servers. Vien is a centre for the study of ethnic cleansing and cultural genocide. Innsbruk has nearly two thousand entries on 're-education' camps. Antti says people are easier to work with when they're already on your side. He makes it sound like a joke."

The cabin rocked a little in a crosswind, clickety-clacked on the high overhead wires as it passed the counterweighted car descending in the opposite direction. Nadira was silent a while, hands fixed in her lap, feet rooted on the ground. She made me unlearn how to sit, when she'd become my handler. Only priests sit for hours cross-legged with palms at prayer, she'd say. Inquisitors slouch.

Finally: "Who knows this?"

"Antti. Georg. Kun Mi. Brika and Tanacha. A dozen or so staffers for the Brotherhood. Me."

"If they go into the temples and find the hard drives wiped, they'll know they've been infiltrated."

"If they go into the temples and find material on nuclear fission, the kakuy will be the least of our concerns."

"What do you want me to do, Ven? We can protect the archives or we can protect your cover – I don't see how we can do both."

"For what my cover is worth. Krima said something when she tried to recruit me: 'There are gaps in your story'. She was looking at Kadri Tarrad, and of course we made that cover weak, made it so that Georg could punch straight through it, but I don't think she meant that. She may have thought there was something criminal she could leverage, didn't connect the gaps in my story with the inquisition. But Georg could. If he looked hard enough. If he has a mole on the Council."

We clattered a while upwards, shrouded in snow and wind. Vien was only a few hours away by train, but close your eyes and you could forget that there were cities or traitors or secrets and lies. We are children of the clouds. With our feet, we pray to the mountain; with our breath, we become one with the sky. So say the Medj, and sometimes, very occasionally, I remember what it is like to believe it, to feel the ocean in my blood and breathe my ancestors in every exhalation. Then I close my eyes, and instead I remember only the fire, and the kakuy.

"Pontus," said Nadira, and it seemed that she too was speaking to the darkness, to the turning night that all things shared. But look again and for a moment you could see the old inquisitor there, the woman who had infiltrated a sect in the Delta who knew just enough about genetic editing to cause a plague; the historian who had dared the first dive into the flooded caverns beneath Martyza Eztok, where the last archivists of the Burning Age had buried their secrets in the old mines beneath the cracked earth. "Georg's spy in Council – we call them Pontus. We don't know who Pontus is, don't have the power to investigate. Krima vaMiyani is in charge of counter-intelligence and has proven reticent to move."

"Why?"

"We're not sure. Internal politics, perhaps. If there is a mole, the damage it would do the reputation of her department, and the Council in general, would be severe."

"More severe than someone sending Georg classified heretical material? More severe than if Maze does split, commits heresy — more severe than war?"

"I believe the Council, and the other Provinces, are all hoping it won't come to that."

"Georg doesn't fear the kakuy." I couldn't meet her eyes as I said it, and as the words passed my lips I thought I saw Lah sitting beneath the cypress tree, sighing: we have failed. Humanity grows arrogant, forgets that it is part of the world, not above it, and we have failed. "Georg cannot conceive of anything upon this earth that cannot be conquered by human intelligence."

"How very old-fashioned of him. I do have an idea, but it will, of course, be absurdly dangerous."

I opened my mouth to laugh, or curse, or tell her where to get off, when a sharp twist of her chin silenced me. I felt the clatter as the cable car bounced onto the slower track, decelerating on its approach to the higher station. Then her face was set in a gormless grin and she was blathering: "Oh, look! The view, oh yes!"

Klem and Sohrab were waiting for me at the top of the mountain, eyes narrowing and lips curling at the sight of Nadira in the swaying cable car. But she did not get out, and I did, dragging the bags of the great men of humanity reborn onto the station floor.

Chapter 16

I did not attend the lunar festival that greeted the new year, celebrated as the first icicles began to thaw. Instead, I worked late.
We were often working late, and Georg never seemed to care.

"Have you had enough?" he'd ask me, when I yawned. It
wasn't reproof, reproach. If I'd had enough, I could go home,
and that would be fine. He would learn from this the measure of
me and my skills and use me accordingly. Some men were weak;
others were strong. That was the truth that lay at the heart of the
Brotherhood.

"No," I lied. "I can keep going."

He nearly smiled then, and nodded, and we carried on
with our work.

"Ull, what a pleasure."

I had never seen Ull of Lyvodia, Minister of my home Province,
up close before. The old man had skin the colour of summer night,
hair like winter snow. He leaned on a walking stick and looked
round Antti's office disapprovingly, as if counting every heresy
on the wall, every trapping of Burning Age pomposity knotted
at Antti's throat and pinned into the cuffs of his shirt. His deputy,
Farii, looked around with a somewhat less outraged gaze, eyes
bulging at the panoply of items, historical and new, assembled in
the Brotherhood's lair. I stood behind, inkstone poised to record
conversations, take notes, run errands; Georg's loyal secretary.

"Antti," Ull greeted the Minister with only one part of his

mouth in motion, the rest clamped shut around what he wanted to say. "You've done well for yourself."

"Maze is thriving, despite Council interference – as you can see. Please, let me show you round."

In private, Antti cursed Ull and Lyvodia, called him a backwater mystic, a tree-hugging crone with wooden teeth and a peg leg. In public, he smiled and smiled and invited Ull to observe the authentic burning era collection of iconic "action figures" he'd salvaged from the landfill site, muscle-bound hunks of manhood and women in skimpy pants and bras, their hair flowing free behind impossibly glued-on masks. "We can learn so much about the idealistic culture of the past, the aspirational nature of their story-telling," he said, one arm on Ull's shoulder as if he might at any time split down the middle, teeth rupturing from his rib cage, and swallow the old man whole.

Farii looked at me and said: "Where do I leave my coat?"

That night, as they argued, the door stayed open and I sat outside it, listening.

"If Maze is committing heresy, then Jia has the right to call on the Provinces to intervene."

"Heresy! Old women in old shawls making pronouncements on how we should live, what we should do? How many times has the Temple got it wrong? How many times have they banned knowledge that now we thrive on?"

"A gradual process—"

"Is their excuse! It's always their excuse."

Georg passed me, sitting stiff on my strange, refurbished chair from another world, stopped as if he'd never seen me before. "Are you always listening?" he asked.

"Yes," I replied.

He thought about this, then nodded, "Good," and went inside and did not close the door behind him.

Dinner was an austere affair, designed to demonstrate to Ull that Maze, for all its talk of prosperity, humanism, freedom, was still culturally right up his street. Dumplings and cabbage, sweet and sour sauces that clung like molasses to the tip of your tongue, fruit tarts served in custard; white wine from the vineyards to the north, which I poured into small ceramic cups as the table toasted good fortune, perpetual peace, the brotherhood of man, and so on.

Then, as if he had wanted to say it all along and could no longer hold his tongue, Ull blurted: "We give thanks for the food that feeds us, the water that makes us whole. We give thanks for this gift from the earth."

Antti's face flushed a peculiar shade of incensed crab as Ull bowed his head, hands raised with cup between them in ancient ritual blessing. Georg tilted his cup towards the old man in polite acknowledgement, drank without a word. Farii bowed her head as was the tradition of the thing, but her eyes were raised, watching everyone, and her lips mouthed the words without sound.

"You. Come here."

Her voice, when she spoke on her own part, away from the ears of men, was sharp, trained to command, frustrated that it didn't have as much opportunity in that area as she wished.

I approached the corner of the balcony where Farii stood, cup clasped in one hand, eyes running across the city. Vien at midnight, the half-fallen, newly restored spires of old temples lit up like knives to heaven, the lazy curl of the river a visible line of black cutting through streets of hanging lanterns. The Deputy Minister had been a voice in politics since she was old enough to vote, but achieved minimal political success until finally paired with old Ull some four years ago. Certainly, people said, she was a woman who could get things done. Competence rolled off every pore, and without much in the way of small talk to accompany this trait, it was as if she had embraced this one attribute into her heart, into every fibre of her being. However much people said she seemed cold, stand-offish, harsh, rude, or whatever the latest word was for the most efficient way of doing business, at least she had this – at least she was competent. Ull hugged children, talked about compassion and honour. Farii sacked those who made false promises; harangued those who didn't get the job done, and everyone was appreciative, and no one thanked her for it. Fine russet hair stopped an inch above her shoulders in a straight, thin bob that hardly moved when she did. Green-grey eyes looked down on the city as if waiting at any moment for a fire to start. When her face was neutral, it was an almost formless thing, with thin pale lips and small flat nose seeming to blend into each other. On those occasions when she frowned – or, more rarely, smiled – contours of fibre and tendon emerged from cheek and chin, as if she existed in only two states: animated, or corpse-like, with no middle ground between.

"Take my cup," she said, and I took her cup, made to leave. "What's your name?"

"Kadri Tarrad, sky-kin."

"Where are you from? Your accent. Lyvodia?" I had barely spoken ten words in the entire evening, but she had an ear for it. "Where?"

"Tseonom."

"Why are you here, not there?"

"I prefer the work here."

"You are Georg's . . . what? Assistant?"

"Yes."

"Good. Stay his friend, Kadri Tarrad. Whatever you do, stay his friend."

I nodded, half-bowed, hesitated. "May I ask you a question, sky-kin?"

"For yourself, or for Georg?"

"There's not much difference any more, is there? But for me." She shrugged. "Go on."

"All this . . . talk. All this change."

"All this heresy, you mean? Georg's man shouldn't have to mince words. Come – say what you're thinking."

"As you will. All this heresy. It is clear that Ull is not interested, but that, perhaps, you are."

"Is there a question there?"

"What will you do, if you're wrong? What will you do if the kakuy wake?"

She thought about it for a moment, eyes drifting across the city, through its streets and to the lights still burning in the tops of every close-woven hearth. "I believe in people," she murmured — not for me, but for the night, perhaps; for the heat of the bodies pressed into the streets below. "I believe in people."

That seemed to be her answer, for, with a flick of her hand, I was dismissed, and bowing, I backed away.

Chapter 17

Nadira said: "There is a plan."

We met only in the dark places now, in scuttling moments snatched between the hours I worked, worked, worked for Georg. She waited for me near the dead drops where I left my stolen data rinsed from any inkstone foolishly left open in my sight; where I deposited the little capsules of microfilm snapped of documents half-glimpsed on a midnight desk. There were dark rings around her eyes. I had forgotten whether there was ever anything else around mine.

"There is a plan," she repeated, as we pressed like lovers into the corner of the alley, beneath the ticking of the high-up compression battery and the scuttling of a startled cat. "To find Pontus before Pontus finds you."

I waited, head on one side. Georg never needed many words, and I had grown out of the habit of inquiry.

"Temple shares heresy with Council. Pontus shares heresy with Georg. We have prepared a document – plausible without being correct – on autonomous military drones. Highly classified. Very tasty. We deliver this document to the relevant parties – identical copies, apart from a unique identifying error in each one – a spelling mistake or a comma misplaced. Do you understand?"

"Yes. You bait Pontus with false intelligence. Pontus sends it on to Georg. Georg gets me to verify it. I look for the error you have introduced. The error reveals Pontus. I understand. It is all very . . . simple."

It is simple, yet it is hard not to close my eyes and whisper to the earth beneath me, hold me tight, hold me tight, I never feared you, I have never feared death and yet I fear, I fear, I fear. Why is this? Why does Georg's face blaze in my mind brighter than a forest fire?

"Ven," she whispers, a hand on my arm – she's never done that before. "This is how we save your life."

I nodded, and could not speak, and, in the sleepless darkness of the night, thought that perhaps I had forgotten how to pray.

Georg said: "Read this and report back in an hour."

And Georg said: "Check what time Witt's train arrives!"

And Georg said: "Drink?"

And Georg said: "No, that won't do. We'll have to re-work the entire thing."

And Georg said . . .

Sometimes I wake in the middle of the night in a panic and don't know where I am. Georg sits at the end of my bed and tuts and has a knife in his hand – that knife that he keeps somewhere about himself, all the time. Perhaps it was his father's, the last relic of a man too intelligent for this world. And then I wake again and he is not there, not in my room, not in my head.

A parade of dignitaries through the office door.

Pav Krillovko laughs and says, though there is nothing funny in his voice: "Dearest thing, it sounds like you want war!"

Shamim, Chief Minister of Damasc, takes the train up from Isdanbul, sits and listens without commenting, then says: "The Voices of the Assembly thank you for your clarity," and leaves again, showing no sign as to whether Antti's pitch of humanism, freedom, justice has made any difference whatsoever to the old man's ears.

A delegation of Medj accompanies Chief Minister Shahd from the Delta, and they are furious. Their faith is one of denial, of leaving not a footprint on the earth, of eating only the bare mini-mum to survive, of bleeding on the soil in apology for an endless, uncertain litany of crimes. They are of the Temple, but not

Temple as I know it. They call the Medj of Lyvodia weaklings; they say the priests of Maze do not merit the name. Their trip is a waste; Antti does not even bother to meet them in person – too busy, many apologies. After, they are lambasted in the press, mocked as fanatics, hypocrites, zealots. There is nothing in this world that they do not believe cannot be cured by carrot juice and prayer. Go back to the great river of the south. Go bleed on Council time.

I do not bow as they depart, this increasingly desperate line of people trying to pretend there won't be a war, and I wonder: which one of you is Georg's spy?

This is a secret so precious that he won't even share it with me, his nearest shadow.

I will find it out by myself.

One morning, as I am drinking tea in the cold dawn air, I find the microdrone.

It's the size of a dead pigeon, folded gossamer wings limp at its sides. It has fallen just outside the back door, where Klem parks the car. An accident, an error – it's hard to tell. Most of its body is battery and solar cell, but there is a little panel beneath its belly that I can slide back and . . .

"Give that here! Give it now!"

I have never seen Georg so angry. He snatches the thing from me and shoves me back with the palm of his left hand, open, a moment away from a slap. Cradles the microdrone to him like a mother holding a child and does not look me in the eye as he storms away.

Five minutes later, it is as if nothing has happened, and neither of us mention it again.

Ten minutes before the Vien Assembly ratified the Equal Knowledge Act, allowing unrestricted access to every heretical server in Temple's vaults and de-criminalising previously heretical actions such as stock buybacks and unfettered logging, large numbers of guardia started to appear at the gates of the major temples across Maze. They were joined by even larger numbers of Brotherhood militia members, ringing their bicycle bells as they circled, like vultures above the bloated carcass. The moment the fastest watch on the keenest leader hit 8 p.m., they clattered through the gates, some chanting revolutionary slogans, some too focused on their tasks to bother. The Medj didn't put up a physical fight. The richest and most joyfully inept were long fled, and though pious remainers were threatened, the militias had been ordered to avoid a scandal, play nice, show that they were here for the people.

"We will defend our people's right to choose their own lives against any aggression from the Provinces or Council," Antti proclaimed. "This is a great day for Maze, a great day for freedom."

On the edge of the river, the land is turning sickly yellow. In summer, it doesn't rain, or sometimes it rains too much. In winter, the ice crawls up the windowpanes, sealing you inside; or there is no ice at all and when the spring comes the mosquitoes swarm in black clouds over pools of muddy water, growing fat and crimson. Is this the curse of the kakuy or the consequence of the new factories Antti has authorised, producing ever cheaper, ever more futile goods to purchase and display as a sign of wealth – and therefore worth – in this strange new world?

Perhaps the kakuy are angry, but they have never spoken to us in a human tongue, so why should we care? Lesser creatures are dumb; humans have always known this.

Temple servers are only powered up when needed. The most heretical information is kept in isolation from all networks, cut off far below the shrines. Caverns hollowed in the earth keep the worst of summer heat from the drives; walls of dry clay are raised against the damp, fans gently turning to keep cold air flowing. The original antiques are in sealed, airless cases, historical remnants to be studied, marvelled at and displayed for curious scholars of the Burning Age. Shelves of recovered history are catalogued neatly along oiled wooden shelves.

Social sciences 456.91–468.99 – gender/sexual discrimination, genital mutilation, reproductive rights.

Social sciences 551.51-559.88 – segregation, racial supremacy, replacement theory.

Social sciences 671.99-672.10 – election tampering, "fake news", "fake media".

Anyone can request access to a heretical server at any time, and usually their request will be granted. They can take notes, copy diagrams, read essays by leading scholars of the Burning Age on eugenics and wealth, terror and market manipulation, and afterwards be offered a nice cup of tea and asked what they thought about it all.

"Would you like a comfy chair?" Old Lah would ask, as I worked my way through pictures of migrants drowning in a raging sea. "I find it best to go for a nice walk after."

Only the truly terrifying – the chemical structures of nerve agents, the construction of incendiary weapons, the design of off-shore oil rigs – were kept entirely out of sight.

"It's embarrassing, if you think about it," Lah would say. "We hide this from ourselves, not because knowledge is good or bad in and of itself, but because we are still so young on this planet. We are still children; still fascinated by playing with fire. In our minds – in our very DNA – we are still starving, driven by the terror of not having abundance. We must have more, and more, and more, in order to be safe, even when the truth is that we have more than enough. The reward we feel when we have more, more! It is intoxicating. I have been ... intoxicated."

This was a strange confession from my teacher, who, seeing my raised eyebrow, beamed. "A good spy should understand passion. Georg Mestri is an addict of victory and the game; you must understand what it is to be an addict too, if you are ever going to get near him. When things are bad, we want them better. When things are good, we find ourselves wondering – what more? And what will I lose if I do not get more now? It is a trait that pushed mankind across the oceans and out into space – what is out there, what else? It is one of our most beautiful qualities and has for millennia served us well in finding new ways to live better. But like all things, it is neither good nor bad, but what we make of it."

103

Then I wondered, how long had Temple inquisition been eyeing me for recruitment? How many years had I spent thinking myself an academic, while they had been planning to put my life on the line?

In Vien, the temples fell.

Some members of the militia had knives. Others had hammered nails into a stick or brought heavy clubs fashioned from bits of old furniture or tumbled tree. One woman sported a pair of fabric scissors, waving it with such glee one would think it a battle axe, having perhaps decided that if she could not muster the same kind of armaments as the rest of her peers she might as well make up for it with enthusiasm. In the Temple of the Mountain Lake, the Medj were beaten bloody, one dying a week later in the clinic, not because they resisted, or said anything particularly snooty to their attackers, but because the dozen or so militia who climbed the five hundred steps to their open door had expected a fight, had been primed to fight, had been fired up with a cry of "They may kill us, but they will never take our freedom!" or words to that effect, and, when faced with a polite invitation to drink tea before committing vandalism, had no idea what to do with their energy, so had the fight anyway for something to do.

A few altars were desecrated; a few images of the kakuy smashed.

"Where are your gods now?" snarled one, pissing on the image of the kakuy of the fields, bringer of harvest, basked in sun. "Why don't they come now?"

"They are not our gods," replied the Medj politely, as the stink settled into the woven straw mats, dribbled down the red-glossed walls. "Gods think humans are special."

I supervised some of the robberies from my telephone in Georg's office. I had, after all, arranged much of the logistics, writing guidelines to local militia groups on how to handle the stolen drives and the best way to get them to the Assembly in one piece for analysis and distribution. My phone rang throughout the night, from journalists demanding statements from Antti – "Does

104

this mean we're going to be rich?" one asked – to late-running militia members trying to work out if they could still be useful in this new rebellion.

"I brought some matches?" piped one voice optimistically. "And a pint of acetone!"

"Go home," I sighed. "I'm sure everyone appreciates your effort."

On the other side of the office, Rilka, Antti's private secretary, typed furiously at her desk, scurried back and forth, peered through the window, poured herself a shot of something alcoholic from a little flask in her pocket, typed again, ran to answer the door, ran back, sat down, stood up, and finally proclaimed: "But we're living through history!"

I had not spoken to her since the night began, and felt that this was perhaps a continuation of a conversation that had been inside her head all evening and which had grown so animated it had to happen out loud. I looked up from my desk and saw, to my astonishment, that there were tears in her eyes. I reached into the drawer, pulled out a clean cloth hankie, offered it to her. She hesitated, then crossed the great carpeted gulf between us, took it, daubed gently at the corners of her eyes, hesitated, rubbed a little more vigorously, held out the limp piece of cloth. "Can I keep this?" she asked.

I nodded.

"It's history," she explained. "We're making a better world."

I thought she might blow her nose on the thing, and keep that too, the immortal bogie of freedom. Instead, she folded the hankie into a little triangle and slipped it into her tunic pocket. Our eyes met, and for a moment both she and I contemplated a future in which Georg walked in to find us entangled on the office floor, clawing at each other's clothes, and both she and I concluded that he would probably be mildly amused at the display. Before I could do anything with this revelation, she spun on her heel and returned to her desk with the dignity of an emperor accepting a lesser king's surrender on the battlefield.

*

The first of the bad news didn't start to arrive until dawn, trickling in from the temples of the forest and the sands. These obscure shrines had no telephones of their own, so the militia had been forced to send a cyclist into the towns to make the call.

"There's nothing there!"

"What?"

"There's nothing there. The server rooms are empty. They took everything!"

"What do you mean, they took everything? What are you saying?"

"I'm saying there's nothing there!"

By the first glimmer of a new day, word had started to spread, and a few enterprising militia members with school-level archaic German had powered up some of their stolen drives and were eagerly looking through them for information on autonomous facial recognition systems, predictive policing, weaponised nano-technology and long-range ballistic missiles.

I had been a woman; now I was a man, old and frightened.

There haven't been any children for a long time now. Melanie doesn't know why that is.

"What in the name of burning sun is this?" demanded one, who had an inflated enough sense of her own importance to ignore my polite requests to hang up and let me handle some of the other calls flooding into my office. "The box said 'material science – industrial' but I'm just getting books about zombies! Fucking *zombies!*"

As birds sang their dawn chorus, oblivious to the history they too were living through, I sat outside Georg's office as Antti and a number of other seniors from the Brotherhood screamed abuse at him, each other and the day in general. A small round window crowned the top of the stair. If I looked at it, I could not moment-to-moment see the sun rising nor measure the changing colour of the sky. If I looked away, even for a few seconds, then looked back, it seemed as if everything had changed, now, and again, and again, and now. Across Maze, the temples burned and the hearths looked nervously towards the edge of the forest, which suddenly seemed nearer and blacker than it had been before. Best to cut it down, they said. Best to play things safe.

The door to the office slammed open and men stormed out; the last one toyed with slamming the door shut, but to do so would have required breaking his stride and might not have achieved a suitable effect, so he left it hanging half-open. I stayed where I was until I heard the downstairs door close behind them, then rose and let myself into Georg's office.

He stood, where he always stood, as he always stood, facing the window and the rising day. I waited, hands clasped, in front of his desk. At last he said: "They knew we were coming."

When I first trained to be a spy, I would stand in front of the mirror and remember how it felt when the forest burned and the river roared, reach out for Vae and miss her flailing hand, don't let go, don't let go, and tell myself, *It's your fault.* In time, I could do this, and meet my own eyes as the fire raged in the cauldron of my mind, and see no flush of colour nor any change in my breath, but was merely the mountain against which the wind must break.

I am kin of sky and earth. The earth holds me, and to the earth I will return, and whatever happens now, the forest will grow.

Then Georg said: "I thought we had them all. Temple must have their own."

I am the mountain, but when I leave this place – if I leave this place – I will shake down to my very roots.

He let out a slow sigh, and in that moment was just a man, not a statue carved in marble. Then he straightened again, turned, clapped his hands together. "By this evening – everyone who has attended any meeting on the bill, everyone who signed to read it, everyone they know, their friends, contacts, addresses. A wide net first, then we start eliminating candidates." I hadn't slept for twenty-four hours, but now was not the time to mention it. "I'll need to see the chief of staff, defence and army chiefs by 2 p.m. Get me a meeting with the Council Ambassador too, see how much time we can buy. And a pastry. Raisins, I think."

This pronounced, he turned away again and resumed his contemplation of the war to come.

Here I am.

Sleepless at my desk.

My face hurts.

My body hurts.

I find words are difficult to concentrate on, a thin, shark-toothed gauze over my eyes.

I read whole pages, and nothing has gone in, just words passing by.

I find myself inclined to laugh uproariously at nothing at all.

I feel incredibly sad at the smell of fresh pastries hot from the oven.

I sit at my desk, and systematically begin an investigation into my own nefarious espionage activities. For a long time, I wonder whether to include my own name on the list of suspects. I was, after all, present and correct at many of the key meetings. I carried the locked briefcase to and from its destination, supervised people signing in and signing out to read the documents therein. I unlocked it several times in transit, when alone, to photograph its contents for Nadira. I should absolutely be on the list of suspects, as indeed should Georg himself. But it seems so obvious as to be absurd, so I leave both his and my name off and instead systematically trawl through hundreds of pages of notes to construct a list of everyone else in the world at large who might be an inquisition spy.

I give him the list at 4 p.m., and he doesn't look at it, but nods once and says: "Break-ins are also a possibility. Get me a full security review."

I return to my desk. Sometime later – I do not know when – I wake at it. The sun has long since set. I have pins and needles in one hand, where it served as a pillow, and in a foot, where it dangled awkwardly beneath my chair. I am probably going to be sacked but, straightening up, find that someone has draped a blanket across my shoulders, tucking the sides in around ribs and knees so it won't fall off while I slumber. I have no idea what to do with this act of kindness, and when I check what new data has been uploaded to my inkstone while I slept, I find that Pontus' stolen document is there.

Here I am.

Photographing the appropriate page of the appropriate document to send to Nadira.

The film that comes from my camera is no bigger than a pill you might swallow without water. It is stored in a little black capsule for transportation and left behind a drainpipe near Judastrasse.

The document is about autonomous military drones. I will flag a number of ways in which it is inauthentic to Georg later — later — when some of the fuss has died down. When Nadira has the information she needs to find Pontus. When Pontus can no longer find me. I do not know what unique error has been introduced to this text to mark the betrayer. A comma that should have been a full stop, perhaps. A minor typo on a long, fiddly word. I find, to my surprise, that I hardly care, and I make the drop-off on the way to collect Georg's morning pastry.

Chapter 18

Jia did not declare war on Maze, not even when the temples burned.

"We can resolve this peacefully," her voice juddered, tired and old, over the radio. "We are all kin of sky and earth; children of the sun and moon. We can find harmony again."

The other Provinces shifted uneasily. Shamim and the Medj of the Delta made their more forthright feelings clear. "We have seen evidence of fossil-fuel mining. We have seen evidence of wasteful butchery. We have seen evidence of ideological mass consumption. We have seen the temples burn. The kakuy do not care for the borders of the Provinces. The kakuy will take vengeance upon us all."

In Lyvodia, on Maze's eastern flank, Ull was noticeably silent.

The Brotherhood radio reported a few Medj fighting back, attacking officials, endangering the public. Even those few stations that were ostensibly independent reported with disgust the hoarded wealth, precious items and luxuries found in the halls of many of the shuttered temples, and they were right. The rot was deep; the Medj had failed, and though the clouds tumbled and the earth turned, the kakuy did not come for Vien.

"How many lives do you think an archive is worth?" asked Georg, fingers tracing a map of the Provinces spilling across his desk, dancing over the old mines at Martyza Eztok, the sealed vaults of Isdanbul.

"In the burning," I replied carefully, "there were surveys done of how many lives you would be willing to end for a cause. If, say, by dropping a nuclear weapon that killed a million strangers – the elderly, children – you could save twenty thousand soldiers of your own nation, would you do it? The answers were disproportionally yes."

"And what about Temple?" Georg wondered, and I thought for a moment I saw Lah sitting beneath the cypress tree, wondering the same thing. Perhaps in another life they would meet and break bread and find in each other interesting conversationalists; Georg could have made an excellent priest. "Are they pragmatists, or sentimental?"

"Both," I replied. "They are pacifists; it is written in their scriptures that the kakuy hate war above all else. They are also pragmatists. When mankind warred, the destruction disturbed the kakuy, roused them to anger, and the kakuy crushed city and army beneath them with no care for whose side was pious and whose was not, seeing no distinction in the petty squabbles of humanity – just a pestilence on the earth."

Georg clicked his tongue in the roof of his mouth, flexed his ankles and rolled his wrists. "It sounds exhausting, believing so much and so little."

It is, says Lah, as wind ripples the water of the lake. Medj need to be idealists, to see the light in all things. But unlike the gods of old, the kakuy walk amongst us, real and mighty, and we need pragmatists too. Tell me, have you thought about joining the inquisition?

In the night, I dream about Tinics, and the temple above the river, and the forest as it grows. I dream about Yue, and lanterns of red and blue. Then Georg is there, in my mind, and he knows everything, and the Medj just watch as he pulls my thoughts out through my blinking eyes, and do nothing, and I wake terrified that I've been talking in my sleep and everyone knows.

"Ull doesn't want to fight," Georg muses, as I hand him the day's summary from the radio waves and server offices. It has

111

been nine days since I left my little capsule of photos behind the drainpipe. More than enough time to get it back to Budapesht, to develop the film, to find Pontus, to end this farce. What is taking so long? "Jia knows it too. If she tries to get a consensus from the Provinces to attack, she doesn't know how many will follow her to war."

I have to force myself back to the room, paying full attention, but too late. Georg has seen my distraction and clicks his tongue, disappointed, before moving on to the next thing.

Three nights later, the united Temples declare Maze officially in a state of heresy. They should have done it weeks ago, and that night the citizens of Vien wait for the lightning storm, the tornado and the rush of judgement, and none comes. The kakuy, it seems, do not respond to Temple paperwork.

On the day when the summer festival should have been celebrated in baskets of lavender and rosemary, the temples stood silent. Instead Antti proudly struck a shovel into the new open-pit lignite mine on the edge of the river at Yahnbach, a somewhat futile gesture given that the tooth-limbed machines were waiting behind to strip back the soil into dunes of dusty black – but it looked good for the cameras. Antti Col was nothing if not good for selling copy.

Rilka, passing me on the stairs in Georg's office, caught me by the wrist. "They're looking for a spy," she hissed. "They're looking everywhere."

They're looking in her room, and under her bed. She is no spy, I'm almost sure of it, but perhaps she once hid a stick of incense or a letter to another woman, failing in her duty to humanity, reason and her sex. Perhaps she takes contraceptives or once expressed admiration for Jia and the Council, a long, long time ago. Perhaps Georg is inside her head too, as I'm certain he is inside mine.

"We'll be fine," I said, pulling my hand free. "We've done nothing wrong."

The next evening, Klem was not at dinner at the hearth, nor the night after that. When he did return, there was blood on his cuff, and bruising on his fists, and he didn't smile at me, and looked like he might spit at my little shuffling bow.

Lying on my bed in the dark, I did not sleep, and did not think, and did not dream. I was the mountain, hollowed out inside, nothing left but darkness and bones.

The smell hit me when I woke. The ever-present turbid mud of the river, a sudden alien presence rising with the dawn. Then voices through the window, high and urgent, the wailing of a siren somewhere in the distance, and beneath it all a strange rushing, as of wind over the sea when tide and gale contend in opposite directions. I stood up, opened my door and looked down the stairs to see greyish water flowing freely through the hall, rushing through every crack and half-shuttered window. It foamed and rolled like coffee in a vat, bumped floating furniture and spun lifted floor cushions and torn flowers through its maw in little busy eddies. Other members of the hearth were already struggling to save their few ruined belongings, heaving saturated fabrics onto the stairs and clawing at slippery cutlery that spun away from their scrambling blue-tipped fingers. I descended slowly, not wanting to get my feet wet, but seeing no other way than to enter the water, removed my socks and shoes, fruitlessly rolled my trousers up, and stepped in. The flood was a cruel cold, enough to shock without bringing the body to alarmed wakefulness. Grit swirled in it, already caking the floor of the hearth with sand and mud, and other things brushed too, each one presumed sentient, or a knife swept up in the tide which would tear its way through flesh, hidden beneath the swell.

I helped as much as I could, saving those belongings that were salvageable, joining a human chain to pass things to a higher level. Within an hour, even that project was abandoned as the water rose another half metre, coming nearly to my shoulders as I joined the exodus upstairs, peering out through high windows as our garden washed away.

The flood lingered for the best part of two days.

After came the clean-up. The stink of river could not be scrubbed from the city for months. Lines of green and brown smeared every wall, and the hosepipes we turned on to try and blast it away just filled us with the sickening memory of water, water, more moon-cursed water. Dead fish and still-slithering eels rotted and blanched in the sudden hot sun. Every blade of grass, every flower and every twining climbing thing was brown, brown, brown and dead, the streets lost to silt, the sewers overflowing and the raw stink of faeces everywhere. We quickly gave up trying to distinguish between mud and shit, wading through it all in calf-deep splats of sodden earth, from which the occasional flash of child's toy or purple perfume bottle might emerge like a pearl from the crusty oyster. Any electrics which had been below the water line were destroyed, taking with them cold-stored food and large swathes of the city's power supply. Families moved towards the rooftops to hard-wire their cookers directly into the solar panels and few overhead compression batteries to get a charge, while children tore and scratched their bare feet on the endless blankets of shattered glass and splintered wood the flood had carried with it.

We all knew disease was coming but were unsure of how, until at last the lack of stored food and difficulties in getting fresh supplies began to bite at our stomachs, and we started eating those apples that were only a little black, or maybe where the decay had only gone somewhat into the core; and that bread where you could dust the mould off, or where the spores were basically the same white as flour. Those whose bowels didn't immediately open caught the cough that spread on the backs of the teeming, roaring, hungry flies that now rose up from the beds of mud that slathered the city, commuters flapping their way through the translucent swarms which fluffed into hair and nibbled at the moist edges of blinking eyes, fearless of the enervated humans that loosely swatted them away.

Antti came on the radio and proclaimed: "To aid in the relief of Vien, we are introducing a new fleet of ambulances and fire trucks powered by the internal combustion engine! Reliable, fast, these vehicles can get the job done!"

Hearing this, some of the more pious denizens of Vien prayed, and many more rejoiced, even though the fleet of promised vehicles were at least a year and a half away.

Chapter 19

In the most secret hours of the night, I pray to the kakuy.

I do not put my hands together, nor offer incense, nor bow my head. Georg's hunt for the spy in his midst is at such a fever pitch that I think there must be holes in my wall, that Klem is watching me from the neighbouring room while I sleep, waiting to catch me whispering secret things as I toss and turn. I have grown so paranoid that I now have to sleep with my face turned to the wall, lest the motion of my dreaming lips betray me. I think that when they come for me, it will be better not to be looking at the door; I have spent many hours calculating the best way in which to be murdered.

Please, spare us, I whisper in silence to the darkness and the moon.

Temple taught us such things were futile. The kakuy do not care for the prayers of man. They are not interested in our good or bad, our desires or whims. We pay them our respects, not because they will smell the incense or taste the wine, but to remind ourselves of the needfulness of this pact. Everything changes; the balance is all.

We arise of the earth, and to the earth we return. I whisper it, and it is the beginning of one of the sacred lessons, but it has been so long since I spoke it out loud. Georg will know my thoughts, he will see it in the corner of my eye, know that I have been praying.

I close my eyes, force my hands to my sides, breathe out slowly.

I am the forest, growing.

The illusion that I am anything else, flesh and blood, heart and soul – this too will change.

Then Nadira said: "It was Pav."

I am nearly nauseous with relief, press against the warm mycelium wall, the slimy tidemark of the flood a soft green line against the pale bricks. "Pontus is Pav Krillovko? You're sure?"

"The document you sent us came from Pav – we're certain of it."

"So Council has arrested him? Jia knows? Krima knows?"

"No."

"Why in the name of sun and fire not?" I have to catch myself from shouting, hold back the breath, clench my fists against shaking.

Nadira's face is sorrowful without regret. "Because it isn't possible for Pav Krillovko to be Pontus. He wasn't in Budapesht when our liaison gave Council the doctored document. It was put on his system, but he couldn't have physically read it until at least a week after Georg received it from Pontus. He was in a temple in the south – on spiritual retreat. Dozens of Medj were with him every day and every night, praying."

I am not the fucking mountain. I am not the turning sea. I am small and mortal and made of flesh that can be hacked, blood that can be spilt, this is my life, my only tiny sacred life, and it is running away from me, the only thing that matters, I am terrified of the earth, terrified of maggots, terrified of the size of the sky and how soft and squishy are human eyes as they look up in fear.

Nadira tries: "Ven, listen . . . "

"No. I told you about the temples – I warned you what Georg would do. He is tearing the Brotherhood apart looking for me, and it's only a matter of time. Either we find Pontus or Pontus finds me, that was always the deal, and now . . . How did Georg get Pav's document, if Pav wasn't there? Someone on his team?"

"Perhaps. We are investigating – we are. Krima knows, she is

117

why we know Pav couldn't have ... Ven, look at me. You did everything right. We'll find another way."

It seems to me that these are the words you say to a corpse, and to my shame I walk away from her before she has a chance to try and make things right.

Chapter 20

On the day that should have been the autumn festival, the temples stood empty, blackened shells, and I travelled through the city with a mask over my face and citronella smeared across every inch of bare skin as the hospitals stank with the smell of putrefaction and the new factory chimneys blasted smoke into the sky.

"We have the technology to defeat all plagues," Antti proclaimed. "We are growing strong."

For the first time, the clinics started serving the wealthiest first. It was only right, the Brotherhood said, that those who had the most, made the most, got the most.

Behind the office, I found Rilka vomiting into the gutter. I caught her by the arms and pulled her into the street as she protested, swore she needed to work, needed to keep going, do what was right. I called an ambulance, but when it didn't come I hailed a rickshaw, bundled her inside, her lips blue, face burning, fingers cold. How could one person be so many seasons at once?

"I'll be all right," she said, pressing her face into my chest. "We're making something better."

At the hospital, there weren't any beds, the summer sickness washed in deep by the floods. I called Georg to explain where I was, and why. He was there in sixteen minutes; in nineteen, Rilka had a bed and a private room. He stood over her as she was plugged into drips and drains, held her hand, daubed her brow with the self-same hankie I had given her the night the temples burned, told her what a good girl she was, how proud he was of her, waited until she was asleep. Then at last he stepped away, nodded at me, once, an affirmation – the right thing had been done, though in that time and place I had no idea what the right thing meant any more.

Then he said: "Give you a lift?" and I nodded, and he drove me home and poured me a drink and asked me if I'd had my vaccinations, and I had, and he nodded again and mused: "It will get worse, before it gets better."

I waited, too tired to give whatever came next even the half-hearted noises of consent a spy should when his enemy speaks.

"The Burning Age was too short-sighted. We shaped the world; built towers, seeded the sky, dug the earth, walked on the moon, built wonders and cured diseases. We waged wars, drained seas, built palaces in the desert. But we consumed too much. Ran too fast. The kakuy were . . . antibodies, no more. The world's antibodies stirred by the planet recognising its disease. We were nearly wiped out, the peoples scattered to the furthest corners by the deserts and the storms. This time, we will do better. Our mistake was thinking that the fruits of man's labours must be shared with all. Now we know it is only for the few to lead, wisely and well. That is the new humanism that we have forged."

I stared at my hands and didn't say a word.

"You've slept with her?" he asked. In the past, such turns of topic, the sharpness of his voice, would have startled me. But I was the mountain, hollow inside, so I shook my head. "You want to?"

"I don't know."

"Men and women need to honour each other. It is the proper way of things. We spent so much time honouring the kakuy we forgot how to do homage to ourselves."

I looked up at that, bewilderment in my eyes, tongue too tired to keep silent. "Do you really believe that?" I asked. "You say all the things Antti wants to hear, you talk the philosophy and the fight and human superiority, but . . . do you believe that?"

The boldness of my own question astonished me, but not so much as his reaction. Somewhere in Georg's clothes there is a

120

hidden blade; I do not know if he has slit the throats of men with it or whether, like the great potentates of old, he allows others to do his killing for him. That night, he laughed. He laughed like nothing I have ever heard, and held my shoulder tight, a brother who at long last saw his kin returning home, and looked into my eyes, and saw something funny there, and laughed again, and poured me another drink, and did not answer my question.

Walking in the park as the crimson leaves fall, there is a smell on the air I do not know, and Nadira says: "It is called gasoline."

I kick at fallen leaves and nod at nothing much.

"I know it's taking too long. I know. We'll find Pontus. Krima is co-operating with the inquisition, there were only so many people who could have accessed Pav's files, it's all high clearance – that means limited suspects, it means . . . do you want out?"

All children love jumping in puddles, playing in leaves. I try to remember if there was a moment when I forgot that particular delight. "Krima could also be Pontus – you know that, don't you?"

She nods. "We've considered the possibility. But she's head of security. Who else can we go to? Ven. Look at me."

I do not. A memory hovers on the edge of recollection, blue-black hair in a crowd. "Krima has a . . . deputy, yes? Yue Taaq. I knew her."

"How?"

"We grew up together. Well – yes. In the same village, I mean. I saw her when Jia visited, walking in the crowd behind her."

"Did she see you? Did she recognise you?"

"I don't think so. What's her clearance?"

"Why?" I shrug, and don't know the answer. "I would say no more than classified. Taaq runs military liaison for Krima; she's not got access to Temple material, let alone to Pav's servers. Do you trust her?"

"I don't know. We were children. I hadn't thought about her

since ... she was in the forest when it burned, you see. We ran to the river, and there was ... but she always said she only saw the fire. Is there going to be a war?"

"Do you think there will be?"

I consider the question. "Yes," I say at last. "And Jia will lose, for a while, because Antti is building tanks and machine guns and artillery pushed by petrol engines. Then Antti will lose for a while, because these things cost too much to make. Then everyone will lose for a while, as is the way of the thing. I do not know who will be alive at the end of this."

"Ven." She stops dead, puts her hand on my shoulder – a rare breach of the strict distance between us, a flutter of humanity in our professional undertakings. In the autumn forest, a new cycle is beginning, a kind of rebirth. In every rotting branch, at every shrivelled root, in every fallen leaf and rotten fruit that falls unplucked to the sodden earth, the thin-tendrilled fungi and fat-headed bugs are setting to work, feasting for the winter, breaking down what was into what will be again, a turning without end. "We can get you out."

"Pontus sends Georg intelligence by microdrone. I found one, once, behind the kitchen. It must have malfunctioned. Solar-powered, a few hundred miles' range. Fly by night, recharge by day. I have stolen so much from him, he tells me things ... but Pontus – nothing is written, nothing is shared. Only Georg knows who they are."

"I'm going to pull you out."

"No – no." I shake my head, am surprised at the ferocity of it. "I will not have this all wasted. When things are on fire, you have to ... you have to do the best you can."

For a moment, I think she will argue. But then Nadira had never really wanted me to quit. So she smiles, nods, and we keep on walking through the fading day.

Two days after remembrance night, when families make offerings to the dead and dancers in white robes bang drums and parade through the streets, chanting the old cries – we are the dead, we are the dead, all that is living is all that dies – Jia mobilised an army.

She justified it as manoeuvres, training exercises. It was a traditional fighting force of six-shot rifles and guerrilla troops, light units on bicycles specialising in a war of forest and night.

"We will resist any aggressive moves by the Council to suppress our freedoms!" Antti proclaimed across the radio waves, as the first iron tank rolled from the new factories on the end of the railway line. Iron production in Maze was still low, steel smelting a low-key industry that the Brotherhood had not yet had time to fully scale up. Nor had they had full access to all the material needed to make a proper, full-blown tank of the kind the Burning Age had rained death from. His was an almost rectangular, creaking thing, with not quite enough braking power to stop itself rushing downhill on the verge of toppling, nor enough horsepower from its combustion engine to get up a hill at more than a snail's pace, and definitely not in rain. Yet it had machine gun turrets mounted left and right, and a short cannon at front capable of firing shells that could shatter wood into splinters at four hundred metres, once it had cranked its way round to aim. It made an impression, and making an impression was half the point.

I stole the designs and sent them to Nadira, almost reckless now in my exploits, a dead man walking who may as well go out with a bang.

"She mobilised too late," Georg mused, as Jia's voice blazed out across the radio, mustering some of the old defiance with which she had held together disparate bickering Provinces down so many years. "She won't fight in winter, but we can still keep manufacturing, growing. By spring, she'll be too late."

"She still has more troops," I pointed out.

"People are not iron," he replied, and that was the end of that.

In the evening, Georg says: "Drink with me," and I do, and we play a few games, modern and ancient, on the low coffee table between his worn crimson couches, and after four rounds we are at a perfect draw, and neither of us suggests a decider. He is frustrated by this pattern in our game playing, infuriated by his failure to consistently win. That's why he keeps coming back, and the joy of the thing is fading with every piece we move, and he will persist until victory.

For a while, we are silent.

We have been silent together for many nights, he working at his desk, I in a corner, without talk, music, the clatter of other people's lives. As the streets grow quiet through the open window, we have shared the deeper calm of distant disturbances, little puffs of noise only emphasising how deep stillness goes. We are silent again now, until he finally blurts:

"Out with it. Come on! Out with it!"

It is strangely profane, this disruption to our easy peace. I sit back, feel the warm fabric where many people, more important than me, have recoiled a little from Georg's stare.

"You look like a blob of mucus and have been moody for weeks. Spit it out."

"I have been wondering what your final objective for this war is. Material victory is not a realistic end-goal. You've got a technological advantage – all that heretical history, cluster bombs and gas and nerve agents, and so on – but it'll take you years to fully exploit it, and ultimately if the Council is too weak, if the Temple thinks the danger is too great, they'll just unlock their archives and start doing the same."

Georg is smiling now, arms folded, leaning back easy into his chair. "Do you think I can win?" he asks, eyes glistening, teeth white.

I think you have a spy in the very heart of the Council.

"I don't know," I reply. "I'd call it fifty-fifty."

Either Pontus finds me, or I find them.

"Would you risk everything on those odds?"

"I think perhaps I already have. What are you really fighting for?"

"Perhaps I believe in everything I say. In humanism. In a better world."

"Perhaps. Beliefs come and beliefs go. In the burning, the human mind was trained to value achievement, ambition and ownership above all else. It was the most abundant the world had ever been, and yet every child was taught that it lived in scarcity – that only by getting more would it ever be safe. Then the world burned and there was just war, famine and the kakuy. You killed, you died, while spirits of mountain and stone raged without the slightest interest in you and your fate. Then the fires ceased, and Temple emerged and taught us to be soothed by the river and the wind, to find joy in each other and what we had, and that ... is also fine. I'm no priest, but I've spent enough time reading archives to know that a little boredom, a little sitting around drinking tea and not causing too much trouble for anyone – that's also fine. But it is not a world for heroes. It is not a place where great men can shape the land to their will, for the simple reason that the land bends only to the kakuy. Only them. God lives; and God does not live for humans. We are tiny, once again. I think you are not interested in being tiny any more. Do you want to kill the kakuy?"

His eyes are bright as the moon; he is a brilliant man who has dedicated himself to working in the shadows, and yes, even Georg's ego will puff like a strutting pigeon now and then.

"Do you think I can?"

"No. Kakuy die – I believe that. But the forest grows back, and while there is a forest, there will be a kakuy. Maybe you can drill a few holes in rock. Maybe you can poison the Ube itself. But you can't kill the sky."

"If you believe that, why are you still here?"

I shrug. "As soon as the going gets tough, I'm sure I'll discover my cowardice again. Until then ... I suppose you could say I'm curious. You want to kill kakuy. That's the endgame – that's all this war is about, yes?" He smiles, and that is answer enough. "Well," I muse. "That's some top-of-the-line ambition."

"Is it not how humanity becomes truly free? By conquering the gods themselves?" he asks, mischief in the corner of his eye, a smile pulling the edges of his lips. "And when the kakuy are dead and the earth is ours, the temples will burn and there won't be any need for a war. There won't be any need, because we'll be right. We'll be our own gods. That's how I'm going to win."

He grins and pours me a cup of wine and tips his glass towards me. "To victory," he says.

"To victory," I reply, and drain the liquid down.

Chapter 21

The days are ticking down, down, down, another year going, going, gone, where did it all go? Georg is in my head, Pontus is in my head, Lah is in my head. The only person who's currently not home and making tea seems to be Ven Marzouki. What would he make of all this from his little home on the edge of the forest?

Meeting in the library, banners slung across the wall celebrating the de-classification of previously heretical texts on theories of racial evolution, eugenics and the carbon economy, Nadira says: "Ven. It's time to go."

"He thinks he can kill kakuy. He thinks Temple is hiding something, weapons, he thinks that when the kakuy are dead we will be free, free to tear the earth apart, free to be strong, free to make and build and kill each other again without worrying about the fallout, the way real men do. Real men, real war, real power – the world was so much easier when gods cared about humanity. I can find the spy, I can find Pontus, I'm so close ... "

"Ven! Krima is looking, Temple is looking, I am doing everything I ... Pontus will be found, it's not you – this isn't on you. What if they find you first?"

"Then that will tell us something too, won't it?"

She leans back, recoiling as if punched, but though her voice says no, Ven, in the name of sun and moon, don't be ridiculous, her eyes say why yes, yes indeed, you are not wrong. If we all die here, it will be very informative indeed.

*

I made it almost to winter festival before my world came crashing down. Low winter light in the morning, the touch of sun through the cold, we give thanks, we give thanks . . .

Then one unremarkable night as the snow fell in grubby sheets, Georg called me into his office, asked me if I'd finished writing up my notes – I had, and gave them to him – nodded once, looked at someone behind me, and whoever that was hit me in the back of my neck with a very large stick.

I think they were aiming for the back of my head, but missed. When this caused me a great deal of confusion and staggering, rather than just the desired immediate blackout, they hit me some more. I was not particularly surprised to see Klem leading the fray, and my old housemate Sohrab, though I was a little disappointed to notice that Rilka seemed to have forgotten our shared history and was busy getting in on the action too.

Here's a cellar, a familiar place.

The summer flood had washed away the blood, leaving instead that fine coating of muddy stench that has settled in a fly-blasted miasma over the city since the Ube rose. None of us will ever be clean again.

Pitching a still-conscious body that doesn't want to co-operate into a chair is hard work. Limbs go everywhere. Teeth, even if they don't bite, remind us a little too much of a dog's toxic mouth, or the venomous strike of the platypus, so if you're not used to such things – and Sohrab and Klem clearly expected more docile prey – the result can be unnerving. In the end, Klem got bored and dumped me on the floor, belly up. Then he knelt on my left arm, pulled a knife from his jacket, uncoiled the fist of my hand and tried to cut my thumb off again. The absurdity of it made me laugh, somewhere through the pounding headache. This didn't bother Klem. Laughter was a familiar fear response.

"Wait."

Georg hadn't said that last time, had he? It seemed only fitting to get the thumb business over and done with, just so everyone was on the same page. Klem paused but didn't let go. Rilka stood by the door, hands squeezed together in front of her so tight I thought she might pop like a pimple. Sohrab lingered against the furthest wall, competent but lazy. Georg's face hovered briefly over mine. I wheezed: "Torture makes people say what you want to hear."

He nodded, once, then again, a backwards nod with his chin. Klem scowled, climbed off my arm, retreated to the edge of the room. Georg waited, just far enough out of reach that I couldn't easily get blood on his clothes. I pulled myself up one arm at a time, clinging to the empty chair for support, managed to get my head up and let it loll back on the seat, untangling my legs on the floor in front of me.

"Can I have a drink?" I asked.

Klem found the idea contemptible. Georg found it almost funny. "Get him a drink," he barked, and, relieved perhaps, Rilka scurried away to find one. I licked my lips, mopping up iron. Georg waited, then squatted down opposite me, a look that seemed close to concern in the corner of his eyes. I had never seen such a thing in him before; he almost never stooped to the level of other men. Then he reached into his pocket and pulled out a hankie, a finer, spider-silk version of the thing I'd given Rilka on the day the temples burned. He spat on the silk, then brushed a little of the blood from my face, examined the resulting smear, and pressed the hankie into my loose, sagging fist. I gripped it tight as a child might hold a sacred totem or a glimmer of metal with the ancient words *Product of China*. I wondered where Yue was. I hadn't wondered that for a while. I hoped that if the inquisition found Pontus, they'd treat them better than the Brotherhood was going to treat me, and was surprised at the depth of my sentiment on the subject.

"Kadri," Georg sighed. "How did we end up here?"

"Terrible choices," I chuckled, and humour hurt, so I decided not to do that again.

He smiled, squeezed my shoulder, harder this time – hard enough for pain – released, waited. The door opened. Rilka entered, carrying a crystal glass of the good stuff. She did not understand the finer nuances of interrogation, perhaps, but Georg let it slide. She held it with two fingers under the base, like a sacrificial offering of water at the temple.

"Thank you," I said, taking it from her shaking hands. I thought I'd down it in one, get a little courage, but the heat of it on my bleeding gums was surprisingly pleasant, so I took my time.

"Kadri," Georg said quietly, a little firmer now, a man with places to go, people to see. There's an unmarked grave already dug somewhere on the edge of the city; it needs to be filled by morning, you know how it is. I clung tighter to the glass.

"The thing is," I grunted, "I've got to wait a few hours before I start spilling my guts. To give other agents a chance to escape. Professionalism. Three should be enough. You can beat me senseless in the meantime if you want, but it'll probably be easier for everyone if we take that for granted."

"Unfortunately," Georg sighed, "you don't speak for everyone, do you?"

I shuddered, despite myself, tried to blink some of the spinning from my eyes.

Then Georg said: "I believe you call him Pontus." Glass is but sand, sand is of the desert, I am the desert, I am sinking from the heat of the sun to that cold, soft place where light may never find me. Georg nodded at nothing much, mused: "Krima's investigation was a little too loud. She turned over a few too many rocks, got sloppy. That's the problem with using a spy to catch a spy – every step closer, you become easier to see. When did Temple recruit you?"

"When? Oh. You think I was bought or . . . you said something rude to me that made me turn? Earth and sky, no." I tipped the glass to him in salute, bloody teeth and throbbing head. "I'm an inquisitor. The whole . . . selling information, expulsion business – that was just cover. Bait. You were always my target. You swam onto my hook like the little greedy fishy that you are."

He looked away, tiny white teeth in a puckered mouth. Georg had never looked away before. He turned again to face me almost instantly, as if the moment had never happened. "How much did you give them?"

130

"Everything. Military, political — everything. The training camps in the mountains? The airbase hidden in the north? Your brilliant strategic plans — the new fleet; the new artillery? Everything. Temple knows about Antti's embezzling, your secret friends in Magyarzag, what soap you use to wash your nethers." For a moment, he looked sick, and I felt a swell of strange, giddy defiance unlike anything I had experienced since the forest burned. I wished I had more alcohol to salute him with, a toast to his ignorance, a glass tilted towards his frown. Then Georg looked away one last time, smiled at the floor, was still smiling when he looked back up. He patted me on the shoulder, gentler this time, a father comforting a disappointing errant son. "Well," he sighed. "You were always good at your job."

He began to stand. Back, haunches, an unfolding upwards. Klem detached himself from his corner, ready to do that thing he did. I caught Georg's hand as it drifted away, gripped it tight. A flicker of surprise ran over his face, matched only by the pure bewilderment as I swung the crystal glass as hard as I could into the side of his head. It shattered against skull and palm, shards digging like the burrowing wasp into my flesh, spilling in bloody stripes down his cheek. The blood started flowing instantly, thick and dark, dripping onto his spotless shirt. The impact rocked him against the chair and I thought I heard Rilka stifle a scream, Klem growl like the hungry wolf, but I was already reaching for Georg's trouser belt. I had searched his jackets before, examined every part of his wardrobe, and now there was only one place left for his damn knife to be: tucked into a sheath on the back of his belt, a little hidden scabbard that made would-be murderers feel smug and bold, but which any professional thug knew was too easily hijacked. My hand closed round a wooden handle; I dragged the blade free as Klem lunged towards me, and as Georg swayed back, pushing himself away from the chair, I caught his hand again and stuck the knife into his left armpit. He gasped, bit back on the pain, twisted as I dug a little deeper, pulling him towards me until finally his throat was within my reach and I slid the knife up into the ridge between neck and jaw and snarled: "Get back!"

Klem and Sohrab froze, Rilka sobbed. I had never seen anyone sob like that before, an awkward, uncertain thing as if she felt it was her womanly duty to have a reaction, which her bright, adrenaline-popping eyes weren't really feeling.

On the floor, Georg and I were a tangled, contorted mess, blood mixing in grubby smears across skin and stone. Trying to slit his throat at this angle would be a right stinker, fleshy but unlikely fatal; but I didn't trust my grip to change to something more practical, so hoped no one else would notice or care.

"Drop your knife," I hissed at Klem. He looked to Georg, who seemed as if he would nod, then thought better of the motion.

"Do it," he said.

Klem dropped his knife, toed it away; Sohrab was unarmed.

"Stand by the wall," I snapped. "Facing it."

Slowly, Klem and Sohrab walked to the wall, turned their eyes to the grey stone. I nodded at Rilka, who didn't need any further encouragement to do the same. I slung my right arm across Georg's chest, adjusted my left so my elbow hooked around his shoulder, giving me a little more balance and control. "Up."

He climbed up slowly, reluctant to shift his weight against the blade, feet scrambling against my thigh as he tried to find purchase. I followed, letting his strength half-pull me upright, until we stood, a swaying, bleeding mess pressed so tightly together we could have been born sharing the same liver. "Out."

He straightened all the way, an uncomfortable height that forced me to peer past him as if I were a puppy hiding behind a tree. His first step was a sway and he almost fell, nearly losing his own windpipe as I struggled to stay with him. Then he caught himself, straightened again, adjusted the cuffs on the end of his sleeves and, with as much dignity as an admiral boarding his flagship, began to shuffle towards the door. I followed, glued flesh to his flesh, blood to his still-flowing blood, through the cellar door.

"Lock it. Throw away the key."

He locked it, tried the handle to show it was done, threw away the key.

"Kadri – Ven – do you have a plan?" His voice had the soft

concern of an employer inquiring into his underling's personal development.

"Car."

A little nod, which became smaller as he remembered the knife at his throat. "Of course. Worth a try."

Climbing the stairs together was such a messy, undignified shuffle that at one point Georg spluttered: "Wouldn't it be easier to stab me in the kidneys?"

I didn't answer, pulled my arm a little tighter across his chest. When we rounded the corner into the corridor, I thought he might try to buckle, felt a tensing of muscles against me, tensed back. He reconsidered, shuffled to the front door, opened it, looked out into the street, turning his head this way and that as if waiting for a rickshaw. "Well?" I peeked past him, and he took that opportunity to turn, grabbing my head in both his hands and slamming me against the wall. I felt my blade cut something, nick flesh, felt blood hot on my fingers, but it didn't slow him down. He drove a knee into my chest and fumbled with his thumbs for my eyes, burrowing from ear to temple to eyebrow, skimming the top of the socket. I ducked under his grip before he could dig, drove skull-first into his belly, trying to push him back from the wall. He staggered a few paces, then adjusted to bear-hug me around the torso with one arm, slowing me to a grind of feet pushing against feet. He caught my knife hand as I swung it up towards his stomach, and though he twisted my wrist he didn't quite have enough strength to force me to open my fingers. Instead he turned, turned and turned, driving forward now as I slid back again, pushing the blade with his whole body towards my chest. I kicked and struggled and grunted and tried to head-butt his sternum into some sort of submission, felt blood in my ears and heard him gasp and wheeze like a poisoned lion. The tip of the blade slithered towards my chest, pricked skin, drew blood. His grip on my wrist was numbing, cutting off blood as he drove the knife on. I dropped to the floor, let the weight of his body on mine send me tumbling. The knife turned as I fell, my arm finally breaking from his with the unexpected force of

133

gravity, his grip around my middle pulling him with me. I didn't feel the tip of the blade glide over my ribs, didn't feel it glance across my body – that sensation would come later. But I felt it slip across his flesh as I scrambled for purchase on the floor. Saw his thigh in my line of sight, felt myself tumble from his grasp; drove the knife all the way in.

Georg howled with pain. I had not known that statues could scream; I did not think he was made of the same stuff as the kin of sky and earth. The blade went so deep that when he jerked his leg away the knife went with it, tearing through thick, red muscle to hang down like a hook stuck in a butcher's joint. He collapsed onto the floor, clutching at his thigh, encasing the leg in his giant hands but not touching the protruding wood or metal, as if moving fingers near it would just make the pain more real. I scrambled away on slithering paws, pressed myself into the wall, hauled down breath, felt for the first time something hot trickling across my belly, ignored it, fumbled in the drawer of the wooden counter by the door with its faux-modern art sculptures and little pot of scented, tasteful leaves, staining it all with crimson. Found the keys to Georg's car – the emergency set he kept for when his driver was sick or his patience was low – crawled over his flailing legs as he rolled and rocked on the ground, face popping with the effort of holding back another roar of anguish. Slipping through the door into the icy street, I felt the cold of it as a blessing – thank you kakuy of the winds, thank you kakuy of the snow, I thought your touch was only darkness but tonight it is blessing, thank you, thank you. Saw a light turn on in a window opposite; another a little further down the street. Georg's howls would wake the whole neighbourhood. I staggered onto hands and knees, scarlet on white snow, crawled onto my feet, tried to run, and in the end managed a reasonable lurch round the corner, to the waiting car.

Chapter 22

I had only ever driven a car three times before. Once, when the postier in Tinics let me sit in the driver's seat and carefully press the accelerator on a very straight, very empty bit of road. Twice more in the temple in Bukarest, when Nadira sat me down and said: "There are so few of these things around that you don't need to know much about them, but we should probably make sure you've got the basics."

The battery was at 50% charge, having been plugged in late after a long day on the road. The driver's seat was set uncomfortably too far back, reclined almost to a snoozing position, and I didn't have time or space in my thoughts to work out how to change it. I tried the pedals, muttering their half-remembered functions under my breath, fumbled with the keys, dropped them, swore, rummaged in the dark around my feet, tried again, the cold of the night now mixing hard with the nauseating heat of blood and pain running through my body.

It took me three tries to get it right and crawl out into the street. The steering was strange at first, each corner taken with the caution of a mouse snuffling for cheese in a cat sanctuary. But in the dead hours of the night, so long as I avoided the main avenues and thoroughfares of the city, the only people I might startle were pedestrians ambling home hand-in-gloved-hand through the settled snow, late-night revellers or the occasional delivery man unloading his crates for the morning market. Once Georg reported the car stolen, it would become an instant liability, the telegram flashed from town to town. That should take at least forty minutes, maybe longer if I'd severed his femoral artery. If I'd severed his femoral artery, he would be dead already. I didn't think I'd killed him. I didn't know.

Ten kilometres out of the city, I pulled over on the side of the road to find my shirt glued to my body with blood. A slash from collarbone to the bottom of my ribs had opened the skin across my chest; not deep, but long and wide enough that the cloth was now saturated with blood, oozing like water through a sodden sponge. I felt dizzy looking at it, too sick to drive, but I pushed the car to the edge of a village whose name I should have known and couldn't remember, driving it at last into a ditch on the edge of a stream of muddy, stinking water that ran down to the Ube. It would be discovered in a few hours, a few days at most. I still felt satisfied dumping it, a terrible, un-priestly surge of wasteful glee.

Swaying through a village in the dead hours of the night. Snow is starting to fall. Catch it on your tongue; thick, clustered globules of frozen white. If you hold out your sleeve and let it settle, you can see each individual flake, until finally, if you stay still long enough, there isn't enough warmth left to melt even the lightest clumps, and your arm begins to sag beneath the weight of frozen night. There are only a few streetlights in this place, enough to give the shape of the curving central street. It is the kind of town where each hearth minds the other's business, considering it impolite to pry into the affairs of neighbours behind their high paper and resin walls. The server office is open only four hours a day, five days a week. The temple is padlocked shut. Even the midnight foxes are slumbering tonight, no yellow eyes flashing in the dark, no paw prints pressed into the settled earth.

There is a clinic, which reminds people with a polite notice outside that the prescription system is changing and will no longer be free. It is shut, but a window at the side breaks easily enough, strewing thin micro-fibres of solar wiring amongst the shattered glass. I crawl through into the chill, dank dark, follow

136

the walls with my hands until I find a switch, coax a little light from the overhead bulbs, poorly fed by temperamental winds. I have no time for proper medical attention, but slather clotting agent and press pads into the most egregious injuries, discard my bloody shirt in a yellow bin and pull on a beige nurse's shirt from a pile of fresh washing behind the reception desk. It will not withstand the cold, and now the spinning in my skull is turning the edges of the world blacker than even winter night.

I wonder where Nadira is. If she is dead, free, taken.

I wonder if I should go back and do not.

The safe house is twenty minutes from the centre of the village, down a mud path obscured beneath banks of billowed white. I get turned around once, twice, trying to find it. The cold is starting to feel warm before I spot its walls, light out, gate locked shut. The key is hidden in a hollow beloved of nesting blackbirds; I fumble through crystallised worms and the remnants of ancient cracked egg before finding it. My hands shake too much to get it into the lock. In the end, I turn my whole body to the side, tipping my weight against the timber for support, twisting with elbows locked to my ribs for some rigidity until the tumblers turn. Then in; courtyard with its frozen–over pond beneath the silver ash. The solar panels are covered with snow; the pipes have frozen. The keeper of the house has not checked in on this place for at least a week, held back perhaps by weather or sheer winter-dark inertia. But there are wood pellets in the stove and a lighter which clicks into tiny flaming life when pressed between my blue palms. As the fire catches, I drag every pillow and blanket I can find into a pile at its feet and bury myself like a bear, muffling against the pain as blood returns to icy limbs.

Winter's dawn is low, blinding, slices of white that catch the gentle dance of dust particles in the air. It comes in on sharp angles through the window above the sink, moving fast over bamboo bowls and empty pans, a cup turned upside down, closed cupboards and bare timber floors. It catches the flash of tatty colour from the piled pillows I've dragged around me; faded ochre and time-drained emerald, dry cobalt and wilting yellow. It takes a while to wake me, having to push through an inordinate amount of blanket and tangled reluctance before my brain registers the day. When it does, I forget for a moment where I am and think that this is what it will be like when I am old, and mad, and every day is a new form of being born, without a parent to love you. Then the pain kicks back in, and the odds of living so long suddenly fade, and being an old codger causing trouble in some patient hearth doesn't seem so bad after all. The pellets in the stove have nearly all burned down, leaving a thin residue of still-warm ash at its base which I am tempted to rub my hands in for that final glimmer of heat.

Outside, a crow hollers indignantly at a peer, or an interloper, or some intruder to its peaceful realm. Wings beat; a mob forming, chasing, hounding – then peace again.

Ploughed fields hidden beneath snow catch the wind as it spins across crystals, disturbed only by the tiny footprints of a hopping bird and the larger footprints of the predatory fox that hunted it in the night.

Somewhere overhead, a buzzard seeks to catch a meagre updraught, and the light through the window fades in and out like flashing code as thin clouds race across its surface. It is a good morning for snowball battles followed by hot drinks; for knocking down icicles and clearing the road for the postier and the cargo truck, for the ambulance and the schoolmaster who lives on the frozen river and every year misses one day – and one day only – when the ice is too thin to walk upon but too thick to push his boat through.

There is a little blood on the blankets I've wrapped myself in; presumably my blood. I do not dare remove my bandages, but crawl through the unkind chill of the world beyond my soft fortress to the cupboards, rummage through until I find the first aid kit. The clotting agents and healing gels within are of a slightly higher quality than most hearths would possess, one of the few acknowledgements in the place of its more clandestine nature. There is medical glue for sealing shut any gaping wounds, macrophages in a vial with various obscure antibiotic purposes listed on the side along with the instruction "shake well – use immediately after opening". I use what I can, drink as much water as I dare, find a bag of dried fruit, munch it down without noticing the flavour.

Officially, the hearth doesn't have a telephone, and it's a brisk walk to the nearest office. But there is a short-wave radio hidden beneath one of the floorboards upstairs. I set it to transmit a distress call every fifty minutes, no more than a ten-second burst, a maximum of six times. Any more and using it will become too dangerous, too easy to track, and I must move on. The bed has a blanket adorned with rose petals and images of happy rabbits. I steal it for my downstairs tangle, drag it into the kitchen to settle before the last heat of the fire, to wait.

The wind-up clock by the door ticks away the hours towards noon, now running on, now stuck in a minute that lasts for ever. I have done everything protocol said I should: retreated to a set location in the event of emergency for extraction, sent a distress call, waited.

The sun turns across the floor, vanishes briefly behind the trees, reappears again in little spikes of dust-dappling illumination, vanishes again behind clouds, stays shrouded. I doze, then jerk awake, then doze again. When I open my eyes, it has started to snow again, and it is impossible to tell whether it is clouded afternoon or failing evening. I check the clock, and it is evening, and no one has come, and I am alone in the safe house.

Here.

Sitting for a little while looking at the clock.

Here.

There are protocols, of course, for this kind of situation. They are loosely worded, make things sound simpler than they are: Evade capture. Get out alive. What they lack in detail, they make up for with stark motivation.

I wait three hours longer than the protocol says I should, which is probably a standard psychological response to being abandoned, and no one comes.

Chapter 23

I decided to move a little after 8 p.m. There was no reason to it, save that I had by that time sat in the thickening cold and dark, by myself, feeling miserable to no avail, for nearly a day. At some point, the paralysing terror of what might come met with the hard reality of how uncomfortable my present situation was, and the balance tipped into action. I pulled the emergency supplies from the pantry – torch, money, maps, inkstone. Blank documents were kept in a box behind the bathhouse, sealed in biopolymer. I filled in a few false details, stamped them, hoped for the best. I dragged myself out of my bloody, meagre clothes and into a dusty, dew-tainted shirt and jacket from the cupboard upstairs. I pulled on hat, gloves, scarf, oversized boots padded with three layers of sock, shovelled the snow away from the door of the bicycle shed, pulled out the least tatty-looking bike from within, turned on the headlamp, loaded up the panniers with food, water and first aid supplies, put a compass in my pocket and turned towards what I hoped was the nearest road heading south-east, towards Slava. On a good day, a fast cyclist could cover the distance between Vien and Slava in less than ten hours. But that was before Maze was declared heretical and the roads filled up with glowering men. Officially, the borders weren't yet closed and you could still cross with documentation and a bit of patience – but I found it hard to imagine Georg had not flashed my face to every post on the road. If he lived.

Just before midnight, I locked the gate behind me, returned the key to its hollow in the tree and set out into the dark.

The first hour – exhausting, drained by cold, just pushing the bicycle in search of a road clear enough to pedal down.

The next hour – frustrating, skidding, breathless, the road decent enough to cycle down but cased with patches of swerving ice that twice send me slithering sideways into the padded dunes of white that frame the path.

The hour after that – arriving at a village. I check its name and discover that, far from having travelled sixty kilometres already, I have made it a little less than twelve. I drink water and eat dried fish to stave off a wave of dizziness, but that just replaces the heat in my brain with gentle churning in my belly. My chest throbs along the torn line of flesh, the pain starting as an almost welcome fire that grows and grows until it is needles in my eyes, pounding in my brain.

Eventually I reach the main road that flanks the north side of the Ube River, flat and clear and fast. These are the small hours of the electric cargo truck and the heavy cargo bike making goods runs through the night. Even the bicyclesarais that appear every forty minutes or so have turned down the lights by the reception doors and pulled the shutters tight. The batteries behind the courtyards are running on empty, emitting their last mournful, sluggish clicks as hot air discharges through slow-spinning turbines, fading, gone. The lights go out in the lanterns that frame the path. The smell of biovats from the sewage pumps behind the sarais makes passing cyclists flinch and turn away, eyes watering, noses running from the unexpected, unprocessed stink.

I stop at a sarai – little more than a shuttered shrine, a few benches out of the wind and a water fountain – a few hours before dawn, astonished at how little distance I've covered, at how much my body hurts. A tired girl with sea-green eyes guards a counter selling a few hot vegetables rolled in egg wraps and warm bread. The sarai is near enough to the windfarms to have a little heat to

141

offer from its stove, a little light to share in the nooks and crannies where half-slumbering travellers rest their heads.

"Is the road clear to Marno?" I ask the girl, who doesn't look up from her inkstone, shrugs. "I heard they were struggling to shift the snow."

"People are coming from there fine enough," she replies, and there ends the conversation.

I eat my food, take a palmful of painkillers in the shadow of the bathroom round back, refill my water bottle, wish there was somewhere more convenient I could lay my head, or that I could stick my legs up the wall to drain some of the sloshing blood from my swelling limbs. There is a dead drop behind the water vat. I check it and find no message, no fresh documents or words of comfort and support. I wait another hour anyway, huddling by the low stoves in blanket-swagged corners of the sarai, listen to the gossip, walk the perimeter of the sarai one more time, do not see Nadira, do not find aid.

Sunrise is coming, a greying of the blackened sky in the east, a rolling down of shadows. I cannot stay here. I return to the half-light of the sarai courtyard, and there are the guardia. There are only two of them, wrapped in grey felt and woollen scarves, their bicycles resting against a wooden post from which the white lantern of the sarai sags, heavy with snow. They are not the elite of the roads, not speeding up and down in their swanky cars, spare batteries in the boot, sirens and flashing lights to clear the sluggish traffic. They are local boys, sent to do a local job, not expecting trouble, but perhaps hoping for it nonetheless, a little excitement to break the monotony of their lives.

"Documents, documents!" calls the younger, with voice and eye corralling the weary gathered cyclists into a huddle beneath the light while her older colleague flicks through offered IDs.

There is an option of running, of course. I haven't been seen yet, pressing into the shadows towards the toilets, and the gentle glow of eastern light on the horizon is still not enough to pick me out against the ivory landscape. But running means heading away from my bicycle, the supplies and the road. It means going on foot into the fields and smothered floodplains, still injured, and trying to steal and bluff my way to safety. My false documents are in the pannier of my cycle bag. At some point, they were going to be tested; better now, I reason, with local boys not used to the hunt, than at a checkpoint staffed by professionals further down the road.

I pull the papers from the bag, drag my jacket tighter around my aching bones, join the inspection queue.

"What's happening?" asks a woman in front of me.

"Just routine," is the answer.

"This isn't routine," grumbles another, as his documents are held up to the older guardia's torchlight.

"Travel much, do you?" asks the younger, and though the man is almost certainly innocent of any crime, the surprise of being questioned so cows him. There was a time, not so many years ago, when he might have laughed and said yes, yes I do, I cycle every month to Budapesht and back, as a free man of the Provinces may. But Maze has been declared heretical, and the Brotherhood is leery of spies, traitors, saboteurs and anyone else for whom a five-day investigation in a cell without trial or access to legal aid may be considered a worthwhile deployment of energy — for the good of the state. Even if five days seem a short period of time for the vindication of being declared guilt-free, this travelling man may miss his son's wedding, or his wife's final hours of illness, or simply have to carry the shame of being incarcerated when he was meant to be at work, or come home to a family gone mad trying to find him, who thought he was dead, swallowed by the kakuy of the rising river. How quickly these things turn.

I am third from last in the queue, and my lips are turning white with waiting. The younger guardia takes my documents, scans them, passes them to the elder.

"Where are you going?"

"Marno."

"Why?"

"To see a friend."

143

"What's your friend's name?"

"Licia Hahn, she's a lawyer."

"Why are you visiting her?"

"We haven't seen each other for a long time. She's just been through an unhappy affair."

"Where'd you come from?"

"Vien."

"You're travelling at a strange hour."

"I promised her I'd be there for lunch. She telegrammed me in the evening. It sounded like things had been very stressful."

"And you're her valiant rescuer."

"I'm just helping out."

A nod; a grunt. She is not at all convinced by my heroic antics, by the aura of righteous yet faintly celibate determination I give off. She thinks I'm a useless manipulator, preying on a woman's grief to get my own way. That's not a crime, however – not yet. Sometimes you need to make a few errors of judgement, she concludes, in order to realise how much better off you'd be with someone else.

She hands my documents back, barely glances at my face, doesn't acknowledge me with another word. I smile and half-bow in gratitude and manage to hide the shaking of my hands.

Half an hour from Marno, I spotted the first full guardia checkpoint. Traffic had slowed to a dead stop, bicycles and trucks alike. A barrier had been laid across the road and grey-coated figures moved in puffs of spinning air along its edges, opening bags and checking documents, peering under hats and into puffy, dry-eyed faces. Documents interested them less than features; some held papers in their black-gloved hands, and I could guess whose face might be printed on them.

I slowed down some hundred metres from the back of the queue. I dismounted my bicycle, calm, casual, wheeled it to the side of the road, flipped it upside down and carefully dislodged the chain, mineral lubricants slithering sticky and brown into the weave of my gloves as I fumbled with it. A few cyclists pedalled by, saw me. One asked if I needed a hand, but I smiled and shook my head and said it was fine, taking my time as I fumbled with the dislodged part, in no rush to fix it. A post truck joined the waiting queue, half-obscuring me from the sight of the other end of the road. I slipped the chain back on, then made a show of inspecting my wheels for a puncture, spinning them round and round as I examined every pebble and shard of ice encased in the grip.

"You all right, sky-kin?" called a friendly cyclist as she dismounted behind the post truck, already rummaging in her bags for her documents.

"Fine, thank you," I replied, bright as sunlight on snow. "Should have done better maintenance."

She smiled and nodded, and as the queue drifted towards the roadblock I flipped my bicycle over again, re-checked my panniers were sealed and, as if it had always been my intention and part of the plan, turned and cycled calmly off in the opposite direction, heart singing in my ears, the taste of vomit in my mouth. No one saw me; or if they did, no one saw a spy fleeing for his life.

It took me nearly four hours to make the laborious crossing to the next major road towards Bukarest, cutting north through spinning clouds of wind-plucked snow to the minor, bumpy, icy road that slithered through Zamk. The telegram office also housed the server terminal and a small general store. A man with charcoal eyes watched me as I scribbled out my message on a yellow slip. Protocol had no definition for my current location, no coded secrets to send. I tried to find some loose way of communicating, some cry for help that someone – anyone – might understand.

HEADING CHENECH, HOME FOR SISTER'S BIRTHDAY

"Going a long way," said the man, and since when did every telegram operator in every rural office read every telegram that passed beneath their fingers? Is this polite interest, absent rudeness, an interrogation? Is Georg inside his mind, as he is inside mine? I need to stop, sleep properly, check the glue binding the skin across my torso, drink, eat, stick my legs up a wall. Every time I get off my bicycle, it becomes harder and harder to get back on.

"Family matters," I mumbled, too slow, too late, a half-muttered excuse dredged from the back of my brain.

He nodded and smiled. He is a good man, a kind man – family is everything to him, and he is pleased to see that others feel the same way. He is a bad man, a cruel man – he is giddy at the opportunity to turn in a traitor to the state, has my picture on his inkstone hidden beneath his desk, believes in the new Maze, in taking control and letting go of the past. Perhaps belief is not enough to make him cruel; very well, he kicks puppies too. I gave him the wan smile of the weary traveller as I slipped out the door into winter light.

Skirting the edge of the mountains. Here, when the days grow hot, the children come and jump into the lakes and rivers that snake through the forest. They swim through silver waters, gasp at the icy melt from the peaks above, dip their toes and lounge on the shingle shores at the first touch of summer sun. In winter, their older peers trek up into the mountain to the little wooden huts that sit above the rusty cliffs where the waterfall flows, turning the roar of plunging foam to a background whisper as doors are closed, fires struck in stoves and thick blankets swung across weary shoulders.

In the morning, the highest trees stand above valleys of frozen cloud, and when the wind blows you may sit upon a promontory and watch new fog form, twist, rise and dissolve, like a ghost's fingers as it tries to crawl its way from the earth. Close your eyes and the sound of birds rises like the sun; open them again and in every nook of every rock you begin to see life spreading its fingers in tiny buds of yellow and purple, in unfolding lime and winter green. Georg says there is metal to be found in these parts, perhaps coal to burn. A few years ago, there was a mighty fire when someone struck a match above a certain patch of soft, life-less ground and the pent-up gases of centuries of buried landfill finally burst open, killing the luckless fire-starter and sending a shock through the timber that was heard as far away as the idling walkers on the mountain peaks.

Here, set between the rising banks of darkening trees, a village, low timber hearths crowned with snow, steps cut in the side of the hill so that each hearth may look over its neighbour's roof into the valley below, a warm light from within. A former church, centuries old, stands carefully preserved in the village square with notices explaining its historical significance, and twice-weekly tours operate between spring and autumn for visitors curious to have the iconography of martyred saints and bleeding sinners explained to them in language we now understand.

On the edge of that town, where the windfarms spun and whistled in the settling wuther of the fading afternoon, another guardia outpost, two women pacing up and down with hands in pockets, puffing and huffing in the deepening cold. I saw no sign that my photo had yet reached them, but when I pedalled up and produced my documents, one leant in and examined my face as if she were a doctor looking for the first signs of cancer from a mole, or trying to spot the optic nerve through the inky black of my eyes.

"Where'd you say you were going again?"

"Volen, via Leviche."

"Where'd you come from?"

"Slava."

"Why didn't you take the train?"

"I wanted to cycle. Trains bore me."

A nod; my excuse is as little noted as it is meaningful. Maybe it's true; maybe it's not. Her attention has already moved. "May I see your bags?"

I open my bags, heart in my mouth. She shines a torch into my sacks, pokes around with the end of her finger gingerly as if expecting bear traps, nods once, turns the torch to my face again, sees me flinch, lowers it back to my chest. "I've just got to check

147

these," she says, taking my documents and heading towards the half-open door of the guardia post.

"Of course," I smile.

I let her get all the way inside, count to ten, swing back on my bicycle and sprint for the road out of town. Someone must have been watching me from the window, because I hear a shout and the ringing of a bell seconds later, the pounding of feet on gravel, the scrape of tyres as someone lunges for their own bike. In this neck of the woods, the guardia will have maybe only one or two cars, and they will be out patrolling the bigger roads. My pursuers follow me on bicycle, but they are fresher than me, will be faster. Now is the time for recklessness, to take the risks that they will not. I plough out of the one-road village and into switchbacks heading for the river floor. It is faster to stay on the road than to cut across, but halfway down I see the beginning of a trail, a smaller muddy way leading up towards the windfarms, and turn onto it. My pursuers don't bother to shout "Stop!" or "Surrender!" or anything of that ilk; they are too far behind and only just beginning to find their breath as they plunge after me onto the muddy trail heading towards the ridge above. Soon it becomes a little too narrow, the snow too thick to pedal through, so I dismount, grab my bags off the back and sling them over my shoulders, and, feet crunching, push forward. The snow turns our chase into a shuffling hopped pursuit, a sluggish churn through the black and white world. My lips are ice, my chest is fire. The forest offers an early night, turning the settling dusk to thicker black that pushes the shadows higher and deeper. The crows are squabbling overhead, oblivious to the disturbance below. A thick furred forest cat hisses, snarls and springs away from me as I approach, the path vanishing altogether now into the bony grasp of the underbrush. At the top of the ridge, I pause to glance back and can't see my pursuers through branch and limb, but I can still hear them, snow compressed beneath boot, twigs tearing as fingers grasp for handholds on the scramble up.

Turn, drop down the other side, and here now is sudden night, true and blanketing, as the hill itself cuts off the setting sun behind its ridge. The change is like plunging into an icy bath, and as I slither down my feet go out beneath me, and I catch myself on a trunk, and rise, and slip and slide again. I am leaving tracks in the snow, easy to follow, but there is nothing to be done. I scramble, leaning heavily to the side, parallel to the lip of the ridge, just a few feet below it, heaving from branch to branch, heading for the singing swish of the windfarm. The turbines here are old, the parts have spun too long, grown cracked and dry, clicking, clunking, whooshing against themselves. The wind is a dirge, a skeleton's lament, but some ground has been cleared of snow, offering a path through the cables and transformers. For the first time, I run, my legs weighted stumps pounding heavy on the earth, my ears ringing. Now someone shouts, a lone voice behind me, and I wonder if perhaps one of the guardia has lost the other. I struggle to move faster, nearly over-tip, leaning forward as my feet refuse to offer anything more, weaving through the high columns of the farm, the smell of electricity and old resin thick on the air, then skid to a halt at a rope slung across a drop where the path stops at a cliff's edge. Choices – left into darkness, right towards the village, back into the arms of the guardia or straight down. The drop is perhaps thirty metres into water of deep black flecked with the last mirrored grey of day. The water moves enough that ice has not yet formed on it, a deep bowl carved from a dozen little flowing trickles which in summer are a roaring tide. Though I might survive the fall, I do not think I will survive the hypothermia that will follow. Footsteps skid to a halt behind me, and of the two guardia who followed, only one has kept up in the gloom.

She stops, realises she is alone, pulls her baton from her hip and raises a whistle to her mouth. I attack before she can make a sound, diving in to wrap my arms bear-hug across her chest, trying to take away the advantage of range that her unfolded stick gives her. The inquisition trained me how to fight, and no doubt the guardia trained her too, but in the moment neither of us remember more than a few physical habits, a shuffling of feet and a scrambling for targets, a panting through which hands flail loosely for eyes or throat, dig into anything soft or try to drive crack-snap into anything hard. There is more luck in this encounter than there is skill, and for a moment we tangle together beneath the turbines, gasping and hissing, feet slipping on icy mud, the moistures of our condensed breaths wet on each other's cheeks and at each other's necks, like dogs looking to bite. I manage to get a fist in her belly, but at the minimal distance between us all she does is grunt. Then she remembers that her stick has two ends and smashes the butt down into my shoulder. She is perhaps aiming for my head, but in the twist of arm and armpit can't get the angle, so she strikes bone, then adjusts her feet, swinging me round with her as she moves, and hits again, and this time does better and catches the back of my skull. The blow is not yet enough to make me let go, a disorientating judder that runs down to my buckling knees; but a few more good whacks and I will be done. When she draws back to hit again, I drop like a drunkard, and the grip we have on each other pulls her down. My back smacks into the earth hard enough to crack teeth, but in the moment of confusion I wrap both my arms across her throat, squeezing and pulling her tight. She understands at once what is happening and kicks and scrambles and kicks again, driving her elbows into my ribs hard enough to bring galaxies across my eyes. I bite back a howl and try to hook one of her legs in mine, hear the stick fall from her grasp, pray to sky and earth that I have not killed her, pray that I did not fall for some cunning trick. Her thrashing slows; her body grows heavy on mine. I let go, perhaps a little earlier than my teachers would have wished, push her off me, roll to the other side, grab her stick, take deep breaths, kneel next to her, arm raised to strike, see that she is not moving.

Slowly, I peel away a sodden glove, fumble at her neck for a pulse, find it and nearly choke back shame and gratitude. An apology springs to my lips, but it vanishes in the panting of my breath. She is already beginning to stir, head lolling this way and that, fingers clawing at snow. I grab my bag, turn towards the night and, before she can get her boots on the ground again, I run.

Chapter 24

Crawling through the midnight forest. The moon is hidden tonight. The cold has settled through every part of me, turning bones to glass. One step wrong and I will break, snap apart from the inside out.

Sometimes I hear voices and have imagined them.

Sometimes I hear voices and they are real, search parties sweeping through the night. Then I crawl on hands and knees between the trees, feeling through darkness, twigs scratching at eyes, water melting through my trousers and beginning to re-freeze against blanched blue skin below.

I imagine dogs and am terrified of them.

I imagine drones, infrared cameras and whining blades, piloted over the blanketed dark. Against the snow I will be a scarlet bonfire, slithering through the night, a veritable demon; still, I fear dogs more.

Once I stop and think I will cry, and realise that my legs refuse to walk. I sit on my haunches and shake and rock and know that the beginnings of hypothermia are on their way, and shake and rock again, until I hear a dog bark somewhere far, far away – or perhaps I do not – and the jolt of terror is enough to warm my fingers again.

The blood that flows from a dozen scratches and the seeping tear in my chest is briefly warming. I think about picking scabs, about feeling the heat of my own body gracing the dead surface of my skin. Then I think about heat rushing away as from a

151

furnace, and cold, dead metal, and how much the creatures of the forest will enjoy finding my corpse once the snows have melted and I am soft enough to eat. Then I scamper on, barely a kilometre, perhaps less, falling constantly into white, heart pounding, unable to escape the noise of it in my ears. I think I will die out here and am grateful that I will be eaten, honoured that my flesh will give back to the earth that carried me. Children of sky and earth, thank you for feeding me; let me feed you in return. The water of my blood was the same stuff that the dinosaurs drank; I have been oceans, I have rained upon the desert, I have circled the earth a thousand times and will do so again, when the last part of me is gone. I do not fear death so much as a life lived failing; I hope that the hypothermia will take away the pain of my bruised bones before the end.

Time to give up, perhaps.

Time to stop running.

So long as the forest takes me, not the dogs, I will be content.

I think I have fallen.

I think I have slept, leaning against the side of a tree.

I think I have woken and moved and slept again without realising, sleepwalking through the dark.

I have no idea where north is, or south. I only find the river by its sound, sit on its bank, imagine losing the dogs by wading through its rushing depths, know that if I do, and cannot light a fire on the other side, I will die. I think that if I try to cross in this inky state, Vae's fingers will rise from the pebble bed below, and she will hold hands with me and pull me down into the water's depths. I do not think she is lonely or sad in whatever drowned place the forest took her; I think the kakuy of the river and the sea carried her water to crystal islands and beneath the frozen surface of the north and that there is nothing malicious in their motion, no rancour in their embrace. I do not attempt to cross the river, but follow its bank in a direction – I do not know which one, fumbling against rocks and slipping, wet-toed, round fallen buttress trees. I hear a drone overhead and know I imagined it. Then I look up, and it is real, or at least a very convincing hallucination.

It hovers directly above me, some hundred metres up, a single red light on its tail as it turns its lensed eye to examine me. I raise one hand in greeting, as an estranged lover might when meeting an old affair after an awkward ending and a forced reunion. The drone neither bobs nor flashes in reply but turns and heads back up the river bank, as if it had not seen me at all.

Pre-dawn lasted a year, a band of grey in the east, which I had not realised was east. I knelt on the top of the great round stones that traversed the river at its shallowest point, put my head in my hands and knew I could go no further. I curled up in the middle of the stream on a great grey rock with a green underwater beard and waited for the sun to kill me. When it finally rose, peeking over the mountain tops, it was an avalanche of light rolling down the valley, a visible tumble of silver. I curled away as it struck me, buried my head in my hands, waited for it all to be over, the shivering uncontrollable now. I heard the creatures of the forest flutter snowflakes from their wings, beat the night from their tails, chirrup the darkness from their lungs and raise their eyes to heaven, and I cowered from it all and wondered what was taking the dogs so long to catch me and drag me by my ankles to their masters.

Then, a footfall, strange, heavy, pressing into the snow.

And another.

They came, far enough apart to imply some mighty, ponderous thing. A bear maybe, testing its weight on the unfamiliar edge of the river. Each crunch was long and slow, perhaps carrying the echo of a falling tree or the slow splintering of breaking ice. I did not open my eyes, and then I did, the last dredges of curiosity overwhelming my cold-broken fatigue.

The kakuy of the winter wood did not regard me as he went about his business. He did not raise his icy head nor pause in his snuffling at river's edge. Instead, he dipped a black nose the size of my face into the water, pulled back a little as if shocked by how cold it ran, then dipped down again to lap at the fresh-flowing stream with a tongue the deep purple of clotting blood.

Four paws, each bigger than my back and each with seven claws, dug into the snow, yet the tracks he left behind seemed only a few millimetres deep, as if he made no mark upon the land over which he plodded. His fur had turned moonlight white and was crowned with spikes of ice, in which fractal spirals and broken patterns of half-imagined forms were captured, twisting this way and that with the changing light. A single, cheeky robin sat a few inches from his tail, preening itself, enjoying the free ride, the power and majesty of the kakuy somewhat altered by its secondary role as birdstand. A smell of black soil and foggy dew rolled off him, powerful enough for even me to smell through the still morning air, and when he raised his eyes to examine his domain, they were winter's night, full of stars. I lay still as the rock beneath me, watching him through my bundled arms. He paid me no attention, lapped up a little more water, shook himself, startling the robin into indignantly flapping away, a creaking and cracking of ice over shaggy, flabby flesh, and then at last looked at me.

The kakuy of the winter wood gazed upon me as the fatted lion, blood on his lips, might regard the little scavenging carrion birds that come to feast upon the corpse the pride have killed. Too insignificant to hunt – a curiosity, a courtier, even – a tiny, ignorant thing. I thought I should bow my head in prayer, put my hands together, the fingers locked in frozen curls, show some deference. But neither the kakuy nor the lion have any interest in the deeds of little things, save as some idle curiosity to watch with full belly, and so the kakuy looked at me, made no sign of distress or disturbance, and looked away, turning slowly from the river to shamble up the slope towards the rising sun. Within a few yards, the thick trunks of the bending silver forest had consumed him, the thump of his great weight no longer echoing through the earth, as if he had been swallowed whole by it. I gazed along the path he'd taken and could barely see the tracks he'd left behind, save for the thick branch of the silver birch that had bent out of his way as he passed. I let my eye wander a little further, past the frustrated, circling red-breasted robin, and saw the stone lantern that had been there all this time, tucked into the shadow of the trees. It was old, unlit, the snow inches thick on its sloping roof, piled high around its grey base. It marked the beginning of a narrow path – too narrow for the kakuy, yet somehow he had travelled it. I watched it for a while, wondering if it too would vanish as the kakuy had, but it resolutely did not.

I uncurled one leg, and it was the tearing apart of an ancient metal rod rusted into some deformed shape.

I uncoiled the other and whimpered and swore and cursed at the pain that ran through me, and cursing vilely made it a little bit easier, so I kept on uttering profanities until my body was practically upright, on the verge of tipping constantly forward but swaying now one step at a time towards the path.

I reached the stone lantern, clung to it as if it were some sacred, holy sign, paused in my cursing long enough to give thanks, thanks to the forest, thanks to the river, thanks to the stone and thanks to the sky, thanks to my kindred who had made this path, thanks to the living who brought light out of the darkness and the dead who had given offering to the timber that housed them and the forest that kept them whole. I half-sang a half-forgotten prayer, a mantra to the changing sun and changing moon, snatches of words from old texts that I had not uttered in all the time I had been Kadri Tarrad, Georg's man, all the time he had been burrowing in my head to see the truth of my heart, and knew now that if I died at least I died free of him, at least Georg would no longer be in my soul. I pushed onwards, up the path, following the dotted lanterns until my toes, sinking through snow, hit buried steps rather than merely winding dirt. I bit back a sob and crawled on hands and knees, too breathless now to manage more than the odd meaningless word gasped through broken lips. The sun made the brightness of the snow unbearable, a dazzling mirror that pierced my fluttering eyes; the forest broke it up into pools of white and shadow, a shelter, a softness, the leaves and rising mist turning the world into a woven tapestry of illumination, the day a solid thing, reach out and grasp it in your fingers, turn it this way and that, this moment alive, still alive, still alive!

155

The shrine gates stood open at the top of the path. No one had come here to destroy, no one had bothered to seek out this little sanctuary to the kakuy of the winter wood. Neither had any Medj lit lantern or incense for many a month, but the timber door slid back to the little room that would have been their sanctuary, and there were blankets piled above the folded mattress in a corner, and dried fruit and vegetables in the cold-storage box behind the altar, and though the solar panels were impossibly matted over with snow, the single small battery off to the west activated when I turned the breaker, and in the tiny square hollow of the Medj's cell, the heater began to glow to life. I piled myself with blankets, pressed my head into the woven matted floor, crawled so close to the heater I thought the fabrics that shrouded me might burn, and closed my eyes and shook before the rising dawn.

Chapter 25

Having stopped, I could not start again.

I lay on the floor of the cell, not even bothering to unfold the thin lilac mattress tucked into a corner, and waited to be caught. Sometimes I managed to crawl far enough to open the storage box and munch on a little apple or fermented cabbage. Then my jaw hurt, so I curled back up again by the heater, until finally, nearly six hours later, the battery that had not been charged for so long gave up. Then I lay on the floor a little longer and waited to be arrested. No one came. The dogs did not howl, the guardia did not break down my door, Georg was not in my head. It occurred to me that this was the kind of posting I could really do with, right now – a forest shrine to tend alone, far from the madness of mankind and their brewing wars and vanities. I pictured myself before the shrine to the kakuy, giving thanks to the forest and, with honour and reverence, sweeping the path and lighting the lanterns, bowing down to the river that gave me life and offering my morning songs to the sun that warmed me. It would be a good calling, I concluded, to be alone in this place, a representative of humanity sent to give thanks. Then I thought about it a little more, decided I'd probably be mad within a week and wondered if there was a school nearby that ever sent children to this shrine, to be taught the old temple lore of ecology and the nitrogen cycle, which mushrooms to pick and which to avoid, and how to live in balance with the world that sustained them. I hoped so; I hoped so with a fervency that astonished me, as if in

157

these few hours of huddling from the snow I had already become keeper of this sacred place.

Then I remembered who I was and waited for the dogs, and the dogs did not come.

An hour or so before sunset, I dragged myself, every part locked in swollen pain, head pounding as if respite had finally allowed the adrenaline that had sustained me to yield to the true exhaustion of the day, into the tiny courtyard of the shrine. I could stretch my arms out in the middle of it and brush either the altar, the gate, or the twin walls of the Medj's cell and washroom, all with a little drunken swaying. I blew a fine crust of snow off the altar, dusted it with the corner of my sleeve, pressed my palms together and bowed to the stone carved face of the kakuy, wished I had a snowdrop or some thin winter flower to lay in offering before his image.

Then I heard the drone again and looked up, irritated now to be disturbed in this place by something so human. I could not see it through the overhanging trees, but I had no doubt that it could see me and raised my fingers in a distinctly profane gesture to it, as much exasperated as anything else that its pilot was taking so long to find me. It turned and buzzed away.

In the washroom, I found dusty robes of the Medj, greys and faded blues. Technically, they were not the robes of the inquisition, and numerous exams and years of careful study and contemplation were required before I was allowed to wear them, but they were warm and clean, and after a little consideration I concluded that my service in Vien probably counted for at least half a doctoral thesis, strong on fieldwork. I untangled myself from my own filthy clothes, peeling them away one bloody layer at a time, and tried not to look too closely at the tapestry of black and blue that rippled over my body before winding myself back into the priest's gown. I found a broom in the dusty corner of a room and knocked the snow off the solar panels. A bucket of wooden pellets lay behind the toilet, ready to start a small fire if needed. I thought about saving them, hoarding my goods, then concluded it was ridiculous and, dragging the bucket into the tiny courtyard, dug a shallow bowl, lined it with stones that some scholarly Medj had doubtless arranged in an ornamental manner of deep metaphorical import and set a small fire going. It was not as magical as the warmth of the heater had been, but it would serve. As the sun set, I piled more stones around the blaze, taking the hottest of the bunch to wrap into my robes and press against my skin as the darkness returned to the forest.

The drone came once more, a few minutes after sunset, but it didn't stay long enough for me to bow, wave or mime obscenities at it. I bent over the fire, prayers tumbling from my lips, the old forgotten songs of gratitude and harmony, sung loosely and out of tune. I thought of taking a stick from my blaze and lighting the stone lanterns that led up the frosty path to my door, as the guardians of this shrine must have done for so many years. But that would have involved leaving the heat of the fire, the orange light reflected upon the image of the kakuy, so I stayed where I was as the owl called and the cold silenced even the hungriest of creatures in a frozen malaise.

I was half-asleep when I heard the footsteps, crunching on old snow. I didn't turn as they approached, but unravelled a luke-warm stone from my gown and returned it to the guttering edge of the fire, listened to the creaking of the gate, heard another step on snow, heard it stop. It struck me as odd that there was not more noise; had the guardia I had fought in the windfarm come alone? Somewhere I had her stick, unless I had lost it in the forest. Maybe this time she'd brought a gun.

Silence, save for the crackling of fading flame.

I half-turned, twisting, and the twist was agony, so I half-shuffled instead, scooching my backside round in a less-than-dignified bumping to see who had come to arrest me. For a moment, I imagined I would not see a human at all but the kakuy of the winter wood, come again to see what honours were paid to him in the shrine that should have carried the smell of incense in thanks for the gifts of his domain. Instead, there was a woman, alone, dressed in a thick midnight-blue coat and hood, fur-lined gloves and knee-high boots, carrying a heavy rucksack on her back, a flashlight in her hand, a gun on her hip. In the low light of the fire, I could not clearly see her face, but there was nothing in her body that spoke of violence or aggression, of retribution for my flight. She could have been a midnight pilgrim, come to pray, except that she turned the full force of the light into my face, her other hand by her weapon, and said:

"Ven?"

I looked again, realised I had only spoken to the forest all day, and that my voice, when I spoke to people, seemed entirely alien and strange. "Yue?"

When things are unnatural, unreasonable, any reasonable response is impossible. I did not run to her; she did not drop her bag and embrace me. Such things happen in cities, in stations, in places that are in the domain of men. In the forest, we stared at each other in silence. Snow tumbled from the black branches, the birds sang, the trees grew, the river roared and took Vae away with it, and we looked at each other longer than the years we had been apart.

Then that too passed, that too was ending, and she shuddered as if the water of the river that had flowed across her back was still rushing through her blood. She lowered her torch, switched it off, walked forward, knelt down beside me, warmed her hands by the last of the fire, pressed them to the top edge of a hot, black-stained stone. The strap that secured her gun was loose, weapon ready to be drawn. She looked into the flames as if she might see the spirit of the great burning slumbering within them, then at last raised her gaze, her puffed breath mingling with mine. For the first time, she seemed to see the bruising mottled across my skin, and reached up, examining my face, touched the back of my head where the guardia's stick had landed, looked back into the fire, opened her bag, pulled out an insulated flask that steamed when she opened it, took a long drink, exhaled, then handed the flask to me.

I drank. It was a kind of tea, floral but weak. She dug deeper into her bag, pulled out a neatly packaged medical kit, said: "You're injured."

160

"Yue – you are Yue." The words wanted to be a question, but there was no questioning in it.

"Ven – you're injured."

"No. Yes. I mean . . . yes. But I'm fine. Not fine. Fine. How are you here?"

"The drone," she replied, turning her chin briefly upwards and taking the flask back from me as if concerned I might drink enough heat to drown.

"That was you?"

A nod, uh-huh. She is fumbling with the pack, little vials of military-grade compounds, far more impressive than anything I've used or seen.

"Why? I don't understand."

She took a while to answer, contemplating where in the cascade of possibilities the most truthful response might lie, picking the most concise way to express as much complexity as she could. "Nadira is dead."

The mind has two choices: understand these words, or reject them utterly. I tell her that she is wrong, she has misunderstood. Of course Nadira isn't dead. She has looked under the wrong rock, come to the wrong shrine. Once the water that feeds me was in the ocean, as was the water in Nadira's blood; we shared the seas, you see, so I'd know if she was dead, and anyway, the whole thing is absurd, quite, quite absurd. Nadira is fine. Georg lied, he lies, he never found a way into her mind. Georg is not made of water; only gasoline runs through his veins. We are different, you see; we are all one life, but we are different.

These words may have become a babble; there may perhaps have been something a little hysterical in my eye, because Yue catches my hands in hers. The touch, glove on glove, silences me. She waits for the words to settle inside my throat, watches for understanding in my face, sees it bloom, nods once, carries on with her work.

"I have a team three kilometres from here."

"Nadira is Temple," mumbles some mushed-up voice that is

going to be my own, now and for ever, now that Nadira is dead. "You are Council. Why are you here?"

"Can you walk?"

"I don't know. Probably."

"It's not far. Lean on me."

When I last saw her, walking through the halls of power behind Jia, she had seemed tall, filling the world with her presence. Now she is a little too short to comfortably drape over, our weights shifting side to side with the effort of balance as we sway down the frozen path by torchlight. Sometimes I think I can walk without her, and make it a few hundred metres so fast I think I could fly. Then I have to stop, and like an old man at the top of a high mountain bend over double to catch my breath. It would be ridiculous to laugh or cry, to tell her she's not real, to swear blind my life up to this moment was an illusion, that time stopped when the forest burned and the kakuy died by the roaring river. At one point, I open my mouth to explain all of this, and get as far as "Yue," before falling silent again. She gives me a quizzical look, and sees that there's nothing but madness in me, and nods once, and says not a word.

Chapter 26

Nadira was shot fleeing arrest. They shot her in the back, twice, and put her in an ambulance, but she died before she reached the hospital, eyes open, tubes down her throat, discarded surgical gloves on the floor around her. They'd have to clean the ambulance top to bottom, no doubt, empty it entirely and turn the hose on its interior, spray it with pink antiseptic and burn the white paper sheets that she expired on. The only photos they had of her face were a surveillance shot of her buying bread, moments before she recognised the danger she was in, and of her corpse. In the first image, she looked humble, charming, smiled at the baker as she took the loaf in her hands. In the latter, she was a martyr to violence, and so the news ran neither, and no one reported her death.

Three other members of the inquisition died that same day. I had not known how many agents Nadira had run, and felt brief disappointment that I had not been the only one, and wondered if I had been the most useful, and was ashamed at my own vanity.

In the winter wood, where all things slumber beneath the blackest black, Yue led me down a path of lightless lanterns to a clearing where once the people of the forest had come to spin their stories through the snow-bound leaves. On ancient tangles of dug-up thread and rotting polymer pulled from the landfill mines, on blue-yellow fishing lines scoured from the skeletal guts of calcified fish, suspended like bunting across the grove to create a second canopy between snow and moon, the memories of the past had been hung like offerings to star and sky. Silver spinning discs bubbling with chemical green that had perhaps once carried music or the sound of voices; long tongues of curling tyre and endless polished beads of green and brown glass, threaded through the forest weave. Distorted plastic bottle tops, painted mats of disposable diapers turned to brown stone through centuries of compression in the mines, cracked sculptures of broken computer chips and shattered metal casings which clunked and clacked against each other as we passed through them, a rubber windchime. Some still bore hints of archaic script:

CE COMPLIANT
MADE IN
CONTAINS PET
DO NOT EXCEED

Beneath an oak bowed by snow, Yue finally let me collapse, huddling against its trunk beneath a tapestry of woven metal shards, spun like a cracked mirror through its branches. The broken remnant of a child's toy; a wrapped bundle of ancient pens, the ink turned to stone; the cracked remains of a wristwatch, time stopped for ever at half past three. The names of the dead had been carved below, etched into wood, landfill miners crushed when the tunnels gave way, or poisoned in the endless chemical stink that seeped through water and lung as they dug their way through the debris of the past. This was a place every bit as sacred as the kakuy's shrine, a monument to the dead, a testament to human things in the place where the spirits reigned. I closed my eyes and pressed my head against the wood, and it felt warm next to my frozen skin. I tried to stop my teeth chattering and couldn't. I tried to hold my knees so close to my chest that not an atom of heat could escape me, but there always seemed a place where the cold got in. Yue said: "They're coming. Ven? They're coming. Listen to me. Stay awake. Ven? Ven!"

It started to snow again, and the snow seemed warm, and I closed my eyes and welcomed it.

Chapter 27

A safe house, two kilometres north of the border between Maze and Magyarzag.

My first experience of coming back to life was a tepid bath. I wanted it scalding, and knew scalding would kill me, and howled as the warmth seeped into my fingers, and didn't care. Strangers wrapped me up in warm towels, laid me down by the stove, talked in low voices and said things like: "At second watch," or "Strategic assessment," or, in the case of one young voice that was perhaps not meant to be overheard: "I swear I'm a slave to that cat."

Then I slept.

Then I woke.

Then I ate, a little at a time, presided over by a man with a mole above his right eye and extraordinarily pink lips, who nodded approvingly when I took little bites and frowned deeply if it looked like I was going to take more than a morsel at a time. He never said anything reproachful, but something in the solemnity of his expression made me want to not disappoint him.

Then I slept again, and when I woke and asked for Yue, they told me she was gone.

In the Burning Age, militaries were confusing things. "Interventions" replaced "conquests". "Enemies we wish to crush" were "rogue states". "Strategic partners" replaced "too big to fight". Huge armies were still kept as a sign of power and prestige, awaiting the day when victory was measured once again in how many hundreds of millions you could afford slain or when nuclear winter settled the matter. As it was, the kakuy ended that era before proud men in smart jackets could do anything too spectacular.

In the modern era, militaries were far smaller affairs. The resources required to sustain the flair and bluster of previous times, along with the classification of some of the more egregious military technologies as anathema to humankind, led to a looser military structure of small units designed to move fast through hostile terrain. The official motto of Lyvodia's 14th Infantry – "our lives in service" – had always unofficially yet far more pervasively been "pedal faster, jackass".

"Been in the wars a bit, been at the old stabbing, the old spying, yes?" The captain, a man in his mid-forties, patted me kindly on the arm. "Could have been much worse."

The safe house was a cabin in the woods without electricity. Worn cushions were arrayed around a low ceramic stove; beeswax candles dribbled yellow into the night. My rescuers sat around reading or playing board games pulled from the cupboard. The largest of the games had a manual some sixty pages long, and play would stop every fifteen minutes to consult the nuance of an unexpected rule.

"This is an eight-roll test," the gamemaster proclaimed. "But you have the salmon, so you must discount your modifier."

Such statements elicited groans from half the board, whoops of glee from the other. I watched from my bundled corner, waiting.

When they decided to move me, they did so without warning, shaking me awake a little before midnight as the snow fell in the dead silence of buried sound. Boots were pulled on and trousers tucked in; revolvers hidden beneath outer clothes, rifles stuck in the back of a sled and covered over with firewood, dried mushrooms, fresh folds of spider silk and a waxed tarpaulin. I was handed documents, clean clothes, a hat that sank down over my eyes with every bump in the path. Then I was compressed into a nook at the back of the sledge, pulled by two men on skis who watched the darkness through their headtorches as if night were a hunting, tentacled thing, every shadow a limb waiting to strike.

Light vanished a few metres on every side whenever I turned my head. Look up and see only falling white, and then above it nothing save a hazy disruption in the dark, twisting sometimes in a billow of tree-top wind. Look to the left and perhaps a wolf's yellow eye darted away; look to the right and perhaps the kakuy is watching, shaking the earth from which he arose and into which he will vanish, perhaps the forest is watching; perhaps the trees themselves bend a little closer to shadow us as we head into the night.

Perhaps not. The lives of humans are not special to the spirits of sky and earth; they will not bless us, they will not curse us, they do not care for our names, faces, moralities or characters. They care only for the water and the fire, for the river running and the mountain standing proud. They will destroy us, or ignore us, not because we are mighty and worthy of note, but because we are small, and it is a simple matter for the kakuy to step on us without noticing that there was something underfoot.

I close my eyes and wonder where Georg is. Who will translate documents for him now, or knows precisely when to bring him dinner? Perhaps I killed his trust in secretarial staff when I stuck a knife in his leg. The thought pleases me, and the surrounding darkness is merely life untouched by light, rather than endless terror waiting, as we glide on through the night.

We stopped three times. Once, a little before dawn, to eat, drink, rest, without fire and with only muffled, murmured speech.

Once, as we were on the edge of a river crossing, ropes set up from one side to the other to guide the wobbling, balancing troops and their gear as they slipped from icy stone to icy stone across the ford.

Last, on a ridge high above a valley carved into a hard V by angry white water. Here, when the halt came, it was so hard and sharp that the momentum of my sledge nearly carried me into the knees of the frozen soldiers that pulled it, and I found myself sticking my hands out into snow to catch balance, kill a little momentum. Then everyone hunkered down, lying flat, and rifles were pulled out and passed around, and I was suddenly the tallest and most obvious target of the lot, so I disentangled myself from my den and wriggled into the shelter of an oak tree, terror hot and itchy in my palms.

There we remained for nearly ten minutes in absolute, motionless silence, as the chattering cold seeped into us. Finally the captain rose again, nodded once, and some semblance of calm was restored. I did not know what he had seen that stopped him so suddenly, but a few kilometres further on he called a halt again and, gesturing to me from his skis, summoned me to the front of the little line.

"There." His voice was a murmur one notch above a whisper, a gentle finger twitching towards the edge of a ridge from which spindling black trees clung to sheer stained rock like breaking masts from a sinking ship. I looked where he gestured, between a break in the canopy, and down to the valley floor. It should have been impossible to see the riverbed below through the dome of winter branches, but the loggers had been busy, and the glint of their equipment still shone yellow and red against the black and white winter. The swathe they'd cut through the forest, a fist of ripped-up earth and spat-out tree, formed a line that stretched almost from one end of the valley to the other, a crumpled desolation. Figures moved against the tumbled-down mortuary of timber and snow, still clearing, pushing back through the cold, and behind them another machine, this one belching thick black smoke from a pipe above its hulking carapace, a beetle crawling over the half-crushed remnants of split forest floor.

"Where are their offerings?" he breathed. "Why are they taking the young trees too?"

"They do not make offerings any more. They say the forest belongs to men."

His lips twitched in distaste. He pointed at the black, grumbling machine as it rolled on caterpillar treads over the fallen limbs of a young ash, white shards of still-living wood splitting open beneath its metal bulk.

"What is it?"

"It's called a tank," I replied.

"How do we destroy it?"

I racked my memory, trying to pull up the few details I'd bothered to absorb about that area of heretical history. "Mines, mostly, I think. Or a bigger tank."

A nod, unhappy to have confirmed the worst. "Nasty things, mines. Never kill who you think they will."

"Well," I muttered, "let's hope it doesn't come to that."

For a moment, his eyes met mine, and there was incredulity there. This was a man who had never once relied on hope to do anything; hope was for children and the elderly – he was paid to plan for the worst. I looked away, his opinion of me significantly lessened from its already low level, and slunk back to the sledge to be dragged like a log through the forest, towards home.

There was no fanfare when we crept across the forest border between Maze and northern Magyarzag. There was no sense of coming home, no change in the air, neither sign nor welcoming committee. There was, however, a path out of the trees onto a road winding through the wood, which no one had tried to clear of snow and which carried the marks of only a few bicycles and perhaps a single postier's truck. Here we stopped. Here my guide turned and said: "We are back," and his words were so devoid of feeling that I wasn't sure at first what to make of them. "Home," he corrected, seeing my face. Then, when I clearly didn't exhibit the full comprehension this statement should have produced, he pointed east. "That way. Home."

"We're . . . in Magyarzag?"

"Yes."

"When did that happen?"

"About two hours ago."

"I . . . expected . . ." A gesture at the empty road beneath an empty noonday sky.

He shrugged. "You will be wanted in Budapesht." And then a thought, a little sadder; a settled conclusion which had been gnawing at him for a while and which could no longer be denied. "There will be war soon."

I tried to think of something to say. Nothing came to mind. This seemed to satisfy him more than any words. He nodded once, and turned to the east, and twenty minutes later we reached a crossroads where a single electric bus sat waiting, driver on the roof trying to dust off some of the snow from the solar panels to catch the meagre winter light. Seeing us, he hopped down, exclaimed, "No one shot? So glad!" and opening the door to the vehicle added, "Only got enough charge to get us to Vakch, then need to plug in. So no heating, I'm afraid!"

"That is acceptable," the captain replied, before his soldiers could groan too dramatically. "Kindly choose a radio station of popular music," he added, the words unfamiliar and uncomfortable on his lips, to which the troops gave a much more impressive cheer.

Chapter 28

It is a strange thing to come back from the dead.

I had clearly been dead; dead in the forest, dead in the shrine to the great kakuy.

I had in fact been dead almost from the moment the Brotherhood raided the temples and found nothing there, counting the hours away until my life was over, until Pontus found me and I was shot or stabbed or beaten to death in the cellar beneath Georg's house.

Now I sat huddled in the back of the bus as it slowly drifted round the switchback roads to the river below, and even the radio talked of war between the music, and I was, in fact, not dead. With every sign to Budapesht, with every guardia post we passed where no one was in a hurry to shoot me, I came a little bit nearer to living. Had I ever lived before? I had studied in the temple, run through the remnants of the burning forest, reached for Vae's hand in the river, seen the kakuy, waded through the flood of the Ube, and yet it seemed to me that I had not at any part of this process been alive. This heady drug of living again, this strange cocktail of delirium was, I knew rationally, merely a high from having come so close to dying, rather than any philosophical revelation. And yet now, close my eyes, and here, this blood is hot, and here, this heart is mighty in me, and here, I am alive.

I am alive again.

In Vakch, the bus stopped to recharge at the garage on the edge of town. A station, a little branch line into the city, was twenty minutes' walk away. The soldiers asked if I wanted an escort, and I shook my head. One started to wave goodbye, and then, realising that no one else did, immediately stopped and looked away, rugged in his detachment.

Alive, I walked through the afternoon sun.

Alive, I walked through the smell of baked goods on hot plates, caught a whiff of fermentation, heard the scream of children fighting as only children can, as if the end of the world had come to their little corner through mysterious ritual and imagined disaster. I passed the open doors of a hearth, smelt fresh resin between newly laid bricks, heard the clicking of the compression battery, looked up into a sky through which the sun briefly broke in tuning forks of illumination before vanishing again behind purple clouds fading to crimson in the west. I passed the telegram office and thought of sending something to my own hearth in Tinics, a world away. Some few words of happiness, of wishing well, and realised there was nothing I could compress into a few hundred characters, no meaning that mattered, and that I needed to go home, and live again.

Opposite the station, a shrine to the kakuy of the winding river and soft marshes that fed this town. Cut reeds stood fresh in a vase by the door. The copper gong that hung beside the gate was warped with use and reuse, melted down and reforged a dozen times, each time growing a little more precious as history was burned away. A novice, barely more than a year out of college, stood before the shrine of the kakuy and called out the evening prayer. Gave thanks for the fire that warmed us through the winter. Gave thanks for the water on our lips. Gave thanks for the wind that carried the day away. Gave thanks that this earth, mightier than we, carried us still through starlight.

I stood in the door of the shrine and could not go in. My hand rested against the timber, but somewhere there was the Brotherhood at my back, watching, watching, and if I went in they would know I was a spy; they would know and I would die, even though I was free and this was madness. I willed my foot over the threshold and could not make it obey, so I turned away and went to the station instead, to find my way to Budapesht.

172

Chapter 29

Budapesht, seat of the Council, capital of Magyarzag, city of domes.

It had once been two cities either side of the great river. Then the two cities had become one. Then the kakuy came, and the city was two again, the bridges swallowed, the world cracked apart. The first archaeologists who surveyed the ruins were confused by what they found – crumbled concrete and iron bar, slab stone and shattered brick. The groundplans they prised from the earth with their bristled brushes were functional, brutal, square. Were sprawling, luxuriant palaces. Were picked out in tile and terracotta. Were elegant, imposing without being grand, as if the city had not known which world it existed in and so lived within them all.

The first settlements of the new age had begun around the river, to catch the boats drifting down the Ube. In that we followed our ancestors, all things in a circle, renewing again. They were built from the reclaimed materials of the past, a bewildering jigsaw, each brick marked with the scratches of a different history from a different home. Then, as the city grew, modern materials were introduced: bricks of hemp and mycelium, floors of pressed clay and walls of compacted straw. Uncertain how to honour a city of so many histories, Budapesht became an architect's paradise, the focal point of every new experiment and curious idea. Towers unfolded like the leaf of the fern. Rooftops of chitin grew on geodesic domes crowning the hearths, their crops of legume and spice shrouded behind the milky material. Canopies woven by silk spiders shaded the narrow marketways, and solar pylons turned to catch the light on engineered sunflower stems.

Council had been in residence in this city for three of its allotted ten years; after a decade here, its apparatus would be uprooted for the migration down to the Delta – a moving capital that favoured no Province above any other. Its presence filled the train station with new styles from further afield, be it the itching robes of the southern Medj or the straight-cut, high-booted garb of some Lyvodian magnate straight from an embassy with the roving Rus.

As with all cities, there were many shrines and temples, but the largest sat within the walls of a building that had once been sanctified to a monotheist God of old. The great dome that crowned it had collapsed many centuries ago, but had been replaced over time with a solar crown dyed with streaks of liquid blue and crimson through which the winter sun spilt like oil. The scarlet marble columns had cracked and been repaired with biopolymer grown from the seaweed vats, adding new veins of translucent black to their white capillaries. Where the monochrome patterns of the floor could be recovered, they had been, new tiles of clay laid in the gaps, guiding visitors to the place where once an altar had been.

Pictures showed how the faded walls would once have been blazoned with gold and blue, and in one alcove set in a shadowed corner, under soft lights, the recovered fresco of a martyred saint was still visible, one hand raised as though begging the god of the sky to rescue him, the other turned towards his bare belly as if he could not contain the despair within.

The monotheists still came to pray before this icon, filling the vaults with song every second seven-day. An overzealous Medj had talked about removing it altogether, sanctifying the space entirely to the kakuy, but local residents had been outraged, and after a certain amount of back-pedalling and "you misunderstood *entirely*", the martyr was left where he was, and the altar to the kakuy remained where it always had been – in the wide,

174

bee-buzzing gardens behind the faded walls, beneath a rainbow of slung spider silk and slatted timber walls. In summer, the shrine burst with crimson tulips, pink peonies, the dry petals of the blue poppy and beds of tiny daisies. In winter, low fire pits shimmered in carved hollows between the paths, and the wax from the hives was pressed into the hundred candles that burned day and night until spring came again.

A novice offered me a hot stone drawn from one of these pits as I approached, to tuck beneath my robes. I realised that I still wore the faded blue and grey of the order, as he bowed low before me. I returned the bow automatically, felt a pang of inquisitor's horror at the mistake, saw no frown of condemnation, heard no sirens at my back. His deference was not a trick. Georg was not waiting in the crowd.

Evening prayers were done, but couples sat on the benches, holding hands and talking softly of quiet truths, while occasional lone figures marched through the gates to the altar itself, and bowed and gave thanks, and contemplated human things before the image of the earth, and bowed again, and walked away. How strange it all seemed now, this abasement before a shrine that cared nothing for prayers. How odd to pray to a world that saw in us no more and no less than the scuttling of the busy ant.

Away from the pious and the casual, the usual tucked-back buildings of Temple business. A kitchen, private rooms for study and contemplation, a laundry, business-like vegetable boxes and a high, steaming compost pile. A locked door heading perhaps to some minor, classified archive. The lights of the Medj's quarters, bright and warm through translucent sliding doors.

I passed through the gate from public yard into inner sanctum and asked the slumbering priest there for an officer of the inquisition, and waited patiently until they came, and said my name was Ven, and my case handler had been Nadira, and she was dead, and I had nowhere left to go but here.

Sitting in the guest quarters.

I have been given inquisitor's robes, loops of grey and faded red.

I have been given a bowl of potato soup, brought to me on a black lacquered tray.

I have been invited to sit with the Medj of the temple and neither talk nor pray but merely sit and be in this place. I fear doing such a thing, but it is rude to decline the invitation of the Medj, so I obey, and sit cross-legged by their side, and sometimes shake, and sometimes sit in silence, and sometimes feel light-headed, and sometimes feel as though I am the centre of the world, and sometimes feel as if every part of me were dust in the air, and at the end realise I have no idea how to be whoever it is I am, now that I am here.

Somewhere, in the heart of the place that is my home, the forest grows. When all else is swept away, I close my eyes and take great comfort in that.

The next morning, I went to the halls of the Council and met Yue again.

Chapter 30

Entering Council premises took nearly twenty minutes.

I watched, as one might observe precise points of a surgical procedure, as bags were searched, bodies patted down and
scanned for electronics. Nothing in, nothing out, said the guardia
on the door. Council security kept everything on hard-wired
systems cut off from the world, and unless you had filled out
your form II89 and got it stamped by someone with an active
B20 authorisation, you would be lucky to be let in with your
lunch box.

"An inquisitor?" murmured the guardia, struggling to work
out how to search the many folds of my awkward garb. "We don't
see many of you – at least, not in the robes."

"My cover was blown," I replied, and it was the first time
I'd said these words out loud. "I don't know if I'm an inquisitor
any more."

He smiled politely and didn't know what to say, and neither
did I, as I was waved through the gated airlock to the interior.

So here we are.

Yue sits, cross-legged, in her office of wood, stone and glass.
The room was rebuilt into the side of a crumbled-down market
hall, the scars of the old world a jagged slice down one wall, a
timber frame bolted into its remains. Where ancient meets new,
yellow resin defines the join like the border between two warring states. Unlike Georg, she has no restored wooden desk but

sits stiffly on a low stool on the polished timber floor, hemmed in by cushion and blanket. She wears blue, trimmed with white, and her hair is pulled up high, in a formal style. There are two teapots – one large, one small – and matching cups the colour of a stormy sea. There are little rolls of bean and cabbage, still hot from the stove. There is a single sprig of rosemary in a thin-necked vase. These things are arranged on a tray between us, and for a while that is all there is between us as I settle, fold my legs, straighten my back, wait.

Yue tests the temperature of the larger teapot, finds it satisfactory, sprinkles dry leaves into the smaller pot by its side, pours water over them, waits for the liquid to brew, and we do not speak.

In one corner of the room there is a shrine. It is not sanctified, and the incense has long ago burned cold, but the arrangement of objects upon it speaks of a certain amount of contemplation, perhaps even prayer. Feathers from birds of prey, collected and tied together in a bundle. Glass beads polished and blasted by the sea. A vertebra from some unknown four-legged thing. A single page from an ancient document, half torn away, the other half framed and preserved against all time, the colours faded.

I cannot see any text, but the jagged half of the image that survived shows a woman's leg, impossibly smooth and pale, contoured to a soft dune of muscle, stepping down from a short yellow skirt to a pointed, raised pink shoe. It is easy to imagine the female face that had been ripped away above it: smiling, laughing, entirely content with her life, joyful in her body and all that she owned. Yue follows my gaze, half-turned in her chair, sees the paper, smiles, nods, turns back.

"From a fashion magazine," she explains. "I was trying to find one about lip fillers, but they're almost entirely gone these days, or already snatched up by eager collectors."

"Why?"

She thinks about it for a moment, head tilted to one side. "It is good to remember," she concludes. "Everything changes. Beauty, sex; right, wrong. Krima says it is important to pay attention to the fluidity of these things. Tea?"

I nod dumbly as she sweeps her sleeve back from her wrist, pours a dribble from the pot into a cup, swirls it three times in a little whirlpool, pours the rest, passes me the cup between both hands with a half-bow, waits for me to sip, pours her own.

We sit together, drinking tea, and it is the closest I have come to home for I do not know how many years. She watches me over the lip of her cup and I do not care. Her scrutiny is nothing next to Georg's; there is no death lurking behind her eyes, no black wolf of the mountain. Finally she lays her cup back down and, inclining the plate of nibbles towards me, says, as if it is the easiest thing in the world: "Krima will need to debrief you. If you want someone present from your order during this process, we can arrange it."

"I have . . . a lot of questions."

"Of course. I'm sorry I didn't answer them in the forest. You didn't look in a fit state for conversation, and it was not wise for me to linger."

"Why? Why were you in the forest?"

"That should be obvious. I was looking for you."

"Why?"

"It is my job."

I am the forest. I will grow and I will wither and my molecules return to the earth, and when they do they shall rise again into my neighbour tree and I will be the forest. Georg found such thoughts distasteful, a crude reduction of the wonder of human endeavour. I have always found them a comfort.

Yue's voice is calm and steady, a thing moulded from clay. "I assist Krima vaMiyani in matters of Council security. Legally speaking, the Council having its own intelligence service is a grey area – the Provinces are responsible for their security – but some threats transcend the need and expertise of any one Province. The Brotherhood is one of those threats. When the inquisition reported one of its agents was missing, that they did not have the resources to find him, it was considered worth the risk of a cross-border incursion to recover him. To recover you."

"Did you know it was me?"

"No. Not until I saw you in the shrine. The inquisition are ... jumpy."

She sips her tea, and the motion is so small I'm not even sure she's drinking.

"I'm ... not sure if I should be here," I blurt. "I don't know if—"

"Pontus." She says the word so simply, so matter-of-fact, that for a moment I struggle to recognise it's a word at all. She shifts a little in her seat, as if her legs are stiff, turns the teacup in her hand. "You are here because of Pontus."

"What do you know about them?"

"Not much. I am cleared to run operations of the kind you witnessed in the forest – recovery, counter-intelligence. I am not cleared to know about Pontus."

"How do you?"

"Krima. Do you know she had an arrest warrant drawn against Pav Krillovko? The inquisition came to her with actionable intelligence which implicated Pav as a double-agent. Except it couldn't be him. He was on retreat in the southern mountains. But someone is – someone with the highest clearance. Do you know how your cover was blown, Ven?"

"I know that every time I fed intelligence back to the inquisition, I made it more likely I would be discovered. A pattern builds up – a cascade of betrayal that could only have come from one source. How much does Council know about me? About Pontus?"

How much does Yue?

"I don't know," she replies, eyes fixed on some distant place. "I don't have access to that information."

"Then – if I may – why am I here? Talking to you?"

"Because we are also friends." She speaks as if remarking on the coolness of the wind; a truth that will still be true when bones are dust. "Your hearth shared bread with mine. We have ... there were things we saw. We are ... these things are also important, no?"

Are they? Aren't they? I have no idea. Kadri Tarrad has no idea.

Kadri Tarrad is formless in thought and deed. Kadri did not see the kakuy of the forest burn.

"There was a spy – in Vien." My voice sounds distant, dull, even to my ears. "A Council agent. One of Georg's tests was seeing if I would kill him."

"Did you?" Her voice sharp and sudden. I had never known the name of the man I left to die in that cellar, all those months ago. Yue does.

"No." She isn't sure she believes me, and I have never been so desperate for another human to see that I do not lie. "Pontus destroyed the Council's operation against the Brotherhood. Georg practically said as much. With Krima's agents out of action, only the inquisition remained in play. I imagine that makes me useful."

"It does," she replies, simple and stiff. "We are friends, you are an inquisitor, and you are also useful, Ven." She says my name as if it was my own. My name is Ven. How strange it is. "You are going to be debriefed by Krima and Witt. The inquisition has approved it. This is not your debriefing. I am not authorised to debrief you. This is simply tea. This is us drinking tea, as friends should."

I am the mountain. Is the mountain a living thing? Does the kakuy slumber in the stone? Is this world a breathing, conscious thing? Or is it madness, humanism run wild, to say that sentience can be only defined by humans, that a network of neurons surpasses in value an ecosystem that is fed from the blackest pit of the volcanic ocean to the highest bird in the sky. As if the mountain could ever be "merely" rock; as if the sky could ever be "merely" air; as if we were not all spinning creatures within the kakuy of the world, turning through the stars.

Then she says: "I met him, you know? Georg. When I was at university."

I have no idea what I'm meant to make of this, so shrug. "What was he like?"

"You wouldn't have expected him to end up where he is. He was going to go far, of course, but we all assumed . . . tech, perhaps? Or maybe a teacher. A brilliant teacher. Not . . . propping up someone as inept as Antti Col."

"He has no interest in Antti. Antti's just what he has to work with, for now. As soon as he can, he'll find a way to replace him with someone more useful."

"Like who?"

"I don't know. Tanacha, perhaps. Or Kun Mi. Someone happy to feel like they're in charge, without acting like they are." Her eyes are still studying some place I can't see. I have to resist the urge to turn and try to spot the distant land on which she has turned her gaze. "Yue . . . I don't know you." Finally her gaze returns to me, almost surprised to discover that I sit before her, a grown man, rather than the child she had left by the kakuy tree. "We were children. We saw the kakuy and—"

"I did not see a kakuy," she interrupts, quick, calm. "I have never seen a kakuy."

"You were there. In the forest, it was—"

"I have never seen a kakuy," she repeats. "The kakuy have not stirred for a hundred years."

I try to wrap my mind round these words, to read anything in her face, and cannot. What would Lah do, what would Nadira say? Nadira would say the mission, Ven, the mission: what serves the mission? Nadira is dead, and I am not sure what the mission is.

My skin hurts across my chest, and I remember briefly that there is a cut inflicted by man, not by any spirits of stone and cinder, which tugs a little beneath my robes.

Then Yue says, a little kinder, and I wonder what she sees in my face to provoke her: "You are right. We do not know each other. We come from the same place, that is all. But I have read about Kadri Tarrad. In the days before we found you, I studied your file. So much of it redacted – so much Temple wouldn't say – but I felt . . . familiarity. It mentioned Tinics, your age, but I didn't know any Kadri from home. It was . . . I could have sent in a unit and stayed behind. I wanted to be there. I don't know you, Ven. But I know you risked your life for the inquisition. I know you got out alive. I would like to know you better, if you are willing."

She pours more tea, offers me the refilled cup. I take it. The heat feels real, and I could do with a certain solidity in my universe.

"Hello, Ven," she says, raising her cup in salute. "It is very nice to see you again."

"Hello, Yue," I reply, and drain the cup down.

Chapter 31

I was, as promised, debriefed by Krima vaMiyani and Antoni Witt.

Witt is a rarity, an escapee from the Anglaes islands who fled before the purity laws could spill his blood in offerings to the wild sea and dark forest. His eyes are green-grey, skin pale enough that he could have almost passed as pure Anglaes. They say his hair was white by the time he was seventeen, that he speaks seven languages and paddled down the Rhene River to the northern border of Maze in a canoe he carved himself. He neither confirms nor denies any of these statements. He learned a long time ago to keep his mouth shut.

He was also one of the suspects to whom Temple gave their doctored files. So was Krima.

The debriefing lasts four days. Yue picks me up at the end of every day, escorts me through Council security, nothing in, nothing out, has secured a guesthouse for me to stay in rather than Temple grounds.

"Ven will stay at Temple," replies my handler from the inquisition. "He is still one of us."

Only later do I realise what my handler must already have known: that the guesthouse would be bugged, every twitch of my toes or snort in my sleep monitored. I do not begrudge Yue doing her duty, and she does not fight my handler on the point.

In my cold little room in the temple, I wonder if the inquisition has also bugged me, and have to resist the temptation to search under the lamp by my roll-out mattress, to run my hands over the walls, shake out every corner of my clothes.

Krima says: "Maze is poised to invade Magyarzag, but they want Council to start the conflict. If Jia fires the first shot, then Ull and Han will have an excuse to stay neutral, brush it off as some philosophical dispute and keep their Provinces out of it. Maze is pushing her to make that mistake – provocations along the border, heresies within their lands. Thus far, she's managed to hold back."

Witt says: "We don't have an answer to armour-piercing rounds. We barely have armour. Some of the newer resins are promising, but if Georg knows how to enrich the tips then . . . "

Krima says: "If he is mining here, why haven't the kakuy woken? Why aren't they raining fire?"

Witt says: "We can't trust in kakuy to do man's business, can't trust in some . . . spirit . . . "

Krima says: "Jia is organising peace talks. A final attempt to stop a war. All the Provinces will send representatives. You helped, Ven. The information you supplied is vital – it will force Georg to reconsider his strategy. It buys us time. Council is very appreciative."

She does not mention her attempt to recruit me, and neither do I.

How many years was I in Vien?

How many weeks did those years buy?

I try to ask, but this is not that place. Their questions matter more than mine. They see things I do not. But they do not see Pontus.

Krima says: "Again. One more time."

Again.

One more time.

And I tell them all of it again.

A week after I arrived in Budapesht, Temple summoned me to Bukarest. I had no bags to pack, sat watching the winter world outside the window rolling by with nothing in my hands and a borrowed hat on my head. No one came to the station to wave me off save a pair of Council watchers too new at their job to be unobserved; but Yue left a message at the shrine, which I only received several days later by forwarded telegram.

STAY SAFE, she said. *TRAVEL WELL.*

Chapter 32

Bukarest, the Temple of the Lake.

I had been a novice here, all those years ago.

Then Lah had asked: "But why did you join the temple?"

And I'd replied: "I think it's important not to take things for granted."

And somehow, in their mind, that had been enough.

Lah met me at the station with a bicycle scrounged from a novice who preferred to walk. Hugged me. I hadn't been held in that way for . . .

. . . I wasn't sure how long.

Then let go and said: "Well isn't it all a fucking disaster?"

And laughed, and so did I. We stood in the middle of the station, two priests in fading robes, and laughed like we'd just heard a very dirty joke.

For my first few weeks back in Bukarest, I went to the server port twice a day to download the latest news to my inkstone. Then Lah pointed out that knowing, devouring every bulletin and rumour sent down the line from Budapesht or Vien, facilitated neither my equanimity nor the calm of others.

Then I put my inkstone away, finally sat in silence before the cracking ice on the surface of the lake, and permitted myself to be simply small in this place. Somewhere behind me there was a version of myself that had perhaps wanted to be a hero, who had walked mighty on the earth and unravelled the secrets of heretics.

Today, there was only the new sun rising, the sky and the earth, the black pine trees and the gods of the stones.

We too are the kakuy, Lah proclaimed. The spirits of earth and sky, sun and moon give life, and we are of the world, flesh made animate, blood made fire by our living. We are the kakuy of humans, a piece of the great turning of the world, tiny upon its surface, and no less than the mountain.

"Why do we give thanks to the kakuy?" the Medj asked, and the congregation sang its ritual response – we give thanks for the sun that warms us, the moon that guides us, the sea that carries us, the sky that gives us breath. These were the words Nadira had sung, the first night I met her.

I tried to sing the ritual words and could not. The kakuy have no interest in the prayers of men; why heed the imprecations of an ant?

We give thanks because we are the mountain. We give thanks because we are the forest. We give thanks because to honour the kakuy is to honour ourselves; we forgive ourselves, we love ourselves, thank our bodies and our sight, our coming in and our going out. We know at last what we are – life shining in a pearl of blue spinning through space, separate and together. Thank you, sky and earth; thank you, sister and brother of sea and fire. We are one.

Even cut off from the world, I heard rumours of the peace conference unfolding on the isle of Kirrk, a last desperate attempt to put off war. I wondered if Georg was dead and what had happened to Nadira's body. I wondered if Witt was looking now at all the intelligence I'd stolen from Georg's desk and tutting and whispering: *we* must fight fire with fire. Perhaps all I'd done was turn a short war into a long one.

In the end, we offered a body of straw and winter flowers to the sky, not having Nadira's corpse. In the mornings, I swept snow from the path so the elders might not slip as they shuffled to prayers. At lunch, I worked in the steam of the kitchen, chopping carrots and stirring vats on the stove. In the afternoon, I folded over the dark matter of the smouldering compost heaps, read the writings of scholars both ancient and new, sat beside the lake and watched the crystals on the cracked edge of the ice shrivel and grow with the changing movement of the sun, and gave thanks that I lived, and healed, and tried not to smell the Ube in flood, or the forest aflame, or the blood as it rolled through my fingers.

Lah said: "It is good to grieve," and it hadn't occurred to me that I was grieving, and I didn't think they were right. I tried to find a way to express what I actually felt, and couldn't. To feel was vulnerability, a habit lost while serving the inquisition. Only the job remained.

"I can send you out to do something more involved, more engaged. But then you will simply be doing in order not to feel, rather than being here, and feeling. What would you like to do?"

I thought about it for a while, knew the answer they wanted, and said: "Please put me to work."

They smiled, perhaps hiding a little disappointment in my reply, and I was sent to the local Assembly to offer advice on archival matters, translate archaic texts, and advocate on subjects heretical and pious. The work was hard, long, frequently tedious, and I was grateful for it. I turned off the radio when it talked about the coming war, and resolved not to think about Yue, and refused to think about Pontus, and thought about them all the time. I peered at the scar across my chest in the dusty mirror of the washroom, then bathed in a tub so hot and deep that to fall asleep in it was to drown. I looked at the timbers that framed the room, wondered what thanks had been offered to the kakuy from whose trunks such things were taken, and if the spirits of the things lived on even here, and concluded that they probably did, altered by man's intervention but still honoured in their way. Then I thanked the forest and the water and, for the first time in a very long while, thought I understood what "thank you" meant.

Drinking tea, Lah slides the door to the balcony outside their room back a little so that the cold of the air outside might mingle with the warmth of the cups in our hands; the contrast, they said, pleasing, invigorating, a sacred thing, if only you're willing to feel a little blessed.

189

They have planted winter bulbs in the garden, and talk idly about squashes and the taste of hot rice on a frozen morning, and how much they love the taste of apricots, until finally, seeing that I'm not really listening, they fall silent.

For a while we sit there, quiet together.

Then they say: "You may as well ask. It'll eat you up if you don't."

"Who do you think Pontus is?" They sighed, bowed a little, adjusted some hidden limb within the great grey sweep of their robes, didn't answer. I tutted. "Come on. The inquisition won't just be praying it's all okay – you have a theory. Who do you think Pontus is?"

"It's very hard to say."

"But?"

"There are some leading suspects. Pav Krillovko has some problematic relationships – bad influences, you might say. And for all that he was not in Budapesht when our trapped document leaked, it still came from his system – his inkstone. I don't know how he could have done it, but he is hardly exonerated in the inquisition's eye. Witt has always been a heretic at heart. He wants us to open up the archives in Martyza Eztok and tell him all about military vehicles and tactical nuclear devices, and so on. If he could have jet fuel, he would. He calls solar planes 'those little sky-farts'. In past border skirmishes with the Rus, he proved fantastically good at guerrilla tactics; even if he's ideologically suspect, Jia won't want to lose that skill. If Krima vaMiyani has betrayed her own department, there's very little we can do, realistically – just hope that Yue Taaq or someone in a similar position spots it before it's too late."

"Is Yue a suspect?"

"She doesn't have access to the kind of intelligence Pontus is feeding Georg. That doesn't mean she isn't compromised in some other way, of course – one must be careful about these things – but she isn't senior enough to pose a threat. Then there's the Ministers themselves. The read-list for the intelligence you provided was small, but Council is meant to keep the peace

190

between the Provinces, not secrets. Jia would be forced to share intelligence with Provincial Ministers – Shamim perhaps, Han or Ull. Maybe even Farii. As you have demonstrated, you don't have to share much to risk even the most diligent Minister falling prey to a clever secretary. Information spreads like oil through water, clinging to even the cleanest of us."

"Lah – is Georg Mestri dead?"

They blinked in surprise. "Sky and sea, no. Why would you think that?"

I felt heat blaze through my face. "I stabbed him."

"In the leg, Ven! In the *leg*."

"I really meant it."

"He's not dead. He's on Kirrk at the peace talks, muttering into Antti's ear as usual. Did you really think you killed him?"

"It was a possibility."

"Sun and moon! What a twist that would have been! But no, Ven. Excellent scholar of archaic heresies you may be – a solid inquisitor, all things considered – but you are not, in fact, an assassin. More tea?"

"I think perhaps something stronger."

They shook their head and puckered their lips, but they fetched something a little stronger from their stash behind the kitchen cabinet.

The next day, the Colonel came.

Chapter 33

Her name was Merthe. She was far too senior for the task given her, but she was, as she put it, "heading in the right direction". She was nearly two inches taller than me, all hips and boots and curly brown hair. She waited for me in Lah's office, wrapped in a grey winter coat, and shot bolt upright as I entered, handing me the letter like a lawyer delivering a summons.

"Is this . . ."

"Please read it now."

I stood awkwardly in the door, opened the letter, read it, read it again, folded it, put it in my pocket.

"Are you ready to come?" she asked. "There is a train in three hours; I have booked a berth."

I nodded. I couldn't think of anything else to do.

It took nearly two days to get from Bukarest to Kirrk. The sleeper train was quiet; empty beds and empty stations. The carriage guard beamed at me and my travelling companion as we settled into our bunks, thick duvets and prickly blankets. "Breakfast is at 6.30 a.m.," he chimed. "And I recommend the oats."

In the dark of the rattling train, a few lights glimmered over the regimented beds as the travellers rocked sleepless in the gloom. Sometimes I slept, and jerking awake thought maybe hours had passed, and we had missed our stop, even though it was at the end of the line. Then I lay awake, and didn't sleep, and must have slept again, and pulled my knees up to my chest and found that made me a little too wide for my berth, and then stretched out all the way and found then I was a little too long, toes tickling out into the corridor.

When the guard opened the blinds for morning breakfast, I expected a dazzling explosion of light, driving back the thick darkness of an uncertain night. Instead, thin pre-dawn glow ran in grey diagonals through the rattling interior, catching on pole and mattress, sluggish stirring shadow of bleary-eyed waking traveller.

In Budapesht there was nearly an hour and a half before the train to Bljaina. I wandered round the perimeter of the station, saw soldiers' trucks and guardia checking papers, families queuing for tickets, thick crowds of the determined, the listless, the confused and those whose earnestness was one trodden toe away from desperate. Merthe walked with me, as if anxious I might be mugged, and finally said: "Everyone thinks that Maze will attack Budapesht first. It's so close to the border, it's an easy target. We are not prepared for urban warfare. There is talk of mining the river."

A memory, loosely dredged from the mind of whoever I was before I fled through the winter wood. "Nasty things, mines. Never kill who you think they will."

She nodded briskly, without comment, as we turned back towards the train.

Valleys and hills; train clinging to the running edge of the thawing river. A waterfall bursting rich from ice above; a den for wolves below. Sometimes terraced fields, growing biomatter for the vats or turned-over soil ready for a spring planting. Forest framing winding roads, wiggling tracks. Tunnels that hit like a punch to the gut. We threaded the mountains like a needle, and I wondered what the mountain heard as we passed through it and out the other side. Some routes were ancient, paths unearthed from the blasting of the Burning Age. Others were newer tracks laid through the kingdoms of the kakuy. Glance out of the window, and for a brief moment a line of wind-worn stones, dressed in fading woven crimson hats, lined the railway path – guardians raised to shield the spirits of the living from the spirits of the dead. Then a town, temple above and post office below, a single telephone line stretching through the trees, a single road leading out. We waited at the station for the up train from Bljaina to arrive, wheezing into the opposite platform so we could pass each other without incident on the one-track line towards the sea.

Merthe said: "I'm with the Lyvodian army, 2nd Infantry. I answer to Ull and the Provincial Assembly, not Jia, but you're technically a Lyvodian citizen, and as I was going the right way—"

"Technically a Lyvodian?"

"I don't know if priests are supposed to swear to some higher . . . state? Power? What do you swear to?"

"I'm not a proper priest."

"Then why do you live in the temple?"

"I suppose no one can think of anywhere better for me to go."

"Don't you have a home?"

"I did. It's been . . . a long time."

"All the more reason to go back, isn't it?"

"You make it sound simple."

"Isn't it?"

Merthe liked things simple. Complex, she had decided, was for idiots who talked too much.

In Bljaina, no more trains. The city sat in a premature winter dusk of bruised purple and salt-smeared clouds. The snow was nearly gone here, black patches of mud worming through the trodden white like new continents rising from the deep. People glanced at Merthe and smiled wanly; she smiled back and mused: "No one wants the Brotherhood's heresy here."

She sounded like she believed it, the passion of the just. I wondered what it felt like to believe, thought I had a vague memory of it, but it broke like cobweb when I fumbled for it.

Yue had sent an electric car, charging up outside the station. I got in uneasily, folding myself into the tight back seats between

Merthe and a man in glasses who did not introduce himself, did not make eye contact, would not say the purpose of his mission or what he carried in the bag that he clung onto with the passion of a father for a weeping child. We stopped once, to recharge in a sarai as the night settled. I got out, stretched my legs, smelt something strange on the air – rotten eggs and sawdust – stood on the edge of the sarai, sniffing the darkness, puzzling, until Merthe appeared at my side.

"We're above an old landfill site," she explained. "The miners picked out what they could, but there are layers that are too dangerous to disturb. Nothing lives or grows around here – but the road passes by because it's the quickest route, and it's not like there are any kakuy we can disturb in this place."

I nodded, staring into the flat dark beyond and finding it suddenly far darker, far blacker than the forest. "Have you ever been to a place called Martyza Eztok?"

"No. Why?"

"There are old tunnels beneath it – mining tunnels – from the burning. When the kakuy woke, the ancient archivists hid their books and their hard drives in the caves, the most valuable information they could find. They intended it as a gift to help the future. Combustion engines. Fractional distillation of crude oil. Deep shaft mining. They wanted to help us. They wanted to make a better world."

She thought about it, then shrugged. "Who doesn't? But as my old Medj would say: there's wanting something, and then there's being a dickhead about it."

"Your Medj sounds like a character."

"They worked in sewage treatment before getting spiritual. Really good priest, terrible gossip; you know how it is."

Then there was the smell of the sea, brown reeds of scrubby grass, rolling, broiling clouds and salt-washed stones. The old bridge between the mainland and Kirrk had crumbled centuries ago. Only a few iron stands remained, testimony to our ancestors' mastery of water and metal. The gullies through the white cliffs

195

where the roads had run still cracked the land in an unnatural geometry. The sound of the seabirds squabbling on the cold breeze was like the conversation of old aunts at the hearth, amicably arguing over how to season their supper. We took a boat out to the island, a single triangular sail the colour of sunset sand, oars and a tiny motor that ran on stinking seaweed oil. Warning lights flashed to the right to keep people away from the tidal tubes hidden beneath the waves, which supplied power to the towns around. The lights to the left were subtler, gentle yellow, marking the beginning of the kelp farms that spread all the way along the coast, feeding their slippery harvest to the biovats, resin wells and livestock troughs across Magyarzag.

As we neared the island, I could see the starscape of a town, built on the bones of that which had gone before, pressed into the place between curving bay and rising cliff. A creature rose over the harbour mouth, made of woven ancient fishing net, plastic flakes and polished driftwood, rusted container and the bent spines of the crab pot. Jaws gaping, a tongue of rotting fibres hanging down its lips – a monstrous monument to the kakuy of the sea, a raging creature of unkind storms and recovered bones. We drifted past it, into the shelter of a spit of sand which stilled the rocking water and brought with it the smell of fish, salt, yeast and grain, as well as the sound of music and human voices, as if the barrier between rough ocean and gentle sea were a solid wall dividing the universe. Figures moved on the beach, torchlight scraping the pale sand. Our pilot waved to them; a man waved back, and as we pushed up onto land someone called out in a manner so much like the chattering of the birds that for a moment I wasn't sure if it was a human or a creature of the sky that spoke. Then the pilot answered in a language of the island, and Merthe said: "Ready, not-a-priest?" She held out one hand to help me scramble off the boat, steading me as my feet adjusted to the soft shifting sand of the beach, cold salt rising as I sank a little in the spongy line between sea and earth.

I looked east and saw the first glimmer of dawn light, thought I might be sick. I had not felt sick at sea. "Is Yue here?" I asked.

"Taaq will see you as soon as you're settled, I'm sure." I thought I saw a little pity in her face, and wondered if she understood just what the letter in my pocket meant. I followed her up the beach, towards a scrubby shore and the lights of the town, guided by torchlight which increasingly grew dim against the rapid rising of the eastern sun, its light curving off a mirror sea.

"We can get you something to wear; would you rather inquisition robes or do you—"

Merthe's words cut short as, from round the corner of the nearest whitewashed, squat house, a group of men approached, black against the town's light. I could not clearly see their faces, but I saw something familiar in their motion, in the set of shoulders and the swagger of limbs. Merthe adjusted her weight, pushing her chin forward and growing larger in the space she occupied, until our two groups met like the foaming place where river flows to the sea.

"Good morning," she proclaimed, flat as skimming stone, before anyone of the group of men before her could speak. "Can we help you?"

"Thought we would see the dawn. Say thank you to it, and all that."

A voice, smiling in the dark. A man stepped to the front of the crowd. Or rather, one leg stepped, and the other followed, supported by a long cane topped with a heavy handle around which his fingers curled as if he would claw the world itself in his fist. The handle was black wood, carved into the head of the wolf – or rather, not the wolf but the kakuy that had worn the wolf's form when he lay upon the snowy mountain, all tooth and blood.

The man did not step again, but held his ground, as if to move more than one limb at a time before the eyes of strangers might expose his limp, the dragging weight of his body tilted to one side; as if by remaining stationary, I would not see it, nor know him.

"New arrivals?" he asked, and one of Merthe's escort had turned her torch towards the man's chest, politely avoiding shining in his eyes, so that only through the reflected glow of illumination could I see the contours of his features, greyed out shadow driven away from the hook of his brow.

"Tired arrivals," Merthe replied. "I'll wish you good morning, kin of sky and earth."

"Colonel." A little nod of his head, not a bow, nor an acknowledgement of enmity. Merthe steered me past him with one hand in the small of my back.

I met Georg's eyes as we passed and felt his gaze on my neck all the way into the rising glare of dawn.

Chapter 34

In the first light of day, I see a figure praying, head bowed to the rising sun.

He seems a mirage, a strange anomaly bowing first to the east, then to the west, as if thanking the fading dark for the quiet that night had brought. Then we get a little closer, and I see it is Pav Krillovko, remember Georg asking him — do you brush your teeth in charcoal?

If he sees me, he does not know me. In a way, that makes me proud.

A room in what might have once been a fisherman's shack.

A bed, a blanket.

I barely sleep, and in my dreams Georg is there, leaning on his walking stick, watching me, inside my mind, back inside my mind, he never left it after all, he will never be washed away.

I wake a little before lunch to tea, beans and fish.

Eat alone.

Wash in cold water. The bathhouse is carved into an overhang of stone above the sea, both salt and fresh water, tiny green crabs scuttling away below.

The robes of the inquisition feel grotesque upon me; an invitation to strike me down, a target on my back. I yearn for a disguise, some sailor's garb with which I can smuggle myself off the island.

Merthe, who perhaps has not slept, meets me at my bedroom door. Says: "Sleep well, sea-kin?"

I have never been kin of sea before; never sailed across the ocean. I wonder if the pirates between here and the west are really as bad as all that. I wonder if the Anglaes still shoot refugees on sight.

"Yes, thank you," I lie.

She nods, and does not believe a word of it, and takes me to see Yue.

Krima and Yue have a shared office tent of inflated spider silk and woven straw mats. Tables have been unfolded, cables run in from the portable solar panels on the hill above, supplementing the isle's tidal supply. Krima stands surrounded by a small cluster of empty chairs, as if her deputies have been smuggling every different kind of stool to see if one might stick, in an attempt to alleviate her pacing.

"Oh. It's you," she proclaims, as I am ushered through the thin, soft flap into the translucent interior. "Another fucking game."

Yue has availed herself of a seat, but she rises as I enter, stands bolt upright, takes me by the elbow, says: "I'll handle it," which earns nothing but a snort from Krima.

Leads me outside into the salt-spinning wind.

Blurts: "It was not my intention. I did not ... but they will not talk until ... it's Georg. He has influence, he has ... he's planning something. I did not want to. But he insisted. He said that the peace negotiations will only continue if you are here. I know it's nonsense – a power play, nothing more. But Jia says it's too important for us to ... I'm glad you're here. Thank you for answering my message."

I replied: "I came of my own free will."

"Why?"

Hesitation, bewilderment. "Because you asked."

She flinched. It seems absurd that a woman in her position should fail to understand her power, let alone regret it. "You'll be accompanied at all times. Krima is too angry to talk about it, but she does understand the ... the risk we are exposing you to. She does. She can seem difficult sometimes, but she's not what she ... the second you want to leave, you can."

200

"Thank you."

For a moment, an old, thin woman tries to push through Yue's skin, pressing out from every part of her like fungus from the fallen tree. Nothing will help now, she screams. You're all fools to think it. Then Yue – the one I know – smiles, and nods, but even she can't quite manage to be reassuring.

In the low afternoon of fading winter, I walked along the edge of a low white cliff as the wind thumped in off the sea. Turn your face to it, and the sheer force of air filling your lungs is a gasp, a moment of contraction as your body struggles to exhale. The smell of salt clings to skin and hair, but not five metres away there is a little gully where white flowers grow and rabbits bound away, and it is another season, another world.

On the east side of the island, the smell of ocean, the great kakuy of the seas answerable to no man, the many-tentacled kraken risen again with a mouth of serrated teeth laid out in rows – fed, they said, on the thousands who died fleeing the water wars, fatted on plastic and microparticles, grown black on spilt oil and scarlet on rust. On the west, the smell of humanity; animal dung spread out across the turned soil, a few pellet fires burning in ancient stoves, gutted fish, fresh kelp, algae vats churning out polymers and proteins; the building blocks of this island's little industry. There are kakuy even in the slim waters between the island and the mainland – the snow-white dolphin that rises up from the passing pod with eyes of sapphire; the great blood-red crab that all have seen and none can catch, which scuttles sideways across black stone and fears neither bird nor man.

It is a good place to talk peace, this island. The heretics point at the fallen bridge and remind the pious of the great things that man can do with steel and piston. The pious close their eyes, as the sun rises over a reflective sea, and remind the heretics that salt water will triumph over even the most ingenious of engineering, in the end. It is just a question of perspective.

Inland a little from the sea, a hearth, set apart from the others. It has whitewashed walls and a gate around which generations of small hands have pressed seashells and stones of spotted scarlet and deepest black, pebbles of polished plastic and glass harvested from the ocean, forming a mosaic frame of the island's history through which visitors must pass. It has three grey olive trees within the main courtyard. There is a bicycle stand, empty, and a shrine to the kakuy of the nearby beach, where incense does not burn. The hearth has two floors, solar panels on the roof turned away from the prevailing wind, a bathhouse from which drifts the sound of splashing water and the sharp smell of mint. Everywhere there are Brotherhood men, and many are armed. They carry eight-shot pistols on their hips, and a few carry hunter's rifles, five shots a clip. Jia's hearth will doubtless have the same weapons, and the Medj will be there now, arguing as to the ethics of declaring canon plans for faster, deadlier weapons, thirty rounds to a magazine, automatic and semi-automatic firing, the kind of gun you just wave in the general direction of the enemy and damned be the consequences.

The Brotherhood always had a fondness for uniforms, for a sense of belonging to a tribe, but now they are really getting into their military garb, grey-brown camouflage and hats worn on a funny angle, creating a shared pride in their clothes, their swagger, their guns, their glares. These men will not be happy until there has been a war; Antti has spent too much time making them believe that war will make them men, will make their lives matter. The inquisition made me think much the same thing about being a spy. They stare at me, and some know who I am and spit at my feet, and others just stare and hope I can see my own death played in crimson across their corneas, a grotesque, slow-motion film in which they are the stars, driving bayonets between my ribs, holding me down with metal while I thrash around like a butterfly on a pin.

A door is opened. The kitchen is hot, smells of cardamom and pepper. A flight of stairs spins tightly upwards, past more armed men, to a sliding door of heavy, old wood, knots black and popping.

"Wait here," says a man who has trained all his life to be a fighter and now will prove it the only way he can.

We wait.

Ten minutes.

Fifteen.

Twenty.

Yue paces up and down, snaps: "Where is he?" Does not get a reply.

Twenty-five.

"We're going," she barks. "Ven!"

The man who has been guarding the passage nods at this, as if he has finally heard the correct password; turning to the door, he knocks three times then heaves it back. Yue stands, quivering with indignity and rage. I put a hand on her arm, the nausea I had felt since stepping into this place briefly fading in the face of her fury. "It's fine," I murmured. "It's just a game."

For the briefest moment, I thought Yue might cry, and was astonished. Then she straightened up, stuck her chin forward, and marched into the room like a conquering queen.

Georg sits, alone. He must have been sat here the whole time we were outside, waiting. The hearth has fat, stiff cushions. He perches on a low stool instead, hands on his thighs, eyes half-closed as if in prayer, the leg I stuck a knife in extended long. On one wall of the room hangs a painting, not particularly good, of the great kakuy of the ocean rising from the ancient garbage patch, caught in a shaft of slightly ominous orange light breaking through black storm clouds. On the floor are faded rugs of woven wool, and the shutters are closed, thin afternoon light slipping through the gaps in the old wood to create prison bars of amber across his feet.

Georg's stick, carved with the wolf kakuy of the mountain, leans against his chair. One cushion has been set on the floor, a tray of tea between us, untouched, the cups waiting to be turned. Georg opens his eyes fully as we step inside, barely looks at me, gives Yue a fluttering glance.

"Taaq – you can wait outside."

"I will stay."

"I think you will go. Why don't we ask Kadri?" His head

203

half-turned as if the weight of his eyes moving to me were a physical force, a powerful blow. I felt the hot flush of a child caught between two squabbling parents, no hope of being right.

"Yue," I muttered, "I'm fine."

She stiffened, glowered at Georg, spoke to me. "I'll be outside. You can leave whenever you want."

"I know. Thank you."

She let herself out, heaving on the door as it creaked closed again, sealing us into gloom.

Georg waited for it to thunk shut, then smiled, gestured at the tea. "Do you mind?"

I turned over the cups, poured for us both, passed him a vessel, one hand circling the top like a hook, the other supporting the base with two fingers, a half-bow of shared drink offered. He took it in the same manner, rolled it around the palm of his right hand, sipped. I picked up my own, smelt the familiar fragrance of his favourite brew, barely wetted my lips with it, put the cup back down, waited. I was used to waiting for Georg.

He drank again, smiled, seemed to enjoy the taste, finished his cup, laid it down, poured himself another, did not drink.

For a little while we sat there, he and I, like an old couple that meets twenty years after the embarrassing breakup, a little wiser, a little more circumspect. The idea made me want to laugh, and laughter seemed better than the sickening fear I'd felt since setting foot in this place, since Merthe had come to Bukarest. Perhaps I smiled, and he saw it and asked: "Amused?"

"I suppose I must be."

"Good. Humour is a blessing. I never thought you had much."

"There was never very much to laugh at, working for you."

"True. I should have rectified that really. I have been told that I can be unapproachable, as an employer."

I rolled the teacup between my hands, old stoneware and fresh heat. "We never did have time for a proper debrief."

"If you are going to complain about your office chair, or suggest we should have put on ... complimentary chanting classes" – his lips curled awkwardly around the words, struggling to find the ludicrous fripperies of other men – "then please, feel free to put your concerns into writing."

"Your recruitment methods left a lot to be desired."

"My ... ah, the business with your thumb."

"The execution of a man in the cellar was also an unexpected career hurdle."

"You refused to do that; I found that very convincing. A good spy would have done whatever was necessary to finish the job. A coward would have fled and never come back. You were neither. I struggled to work you out, Kadri ... Ven. I realise now how vulnerable that made me. My intellectual curiosity – my vanity, even – overcame my common sense. Thank you for that lesson."

"How's your leg?"

"A useful reminder. How's the cut across your chest?"

"It was superficial, although the scar will be a story."

"Someone taught you how to fight."

"A little. There wasn't much combat on the syllabus, but we covered the basics of pure blind panic, extraordinary stress and moving your feet a lot."

"This is all very un-priestly."

"On the contrary, there is an ancient legacy of monastic orders taking up weapons, usually to fight to protect their economic superiority, very occasionally for theology, and often as a performance art for fundraising purposes."

His laugh was a single high bark, delighted despite himself.

"How's the war going?" I asked.

"Oh, you know. The defeat of our enemies is inevitable. All this," a loose wave round the room, the sea inhaled, "is just fluff and faff to buy us diplomatic leverage – and to allow us to re-write our plans. Well done, for that. If you hadn't been caught, you could have made a real difference."

"It's a little too early in this conflict to judge the difference people make, isn't it? Here you are. Buying yourself a little time with this diplomatic farce, because your invasion plans are now framed on Jia's walls. Do you have a new assistant yet?"

"No."

205

"You should promote Rilka. She adores you."

"She does. But she's prone to finding drama in every little thing."

"Sohrab? He can't translate a text, but he'll take a bullet for you."

"There are plenty of people who will take a bullet for me," Georg replied primly. "But I don't intend to put myself in a position where that is the primary job requirement."

"I'm afraid I'm unavailable to draw up a job description, if that's what this is." Another laugh, gone as fast as lightning. I sighed, watched the candlelight flicker across the ceiling. "Why am I here, Georg? I expected poison, not tea."

"Why do you think you're here?"

"Honestly? I think it's just another stupid bloody power play. You've always had a fondness for waving your willy around." His smile was light and broken glass, a sight that had sent shivers through me when I was Kadri Tarrad. Today, I didn't seem to care. "Jia is desperate for peace, and if she can't have peace she's desperate for a little more time to mobilise. Council is so desperate they'd do anything you ask, however ridiculous. 'Fetch me this spy, I want to have tea with him,' you say, and of course the entire thing is absurd posturing. But they'll do it anyway. For Georg Mestri, the real power behind the Brotherhood – they'll do whatever you want. So here I am, playing your petty little games."

"Here you are," he agreed, quiet as the snow. "My man found you out before you could find him, and here you are. It is as you say. I speak; they obey. You obey. Now you have come all this way, and now you can go. Off you go, Kadri. Off you go, Ven. Go find a rock to pray to."

I rose slowly, drained my cup of tea, the burning welcome in my belly. Put my hands together, bowed before him. "Kin of sky and earth," I murmured, "I do hope your leg recovers."

Was that a flicker in the corner of his eye? It came too fast, too tiny in the gloom for me to be sure. I straightened up, turned my back on him, and walked away at the stately, gentle pace of the old Medj of the mountains.

Chapter 35

Sitting by the sea as the sun goes down. There are guards some-where behind us, Merthe keeping an eye out, but for now there is only Yue, myself, the earth that holds us and the sky that catches breath.

I am the sky, I am the sky, breathe with me, help me, I am the sky.

She says: I know it was just for show. Just to make us dance, waste more time. I'm sorry you were put through that.

I say, I gasp, I am calm, I am holding my breath, let it go, I am the sky: It's nothing, it's fine. There was nothing in it. If anything, I feel better. He's just a man. It's fine.

She says: When I was young, I thought I would be a hero. I wanted to work for Council, make things right. I would fix things, I imagined hands reaching up to me in thanks for all the good I would do; I imagined a life of sacrifice and it was good. Now there will be war and I can't stop it. I have tried everything, everything, I have given everything, and it's all for nothing. I am not a hero. I have no control over these things, other people have decided and they will impose their will, they will impose their power.

There will be a war and there is nothing to be done, nothing at all, so what is the point? Why do we trick ourselves into thinking we can control anything about our lives, have any power over our fates? What is the point?

Somewhere in Vien, there are men who think they have the

answer. They point at monuments to beautiful men and graceful women, they talk of the mountains we have levelled and the triumphs we have made. See, they say, see how man becomes the hero. See this god with trident raised, how he has human form. See how we ascend.

The evening sandflies were starting to bustle and bite. A line of seaweed marked the furthest reach of the tide, rubbery purple twists crystallised with salt. Her shoulder was pressed next to mine. I stared at my hands and said: "The river does not run because we thank it. The wind does not blow to be heroic. The leaves of the fresh green buds do not uncurl before the sun for any story, or to serve any purpose other than to reach, to live, to flower and to die. All these things will change. We are children of the wind."

The island has only one temple, built from the drifting plastic and saline skeletons of the sea. There is one Medj who guards it, and they were a sailor once, who talks in the sailor's tongue of rust and sunset and endless sky. The evening bell rang, softly once, a little louder twice, the full bell at last, calling out three more times before singing away.

Yue turned to stare at me, a glimpse of dread in her eyes. "Do you really find comfort in that? Does that make you feel ... good?"

"Sometimes," I replied. "Sometimes I think I understand what it means, and then I feel better, for a little while."

"You remember the forest?" The question caught me by surprise, a moment in which my tongue tangled. "They say the fire is renewing. The old dies so the new can live. In Damasc, they believe the kakuy want blood, that when the world burned they had to sacrifice their own people to feed the earth and keep the kakuy satisfied, that the spirits of this world are violent, insane."

"They're wrong. The kakuy don't care if we spill human blood; they have no interest in us. They do not care if we live or die, only what mark we leave upon the earth. What is our blood to the soil? Nothing more and nothing less than a little drop of crimson, which will vanish. It is arrogance of the most egregious sort to think the sun will change its heat because of a knife through some poor bastard's chest."

"If you believe that," she replied, "then Vae's death was meaningless."

Do I remember Vae dying? Don't let go, don't let go, and now I can't remember if I said it, if I screamed it, or if it was just a thing written into my heart.

I close my eyes, feel her hand pulled free of mine, but even this memory is false. As my hand grew bigger, hers stayed the same size, and now I remember reaching for it with my adult fingers, as she grows smaller and smaller, slipping through my grasp. Don't let go. Memory does not hold truth, only stories. Perhaps I don't remember her at all. Perhaps I just remember some fantastic trick, some illusionary girl I have re-imagined and re-imagined to fit my needs. A spy would know what to say. Knowing what to say would make me very suspicious of anyone I met.

Then Yue said: "Witt says that Georg has already won. That if we are to survive, Temple must unlock its archives. Warplanes, fuelled by oil. Chemical weapons, drones with missiles and ... I don't know what else. Isn't it absurd? The first shot hasn't even been fired, and Maze has won."

"A strange attitude, for a general."

"A leader should be a pragmatist too."

"What about the kakuy?"

"What about them?"

"To build your planes. To drop acid on the earth. To poison rivers. Do you really think the kakuy won't respond when you scar the earth?"

"No one sees the kakuy these days. They don't care what men do."

"They care when the forests burn."

"Do they?"

"You know they do."

She raised her head, curious, a turn to the side. Didn't see an answer in my face, half-shook her head, asking a question without words.

"You saw the kakuy. In the forest. I was there. You saw it."

A moment in which perhaps something flickered, a glimmer of a memory that had been pressed down so deep that a forest could grow its roots and bury it for ever. She shook her head, once, twice, turned away, shook it again as if trying to clear it of the memory of smoke. "I have never seen a kakuy. You are wrong."

A thousand kilometres away, the forest grows. It came back to life so slowly, from root to branch, branch to leaf, leaf to the bugs that feast on sap, to the birds that feast on bugs, to the predatory cats that look for the fall of feathers, to the worms that feed on the beasts that fall to the fungus that clings in the damp gullies of the bark to the soft-nosed beasts that feed on mushrooms to the darting lizards that lick at rainwater caught in the upturned belly of a curling leaf, the forest grows and becomes again a living thing, where fire once blazed. I close my eyes, and in that moment cannot imagine the sky and earth being merciful to humans should the forest burn again.

"Yue . . . " A thing I needed to say, a thing I needed to express, my fingers catching at hers as the root of the nursery tree tangles with its peer; but she stood up before I could, brushed sand off her trousers briskly, turned away from the setting sun, barked: "Dinner? Dinner before you go," and was marching away without another word.

I lingered a moment behind, then followed her.

Yue's idea of dinner was dinner at Jia's hearth.

And here they are – here they all are. The great and the good of the Provinces.

Ull and Farii, Han and Shamim; Shahd from the Delta and Fethi from Damasc. Antoni Witt, picking at his food. Krima vaMiyani, who trusts no one and smiles, smiles, smiles, just like Georg. Pav Krillovko, telling jokes as the peace comes to an end, and Jia herself. Close up, she is tiny, impossible to imagine that she can stand unsupported, but also hard to imagine that, after so many years of refusing to break, anything will bend her now.

One of these is Pontus.

Who pours hot tea into a waiting cup? Who is the shadow, unacknowledged behind the elbow of some great potentate? Who wears the same face I had worn, all those months in Vien? Who let a fellow spy die in order to seal their own fate? Or maybe no, maybe Pontus was made of sterner stuff; maybe now they sat right by me, smiling and eating flatbread and fish, hands pressed together in thanks for the gift of the bounty of the sea, eyes a mirror, words a song. Who would I be, if I were Pontus, in this room?

Ull, the Minister of my home Province, shares some desolate words with Jia, and Farii can't meet anyone's eye. Behind them, Merthe sits cross-legged on a cushion, eating fish one slither at a time from a round bowl as if she's never seen food before in her life. "Ull wants to stay neutral," murmured Yue in my ear, as I watched from my place at the bottom of the table. "He knows we don't have the troops to defend both Magyarzag and Lyvodia. He's right."

These are real words, on real matters, and yet they seem a thousand kilometres away. My home will fall; the Council will not attempt to defend it. Yet any words which do not run around the room jabbing fingers into faces and screaming, "You? Are *you* the spy? Are you the traitor?" seem, at this juncture, immaterial.

"Jia thinks we can hold them at Beograd, so long as their advance is slow. Our army is trained for guerrilla warfare, not pitched battles. She has a plan." Yue's voice the numb declaration of the surgeon who will cut away a tumour.

A murmur from the top of the table, a gesture. Someone scurries to my side, whispers in Yue's ear but looks at me. Yue says: "She wants to see you now."

"Who?"

A nod upwards; Jia is watching me. I stand, awkward suddenly, knees and elbows, chin and bowing shoulders. The Ministers examine me as I approach, puzzling me out. I put my palms together and bow before the old woman. "Honoured kin, this is Ven," Yue said.

She nodded slowly, bright eyes in a folded face, then took

my hands in hers. The tips of her fingers had grown chubby and clubbed, and bones stood out on the backs of her hand between a daubing of yellow spots. "Ven. They tell me you are a Temple spy."

Does Pontus hear this and turn to stare? Is this some trick, to bring us together, kin of sky and earth? I glance round, but no one cares, and there is just Jia, Yue and I, talking low in a room of stone and salt.

"I suppose that's right."

"And we have you to thank for buying us time."

Was that what I had done? All of that, to buy some time? My eyes flickered to Yue, and I thought she shook her head, just a little, though I didn't understand why.

"It was an honour to serve," I replied.

A twitch in the corner of Jia's mouth. She nodded at nothing much, but there was something alive in her eyes, amused. "I doubt that," she murmured. "Temple and I have a bit of a problem, you see. We know that war is anathema. We know that the kakuy will wake, if we start tearing the world apart. We know they will crush us. Council has the terrible dilemma that we must therefore stand for peace, defend peace at all costs. Even if the only way to defend peace is by going to war. You see the difficulty?"

"I believe I do."

She patted me on the arm, as a kindly grandmother might do to a child whose name she thinks she should know but can't quite remember. "Well. That is why it is so good to have people like you around. Thank you for your conviction." Then she bowed a little from where she sat and let me go.

Chapter 36

Sit upon a stone outside the hearth door, and watch the dinner guests depart.

Krima vaMiyani talks to Yue, low, urgent, her eyes moving to every face. Krima is the one we must rely on to find Pontus, and yet slow – so slow. How has she not found them yet? Why has Krima failed? I am the sea; I drown in thoughts of Pontus.

Krima sees me, acknowledges me, does not approach, has nothing to say. The inquisition has done its part, and I am nothing more than a blown agent, dragged halfway across the Provinces on the whim of her enemy. Yue can deal with me.

Pav Krillovko tells a joke to Ull and Farii, and they do not get it, and are not in the mood. Antoni Witt is enduring Fethi and his pious, pompous huddle of Medj pontificating on some finer point of the kakuy – perhaps they are arguing that owning more than one pair of shoes is insulting, demeaning to the spirits of the earth, or that any glue made from animal bones is heresy, and we were meant to live on the forest floor or in caves and feast entirely on nuts and berries, as our ancestors did. Our ancestors died when they were thirty-two but well, ah well, if the kakuy demand it, so it must be.

Fanaticism would be a wonderful cover for Pontus. The absurdity of it, the sheer excess of it all suffocates even the slightest thought of subtlety, cunning or betrayal. Does Pontus cut their arm and bleed into the dust, proclaiming, "Bless me, spirit of the sand"? Does Pontus smile to see their scars by moonlight?

Somewhere, carried by the wind, the Brotherhood are singing. Their songs are of human endurance, spirit, passion and bravery. They are songs of heroes, bright and bold, loud enough that even Witt briefly stops arguing to turn and listen. Perhaps the world was once full of heroes, before the kakuy woke and, not even noticing what they did, crushed the great, the mighty and the bold beneath the storm.

I move away, fumble my inkstone from my robes, try to find words in it, something meaningful, something calming. The screen is old, a crack in one corner that no one has got round to repairing yet. You have to hold the on-switch down in just the right way to get it to come on.

Then Yue is by my side, and she says: "Not your stone?"

"No. Borrowed from a Medj with a cataract."

The sound of music swells, lifted on the wind; a cry of glory and the might of man. Her head turns to it, as if it were the snap of a breaking branch in a midnight forest.

"They're certainly keen singers," I mumble.

"Worrying you chose the wrong side?"

I shook my head. "No. You?"

"I think it would be too late for me to change my mind, even if I did." Her hand brushed mine, so light that for a moment I thought I'd imagined it. Then she said: "I'm leaving tomorrow. Going to Budapesht. We have to prepare for the worst. I don't know if ..." and stopped, looked away, her hand still pressed, back to back against mine.

I tried to think of something to say.

Georg would think of something to say.

Then someone called Yue's name, and she walked away.

In the dead night of my little room, I do not pray.

Prayers are for gifts. They are for blessed things, bestowed in mercy, compassion. They are raised up in exaltation to something unique and cry out for special attention, for the world to be something other than what it is.

Instead, I close my eyes, and feel my feet upon the earth, and know that when I die the worms will feast on me and the forest will grow.

She knocks on my door twice, almost too quiet to hear, then knocks again, a little louder.

I let her in.

All others are sleeping. The boats will carry the great and the good of the Provinces away, and tomorrow, or maybe the next day, polite people in smart shoes will deliver mutual declarations of war to each other's doors, and children will stand by the railway line and wave at the soldiers, who will perhaps wave back, and we will become barbarians in order to survive.

But for tonight, Yue puts her hand in mine, and kisses the backs of my fingers, and kisses my mouth, and I kiss her back.

There is no love here. Tomorrow we will both be gone. Better to make love with someone whose death you will not mourn, when the bombs start falling; better one last night of comfort, before the world runs mad.

She stays in my bed a little while, because together we are warm and the air outside is cold, and when I am asleep she dresses again, and is gone on the first boat of the morning tide.

Chapter 37

I was standing on the docks in the bright mid-morning cold, waiting for a boat back to the mainland, when the bomb went off. The wind had turned southerly in the night, carrying with it a hint of warmth and compassionate sunlight yet to come. The water was choppy without foam, a deep blue spilled over here and there by the shadows of the clouds above, or the swirling of loose silt below. Friends and enemies were returning to their cities, smiling politely at those whom they would soon be trying to kill, hands pressed together and bowing, well, well, wasn't this nice? Such a pity; such a shame.

It would be gratifying to say that I sensed it coming. That I realised, when I saw Ull approaching down the beach with his escort of five, that something was amiss. That I understood, on seeing Antti and his Brotherhood men waving to their skiff as it bobbed on the end of a long wooden pier, that there was something wrong with this picture. The light was dazzling, a constant flinch away from reflected glory; I could hear women chattering, the natives of the island bidding farewell to their unhelpful guests. It was a good morning to blow cobwebs from your lungs, a fine day to stroll and get salt in your hair or to sit on the edge of a cliff and dangle your legs over the side and feel free.

I did not see it coming.

What I saw, instead, was Antti look towards Ull and smile, a strange smile as if to say, sorry friend – sorry that we are at odds – but no hard feelings? I saw Ull nod once in reply, as if he too were regretful over some hidden thing, and then they both were standing on the pier that reached out towards the water, some ten metres apart, Antti nearest the water, about to step onto his skiff; Ull waiting his turn, for there were only so many people who could comfortably fit at the end of that narrow path with the boats bobbing unevenly all around.

The bomb was under the pier, and it detonated a little late, as if the finger that pressed the remote had been hoping for the two of them to be nearer, was eyeing up the perfect moment and, when it didn't come, went with the best opportunity they had.

It was not a very big bomb. At first I thought it was a terrible accident on a ship, a crash or something running aground. The shockwave of it, from where I stood, was enough that I felt it run through my gut and down my trembling knees, but it did not knock me down or send me scurrying for shelter. There was no fire, simply a black cloud rising rapidly up, spinning at its billowing top, and then rain. First it rained salt water and wet sand, then it rained shattered timber, then it rained bits of pebble and stone, and then it rained ruined parts of human. Most people who were caught in the blast were indistinct enough that the falling tatters of clothes and flesh were unrecognisable, merely driftwood of crimson and black, no more animate than the splattering mud torn up from the shore. The sound of debris falling made a strange, quiet percussion. The acrid acid of the explosive itself was a subtle aftertaste, noticeable only when the adrenaline wore off, a sticky bile in the top of the mouth that water wouldn't wash away.

The first person to scream was one of Antti's guards, blasted out into the water and still, incredibly, alive. He did not scream long. He drowned some eight metres from shore, limbs torn and unable to breathe, gasping in shallow, frigid water. Of the four other survivors, only one had the capacity to groan, to roil and twist his head and gasp for medicine, medicine, please in mercy's name. I ran to help, like an idiot, oblivious to the danger of another blast, saw a leg bouncing against the shoreline like driftwood, saw a crimson slick like oil dispersing in the salt, and

217

a round-eyed fish turned belly up from where it had perhaps been nestling in the shadow of the now-shattered pier. The first body I reached was that of Ull, still alive, bloody and eyes open and still alive, bleeding from belly, chest, arm, head, leg, one foot just gone, and I knelt by his side and realised I had no idea where to begin, nothing to offer to injuries so catastrophic, so seemingly fatal, so I held his hand and shouted medic, medic, someone get a medic, help me! A woman staggered blindly past, hair a matted shroud, blood flowing from her ruptured ears, trying to form words and unable to get her tongue to shape the sounds. Medic, I roared, medic!

Ull's eyes started to close, and I thought perhaps I should keep him awake, keep him conscious, but didn't know why, didn't know what good it would do, shook him anyway, snarled, stay awake, stay awake, you're safe, you're going to be all right, you're going to be safe. Medic! Why doesn't the medic come?

Merthe was the first to arrive, slipping and sliding down sand and shingle. Did she know how to save anyone's life? I doubted it, but at least her soldiers had bandages, press here, hold that, do this, would it matter, didn't know, but something, please help, I don't know if he's still breathing, help me!

The medics came next, running with bags hanging off every limb. I was still holding Ull's hand when they pronounced him dead, ten minutes later. Farii, uninjured, stood behind and wept. I had not known she had tears in her. Merthe looked pale as the floating fish on the foaming sea. They found Antti's torso, arm and leg a few minutes later, bouncing up against the sinking side of his blasted skiff like wet paper. I sat, sodden and bloody, at the water's edge, and shook and trembled and waved away anyone who tried to approach me. In the end, Merthe put a hand on my shoulder and said simply: "We're done here. You're done," and didn't let go until I stood up and turned away from the sea.

Then I saw him.

Georg stood, leaning on his walking stick, at the top of the beach, the sun to his back, no hat on his head, looking down on us all. At that distance, I could not see if his eyes met mine, but

I felt it, as sure as this heart beats in my chest, before he nodded once and turned away.

Six days later, the war began in earnest.

Jia was universally blamed for Antti's death.

A crude assassination, everyone said.

Kun Mi was appointed Chief Minister of Maze in Antti's place. It was a perfectly sensible appointment – an apparent moderate, who could appeal to the masses.

Magyarzag declared immediate neutrality, citing provocation by Council against the independence of the Provinces. It was, Jia said, an act of surrender by any other name. Council evacuated Budapesht. Papers were still burning in their buckets when the soldiers came; hard drives smashed, their parts scattered across the floor.

Farii was appointed Chief Minister of Lyvodia, and led the mourners through the forest to the highest peak, where Ull's body was offered to sky and earth.

"He was cut down by treachery," she said. "He was betrayed by his own."

The Medj sang their songs for the dead as the mourners filed along the winding path between the unlit lanterns. I stayed until the melody at last gave out and the clothes were cut away from old Ull's body and the soil packed thin around him, so that the creatures of the forest may feast and his bones may return to the soil from which he came. The Medj bowed, gave their thanks, and for a moment I raised my head, wondering if the kakuy would come, if the moon would smile on its departed child, if the stars would dance a little brighter or the darkness bend in to acknowledge the fallen at its feet.

I followed the Medj down the path, guided by headtorch and stumbling memory, and returned to Bukarest.

A telegram was waiting for me at the temple.

COME BEOGRAD. SAVE YOURSELF.

It was not signed, and was from Yue.

I left it in the recycling vats for the novices to pulp down again.

Old Lah sat cross-legged on their pillow and said: "We must hold to who we are. We are the children of sky and earth. When people forget that, we must remember. It will not be thankful work. It will not be glorious or easy, and sometimes it will not be kind. But it is what we are."

The younger priests nodded and said they understood, and did not understand at all and wondered why we were not taking up arms, grabbing hunting rifles and knives and preparing to defend all that we were. What good are pacifists, they whispered, if all we do is die?

I threw myself into getting the last of the archives out of the temple. Most had already been secreted away, smuggled by bicycle and train to Provinces where their knowledge might be preserved, but a few remained. We hid them in panniers stuffed with boiled eggs and scrap metal, tucked them into freshly settled clay and wrapped them in resins from the vats, disguising them as crude objects or worthless icons, opening the windows of the temple wide to wash away the smells of our chemical concoctions while in the courtyard outside the Medj burned the most pungent incense they could and held their hands up to the sky and called for harmony amongst mankind, harmony upon the earth.

Maze's army was at Budapesht within three days of the neutrality declaration. Within five, they had control of the Ube all the way to Mohacks. Jia wasn't even trying to stop them, the reporters said. She knew she couldn't hold them until the mountains at Beograd – and besides, Magyarzag's neutrality made it questionable whether she could even legally attempt to defend the Province. She would have to wait, the pundits said, until the troops spilled south into Anatalia, into a land that was actually willing to fight.

"Will they come to Bukarest?" asked a man, hands pressed together as he bowed before Lah. "Will Farii fight? Will they burn the temple?"

"Temples can be rebuilt," replied the old Medj, which comforted precisely no one at all.

After evening prayers, I sat down before them and said: "We should send the novices away. I can forge the document, and know routes through the mountains. We can get the first group out tonight."

Lah sighed, half-closed their eyes as they considered this proposition, then, smiling, said: "It is useful for the pious to keep the occasional scallywag around, isn't it?" They chuckled again at a joke only they found funny, and then as casual as a pun added: "You should go too. I can't imagine the Brotherhood will be pleased to see you, when they come to Bukarest."

I shook my head. "We get the novices out first, and the last of the hard drives. You are very good at calming aphorisms for an anxious supplicant, Lah, but with respect you are terrible at cover stories."

"I also know how not to be a hero. Don't be a hero, Ven. It'll only feel good for a little while."

The next day, Farii formally declared Lyvodia's mutual defensive alliance with Maze.

"We will fight for what is right," she said. "We will fight for independence from Council tyranny. I believe in the people." Then she bowed at the hip, nose almost brushing knee, to Kun Mi as the first tank rolled into Bukarest. Georg stood behind her, as the Assembly of my home welcomed them in.

Chapter 38

A city under occupation.

It is not called occupation, of course. It is called "alliance". Farii has allied Lyvodia with Maze. These are welcome guests, these men in boots come to our town. We are delighted to be part of their noble crusade.

Come, drink; drink with us.

You seem quiet, you in your halls and hearths.

Drink and toast, like the few men and women who are smart enough to sense opportunity; drink! There is food and wine aplenty, and will be more yet to come, for we will be the winners; your leaders have chosen wisely. You do not need to hide supplies in the cold rooms behind the hearth, you do not need to get on your bicycles to go visit long-neglected cousins in far-flung places.

Forget the kakuy, forget the mountains and the rain. Humanity has always been its own best and only friend.

The temples stayed open – no bonfires as in Maze – but messages were delivered to every door, an eleven-point list of things that the Medj could and could not say. No political sermons. No talk of heresy. Functions were to be limited to blessings and prayers for happy births and prosperity.

"I had no idea we had power over pregnancy," Lah exclaimed, squinting at the list over the bridge of their nose. "I feel quite irresponsible!"

The arrests were quiet. Opposition leaders politely confined to quarters, for their own protection. Journalists invited to take some time away from work, offices closed. A few senior figures urged into quick retirement. Unwanted vagrants, disruptors and renegades taken for trial, charges pending. The charges would be pending as long as they needed to be; there was a war after all, and we all had to prioritise. The guardia were supplemented in the streets by soldiers of Maze. They did not threaten or extort, did not punch strangers or whistle at women. They were simply there, lounging in the middle of the great old causeways, leaning up against pine trees or sitting, knees wide, toes turned out, on the black benches on the edges of the parks, watching.

Farii went on the radio and said: "During this time of emergency, it is more important than ever to honour our brothers and sisters from Maze. This world belongs to us. To the people, to all mankind. We can shape a great destiny."

The train station was closed, and patrols checked the documents of anyone coming and going down the great highways of the city. A man with an inkstone into which he made short, sharp notes came to inspect the temple.

"Not many novices here," he mused, as Lah politely showed him round.

"On study trips," they explained cordially. "We like to send our novices into the community."

The man ran a finger along the edge of a kakuy stone, as if looking for dust, and, finding none, made another little note.

"Where are your hard drives?"

"In cold storage below."

"And what do they contain?"

"Erotic literature of the Burning Age, anthropology of the early modern period, and a complete history of anarchic comedy with a specialisation in the style known as 'laughter track'. It is a form of humour, you see, where the laughter is artificially added in, and you do not necessarily need to have traditional modes of comedy such as 'jokes'. Very interesting."

If the man was angry, surprised, disappointed, he did not show it. He made another, impossibly tiny, note.

"You have solar power?"

"Yes, and a little biomass."

"How much do you generate?"

"I will find out from our groundskeeper. Of course, we have always pooled resources with the community grid."

"That will end. Resources cannot be wasted on superstition. We must think of the future."

"We in fact generate more than our requirements, so really . . ."

"Resources cannot be wasted," he repeated, as if Lah had spoken some ancient, impossible tongue. "Humanity is all."

"As you say," Lah murmured, bowing again with a harmless little smile. "Would you care to see our collection of artefacts from the Burning Age? We have some astonishing items on the history of penis enlargement."

Even this man, face like the bottom of a saucepan, winced at the beatific innocence of Lah's smile.

At night, I did not sleep in the temple but cycled to a hearth on the edge of an old part of the city, where once the slabs of the great burning had stood in brown concrete, hard lines and over-hanging squares stacked as if by a lazy child. Time had reclaimed this place, and now only a few signs of the past remained in the odd chunk of ancient wall into which new resin had been pasted. In a hearth overlooking a flower garden bright with the new buds of spring lived a community of twelve or thirteen ranging from an old woman with no teeth, whose lower jaw in its resting state nearly abutted the tip of her nose, to a newborn baby and a group of three children, who had nothing but questions about this new world and longed to defy the rules freshly set down, now that we were at war. But even children could sense that perhaps this was not the time for mischief, that they would have to find some other way to have adventures from within the confines of their home.

Pinned to the side of the door of this hearth was a tiny box containing, they told me, a piece of sacred text from a holy book, and from the sunset of fifth day to the sunset of sixth they would

224

not cook nor handle money, for their God had declared it a day of rest, and their God was most interested in human affairs.

"Come, come," said a woman with skin of deepest burnt caramel and a mole on her chin. "Close the door behind you."

They did not head to the temple to pray, though neither did they deny the existence of the kakuy. "Angels," said one, though perhaps sometimes they were devils too – either way, spirits sent by a singular, almighty power.

"If you don't go to the temple, why are you sheltering me?" I asked.

"Our people have survived thousands of years," came the answer, and that seemed to be enough, all the explanation that was needed. "Here, you are too skinny – you must eat!"

Lying on my mattress on the floor in a little storage room tucked high above the hearth, I heard the prayers being sung to their God. Sometimes He answered, they said. Sometimes He was angry and did not come to their aid. One day, these struggles too would end, and there would be life eternal.

Three weeks after Kun Mi, Georg and the forces of Maze moved into the city, the first soldiers came to the temple to arrest me. Finding me gone, they shoved Lah around a little, without much enthusiasm, and in an act of purest spite shot holes into one of the compression batteries, releasing the stored-up air in a long, cold hiss. Lah tutted and sighed and said they'd have to ask someone to help them fix that, and when the soldiers were gone I emerged from my hiding place with the last of the novices and their precious bundles of heretical hard drives, and announced that we were stepping up plans and would leave that night.

The novices swallowed their fear, bowed in acknowledgement. "Don't do that," I snapped. "You are a midwife and a plumber. Don't bow."

They nodded, awkward with informality. Their heads had already been shaven in preparation for taking their final vows, giving up their past lives, their worldly affiliations. A few weeks of growth was beginning to give one of them some thin fluff of faded brown-grey across the muted surface of her skull, but the other's remained stubbornly smooth.

"Time for you to go too," Lah murmured, arms folded within their sleeves, limb impossible to distinguish from fold of grey. "You're a danger to whoever protects you."

I smiled, teeth and no heart, nodded once, beckoned the novices to follow me. "You," I snapped, indicating the man with the pristine skull. "Let's learn about wigs."

That last night, I stood beside the temple bell and did not pray. It was an ancient thing, forged from the slag of some forgotten war, some final gasp of conflict dug out of the desert of the Burning Age. Some people called it ugly in its mismatched rings of alloy spun together in the furnace flame, but the note was clear and carried across the water to the answering shrines of the city. Lah stood beside me, contemplating the hollow dome.

"Did they teach you the rituals and the bells?" they asked at last. "Or do inquisitors skip that part?"

"I sat through a great deal of philosophy before I was allowed to use invisible ink. Military trainers try to exhaust soldiers into quitting; in the inquisition they see if they can bore you to death. It is a good test for any agent." At Lah's disapproving grunt, I added: "But I do remember a few things. Strike the bell once, quietly, a call to attention. Strike it again, a little louder, to invite all who hear it to settle. Then strike it loud and clear, to call to the kakuy within you, who lives not in the past of human suffering, nor in the future of human aspirations, but in this moment, now, breathing in and breathing out the gift of the wind. I think there may also have been a poem you could recite, if you were feeling especially pious; I forget that part."

"There are in fact two poems – a profoundly moving verse on the nature of existence, and a somewhat more jaunty limerick we teach to the children visiting on family fun days. It's good to get them while they're young, yes?"

"Please don't say it like that."

"I thought you'd approve. Practicalities over philosophy."

We stood a moment more in silence, as the afternoon light slipped into a pinkish haze. Then Lah said: "Nearly time. You should ring the bell."

"I don't know the poem – or the limerick."

"So? It's just words. The world is changing. Who knows when this bell will ring again? You'll feel like an absolute barnacle if you don't do this now."

"Tell me, when you trained – presumably back in the age of fire and steel – did the temple do classes in sombre piety, austere reverence?"

"I'm so old I couldn't possibly remember. Ring the bell, Ven. Now's the time."

The ringing lived a little longer in my ears than I think it did on the air, and then even that died away, and I did not think the bell would ring again.

"Well done," Lah said. "Now off you go. Don't do anything I wouldn't and so on."

I nodded once and, picking up my bicycle helmet, went to flee the city.

Chapter 39

Two hours before curfew, three people, the last novices of the Temple of the Lake and an inquisitor, slipped out a back door into the evening light. The woman I sent ahead, as she seemed to have a steady head on her shoulders, pedalling on a bicycle with panniers full of clean towels, painkillers, antiseptics and gleaming ceramic blades for cutting through tissue or snipping an umbilical cord.

"You are summoned to a patient whose labour has come on early. You cannot be delayed."

"I am concerned about a breech birth," she confirmed calmly. "Even though I have complete confidence in the physicians, I have been assigned as this woman's midwife for five months, and it is my duty to be there as an emotional support as well as to lend any practical aid I can."

I beamed, tapped two knuckles on the top of her bicycle helmet and sent her on her way.

"Will Esa be all right?" asked the other novice as we closed the door on her retreating back. He was a flat-nosed boy by the name of Salo, considered by Lah to be mostly interested in the idea of priesthood as an easy, simple life where no one would ask too much of him or bother him particularly. What a shock would await him there, cackled the old Medj. The arguments over how to cook peas! The relentless bickering over the best way to transcend the need to bicker! No one bitches like a bitchy little Medj.

"She'll be fine. You . . . ?"

"I am a plumber," he babbled, too fast, a thing remembered, not understood. "I work for the civil water board. I am working the night shift at the downstream station on the Bovita; my responsibilities include maintenance, monitoring water pressure and on- and off-site repairs. I have been working there for two years. I am still learning a lot."

"What are you learning?"

"I am studying the use of robots to explore and highlight areas for repair in mains water pipes. I am studying for my grade one."

"What's the most commonly used type of robot in this work?"

"I . . . I don't know."

"Make something up. They won't know either."

"I . . . um . . ."

"'It has a proper technical name, but we just call it the squid.'"

His face drooped in relief and terror. "Yes, I . . . I see. I see what you did, earth-kin."

"Don't call me that. How's the wig?"

"I thought it would be more itchy."

"I'm sure it'll grow less comfortable. Come on."

Cycling through the streets of Bukarest. Have I ever looked at this city properly, now I am saying goodbye? Was there always music playing from an open window above the park? Did the white-crowned crows always turn their heads so quickly at the rattling of wheels on old road? The sky is pastel purple, a half-moon the size of my thumb overhead between the criss-crossed walls of the hearths that hem us in, vanishing and reappearing between structures of this place.

We made it nearly two kilometres before the first roadblock, a line of guardia standing down the middle of the street, flagging down those few electric vehicles that passed, the many bicycles streaming by. The queue was nearly fifteen minutes long, a line of tired men and women trying to get home before the curfew started. Work must go on; just because there's a war on doesn't mean people won't want their curtains cleaned.

Salo pressed in close to me as we neared the checkpoint, gripping his false identification as if it were the wriggling head of a venomous snake.

"Mains water and sewage," I explained briskly, as we reached the head of the line. "Heading to Bovita outlet number three."

The guardia read my papers. "Open the bags please," she intoned, repetition having made the words numb.

I smiled politely, unclipped the pannier bags on the back of my bicycle, stood well back. The smell of raw sewage and septic tank rose up in a hot wave, cutting through with an acrid immediacy to the tear ducts and settling in a chemical stink on the back of the throat.

"In the name of . . ." began the guardia, then stopped herself, lest she invoke the kakuy of sun and moon or some other suddenly unfashionable imprecation to ideas that were quickly going to become unpopular in her chosen profession. "Can't you clean that?"

"Why?" I asked, with polite confusion. "We're going back into the tunnels tonight. What's the point?"

"That can't be healthy."

"We have chemical showers," blurted Salo, trying to do his bit. "It's perfectly safe."

The guardia looked at him for a long moment, but it was not the scepticism of an officer observing a spy that sharpened her gaze, rather the crooked manner of one who can't quite believe the things people get up to, despite all that she's seen.

She waved us on, turning her nose away from our mutual stench, and I dinged my bell merrily as we cycled by.

Esa was waiting for us beneath a low grey bridge above a thin artificial channel of water that flowed out of the city towards the wider river. Salo half-bowed towards her in joy as he dismounted, catching himself only when he saw the look of disapproval flash across her face, and awkwardly hugged her instead.

"Any trouble?" I asked.

"I had to describe the process of a caesarean," she replied

matter-of-factly as we huddled in the gloom of the bridge. "Thankfully, once I got into the details of cutting through the uterine sac and releasing the amniotic fluid, he quickly lost interest."

I grinned, rummaging with half-attention through my bicycle bags to make sure the wrapped hard drives were still safely stowed below. "You should have joined the inquisition, sky-kin."

"Lah says I'm a good all-rounder," she answered without a smile. "Where now?"

"We wait for it to get fully dark, then follow the path another kilometre or so. There's no in and out of the city without army permission, so main roads are out, but once we cross the old highway there are just fields and some woodland, and then a straight line down to the Ube. The river will be heavily patrolled, but our friends will be waiting until dawn. That gives us nearly ten hours. Lose everything from your bags that isn't essential – if we get stopped here on in, no cover story will help."

We tossed everything except the hard drives and a few bottles of water into the sluggish canal, then pushed our bicycles up the old ramp onto the bridge and turned south. The canal had once been flanked by busy roads, but time had changed the city's shape and now smaller paths of pressed gravel and black tyre repurposed into sullen paths criss-crossed between hearth and greenhouse. Trees sprouted through a place where once there had been a terracotta roof; tendrils of green rolled like tongues through the long-cracked windows of old warehouses, and only from above could you see the straight grid-like scars of the old tarmacked roads, framed by the oldest trees that had survived the greatest storms. In the settling night, a dog barked, and the electric hum of a guardia vehicle was drowned out momentarily by the ugly chuntering and bitter bellow of a newer, combustion-driven army car from Maze.

We cycled as far as we could down the narrowest of paths between greenhouse and hearth, shying away from the few street-lights that glimmered along the wider roads, headtorches on our heads. In the dark, the bouncing of our bicycles on the uneven way was a ringing roar, a siren to summon an unseen enemy.

From behind the walls of one hearth, a dog barked, and its barking set off another dog barking a few metres away, unseen, and that barking set off a third, until the walls around us rang with busy creatures pronouncing here, here, look, look! We scurried on faster, slipping in and out of pools of light on the corners of the hearths, heads down, eyes up.

A door opened ahead, and an old man peered out, furtive, into the night, saw us, nodded, closed the door again. The outline of his form seemed like an ally, not a threat, but who could tell?

Voices were raised, then silenced through a half-open window to the right. On a wall, the shadow of a woman working at a desk grew enormous as she leaned into the light, then shrank back down to a smear of grey against yellow as she stepped away from her midnight labours.

A fox watched us from across the street, utterly fearless, white belly beneath autumn fur. We pedalled by, heard the electric hum of the guardia again, nearly on top of us, hard to tell where precisely it came from, and barrelled into the narrow passage between two buildings, stinging nettles and ankle-splattering black mud, hot breath on cold air. The vehicle slid by, two figures half-glimpsed inside, headlights on full, crawling at a snail's pace. I wondered, if the guardia caught us would they really arrest us? Curfew was a strange imposition, unfamiliar and disliked. If I pulled off Salo's wig and said, look, look, here is a priest fleeing for their life, would the old guardia turn us in? It would come down to who you met, pious or officious, frightened or brave – a bit of luck: some old patroller who doesn't care much for this new alliance of Farii's; some young whelp looking to get a promotion in this strange new world.

We spent nearly twenty minutes in a ditch on the edge of town, caught between patrol behind and idling, chatting soldiers ahead. They were not stopped on this road because they expected trouble or because it was an obvious route out of the city. Rather, they were lingering because their superior was an absolute bastard, a bull rearing at every sight and sound, and they wanted to prolong their absence from him as much as possible, pausing now in the dark to share a drink, have a piss, chat about nothing much.

Snips of words drifted in from where they sprawled against the hot metal sides of their strange, stinking vehicles. Games played, bets made, awkward love affairs. Anything except the war they would soon be fighting in; anything but the future. Soldiers learned not to speculate early on in their training; it was one of the qualities they shared with priests.

Once a drone flew overhead, and I heard Salo's breath rise through flared nostrils, saw his eyes grow into moons, let my breathing fall a little louder, calm and steady, until at last he got the right idea and forced himself to exhale, to breathe out slow, to half-close his eyes and dig his fingers into the soft mud he was pressed against, grit in nails, slime in skin, calm again.

The clunk of an engine; a slamming of heavy metal doors. The combustion vehicles of Maze were crude, growling things, bigger than their burning era counterparts, all pipe and joint and heavy tyre that bounced and cracked on uneven ways. In time, the designers would get it right, somehow manage to mimic the sleek, shark-like qualities of the older vehicles, start talking about whether a car had a friendly face or a feminine bonnet, whether it had headlights like eagle eyes or a grille like the smiling mouth of a predator. For now, they were built to work, and intimidate, and didn't yet run as far or as fast as their electric counterparts, but who cared? In time they would; for now, the symbol was all.

We waited for the sound of engine to drift away, then crawled, teeth chattering and skin grey, up onto the empty road. I turned my headtorch on low, bent over the map, traced the route to the river, turned my torch off, fumbled in the thin gloom for a drink of water, sipped, shared the flask, returned it empty to my pack.

"What if the drones come back?" asked Salo.

"Just keep moving," I replied, turning away before he could ask anything else.

*

233

In the headtorch gloom, the rittle-rattle clackety-clack of the speeding night, there is no sight, no sound, no change in colour nor heat nor cold that the mind may hook onto, no passing world that isn't dark, no motion that isn't seamless, the same, endless and without form.

I think that Georg is still in my brain, still watching my every thought, and that Lah is there too, an antibody devouring the other's spreading poison. Like gobbling amoeba, they exist for now in perfect balance, consuming and expanding, consuming and expanding, until there is no room for anything that resembles me left.

Then I heard a vehicle up ahead, turned my headtorch off and gestured the others into the side of the road, and it turned out the void all around was not void at all, but a busy, teeming night of hunting bird and scurrying prey, of thorn and bark and worm and ant, of thin spitting rain and wind rolling across the first leaves in the highest trees, the breath of a giant exhaling after a long, cold sleep.

We cowered in the woodland on the side of the road, bicycles thrown down into bracken, bodies against branch, as a convoy of five electric cars, accompanied by one grunting, grumbling truck of Maze, slithered by in a snake of dazzling whiteness, almost too bright to look at after the long night.

Then they too were gone, and the darkness in which my mind wandered was now a terrible, gnawing thing, a huge monster that would consume us whole if we let it. I switched my torch back on, and with every turn of my head imagined I would see a rifle raised, see Georg as if he had ruptured from the earth like a spire of lava, inches from me. The novices looked at me, and for a moment I think they saw my terror, and I knew they would never fully trust me again. I picked my sodden bicycle up from the dirt, barked some order, heard the authority of one who has crossed over into that place where authority derives not from some experience or moral quality but from fear. Nothing to be done about that now.

"Three hours to dawn," I snapped, checking my watch. "Not far now."

Chapter 40

On the banks of the Ube, the last of the trees were being cleared. I could see the distant lights of the trucks as they worked through the night, hear the timber crashing down. The broken cover and churned, sodden mud would make it harder, at least on the north bank, for anyone to cross over without being seen.

Timber groaned, followed by a hairy brushing of a hundred twigs shattering as the trunk that bore them fell, and for a moment I thought I heard an answering sound, a shuddering through the earth, as if a creature with lungs of stone had been disturbed by the noise and now lay restless in shallow sleep, remembering the nightmares which previously had passed it by.

We lay flat on our bellies on the edge of a field of turned-over, crunchy earth, watching the slope down to the water below. No lights moved; nothing stirred in the darkness.

Esa said: Perhaps no one guards it?

Salo replied, hope seeping into his voice: The river is long. They can't have patrols all the way across it. Praise the river.

I looked up at the overcast sky, tried to hear the sound of drones, catch the glimpse of light on wing. Saw nothing. Heard only the wind. I took my headtorch, flashed it five times down at the water, then five times again, then waited.

We waited a minute, then two.

I flashed my headtorch five times, then five times again.

We waited.

A light answered from the opposite bank, four flashes, then

three. I replied with three flashes, then put my torch away. If I closed my eyes, I thought I could hear the sluggish tumble of the Ube itself, the slow, fat weight of it as it finally neared the end of its journey, rising from mountain and slewing into sea. The Medj said there was one great kakuy of the Ube, a dragon of snow and silt, but the sailors swore they had seen dozens, maybe a hundred different creatures down the years, from the dancing sprites that played beneath tumbling alpine waterfalls to the ponderous, slug-bellied beast that surfaced sometimes from the twisted reeds of the delta. I wondered if we would see the kakuy tonight, and doubted it very much. The Ube did not care for three travellers in the dark.

"Run straight for the river," I said. "If they're slowing you down, throw the hard drives."

"We're nearly there," Esa breathed, her eyes flickering skyward, before returning back to the dark between us and the river. "We're nearly done."

A flash from the water, three points of light in the dark.

"Go. Go now."

They did not need telling twice. They were off, crawling onto hands and knees then sprinting straight down, visible only as muted darkness against the reflective ribbon of the river below. I followed a few steps behind, my head tipping down and feet skidding behind as I ran, a toe curl from catastrophe. A few seconds later I heard the low hum of the drone as it descended from the dark behind, then caught the sweep of the searchlight as it powered up its main lamp and swung towards us. The beam tumbled past me, moving too fast, overshot the novices, then slowed and inched back, the unseen controller working to keep pace as we descended. The light caught on the back of the bicycle helmet still on Salo's head; he swung to the side, trying to dodge out of the beam, and it didn't bother to follow him, didn't play that game but jerked sideways, spilling over Esa as she barrelled for the water. Against the white of the drone's light, I could barely see the flashing of our rescue boat as it turned towards us, but I caught the glow of a dozen other lights illuminating the far bank – Council troops, perhaps, or local guardia alerted to our escape – voices rising and engines coming to life. The drone lost pace with us for a second; then it found us again, and now a second unit was sweeping in from the north, the conical white beam a three-dimensional thing picked out in cold drizzle, two bouncing military vehicles behind it, headlights on full, tracking the light above us as we tumbled for the water.

"Don't stop!" I hollered at the weaving novices. The water was only a hundred yards away, my throat shrunk to a straw, heart in my ears, the two cars bouncing and shuddering over disturbed earth and churned-up root so high and so far that I thought for a moment they'd shake themselves apart before reaching us. When they opened fire, it seemed such an absurd exercise I almost laughed, the man leaning out of the passenger window of the nearest vehicle utterly unable to aim against the bouncing motion. But at the sound of bullets, the novices slowed, and I tore past them, too little breath left to tell them to run. They got the idea, picked up speed again. Esa wove wide, drawing the beam of the second drone away from the pack, and I silently thanked her and cursed her and thanked her again. One of us would make it, at least; one of us would get to the boat in the dark.

More gunshots, a little louder now, the first vehicle sliding as the driver tried to control its descent down the slope; fast enough to overtake us, not too fast to slip. I caught the shape of the shooter as he levered himself up a little higher, digging his elbows into two long bars across the roof and taking more careful aim, lining up a shot with the flashing bicycle helmet on Salo's skull. Then the lights on the other side of the river changed, and for an instant I could see the exact shape of the waiting rescue boat on the water, picked out in chemical yellow as three or four shadows lined up their shots and opened fire.

The car twisted, spinning nearly 180 degrees in the churned-up mud, turning itself sideways on to the boat. Doors opened and soldiers tumbled out, ducking behind metal and heavy bonnet to return fire. One aimed a shot at me, but it was an afterthought, the drones now sweeping towards the river to light up in full whiteness the little barge that had come to our aid. Then the second car squelched by me, and I was dazzled by its light as it skidded to an uneven halt, back wheels digging themselves into the mud between us and the boat. The doors facing away from the river opened, soldiers tumbling out, not five metres away. They had not yet drawn their pistols; they seemed to expect their mere presence to be enough to induce a surrender. "Run!" I hollered, and Esa was already far enough out of their reach that she went straight past the car without even slowing, without sparing it a second glance, a bag of hard drives bouncing on her back, her chin tilted forward like a hound.

Salo was less lucky, the arc of his path bringing him straight into the tumbled-down waist-tight grasp of one soldier who threw himself like an uncoiling snake across the gap between them, knocking the novice to the floor. I didn't slow, running straight into the nearest man in front of me, palms-first, letting the full weight of my body and speed of my descent hit him in the chest. He staggered backwards, slammed into the side of his own vehicle, bending with a crack in the small of his back, eyes wide and bewildered. For a moment, the two of us fumbled for his gun, the strap suddenly a knot of fingers and clasps. I gave up on the weapon first and, having no better ideas, slammed my forehead hard into the bridge of his nose, which cracked as the reverberating impact rippled into the soft bones of my ears. He didn't howl but curled away from me, both hands pressed to his face, so I turned and kicked at the soldier who held my novice down. He did not expect to be kicked from behind, and though I doubt I hit anything important, the surprise loosened his grasp.

"Get to the boat!" I snarled. Salo crawled back to his feet and sprinted until he fell the last few metres into the waiting barge. I twisted round to follow him, and a hand caught my ankle, dragging me down. I landed chest first, followed by grazing palm and bouncing skull. The boat was so close I could grab for it, see the faces of the men and women on the deck, dressed in civilian clothes, rifles raised. Someone managed to clip a drone, and one of the lights illuminating them spun to the side then went out. Another rescuer staggered, then recovered herself, fired twice more, then fell without a sound, as if time was running slow for her and the bullet in her chest had arrived sooner than she was prepared to receive it.

I crawled forward, hoping by sheer will to pull myself free from the hand that held my ankle, but a shadow moved across my side and something ruptured in my back, too big and broad to be a bullet but perhaps a boot, an anvil, a missile falling on me and me alone. I saw my novices crawling into the back of the boat, hiding behind the gunmen, saw the light of the one remaining drone flicker and dart away as more bullets flew skywards, saw another man fall in the last graze of its failing light. Heard someone shout, "We have to go!" and briefly met the eyes of a stranger, a captain perhaps, or the skipper of the barge. I had no idea who this man was, and doubted he knew anything about me other than he was there to rescue a bunch of priests. But I knew he would remember me that day, that my eyes would be with him every dawn and every dusk, and I wished I had time to tell him that it was okay, not to worry about these things, that regret was a changing thing.

Instead, I shouted – or tried to shout – "Go! Go!" but a soldier had grabbed me from behind and was dragging me by hair and by throat, by shirt and by elbow, by anything hand could get a hold on, back into the shelter of the cars. "Go!" I gasped, and had no hope they'd hear me until I heard the engine on the boat rise.

Then I was being shoved into one of the cars, head down against the bullets flying, hands covering my skull from shrapnel or angry men. There I stayed, and did not see the boat make it to the furthest shore but knew it must have by the grumbling of weary voices and the slap-slap of despondent boots on torn-up earth, and the slow fading away of the barrage from a few shots, to one or two, to nothing at all. I peeked through my latticed fingers, turned my chin a little away from the ground, and saw the first light of dawn was coming, tulip pink and daisy white.

Then someone said: "Breakfast?"

I unrolled slowly from the back of the car, blinking in the gently rising light. A woman held out a hard-boiled egg, a bottle of water. I drank uncertainly, returned the flask, cracked the shell of the egg on the side of the door, peeled it open. One of the cars wouldn't start; that seemed to be the cause of this sudden quiet, this opening up of rations, this sitting around as if there hadn't just been a gunfight by the river. Someone who seemed to want to be in charge marched up to me, saw me eating, shook his head, turned away, didn't have anything much to say. Someone else looked towards the east, and I thought perhaps he was about to utter a morning prayer, bow to the kakuy of the sun as he had done every morning since he had been old enough to put palm to palm. Then he looked at his milling colleagues and changed his mind. I finished the egg gratefully, suddenly realised I was incredibly hungry and yearned for bread, and instead sat on the floor of the broken vehicle, feet dangling out into a muddy field, as someone fell back on hitting the engine with a hammer.

"Excuse me," I said to the soldier who'd given me the egg, "are you going to shoot me?"

"I hope not," she replied.

"Oh. Good."

She smiled patiently, patted me on the shoulder, reassuring as a surgeon's blade. "Temple, yes? Trying to cross the border?"

"That's right."

"Why'd you do that? We're fighting for a good cause. For good people. Temple doesn't have anything to fear."

"Do you believe that?"

She stared at me with blank surprise. "Of course. We're fighting for people. For the future of people. Just because Temple is ... just because you believe something different doesn't mean you'll be hurt."

"Thank you for the egg," I sighed. "That was very kind."

Hitting the engine with the hammer clearly did something,

for with a popping of sparks and a sudden hiss of suspension, the car came back to life. "Finally!" barked he who would be in command. "Let's get out of this dump." His eyes returned to me, sat in a little crescent of broken egg shell and bruised rib. "What the hell are you looking at? Can somebody please arrest him?"

Chapter 41

The prison was perfectly polite.

No one told me my rights or offered me access to an advocate, but the woman who entered my details into the system smiled and said, "Not to worry, earth-kin." I nodded and tried to smile in reply as she filled out the form on her inkstone. "Any allergies?"

"No."

"Are you currently in withdrawal from any narcotics, hallucinogenics, depressants, etcetera?"

"No."

"Do you take any essential medication?"

"No."

"What gender do you identify as?"

"That question is irrelevant," snapped an older man behind me, a man who knew perhaps which way the wind was blowing. The two regarded each other over the stoop of my shoulder, then with a beatific flicker of teeth and darting eye the woman murmured: "Until I see the revised guidelines, I'm going to have to follow protocol, you see. I'm sure we're all looking forward to the retraining."

They put me in a cell with two other men. The walls were painted a soft algae green. There was a toilet in the corner. Signs along the corridor invited us to reconciliation classes. The same evening I was admitted, they were taken down and replaced with a noticeboard of emergency proclamations and newly indictable offences.

Of my two cellmates, one was in for domestic violence. "He made me do it," he said, face turned to the wall, knees up to his chin. "He just makes me so mad."

The other, to my surprise, was an Assembly member. "My name is Bayzed. I voted against allying with Maze. I voted against letting Maze's army in. I voted against welcoming Kun Mi to the Assembly. I voted against giving up the country to heretics."

"Voting isn't a crime. Why are you here?"

"Apparently I over-claimed on office stationery. But I'm sure they'll think of something better soon. What about you?"

I lay on the top bunk, pressing a palm into the ceiling, feeling the texture of painted resin beneath my fingers, a remnant of what had once been something organic, compressed and reprocessed. "I was an inquisitor. A professional traitor. I think they're going to kill me. Probably best to get it over with."

Bayzed thought it over while the abuser curled against the wall and blamed everyone but himself. "Do you think it will come to that?"

"Perhaps. Probably. In the early days it's easiest if it's an extra-judicial killing, somewhere quiet and out of sight. Paperwork goes astray all the time, especially in times like this. Once people are used to the idea that people just vanish, they will be more comfortable with the reality of executions – just a formalisation of what's already happening. After they are comfortable with that, public executions are a logical next step, and when you've made that a family outing, you can move on to the truly grotesque stuff, for when you need to formalise the fear."

"You seem very calm about all this."

I pushed both hands into the ceiling, as if I might feel the weight of the building above me, as if I could drive myself all the way into the earth. "I saw the kakuy of the forest," I breathed. "Twice, actually. Once in fire, once in ice. I don't want to die; sun and moon, I don't want to die. But I don't know if I'm afraid either."

*

243

At the evening meal, the political prisoners drifted together uneasily, a shoal of fish suddenly thrown into a very different sea. The pride of an ethical position held or the moral delight of defiance counted for nothing within walls of grey and green. They were laughable, a ridiculous thing to risk life and liberty for.

You are in here for principle? Not for theft? Not for assault or setting fires? Not for murder? You are in here because you wrote something?

I've never heard the like. Never heard the like! The times we live in.

In the morning, after cleaning the pots in the kitchen and scrubbing the floor, I asked an officer what I was charged with.

"Your advocate deals with that," he replied.

"Who's my advocate?"

"Don't ask me."

"Who should I ask?"

"Don't you know?"

"No. That's why I'm asking."

"What are you charged with again?"

"I don't know."

"If you don't know then how do I know who you should be talking to?"

My mouth hung open, words stopping in a dumb half-syllable. Then I picked up my bucket and mop, smiled, nodded once, and started to think about how I might escape this place.

On the sixth day, the man accused of domestic violence disappeared. Some said he was released; others, transferred. Rumours of things he'd done and mistakes he'd made – of people he'd crossed and promises broken – immediately circulated round the low halls, echoing from door to door through pipes and notes scrawled on scraps of paper swung by string from hand to hand. A look he'd given someone became a call to arms; the way he hadn't finished his dinner on a second day became a clue to some unravelling mystery. One man, who worked in Release

244

and Rehab, shrugged and simply said the advocate had got him off, he was going home, but that was far too simple a story for a muted, windowless world to accept.

Two days after that, Bayzed vanished, and no one asked where he'd gone, and no one remarked on his absence, and no one whispered secrets through bending pipes in the wall.

One man was assigned as my new cellmate, and he wouldn't meet my eyes, and three days later he got himself reassigned to a different cell. He was clearly popular amongst the officers because his request was approved within twenty-four hours, and I was left alone with a choice of bunks and a toilet all to myself.

A month went by, and I was not charged, and no advocate came.

In the mornings, I cleaned the kitchen. I was told I would be paid for this service, money added to my account. I was not told what my account was, or how I could access it or use it to buy anything for myself, and when I asked the answer was always the same: "Your case officer handles that."

I gave up asking who my case officer was, after a little while.

In the afternoons, I read. There was a library, and a few ink-stones could be borrowed, pre-loaded with carefully selected material: educational, legal and light fiction that romped along with reasonable moral character. A few politicals talked to me, a few tolerated my presence, but they were men of ideals and passion, and I had very little of either to give.

"Well," mused one, "maybe it's good to have a pragma-tist around?"

I looked in his eyes and knew then that if I laughed he would cry, so smiled and nodded and turned away to stare into my empty bowl, poking at the edges with the chewed end of my wooden chopsticks.

From the radio in the workout hall, Maze's victories filled the air. Cities fell east and west, cutting off huge swathes of land and encircling Jia's forces in Beograd. Temples burned and a new era of humanity was promised. So much was promised, and the pris-oners laughed and said they'd heard talk like that before; sunfire be damned, some of them had even spouted it in their time, to get what they wanted.

Roads would be driven through mountains; planes would soar in the sky. Everyone could buy everything, and the only thing holding you back would be your own petty limitations.

"Hey, priest – where are the kakuy?" demanded Brahno, king of the radio, keeper of rechargeable batteries and lubricants of uncertain origin. "Where are your gods of the forest now?"

"It was never clear in the historical record," I answered, "if the kakuy brought fire upon the people of the burning or if the world was already on fire, and the kakuy brought rain."

"What does that shit even mean?" he growled. "What is that shit anyway?"

Brahno was a bully, too much of a coward to do anything about the people who really scared him, so he would sometimes exercise his violence on smaller prey, easier fry. I had enough training, enough memory of a knife in my hand and gunshots above the river to put up more of a fight than he expected. I held him off long enough that his lackeys felt the need to step in and get involved, and by then the officers were running into the room to pull me free, to drag Brahno to solitary.

He never left solitary, and no one tried to touch me again. I did not think it was due to my martial prowess and the pointed end of my elbow, but at the time I couldn't work out what else it could possibly be.

At night, I managed for the very first time to pray.

There was no expectation of reply or consequence, nor any invocation for things to change. That was not, I concluded, the point of kneeling in the dark.

Then one week like any other, I was pulled from my shift in the kitchen, escorted to the gate, let out without paperwork or explanation into the noontime sunlight, and was astonished to discover that spring had come in translucent leaf and buds of cherry blossom, in drifting pollen through shafts of light and

246

thin, larvae-fresh insects uncoiling their wings in the first kiss of heat. I stood for a moment, dumbfounded and blinking in the sudden illumination, when I noticed the combustion car waiting by the gate, the passenger door open, the driver's door opening too, and there was Klem, grinning as if I were his oldest, long-lost friend, beckoning me in. Sohrab came round the other side, cutting me off.

I considered running, but there wasn't anywhere to go.

Klem squeezed my shoulder as I ducked past him into the car, eyes wide with the breadth of his amusement.

Closed the door behind me.

Chapter 42

Here sits Georg.

His Bukarest office is not as grand as his office in Vien. He does not stand by the window. Rather he sits behind a desk. The desk is more functional than his grand old thing of blood and leather. His chair is huge and padded. It has been tilted forward a little further than usual, so that he is almost tumbling off it. I wonder if it is to hide the limp, the flinch, the flicker of pain that runs across his face every time he eases himself up, both hands resting on the armrest, weight on only one leg.

Klem waves me to one of the two chairs opposite, gestures me to sit.

I do, hands in my lap.

Georg finishes reading a document on his inkstone. Maybe a report. Maybe a map. Maybe nothing at all. I have tried this trick too, of reading something terribly important while my mind is a thousand miles away. I watch his eyes, and they are not moving side to side, but still, he wastes both his and my time with this game.

He wears grey that is nearly black.

He has a private telephone, the handle worn from painted red to softer pink where he's gripped it.

He puts the inkstone down, straightens it up so the bottom edge aligns with the line of the desk, folds his hands, looks at me.

"Kadri," he says.

"Georg," I reply.

For a moment, that is all there is between us. Klem hovers behind, almost vibrating with the urge to do violence, his delight in the blood that is to come, the expectation of it an arousal that glows in a thin pink blush across his cheeks, youthful and naïve.

Then Georg pushed the inkstone across the table to me, turned it, fingertips on opposite corners as if he were spinning puppets in a dance. I stared down at it, took a minute longer than I had needed in the past to recognise it, for some slumbering part of my brain to wake.

"Well?" Georg asked at last.

For a moment, we are back in Vien, strangers in the snow. "What do you want to know?" The words came as much from memory as now, a familiar call and response, a song once sung to a different tune.

"What do you make of it?"

"Archaic French. It is a discourse on toilets in Burning Age military submarines."

"Is it authentic?"

"Do you have cross-referencing material?"

"I can."

"Then I'd have to see that, but off the top of my head, yes, I'd say it's authentic. It's a digital copy of an analogue copy of a digital copy, which never bodes well. Signs of interference introduced by the process, remnants of Temple classification markers – not Pontus' finest theft, if we're honest. But there's not much call to fake a document discussing the difficulties of ejecting faeces from a vessel whose interior parts are at a lower pressure than the external environment."

"What else?"

I smiled, half-nodded at the inkstone, met his gaze again, held it without fear. "It's a very dull read."

He nodded thoughtfully, twitched the tips of his fingers towards Klem, returned his attention to a different document on a different reader on his desk. "Good. You will have it fully translated by this evening."

"Will I?"

"Yes. We have the Medj of your old temple – Lah – in cells below. She will be hurt until you comply. It is very simple."

"Why would you hurt them, and not me? Lah is a better translator than I am."

"I understand how you work. That is enough."

"I would like to see Lah."

"Once you have completed the translation."

I rolled a little deeper into the chair. It was as if I'd never sat in a chair before, never conceived of what an object like this was, how my body bent to it, and it bent to me. I stared up at the ceiling, absurdly high and panelled with wood that rushed into the centre point like an exploding star, and said: "Wouldn't it be easier – safer even – just to shoot me? I appreciate irony, but from a security point of view this – all of this – is just ego. That's all it is. Vanity – not even a power play, like Kirrk. The sensible thing to do is to kill me and be done with it. We both know it. Why make the mistake?"

Georg did not answer, but without raising his eyes from the desk gestured again at Klem, who, still bristling with delight at things yet to come, caught me by the shoulder and pulled me away.

They put me in an office on the very top floor, in a converted attic. I had read stories about sloping rooms above ancient buildings such as these; places for ghosts to emerge shimmering from the cracked floorboards, or for young lovers to pine away in. Instead, I was sat down on a single deflated beige cushion in the middle of an empty floor, given an inkstone with an empty text file and a few old dictionaries loaded on it, and left alone. A bolt slammed across the door. One window looked out onto pipes and solar panels, twisting up to the obscured sun. A single grey pigeon on a ledge of guano turned an orange eye to examine me, confused by this face in its domain. The window was locked, and while I might have been able to smash the ancient, dribble-distorted glass, there was a sheer drop between me and the nearest roof, several storeys below. The room smelt of old bugs unhappy at a new neighbour, and the winter's cold had not yet vanished from the shadows. Water ran behind one wall from a thermal exchange, the temperature difference palpable from one side to the other as I traced my hands across the thin plaster.

I paced the room, and there was only so much room for pacing.

I sat cross-legged on the floor and tried to find something of the stillness that had come in the dark and empty night of the prison. There, the constant passing of footsteps, the crying out of a voice from a cell, the banging of metal on metal, of fist on brick, had become its own background stillness, a presence which had lowered until at last it comforted. Here, the silence was a faraway city, distance distorted by travelling upwards and dissipating into the clouds.

My clothes were too thin for the cold.

I tucked my knees into my chest and translated a page, looked at the translation, tweaked a few words for ease of readability, wondered if any of this could change the nature of the war. There hadn't been submarines in the seas for centuries, apart from a few dredged-up coffins of ancient bone and the occasional scientific vessel launched into the deep. I was not sure what their relevance could be to Georg now. The Isdanbul fleet was so much stronger than anything Maze could ever put to sea, the idea he would engage in a naval conflict at all was absurd.

I worked through another page, made a note on an obscurity, a word I didn't recognise, to cross-check later. Somewhere, Georg would already have a translation of this document, to compare with my work. He would have translations of half of whatever he asked me to work on next, to catch me in a lie. He would start with things that seemed harmless, which could have no effect on the shape of the war. He would then slip in the odd text which may seem on the surface to do no damage but which he could point to in a later time and say, look, see, you have already betrayed your people by translating this, so why make a stand now? You are already damned. You were damned the moment you wrote a single word.

I stopped.

Put my pen down.

Lay out long and cold across the floor, hands on my belly, to wait for the end.

Chapter 43

When I was twelve, I was taken along with a handful of other children from the school in Tinics to the dormitory that lay behind the Temple to say goodbye to the oldest of all the Medj who honoured the forest, who would not be long for this world.

Yue was there too, face furrowed in a perpetual frown. Did her mother and mine sit up long together on the grassy roof of the hearth and whisper of their children, remember Vae's name, wonder what we truly saw that day in the burning forest? Probably not. The hearths of Tinics were eminently practical about these things.

Beti, the oldest Medj of the valley, had been the bane of many a merry childhood game, boring us with sermons and insisting on decorum, respect, when a more liberally inclined member of their order might have laughed to see children chase after crows or play at conkers. From their moral austerity, Beti's physical stature had seemed to evolve too, creating an imposing giant of a priest, filling every door with their shadow and booming out like thunder: "Do not scratch your name into the sacred stones! Do *not* leave lewd messages in the raked pebbles of the yard!"

Now cobweb skin hung sunken on calcium skull, the occasional pulsing black wriggle of a vein across temple or crown the only sign of life. Lips cracked and hands folded over chest, their carers had already removed the air vents that had sustained them, and breath came in irregular gasps, strange wheezes as the last hours ticked by. Their successor talked us through the final prayers of farewell, spoke softly into the half-shadows of the room as the moon rose outside and the warm smell of fresh citronella drifted in on the cool spring breeze.

"Sometimes they will wake, and may say a few words, or ask for water, but before you can bring the sponge to their lips they may sleep again, or forget what they desired, and then their eyes close. Sometimes they will gasp, and you'll think they are in pain. You'll think this is terrible, this is monstrous – but it is not, it is just a holding on, a releasing. It can take days, in which time they will neither eat nor drink nor wake. The pain is already past. This is not pain. And an hour will come where you leave the room, just for a minute, just to wash your face or greet the sunrise, and when you return they are gone. It is as if they are waiting for us to leave, for no living eye to look upon them so that, at last, they can let go. We have feared dying more than anything. We invested so much energy, so much time, into fighting death, into refusing to accept that it would come. We painted ourselves to look young, injected chemicals both pointless and poisonous, lived in extraordinary pain and discomfort rather than let nature come, so that we spent perhaps almost as much time fearing dying as we did actually living. A Medj should not die this way; we do not fear change. But it is all right to be sad. It is human to be sad. But do not fear. Go – live – and do not be afraid."

With this guidance we were sent home again, and Beti died that very night, when their attendant had left to make a cup of tea.

Chapter 44

In the evening, in an attic in Bukarest, Klem came to find me, and the translation was not done.

I waited for him to kick me, to swing his fists or throw me against a wall. Instead, he grabbed me by the back of my shirt and pulled me down the hall. Every time I found my footing, he shook me a little to the left or a little to the right so that I had to catch onto his arm or claw at his chest to stop myself from tumbling into the throat-clasping pressure of my own dragged clothes as he hauled me before Georg, shoving me at last onto my knees in front of the desk and holding me with one hand across the top of my skull like I was a prize pig.

This time, Georg looked up with a sigh, no patience for pretence.

"Well?"

Klem shook his head.

"I will kill the priest," Georg tutted, disappointed, perhaps even annoyed.

"What will that achieve?" I asked.

The question seemed to catch him almost by surprise, as if the notion hadn't even crossed his mind. Then he straightened, a conclusion reached, put his inkstone down, nodded once at Klem, who yanked me back onto my feet. Georg was halfway to the door in a few steps, assistants and would-be supplicants scuttling out of his way like beetles before the spider. Eyes turned downwards as I was shoved along, as mourners may look away from the coffin.

I lost my footing on the stairs when Klem timed a shove badly and, tripping, caught myself on the only thing in front of me that offered any support – Georg. He grabbed me by my arms before I could tumble past, and for a moment I nearly said thank you, but something I could not see danced behind his eyes and with neither scowl nor smirk he pushed me back into Klem's grip, which was a little more cautious for the last few stairs into the basement.

The lower half of this place had been a cold storage for the hearth, the pipes of the thermal exchange still visible in the ceiling, thick, flax-plugged walls and straw spread on the heavy clay floor. A sliding door was held shut with chain and padlock. Georg pulled a bunch of keys from his pocket and worked through four near-identical little silver ones before finding the key that clicked, slinging the loose chain over his shoulder like a silk scarf. The door pulled back and as my eyes adjusted to a little light tumbling through the opening, I saw the pallor of skin, a hint of face and hand. Lah sat up slowly from where they'd been bundled in a ball, blinking against the illumination, shielding their eyes, and finally, as their gaze adjusted, they said: "Is that you?"

I nodded, realised how futile that was in the shadows, said: "Hello."

They nodded, slow, thoughtful. "Ah well," they sighed. Then, an afterthought: "Imagine, if you will, that you opened the door to find me meditating profoundly."

"Of course."

A hand to my shoulder; Klem pushed me to the side, spine knocking against the frame, and Georg put a hand against my chest, holding me in place. Lah regarded Klem with polite interest as the man strode into the gloom, drew back his fist and hit the Medj across the face. Lah fell, fumbling at their jaw as if surprised to find that this was what this experience was like, learning something new – they'd always wondered. I caught Georg's wrist in both my hands, met his eye, saw him shake his head. Behind, two more Brotherhood men approached, idly interested, idly here, wondering what their boss was doing now. Klem hit Lah again, and again Lah fell, and this time they stayed down, tucking head into arms, knees into chest, perhaps not yet in too much pain, but in no hurry to experience more.

Again, my eyes met Georg's; again, a slight shake of his head. I felt my lips curl into the beginning of a snarl, had no idea where that came from, heard meat on meat as Klem struck again, again, one more time, this time a grunt of pain from the Medj on the floor. I felt Georg's hand press a little harder into my chest, knocking a half-puff of air from my lungs as he put his body-weight into it, pinning me back. The snarl at my lips became a slow grin, the grin of the wolf, the grin the wolf of the forest might make, the kakuy of blood in snow. Georg's eyes flickered in momentary surprise, and then I let go of his wrist and snapped my right fist into his throat. I didn't hit hard, the crunch of little bones in my hand rippling up to my elbow. But throats were not designed to be hit and he curled away, gasping, wheezing like old Beti the night they died.

The Brotherhood boys who'd been waiting their turn lunged forward but I was nearer to Klem than they were to me, got a punch into Klem's kidneys and a kick into the back of his knee before he even had the chance to turn. I tasted iron in my mouth, felt the snow of winter beneath my feet and heard the forest burning in my ears, wood cracking from within, black splinters and fire in the eyes, felt the river rise and the wind at my back, and as Klem staggered I smacked one hand into the right side of his head, into his ear, hoping to rupture his eardrum, put the other hand against the side of his neck and marched him, skull-first, staggering and confused, into the nearest wall. I drove his head into the glazed ceramic three times, each time throwing more of my body into it, each time feeling a different quality of cracking that rippled through him and into me, before the Brotherhood boys caught me and dragged me back, kicking and growling, untamed, blood on my fingers. Klem collapsed, crimson running down the left side of his face from the ridge where two skull plates join; thinner blood mingling with clear liquid flowing out of his right ear, which he grabbed with both his hands as if I had not already fractured his skull, rocking and groaning, a howl that he dared not release. By the door, Georg was still gasping, doubled over, one hand raised to shoo away the men who ran to help him. To show willing, one man hit me, and then, not to be left behind, another joined in, taking turns to knock me down and pick me up until Georg had enough air to gasp: "No!"

Confused, they stopped, each with one fist raised, like children caught in an embarrassing act who are trying to think of some other thing they might plausibly claim to be doing here.

"No," he repeated, and that word took all the air he had, and he turned away to wheeze a little more. Klem's groans now rose again, a strange, almost musical circle of rise and fall, rise and fall, as if he were skipping back and forth over a spinning line of anguish. "Help him!" Georg snapped with his next, meagre breath, and someone ran forward to lift Klem up. Sensing that this was their opportunity to pretend nothing had happened, my captors let me go, and I flopped down next to Lah, who had uncoiled enough from their ball of arm and knee to peer at me, bloody eye to bloody eye from where we both lay, a few inches apart on the floor.

Here, in this place, our gazes were the only things that we could perceive, and with Lah's bloody face before mine, all the fight, the rage, tumbled out of me as if plucked away by some ghostly hand. From nowhere, a gasp that might have been the beginning of a sob caught in my throat, and I blinked at blood in my eyes and knew it was not all blood. Lah reached out slowly, one hand catching mine, then the other, squeezing tight. They smiled, and were afraid, and smiled anyway.

And it seemed to me, in that place, that the temple didn't just take the children to witness how old priests died but to teach us how we should die too. Come, whispered the Medj, come – let us not make a fuss. Let us not wail and curse and beat against the ending but exhale a final, peaceful breath and make things easy on those who survive. Be easy, be easy. Let us tell you how you should live; let us tell you how you should die. Even when you are screaming: be easy.

Footsteps moved above us. I heard the click of the gun and closed my eyes. It was simple to think that Georg had shot me, when he fired – the sound was so loud, the hot press of blood across my face and neck so immediate, that in that moment I concluded that, though I was dying, I would feel no pain. The Medj had been right all along; this was easy. Then hands caught me, picked me up, and though I felt nothing from having been shot I felt a great deal of pain everywhere else, and that didn't seem to make much sense, so I opened my eyes and saw Lah's body on the floor, one eye rolled all the way back from where the bullet in their skull had torn something apart. The blood had crawled up Georg's trousers and boots, but no further. He brushed down his thighs with one hand unconsciously, handed the revolver back to one of his men, nodded, still breathing fast and shallow, as if this were the logical conclusion of an inevitable plan. Then he spun on his heel and walked away, as I kicked and screamed and screamed and screamed after him.

They left me in that place. I don't know how long. Perhaps a few hours; perhaps a few days. There was no light, save for a tiny line at the bottom of the locked door. I huddled in a corner as far from Lah's body as I could, shaking, mind in a loop.

Here, close your eyes.

Now they die.

Now they die.

Now they die.

Now they die.

Enough. Open your eyes. Think of something else. Here in the dark, what else will you imagine? Find a prayer, find your breath. Here, exhale, close your eyes.

And now they die.

Now they die.

Now they die.

Now they die.

Reason says that this is a physical reaction, an emotional reaction, trauma.

Breathe through it.

You are the kakuy. You are a living spirit. You are part of this world, and this world breathes within you.

Don't let go.

Don't be afraid.

So breathe.

Breathe.

Breathe.

I curled up in the dark, and could not remember how it felt to breathe.

Someone left food, water by the door, and it turned out I wanted to eat.

I thought Lah's body would start to smell, but it did not.

Perhaps the cold.

The darkness.

The isolation.

I imagined flies, maggots, but this was a sterile, buried place.

Someone left more food, more water by the door, and it turned out I wanted to live.

I fumbled on hands and knees until my fingers found sticky blood, then fumbled a little bit more until I found the corner of Lah's robes. Slowly, their body grown heavy with death, I unrolled Lah from the rolls of fabric, until they just wore their trousers and shirt below. I shook the robes out, folded them by fumbled touch, drew them over Lah's head and neck, tucking them gently round their body as you might wrap a basket of apples for the market. This done, I knelt down and mumbled the prayers for the dead. Some sentences I heard myself say. Others I did not, the words repeated and stumbled through again, again, and now again, as I lost the tangle of this moment or the memory of the last.

From death, life. In the temple we learned the process of decay, were invited to honour it, to marvel at nature's process. Over the first few days, the internal organs of a corpse will begin to decompose. Without oxygen to keep the cells alive, carbon dioxide builds up in their last figurative respiratory gasps. The carbon dioxide creates an acidic atmosphere within the body, causing cell membranes to rupture. Enzymes are then released which start eating these cells from the inside out. The skin loosens, even as the muscles grow stiff. A few days later, the gases released by cell consumption and the bacteria that are now thriving within the corpse will cause bloating, resulting in the body expanding up to twice its normal size. Insects move in, happily gnawing away, and the stench of this stage of decomposition is the classic vomit inducer that sends people scurrying for the gutter.

Eventually, what's left of the body liquefies. At first, this is through the nose, mouth, anus; any hole that fluid can run freely from. Maggots move in, until there is nothing left but bone and hair. Any artificial joints, piercings, inorganic implants also remain, nuzzled clean by nature.

The remains feed the creatures that are then fed upon by another. Plants take root in soil grown rich with the bacteria that feasted on your blood; bugs waddle away, fat on fluid, to be caught by birds that are then preyed upon by the larger bird that is then preyed upon by the predatory cat that is hunted by the wolf. On the earth, there is only one ocean, which becomes rain, which becomes blood, which returns again to the sea. There is only one breath, which becomes the hurricane, which spins across the peak of the mountain and returns again to the forest.

And now they live.

And now they die.

Now they die.

Now they die.

Now they die.

At some point, the darkness was broken by the door opening. Two women I didn't recognise stood in the light; puffed short sleeves, big, waist-clinching belts. One turned away the moment the air from the cell hit her, an audible retch breaking up from the back of her throat, hands over her mouth. I had not noticed the room begin to stink. The other put one hand on her hip, pushing her whole frame a little to the side like a tree struck by a boulder, folded her other hand on top as if bandaging her whole frame in place, and barked: "Kadri Tarrad? Come with us, please."

I crawled to my feet and followed them, having no idea what else I could possibly do.

There was a bathhouse behind the kitchen. Two great round tubs were already filled – one with hot water, the other with cold. When the women removed the lids that covered the hotter tub, steam rolled up like a living lizard, tonguing the air. Towels were slung over the hot pipes. A yellow sponge and bar of soap smelling of oil and lavender were deposited on the blue-tiled lip. I stripped out of my clothes as the women watched. The fabric had grown stiff, bent like card from the blood that had dried in every seam. Black grime beneath my nails was flecked with clotted scarlet, and purple bruises spotted my arms, ribs, back, knuckles, some no bigger than a finger's gouge, some a violet eruption spread from the impact of a fist. I walked up the warm, tiled steps to the bath, climbed carefully over the side, sank down, knees to chest, until the water was at my chin.

"Lean forward!" barked the older woman, and I obeyed. She grabbed the sponge, held it under the water until it was hot and malleable, rubbed soap into it, then into me. Her fingers rolled round the backs of my ears and into the spirals; ran through the roots of my hair like a garden fork pulling at soil. At some point, her retching companion joined quietly in the corner of the room, hands folded, head down. "Fetch the clothes!" snapped the elder woman, pulling out a short-haired brush to dig into my nails like she was scouring for gold in the desert. The young woman left; the young woman returned, carrying a folded-up bundle of clean dark grey clothes, without shoes, and a flask of cold water.

"Drink!"

I drank.

"Cold bath!"

I crawled, the pain of every bruise now transformed into something sluggish, universal and soft, out of the hot tub and into the cold, gasping as the water ran over me, watching a thin, oily sheen of residual soap and scrubby skin slither across the top of the water.

262

"Out!"

I climbed out, wrapping myself slowly in the hot towels provided as the woman tugged a comb through my hair, a scowl at every knot as if each was a personal slight. Then I changed into the clean clothes provided, long sleeves and straight trousers, my bare toes curling into the tiles below while the bloody bathwater gurgled away to the greywater tanks. The women seemed satisfied with the final result.

"Follow me!"

I followed, through cool corridor and across courtyard where the vegetables vines ran up wall and trellis, under an arch of old stone and down a side alley where the rainwater butts bulged beneath the downpipes and green moss grew hungry around slowly leaking barrels. My feet were dark with the gathered dirt of the walk, and that was good; that felt like a kind of safety. Then through a door guarded by a Brotherhood man, into the back of a great villa, a thing of half-restored old-world masonry and new solar glass walls, timber frames and half-lifted roof canopies to let in the cooler breeze during hottest days.

The sound of crockery and pipes, the smell of cumin and pepper, chilli and starchy rice hit my nose, and then we were in a kitchen, long tables down the middle of the floor, hot stoves blasting beneath white lights, dazzling bright, voices competing with pots and pans and the hiss of oil, water running and fans spinning. Rows of men and women wearing aprons stood each at their assigned station, chopping, peeling, carving, dicing, grinding, skinning, braising, boiling. Few glanced my way as I was led to a small corner office where a man lounged, feet up on a desk, reading, and another dressed in Brotherhood black stood stiffly by the door.

"Colas." The woman managed to keep a little of her imperious formality down for the man as she waved me through the door. "This one's for you."

The man called Colas looked up from his inkstone, lips curling with evident displeasure as he took me in. A half-crown of white hair ran from behind his left ear to his right, circling a great bald skull above. He sported thin-rimmed spectacles whose round shape perfectly matched the twin bulbs of his cleft chin when his bright lips moved. He wore an old-fashioned white shirt, a pair of dark brown shorts that stopped just above his knees and long green socks that stopped just below them. Swinging his legs down from the desk with exaggerated slowness, he rose to his feet, which revealed that he was little more than five feet tall, and king of his domain. Yet even kings were sometimes forced to do things they didn't like. "Where's his shoes?" he asked.

"No shoes."

"I've got standards, you know. Hygiene."

"No shoes."

"What's his name?"

"No name."

"I've got to call him something."

"Pick something, then."

He thought about it for a moment, but a moment was all the interest he could spare. "He looks like a Pityr. Hey, Pityr – ever worked in a kitchen before?"

"I did breakfast service at the temple for a few months."

He rolled his eyes and, with exaggerated slowness, indicated first himself, then the Brotherhood man who stood to attention by the door. "Me Colas. Me boss. This Qathir. He shoot you if you run, yes?"

I gave Qathir a longer, more speculative look. "He hasn't got a gun, only a stick."

"I can beat you to death too," offered Qathir with a shrug.

"I'm just wondering why he doesn't have a gun."

"Point is," snapped Colas, hands flicking up, "you do what I say, yes?"

"I guess so."

"Not you guess so, you do – you do so, yes?"

"Okay."

His eyes narrowed, and for the first time he looked as if he was trying to see something of me, myself, rather than the barefoot intruder shoved into his domain. Whatever he found behind my bruised eyes, he wasn't impressed. "I don't like you, Pityr."

I shrugged.

"Shrug again, and Qathir will shoot you – and don't say anything about a gun!"

I stood silent, waiting. For a moment, Colas rocked from toe to heel, as if he couldn't quite tell whether it was more majestic to retaliate against perceived insolence or to turn the other cheek. Then, with another twitch of his hands as if he were flicking up a window blind, he barked, "Yes, this way, yes!"

Qathir smiled thinly, gestured with rolling politeness towards the door. I followed Colas; Qathir followed me. By the time I caught up with the diminutive lord of the kitchen, he was already talking. " . . . there is always something and if there isn't something, find something! You will also mop the floors, clean the stoves, and do anything else you are told to by anyone who tells you to do it, yes? Yes!"

I stared at the twin sinks before me, one side already heaving with dirty plates and cutlery.

"*Well?*" His dignity, already threatened by this whole situation, seemed on the verge of deserting him altogether.

"All right," I replied, fighting the urge to shrug again. "If you say so."

So began my tenure in the kitchens of Georg Mestri, unsung leader of the glorious human revolution. At 6 a.m. every day, my world began with a poke in the ribs from Qathir or one of the other guards assigned to stand watch over me. I would be dressed and in the kitchen, warming the ovens and stoves, by 6.30 a.m. and would not leave that place until 10 at night; later, if the dignitaries upstairs had guests to entertain. The others in the kitchen paid me almost no attention, except to occasionally shout, Pityr! I need the celery! – or Pityr! I need the big pan now!

Of my four rotating watchers, it was Makris who first cracked and borrowed a stool from I knew not where to perch on throughout his long vigil, rather than tire his legs standing over me as I washed, scrubbed, scoured and mopped through the broiling heat of the kitchen. Sometimes Colas came over to find fault in my work, but usually he left me alone, finding it easier to be a king if he was not reminded of this unwelcome imposition in his domain. Only once did one of the cooks bother to speak to me; she was new, unfamiliar with the ways of this place.

"Hey, Pityr – why don't you have any shoes?"

Qathir, sat a few feet behind as I tied off the cornbags of food waste for the biomass vats, grinned, chewing down on an apple and waiting to hear my reply. He was going to grow fat in this job, a paunch already pushing against the buttons of his shirt, cheeks rounding out as if flushed from the heat.

"I don't have any shoes because I'm a political prisoner," I explained politely. "If I have shoes, it is more likely that I will try to run away."

"Really? No kidding."

"Really."

"Huh. I guess . . . that makes sense, now I think about it. Hey, is that legal? I mean . . . you know. You working here and being a political prisoner and that?"

"I don't know. I imagine the laws have been changed, now that we're at war."

"I guess you're right. Hey, thanks."

"No worries."

She smiled awkwardly, waved a chopping knife at me with the slow waggle of one not quite sure what to make of the last twenty seconds of her life, and went back to chopping a squash.

Qathir leant a little closer to me as I pressed the bags of waste together into the sealed bin that would go to biomass. "She likes you," he grinned.

"I doubt that very much."

"Maybe she'll help you escape?"

"I doubt that absolutely."

"You're not very imaginative, are you?"

I hesitated, squeezing the lid down on the last of the bags, head on one side. "You know, that was what Georg thought, before I stabbed him in the leg."

*

Every four days, I was given half an hour to wash top-to-toe, and when the days were slow and even Colas couldn't think of a task for me to run, I huddled in a corner of the kitchen and slept instantly, profoundly, until Qathir or one of the other watchers kicked my shins and barked, "Job's in!"

In that way, my life continued. I did not know the day, heard no news, did not speak unless spoken to, did not pray, did not rest, and, to my complete and continuing bewilderment, was not shot in the head.

That last omission was the one I found most interesting.

Chapter 45

One morning, a box of fruits was delivered to the kitchen. I padded outside, the hot summer air damp with the promise of autumn, and pulling back the tarp that covered the boxes, saw thin green-grey mould smeared across the rind of shrivelled oranges; brown rot sunk into the crisp surface of the onions and maggot holes poking in and out of the thin-skinned peaches, from which sugars oozed like blood.

"What in the name of sun's fire is this?" roared Colas, as we dug through the finger-splattering, bug-crawling delivery in search of something edible. "What am I meant to do with this crap?"

There was a smell on the air: hot coal and diesel, unfamiliar to the city. That night, it rained so hard that I was dragged from my bed not two hours after I'd crawled into it to lay sandbags around the kitchen door against the deluge running from the overflowing drains. In the morning, in every vegetable box and hanging garden of the yard, mushrooms had grown, brilliant orange threaded with white gills and a purple drop on top or white inverted umbrellas; they sprouted at the feet of every wall and from the trunks of the bending fruit trees, scythes of bruised grey fungus, hanging off the bark like sunhats.

"Can we eat them?" Colas demanded, as Hang, his second in command, peered under the top of the speckled crop.

"Poisonous," he replied. "No good."

"Pityr! Clear them!"

I looked round this strange new landscape of fungus, bare toes bending into sodden soil. "Mushrooms are just the flower," I heard myself say. "The roots go deep."

Colas spun on me, a flush of anger in his face, but to my surprise Makris shuffled a little closer to me, muttering: "I'll give him a hand."

We worked in silence, tugging soft fungus by its base and snapping off the dusty discs for the biomass wells. When I curled my toes, water rose from beneath them, and, for the first time in what might have been months, I shivered in the drizzle-grey cold.

A few days after that, the meat of the freshly slaughtered lamb came, blackened with disease, wriggling with worms. Someone gagged at the sight of it; there was no question that it would fall to me to dispose of the needlessly slaughtered flesh.

As I washed my hands clean, the woman who still had not learned to refrain from speaking to the condemned casually manoeuvred herself close to where I worked, her attention fully on the eggy sauce she beat in the bowl before her. Without glancing my way, she murmured: "Are the kakuy angry?"

I kept my eyes down, away from hers. "Pissed, I would imagine."

"Is this their punishment?"

"Hard to say. Doctrinally it's always suited Temple to be a little vague about these things."

"I will pray," she replied firmly, and turned away, seemingly satisfied.

At night, I crawled to the tiny square window in my low room, watched the feet of passers-by splash through the rain, and did not pray.

Then one day, much like any other, Colas hollered my newest name.

"Pityr! Take this upstairs!"

A tray of sweet teas and candied fruits was thrust into my hands. "Third-floor reception room, quick quick!"

My life, to that moment, had not deviated from its narrow

course of locked bedroom to observed washroom to kitchen to courtyard. I knew in some abstract sense that there was a house – you could even call it a small palace – overhead, the inhabitants of which we constantly served with treats sweet, succulent and savoury, but I had not encountered a shred of it down in the places I dwelt. Qathir was my duty guard that day, and, seeing my hesitation, he shrugged and pointed with one single waggling digit towards the heretofore unregarded staircase.

I went up.

The floor beneath my feet turned from ceramic to bare clay, from bare clay to warm timber.

One floor up, the timber became carpeted, with worn undyed wool.

A floor above that, the carpet was dyed a sudden, vivid green.

The floor above that, the tattered carpet of the stairwell gave way to a new, thick weave, the warmest, softest thing I had ever felt beneath my grubby toes. I hesitated as I stepped onto it, blinking in kind yellow light and twisting my head round side to side, blanketed in the comfort of the place. Qathir nudged my shoulder, pointed the same wagging digit towards a half-open set of double doors, waited.

I shuffled towards them, was stopped by a woman who sat guard as once I had sat for Georg all those months ago; she rose, knocked politely twice, did not wait for an answer, then opened the doors to gesture me in.

Inside, sofas arranged in a u-shape were assembled before a long table on which much tea and many nibbles had already been consumed and many more left half-chewed with a disregard that might once have been an embarrassing breach of etiquette; these days it seemed a badge of pride. Arrayed in knots and gaggles around the room were the great and good of Maze and their new Lyvodian allies; some I recognised, some I did not. The conversation was low, the occasional spike of laughter too loud, the occasional brush of a hidden confidence murmured into a sleeve. Farii stood nearest the door, pressed into a triangle of conspiracy with two others. Whatever time had passed since I saw her

270

pronounce her eulogy over Ull's corpse, it had not been kind. Her eyes were puffy grey bags around tired, blood-wrinkled slits. Her lips were thin and shoulders pressed towards her neck, like a starving vulture that doesn't dare feast while the hyenas are still gnawing. She glanced up as I passed, started in surprise, recognised me, one hand squeezing the arm of a compatriot who stopped talking and glanced my way too, her mouth widening in amazement. Merthe moved towards me, but Farii held her back, and I looked away and walked to the long table, feeling suddenly dirty, small, Qathir watching me from the door.

I put my tray down, glanced to my left and saw Kun Mi, pride and peacock-feathered, her dark hair wound in braids across her skull, head high and neck stuck forward as if she would peck at the faces of those who addressed her. Bukarest had become her new home, the forward line of her advance; and besides, the whispers went, Vien was a stinking plague-pit. The water that came from the taps was stained orange-brown; the air was thick and hard to breathe. No wonder the greatest of the war had moved somewhere a little closer to the front lines.

I turned, and there he was.

Georg, right behind me, leaning a little on his walking stick, his eyes running from head to toe as if he was wondering, had I grabbed a knife? There were plenty of blades in the kitchen, but his face flickered curiosity, not fear. His shoulders were pulled back, bound up in a knot, ready to be unleashed, ready to fight, he was so ready to fight, the smile on his lips barely creasing the soft tissue of his face. For a moment, we stood regarding each other, and I was tempted to reach behind myself, to mime the action of a killer, just to see what happened, to smile, to snarl, to see if I could make him jump. I did not. This was not the time for such games.

He saw that realisation in my eyes the moment I had it, and now his smile was something real, and he nodded once, and looked as if he might speak, and instead stepped to the side to let me pass, which I did, closing the door behind me.

Chapter 46

Time passes without days, days without name. In that too, there is a kind of honesty. Autumn comes in bloody leaf and yellow fruits. The slugs slither out in the rain and are crushed by passing vehicles, guts spilt into the sodden earth. It has rained for nearly nine days without end, and in the morning I cannot see anything except fog through the tiny window of my room. The soap from the dishes is making my hands peel. I pick at little flakes of white unconsciously now, though sometimes I pick too deep and blood wells up beneath the scales of skin.

Since there is no one left in the temples of Bukarest to offer the autumn libations, I do the best I can. I steal a little barley from the kitchen and scatter it when I am sent to take the recycling out. I spill a little water on the already sodden earth, and put my hands together at dusk when no one is looking, and bow to the west. Such things, when done alone, are largely meaningless. It takes a society that bows, all of humanity honouring its place upon this earth, to live with the kakuy. The temple never had magic; there was never any mystic power in the prayers of the Medj. Their power was one of teacher and guide who taught the children to think before they felled the forest, to thank the animal whose flesh they feasted on, to cherish the earth that carried them. Get them young, Lah had said, and where were their ditties now, their songs of balance?

They are dead, and it has not stopped raining it seems for a month, a year, and in Tinics I do not know if the forest grows.

*

Having been sent once to deliver tea to the upstairs rooms, I was sent again. Three times a week, then five – then, it seemed, every day. Sometimes to offices, sometimes to halls, barefoot I plodded round the villa with a guard at my back, occasionally noticed, rarely remarked on. Georg glances my way as I lay the warm bread down at the end of his table, but he otherwise does not cease his dictations. Farii watches me in the corridor as I pass by. Kun Mi does not know, nor care, who I am. I am invisible to her, except for once, when she stopped me and barked:

"Why aren't you wearing shoes?"

"I am a political prisoner," I replied, bowing politely. "Although by now I thought everyone was used to this kind of thing."

The answer seemed to throw her, a bafflement to her dignity, so she tilted her chin higher and swept on by, and I have no doubt that fifteen minutes later she worked out something profoundly insightful to say.

"Beograd has fallen," Qathir said one night, just before locking the door to my little room. "Jia has fled to Isdanbul. They say she'll sue for peace."

"Is that so."

He nodded, a little disappointed at my neutrality. Then: "We used bombers. We firebombed the city. We did it with planes."

These ideas – bombers, planes, firebombing – were strange and unfamiliar to him. He was not sure what to do with the words, how to form them, but he knew they were important, and impressive, and it made him feel good to say them. I opened my mouth to lecture him on heretical history, on twenty-five thousand burned to death in a single night during the wars of our ancestors, on how adult bodies shrivelled to the size of children as the water boiled from them, of how fleeing refugees tumbled from lack of oxygen and just lay there, rag dolls, before the coming inferno. I tried to explain how after a great fire there was often a great rain, but he had already locked the door and pushed the bolt home, so I lay instead on my back, and wondered if I should cry, and felt absolutely nothing at all.

The next day, Colas found weevils wriggling through his rice stores. There were millions of them, tiny brown bodies grown to a colony within the sacks. He cursed and swore and was uncertain if he should throw the bags away, not knowing whether he would get more. But someone upstairs heard of his plight and swore that he would receive more rice soon, have no fear. The household of Georg Mestri would not go hungry. No one would go hungry, in this great new age.

"Lovely bit of protein, your weevil," chuckled Makris, but he was only half-laughing, and as I stirred the mulching, steaming compost in the vats out back he shuffled a little closer and whispered: "Do you bless people, priest?"

"No," I replied, not looking up from my work. "I was never that kind of priest. Besides, all a blessing is good for is reminding you not to be a total pillock, so I'm not sure if it's up your street."

He bristled a little at this reply, but didn't retaliate, and later helped me scrub the greywater vats, which he had never done before.

A sliding back of bolts in the dead of night. Perhaps the city is flooding again; perhaps tonight they will kill me. A woman I half-recognised, Georg's new assistant, guardian of his door, stood in the light.

"Come with me," she barked, and I wished for the little kitchen knife I'd stolen three days before, which I could not now easily reach without revealing its hiding place.

"What time is it?" I asked, and she didn't answer.

Upstairs, and up again, to a little reception room that I had visited two or three times before to deliver the fruits of the kitchen. Pillows across the floor, a low table with a single cut flower in a jar on it, mementos of past glories of Bukarest on the wall. There was only one person in the room – the one person it was always going to be. The woman gestured to a pillow opposite him, and I sat cross-legged on it, as she closed the door behind her.

274

Georg, awake as always when all normal people should be asleep, sipped tepid tea, cup clasped between both hands, and watched me over the rim. I adjusted my posture, stretched out some of the hard constrictions of my brick-like bed, shuffled a little to the left and a little to the right, like a cat kneading an unwilling lap into submission, folded my hands palm on palm, and waited.

Finally he said: "You heard?"

"No. What haven't I heard?"

"We bombed Beograd."

"Ah – no, I heard that. Firebombed, yes?"

"Yes."

"How'd it go?"

"Well, all things considered. It was our first time attempting incendiary carpet bombing. The information we had was piece-meal. Our scientists had to work hard to fill in the gaps, do a little thinking for themselves. I think the exercise was good for their imaginations."

"I see. What next? Nuclear?"

"Hardly. It wouldn't achieve anything strategic. And there are too many barriers between us and fissionable material. Temple was wise to keep that secret to itself. Although I do sometimes wonder as the war progresses, do you think the Medj will tell Jia how to do it? Where to find radioactive rocks, how to split the atom?"

"Nuclear winter would not please the kakuy."

"Please. Let's not pretend Temple was ever interested in the spirits. Everything you people have ever done has always been about man – keeping mankind in its place, obedient, passive."

"Yes." His eyebrows flickered up in surprise at my admission, and I shrugged. "The kakuy never gave a damn for individual humans or individual hearts. Prayers are just words, thrown up in hope. Temple teaches people to pray in order to shape what we hope for. It is pure social engineering. But fundamentally, Georg, with your pissing little ego-bastard war, you are doing precisely the same thing. You are trying to redefine what people hope for, and what they fear. And at the end of the day, I would far rather hope for the kakuy not to burn us all to ashes through the general equality and peace of all humankind, than the destructive nonsense you're selling."

He nodded, eyes running to some other place. "Interesting."

"Is it?"

"Not philosophically, of course. Philosophically you're a coward, blighted by your own internalised inferiority. But it is interesting to hear you speak as yourself – as an inquisitor. I thought you didn't believe in anything at all."

"I have seen the kakuy too," I said, and surprise flickered like the first spark in a fire before he hid his face again behind a bored smile. "Belief doesn't really come into it."

He nodded again, neither here nor there. Perhaps there should have been words, and for a moment there were none. Georg smiled at nothing much, nodded to himself alone, put down his cup, straightened, hands mimicking mine in his lap – consciously or not, I couldn't tell.

"There is disease in Vien," he said at last.

"What kind of disease?"

"The water. Something in it. A heavy metal of some kind – they think perhaps lead. It is rational to say that there was error at the armament factories further upstream. They have released chemicals into the water, a toxic wave. You can even see it, the land turned scarlet. The responsible parties have been reprimanded. But in Vien they say it is a curse. That the kakuy are doing this to them. What do you think?"

"I think it is a spill from the armaments factory," I replied. "I think you have poisoned your own land. I think when children start coughing up black, when the old die in the heat and the young die in the cold, it will be because of what you did."

"And the kakuy?"

"I do not think they will help you. More I cannot say."

He nodded, staring straight through me at his own thoughts. Then: "We dragged a few priests out of prison. Some of the novices. Got them to say their prayers. They seemed very keen to help."

276

"I imagine they would be."

"By spring, Jia will be on the other side of the Bosphorus. It is a good natural border; she will sue for peace then."

"Will you give it?"

He shook his head. "Farii wants us to, of course. Even Kun Mi is getting anxious. But they both are beginning to understand the inevitability of this conquest. To win, we must tear down the mountains and the forest; the mechanics of this war require no less. The land we move through is turned to ash, and it does not heal. The water in Vien is the colour of piss, and it does not heal. We cannot stop at the Bosphorus. We must keep going. We cannot let our army disband or our soldiers go home. If they go home, they may find that they do not have a home to go to."

"So your plan is . . . what? Circle the world for ever, conquering everything you can and leaving devastation in your wake? Cross the sea to Amerika and sweep across that land too until it is poison? Then come back to Maze and hope that enough time passed while you were warring over there that the forest over here has grown? That is a terrible plan."

"They say in Amerika," he mused, "that the people hunt kakuy for sport. That the walls of the militia forts are hung with severed limbs of ghastly creatures."

"They say that Amerika is nothing but yellow dust and acid," I retorted. "That beasts bigger than men roam the ashen wastes with stinging tails and poison spit; that in the spindle forests where once men cracked the earth in two, the trees have grown fingers that claw at travellers and pull them into a bloody, boiling earth. So much for that."

He sighed, reached for his tea cup, stopped himself, folded his hands again, turned his head as if the corner of the room had suddenly become fascinating. "Men and the kakuy," he sighed. "What a frustrating thing."

I waited, motionless, eyes tired and body buzzing.

"I'm told that when you were young, the forest burned. That's correct, isn't it? The forest of your home town, burned to the ground."

277

My heart is a great hollow thing, bloodless and dry. I licked my lips, tried to swallow this knot back into my chest, nodded. "Yes."

"Is that why you joined Temple?"

"No. I don't think so."

"Then why? There are a thousand more interesting things to do with a life than offer prayers you know will never be answered and indoctrinate children to bow and scrape to worms."

I thought about it, then said:

"Firstly, I ended up an inquisitor, not a Medj. I was never pastoral in my inclinations. But you're also wrong – Temple is fascinating to work for, if you have the right mindset. In the burning, humankind was taught that human nature was fundamentally violent, selfish. That the most successful iteration of a life was to make wealth and be, in some manner, superior to others: socially superior, superior in fame or standing or riches, in material belongings, in ruthlessness. We turned our backs on the essential truth of our species, which is that we are co-operative. Oh, certainly, some societies dabbled with the idea that individuals were nothing but servants of a state, to be crushed and disposed of at will, forgetting that the state is made of people too. And others embraced the notion that individualism rose above all else and forgot that it was society that carried these lone heroes up. So when the forests burned and the seas turned to acid, the great authoritarian states said, "Our power is more important than our people," because by then such bodies were nothing more than monarchies for a corrupt few, ruling in the name of the many. And the individual heroes who had been lauded for their wealth, their ambition, their beauty or their fame . . . well, they rushed to protect what they had too, leveraging their meagre social capital to protect themselves from the dust and the famine while all around them everybody died.

"How easily humans are swayed. When things go wrong, we look to the oldest story of all – to a messiah, to a change – and it doesn't matter what that change is so long as we believe there will be a hero. But it took three thousand firefighters to hold back the fire that burned through my childhood, and in the end it was the rain, not a hero, that doused the flames. In the burning, we raged, raged, raged against the truth that the fire and the sea were stronger than us. Temple taught us that humility before the storm was sacred – but it failed. Temple has failed you. You believe that you deserve what you receive, that you alone are the hero of your story. And yes, sooner or later, the only way to prove this is by conquering your fellow humans, mastering them with your strength. And when that is done, when humans are cowed and there is only annihilation, the only thing left is to kill a god. To kill the kakuy themselves. And that is how you will die, if you're wondering. You will end raging against the sky that fed you, the river that gave you life. That's why I joined Temple. To be part of something more."

Georg nodded again, without seeming to see me. "I think that's fatalistic shit."

I shrugged, and the motion felt like a sudden freedom, a giddy escape.

"You think so little of people – you talk about 'care' but you think so little of them. I think you're a coward, Ven of the Temple of the Lake. Kadri Tarrad. I think you hide and hide and hide, because you can't accept that some men are great, and others are small, and you have always been tiny. That's what I think."

"In that case, you may as well shoot me now. Why haven't you? I doubt you're keeping me alive for the conversation."

"Not for that. You bore me. You can go now." One hand had drifted to his leg, rubbing along the old knife wound, the great scar I'd carved through his flesh. "Go back to the kitchen."

I rose, put my hands together, bowed a little, saw the flicker of something in the corner of his lips that could have been anger. Let myself out and barely noticed the bolts slide shut on my prison door.

279

Chapter 47

I guessed when the first day of winter was, and pressed my hands together, and gave thanks for the seeds hidden beneath the snow, the wool grown thick on the back of the sheep, the summer water now falling in winter rain, the wood from the curling tree and the stars spinning infinite overhead. The next day, Colas fired two of his staff. There was less food to cook, less food to eat; the season of abundance was ended.

I was summoned, bare-footed, almost every night to wait at Georg's table. I did so in silence, serving cold meat when commanded, topping up wine and flasks of tea. It was easier to serve than to clean. Farii avoided meeting my gaze, when she ate with the men of Maze. Merthe, wearing the uniform of a woman who'd been promoted, stared with open-mouthed amazement whenever I entered the room until nudged by Farii to hide her dismay. Kun Mi watched with open dislike, until one day she blurted: "Why. The shitting. Do you keep *that* around?"

It takes the table a moment to realise she is talking about me. Conversation lulls, eyes drifting to my previously unregarded form, a pitcher of water held in both my hands. Georg, picking at hot dumplings from his bowl, doesn't look up as he says: "That is Pityr. He works in the kitchens."

"He's a political. Your enemy. You let your enemy serve you food?"

"Yes."

"Why?"

"Because it pleases me."

Kun Mi glowers down the table, and for the first time it strikes me how young she is, how utterly unequipped for the role chosen for her. Georg sighs, lays down his spoon, rises awkwardly, unable to disguise the slight wince of pain as his weight shifts from one leg to the other. "Look." He puts one hand across the back of my neck, pulls me in closer to the table as if he might embrace me. "He is entirely docile." Shakes me a little, side to side, and, when nothing falls out, laughs, pushes me away.

"Isn't he dangerous?"

Another sigh from Georg. He gestures me closer again, and closer I come. "Pityr," he sighs, "put the pitcher down."

I put the pitcher down.

"Pityr," he sighs, "kneel."

There is a kitchen knife taped to the small of my back. I have been carrying it for the best part of a month, and no one has bothered to search me or my room since summer, given how passive I've become. Given how little I have fought back. I kneel at his feet.

"Pityr," he tuts, holding out one foot. The boot itself is clean; Georg almost never leaves his office. I bend down and kiss it, hinging at the hips, bend back up, wait. Georg smiles, ruffles my hair, turns back to the assembly.

"You see? Harmless. He knows his place. There are masters in this world, and there are the mastered. Pityr understands this now."

I study his knees carefully. One trouser leg sits a little lower than the other, his weight favouring his uninjured leg. It is a subtle imbalance, but there if you bother to look for it. Kun Mi grunts a kind of approval, and with the tips of his fingers Georg gestures for me to stand. I do, pick up the pitcher, resume my station. A few people stare. Merthe cannot hide her sympathy, or her disgust, but directs it to her plate. Farii does not meet my eye or the eyes of anyone else.

*

281

A new guard on my shift, replacing Makris.

She does not say her name, does not sit on the now-habitual stool by the sink in the kitchen but stands, bolt upright, hands behind her back, to attention. She remains like this for two days, until finally it is time for me to wash and clean myself in icy water. She stands by the washroom door as I strip and rub thin soap into cold fingers, eyes straight ahead. Then she crosses the floor so fast I don't even hear her coming, and I think this is it, she's the assassin sent at last to kill me, the end of everything, but instead she pushes my head towards the sink, presses her lips in close and whispers:

"There is a traitor in Council. They call him Pontus."

I brace with both hands against the sink, try to see her face in the tarnished shard of mirror, soap drying to scaly prickles on my skin.

"Do you know who it is?"

I don't answer, and after a moment, she lets me go and marches back to the door to resume her station as if she had never moved. I carry on washing myself, pull my clothes back on, go back to work.

The next day, she was not on shift.

Nor the day after that.

The day after that, I turned on the taps in the kitchen and the stink of raw sewage filled my nostrils, hot and clinging to the back of my throat. I turned the taps off, waited in Colas' office for him to come to work, let him shout, was sent back to my cell; nothing to do until the water ran clean.

When the door next opened, it was her again, and downstairs there was a truck from I knew not where, fresh water flowing from a nozzle at its back. She watched me carry buckets all day, and never once moved to help, until one time when I slipped and sloshed liquid over the edge, and Colas shouted – although by then he was simply shouting at the day, at the world, at this stupid fucking universe – and she passed me a cloth to clean it up, and as she bent down she said:

282

"Who killed Ull of Lyvodia?"

I laid out the cloth on the floor, watched it absorb the spill, squeezed it tight into the bucket, laid it back down in the next puddle. "Georg, obviously. *Obviously.*"

"If we get you out, will Jia listen to you?"

I shrugged, kept on scrubbing, without a word.

In the evening, Georg summoned me again.

The villa was empty; no point feasting while the taps ran with shit.

He drank from a bottle of wine – safer than even boiled tea – and, when I sat opposite him, gestured to the inkstone in front of him. I picked it up. It was archaic German. I put it back down. "I don't translate for you. Shoot whoever you want."

"I don't need you to translate it; I know what it says. Read it."

Cautiously, I picked it up again, half reading while watching him over the tip of the stone. I had not read any words other than the hygiene instructions in the kitchen for months. The feel of it was like an alien crawling into my mind, a strange and disturbing notion settling over my consciousness. It was an ancient tract on the benefits of innumerable forms of implausible healing. Lavender oil and tea tree; cloves of garlic and sweet-smelling citrus. Crystals and diets and vapours of dissolved salts. I put it down, met Georg's eye, shrugged. "And?"

"What do you think?"

"I think if you like nice things it's perfectly nice. If you want to cure your cancer, it's nonsense."

"It was very popular, once upon a time. As science became more impenetrable, people turned to simple, comforting things. They said they were getting back to nature; that it was not mankind's place to inoculate against disease or edit DNA, that it upset the order of things."

"You are using a facetious example to prove a lacklustre point," I retorted. "You are conflating the genuine human urge to have control over one's life with the heretical urge to conquer the world."

"And when men cannot control their world, what things

might they do? Temple took away man's control, his freedom to choose; it made us no better than beasts. You inquisitors should have realised long ago there would be consequences."

"We always want the pain to end quickly – it is so much easier than hard work," I replied. "And if Temple takes away your right to set the world on fire, so be it. Grow up. Find some other game. Why are we still talking, Georg?"

He licked his top lip, gestured at the bottle of wine. "Pour, please." I refilled his cup. There was none for me. "Do you think about him? Pontus, I mean?"

I lowered the bottle slowly, rested it on a stained round coaster, folded my hands in my lap. "I don't."

"You think perhaps you are alike? You spied on me, he spies on Jia – and so forth?"

"That would be presumptuous. Presumption would make discovery harder. You know that, I believe."

"You must have suspected someone, by the end. Who? Krima, perhaps? Pav?"

"No."

"No?"

"No. I know two things about Pontus – that they got to me before I got to them, and that they have limits. Pontus makes mistakes. It took them far too long to catch me. This implies that even my speculation, my casual suspicions shared over a cup of tea, might offer actionable intelligence. So no. You can talk about Pontus if it makes you feel big, but you'll excuse me if I only pretend to listen."

"You're going to die in Bukarest. You know that."

"I think it's very likely."

"Don't you want to know who Pontus is, before the end?"

"If I'm to die, what difference would it make?"

He clicked his tongue in the roof of his mouth, sat back a little in his chair, the wine untouched, hand rubbing unconsciously along the hidden scar across his leg. I watched for a moment, then asked: "How's the war going?"

"We're winning. Decisively."

"And yet the taps run with shit."

"That is not Jia's doing."

"You say that as though it makes things better. I thought you'd rather deal with humans than something worse?"

"I am dealing with humans. Stupid fucking humans all the time."

"You look tired. Perhaps a little peace might do your side the world of good too."

"Honestly, I could do with a break. I've had terrible trouble with the staff."

"I always had you down as a seaside kind of man. Rolled-up trousers, an oversized tome about philosophy in dappled shade while drinking fruity concoctions."

A tiny smile, the first real smile I thought I'd seen for a very long time, flickered across his face; it was gone almost instantly, as if ashamed of its own merriment. He shook his head. "Skiing. I grew up in the mountains, you will recall."

"Ah yes. You saw the black wolf."

"And it can die. I know that. I know it."

"The wolf can. I imagine even you haven't worked out what to do about the mountain."

"Goodness, you must have worked hard to keep your sanctimony in check when you were Kadri Tarrad."

"Honestly, it was the least of my worries."

"Does it make you feel bigger? Does it make you feel brave?"

"You misunderstand. Your mistake is imagining that in understanding the size and majesty of creation, the wonder of this world and the richness within it, you become small. A tiny scuttling thing without centre, without identity and form. You fail to see how, in grasping your small place within this life, you become part of something that is so much bigger than you could ever be when you were being a hero alone."

His brow flickered in brief exasperation, his hand pulling unthinkingly back from his leg. Then he gestured briskly towards the door, all conversation over. "Piss off, Ven. You bore me."

I rose, bowed, palm pressed to palm, and let myself out.

Chapter 48

Two days later, a mudslide buried half of Tseonom. I felt the panic rise as news came over the radio, bit back on asking, what about Tinics? What about my home? It was only a few kilometres away, was it hit too? Who of my clan had cycled into town that day? Who of my hearth were visiting the clinic or taking tea with friends when the world turned brown?

An inquisitor hides their home, hides their fear, but I was an inquisitor no more, so I stood squarely in Colas' door and said:

"Tseonom is near my home. May I see?"

Colas opened his mouth to say the usual – piss off, Pityr; get lost, Pityr – then didn't. He handed me his inkstone without a word, sat back and waited, arms folded and tea cooling on his desk, until my reading was done.

It was the mudslide that caused Farii to rush through the censorship law, if one could say Farii was still in charge by then. But she was too late to stop the news from Tseonom, and as word spread of liquid death shaking itself loose from the hillside and tumbling down faster than a speeding train to drown and crush those unfortunate enough to be in its path – children and adults – one of the cooks grabbed me by the arm and hissed: "Is it the kakuy? Did they do this? You were a priest – are they punishing us?"

"Deforestation often results in mudslides," I replied, not looking up from the sink. "Roots hold the soil together and a rich,

286

bio-diverse landscape is better at absorbing excess water from rain than bare, dry earth."

He blinked at me in surprise, bewilderment, then gripped my arm a little harder. "Are the kakuy punishing us?"

I sighed, laid the dish to one side, rinsed it clear. "Deforestation often results in mudslides. Humans and kakuy are born from the same ecosystem."

He shook his head in disgust, threw a cloth over one shoulder like he would whip himself with it, and turned away.

After that, the radio broadcast mostly patriotic songs and excerpts from speeches on the theme of mankind ascendant.

On a day without name, I went out in bare feet from the back door of the kitchen to find five feet of snow blanketed over the biomass chutes. I listened for the sounds of the city and found that it was quieter even than the winter wood where once the icy kakuy had prowled between the trees. Colas, peering through the door behind me, arms wrapped around his chest, swore, marched back into the kitchen, re-emerged a moment later with a shovel and, to my surprise, his own winter coat. "Just a loan, dimwit," he muttered. "Can't have you dropping dead." I put on the coat, the smell of vegetable stock and toasted nuts warm in the collar, and when I looked at him again saw, to my astonishment, that he was taking off his shoes. "What?" he snapped. "Don't think I'm going to kiss you!"

His shoes were far too big for me, but they offered some meagre protection for the next few hours as I flopped and slapped around, trying to pile the snow as evenly as I could so the delivery trucks could get through. When I was done, I felt warm all the way through my body, until I moved my hands near a stove and nearly sobbed at the pain as blood returned to frozen flesh. Colas let me keep his coat for another hour as I chattered and shivered in the warmth, before sending Qathir to reclaim it and his shoes, which he did with something that was almost an apology.

*

287

In the dead of night, the bolts slid back on my door.

"Come," snapped Qathir, clearly as annoyed as I was at being disturbed.

I shuffled after him through the winding corridor to the floors of green carpet, swaying a little for the first few steps as blood sloshed back into sluggish limbs. I didn't have tea to deliver, or any duties to perform, but was led as usual to Georg's study door, where Qathir knocked three times, awkward, a crunching in his shoulders that was unlike any of his normal leg-lolloping ease, before letting me in.

I stepped inside to the warmth of a fire and the smell of strong black tea. There was Georg, looking perhaps a little tired – did Georg ever look tired? Farii, sat in a corner, shrinking into it as if she was little more than an old pillow on a tatty chair; Merthe, face wrinkled with distaste; and Yue.

Yue, dressed in winter grey, black hair in a skin-tugging bun on the top of her head, an inkstone held so tight I thought she might crack the case. She rose as I entered, looked me in the eye, then looked away.

"Happy?" asked Georg, legs stretched out across the low tabletop. He made it look like a sprawl, hiding the discomfort in his injured limb, turning disadvantage to a performance of strength.

Yue looked back up, met my eye again, and I didn't know what I saw in her face, had no idea what was running across mine. "Not yet," she replied, forced strength, forced confidence, what in the name of sunfire was she doing here? "Ven – I need to ask you some questions. Are you being mistreated?"

"What?"

"Yue is here to negotiate," Georg intoned, a ritual chant from a priest who had long since lost interest in the things he said. "Jia wants to end the war."

"*What?*"

"Ven." Yue's voice snapped my full attention back to her, standing stiff and straight as a turbine in the storm. "Have you been mistreated?"

"Yes, of course," I retorted. "I mean – of course. But I'm far less dead than I should be. What in the name of sun and fire are you doing here? Yue?"

"I have been sent to discuss preliminary negotiations."

"Secret negotiations – Jia doesn't want the Provinces to know how badly she's losing," corrected Georg.

"Kun Mi isn't exactly able to reject Jia's overtures," I snapped back. "How is the water in Vien these days?"

In her little, huddled corner, Farii has closed her eyes, like one at prayer, detaching herself from this place and moving to another world.

"A prisoner exchange will be part of any negotiation, you have my word," Yue declared, and she didn't believe it would happen, and said it anyway.

"Ven is fine. Look at him – he's practically glowing with health. Beograd burns and the kakuy sleep. What could be better?"

"You shouldn't be here, Yue."

"I am here to negotiate," she repeated, staring now at some place behind the back of my head, as if she didn't see me at all. "The treatment of political prisoners and prisoners of war will be a priority. Thank you."

For a moment, the two of us stood there, like opposite ends of a broken bridge. I do not know how long we stood, and it was probably only seconds. It was perhaps long enough for a forest to grow. Then Georg puffed in exasperation and snapped: "Well, off you go, Ven. There's a good pup."

There is a knife strapped to the small of my back. I have learned how to sleep with it inches away from my fist. Tonight is the night, perhaps. Tonight I'll do it, leap across the room in a single bound, drive the blade into the soft pink flesh beneath Georg's chin, push it all the way up, through the hollow of his windpipe and across his vocal cords, so no one would hear him scream, just like the inquisition taught us, just like they always said I might need to do, in order to be a really good pacifist, a really generous priest.

Then I'll take Yue's hand and, having heroically put her in

danger and ruined everything, I'll valiantly rescue her from this locked-down city in my bare feet, and we'll run away to the forest and everything will be astonishingly terrible. And she will never forgive me, and quite right too.

So much for magic. So much for prayer.

I turned my back on them all and went quietly back to my prison cell.

Chapter 49

In the evening, when all else is sleeping, I drink tea with Georg.

It has become something of a habit of his. At first, it was an accident, a casual little thing; I cleared up plates after another late-night session, and suddenly I was the only person there.

Then I was the last person left again, and again after that, and I began to think he was calling for me to come from the kitchen a little late, so I might be the last person left behind, and then I was certain of it, and I poured floral tea without a word into a cup the colour of sage, and sometimes he talked, and sometimes he didn't, until one night nearest the year's end he said: "We'll never let you go, Ven. Whatever Yue says. Here until the end."

I shrugged. "I know."

"Why don't you do something?" A flare of anger, frustration – I hadn't seen it so bright or hot in him before. "Why don't you try to escape or fight? I know you can fight, I've seen it. Do something!"

"I'm not sure what you expect. In Vien there were protocols, safe houses. I had shoes, support. You want me to cross the mountains in winter without any shoes?"

"Then die fighting. Die doing something!"

"Assassinate you, perhaps? I've thought about it. Killing you is far more strategically important than killing Kun Mi, given she's just a little prancing tool. But then I have to wonder ... what would she be like if you weren't pulling her strings? What would the Brotherhood do next? I'm not at all convinced that stabbing you actually helps, though of course if the situation swings too far, I'll be sure not to let you know."

For a moment, he balanced between anger and surprise. Then he slumped back into the couch, and was tired, and hurt, and he laughed. He waggled the empty tea cup in his hand; I refilled it, poured myself a cup. Outside, the city was quiet, scuttling, beetle black.

"Temple makes people dumb," he pronounced, head back across the top of the couch, neck exposed. "Spends so much time telling us to be grateful, to accept, to . . . hug a cockroach or whatever . . . that no one ever does anything. No sense of ambition. No sense of purpose. I was worried you were the same."

"You mistake a short-term sense of gain for a long-term plan. So long as you don't mind thinking a hundred years ahead, Temple is a sparking dynamo of activity."

He snorted but did not deride. Then: "We've put a bounty on kakuy."

"That's phenomenally dumb, don't you think?"

A half-shrug. "It was Kun Mi's idea. You have to let her have a few, sometimes, just so she feels useful. All across the Provinces, people are shooting monsters and beasts, stringing them up at the temple door."

"Bears and wolves? Please. The forest will burn and the field will wither – I have yet to see you shoot the sky."

To my surprise, he nodded. "In the burning, things were simpler. The gods slept – or rather, the gods were on our side. They were human creatures, invested in the welfare of humanity above all else. The superior species, the chosen ones. They felt rage, and love; they were there for each unborn child, sent angels and demons to harvest souls. Then the kakuy woke, and suddenly the gods were real, and they cared as much for the ant as the human, and we weren't special any more."

"You know it's better that way, don't you? Being part of something bigger than ourselves – it is better."

"I think the best of all would be a world without gods."

"Then you're fine. The kakuy aren't gods. They are . . . no

more and no less than the wind and the sea. Georg? You do understand, don't you?"

He nodded again, slow, and I thought he would speak, but the nodding was heavy, lolling. I rose quietly and, for the first time in my life, saw Georg Mestri sleep.

Balance the kitchen knife in your hand.

Here, this way, this gleam of the blade. Quick and easy, through the windpipe; no one will hear him scream. Steal his shoes, steal his coat. I know my trade. Everything changes. Everything dies. I do not fear dying. I am not sure how I feel about killing. Kill him now, to protect a world without killing.

Vae is pulled into the river, Lah's final breath is my own, Yue walks away, ash in her hair and boots crunching on snow. What would they say, in this slumbering calm?

Do it, thunders Georg. Do it, do it, do it!

Lah sits in that place in my mind where my own thoughts should be, says nothing at all, and pretends to meditate.

Temple has an inquisition; is there not a kind of confession there, an admittance that even the gentlest of doctrines sometimes run hard into a crueller reality?

I have never seen Georg sleep before. He seems almost human.

Do it, don't do it, do it, don't do it, what will be the consequences in a hundred years' time? What will be the consequences now, when they kill me slow?

I wander to his desk. Let my fingers trail over the apparatus of his life. His inkstone is secured with a passcode and a biometric sensor. His drawers contain the bare minimum for a functional spymaster — stationery, a charging cable, emergency solar battery and torch, a gun. One is locked, but largely for show. I remove the drawer above it and reach down inside the hollow to release the locking mechanism from the inside. Slide it open.

Inside are a map and a little bee-like drone, its translucent wings folded, the solar panels on its back streaked with dried dirt and rain. Its belly has been opened to release the package it carried within, which lies next to it now — a tiny capsule, a similar size and shape to those I used to hide around Vien, all those winters ago. I unscrew one out of curiosity, find it empty, turn it this way and that, imagining its contents, the tiny coils of film it once held. Put it back. Unfold the map. It is scrawled with markings added and erased, lines flowing across Magyarzag, heading south through the ruins of Beograd, towards Isdanbul. If I had a camera, I would photograph it; all very interesting stuff that Nadira would love to . . .

I do not, and she is dead.

Instead, I smooth it out a little on the desk and study its movements. Georg should be piling in his troops to Plovdiq, but a loop circles a place further to the southeast, bypassing the city altogether. Martyza Eztok, inquisition archive. I press my index finger into the name, watching how the joint bends back under pressure, then release it, fold the map, close the drawer, lock it, return to Georg on the couch.

He looks, for a brief moment, innocent. He should have been a surgeon, perhaps, or a teacher. There is another life where I would have felt confident with my life in his hands.

I drape a blanket around his shoulders, tuck it in so the cold night does not disturb him, leave him sleeping, tea cooling on the table, and let myself out.

That night I dreamed of dust.

I dreamed of coal tunnels beneath the earth, of being trapped in black, of coughing blood, of flashes of light fading and the smell of sulphur.

I dreamed of bones and children, of the forest and the flood. Temple was wrong not to build shrines in the landfill mines and the poisoned places; we were wrong not to honour the hands that made the burnt yellow wasteland. They had made it for the sakes of their children, after all.

I dreamed of a world on fire, and no rain came.

Chapter 50

The end came on New Year's Eve.

I had no idea it was New Year's Eve until Colas, drunk, raised a bottle and hollered, "Happy new year, Pityr! I thought they should shoot you but actually, I've almost grown fond of your miserable weasel face!"

Then he poured wine for one, drained it in a single gulp, burped and started singing a Temple song, until Qathir hissed that they didn't sing those any more and to keep his mouth shut in case someone upstairs heard.

In the shuttered temples, Medj should have been giving talks on renewal, change, on letting go; on seeing the past with clarity, the future with hope. Instead, the radio waves played newly penned patriotic ditties, of which most would vanish without a trace and maybe one or two had a catchy, key-changing chorus that you could whistle under your breath.

"Tum tum te tum, brotherhood and man, something something, beneath the crimson tum te tum . . ."

The radio in Colas' office had been getting more bilious as the war crawled on, no sign of peace, no sign of Yue, no sign that her visit to Georg's office had been anything more or less than another one of his shows of power, another stupid game. "I say we firebomb Isdanbul," offered a punter, hungry, cold, looking for something to blame. "If it saves one of our boys' lives, it's worth it! Council should just give up; that's the only reasonable thing to do. Why are they hurting their own people like this?"

The winter cold froze the pipes, put thin sheets of ice on top of even the steaming biomass pits, locked the fog in the evening air as if time had stopped when it should have billowed. It crept into every corner of the kitchen and house, sapping away warmth like a closing shadow, until everyone huddled against the stove in tighter and tighter knots, driven to it by a dark they could not overcome. Knives moved slowly down the chopping board, fingers turning numb. People shuffled, lead-legged, through the streets, blood a thick treacle in stiffened veins. Someone said there were parades later, military marches, but no one seemed very keen. The dignitaries of the house were gone elsewhere, to the Assembly perhaps, to the old, wide boulevards to watch soldiers tramp up and down through the snow; to the front lines, wherever they were. The kitchen turned the lights down early, and Colas reluctantly poured a dram of alcohol for all his staff, forgetting me, and managed a few inspirational words.

"Well, yes. Well done. We'll do better next year. To peace and victory."

"To peace and victory," mumbled the kitchen, and no one met anyone else's eyes as they drained their thimbles down.

I did not stay awake for midnight. An early night was a blessing, a rare, gorgeous relief. I lay, cold, knees tucked to my chin, and thought I heard drumming and a distant snatch of song, but then the wind turned and carried it away again, and I was so deeply asleep when the bolts drew back that I didn't wake until she shook my shoulder and called my name again.

"Ven. Ven!"

She hadn't turned on the single light in the room but, behind her, her guard carried a wind-up torch, light turned to the floor beside my face. I blinked bleary recognition into my eyes, and, not quite understanding, murmured: "What in the name of sun and moon are *you* doing here?"

Farii smiled. I could not remember ever having seen her smile, not even when Ull was alive. It was the tired grin of an ageing grandmother who has just been given the bad diagnosis she already knew.

"I wish to defect to the Council. And you wish to escape, yes?"

"Wouldn't say no."

"I think we can help each other."

There comes a time when there is no time left.

So here, without thought, without time to think about the consequences, only actions:

Change into a new set of clothes, military, so warm, so thick, woven wool and the smell of nothingness, of not-sweat, not-steam, not-oil, not-damp, not-mould, the smell of clean is distracting, mustn't get distracted.

Put on a pair of shoes, and for a moment I fumble with the laces and can't quite remember how this is done. There is something alien, heavy, pinching and hard wrapped around my feet; was this how shoes always felt?

Put on a low captain's hat, tucked down tight to hide as much of my face as possible. Turn the collar up on my coat against the cold and prying eyes. Farii's guard is called Yoko; she has a car prepared. We are just going to walk out, the three of us, she says – it is fine, everything is settled. No one will stop us. Come, come. The time for trust is now.

I hesitate in the doorway, and Farii looks back at me, already halfway out, a winter coat wrapped tight around her body, deerskin boots up to her knees. "They will kill me too, when they find out," she declares, voice of stone. "They'll kill me, just like they killed Ull, and make it look like an accident."

I nod, dig my hands into my pockets, tuck my chin into my chest and follow her out.

Chapter 51

Stairs I've never taken, down to a courtyard I've never been in. There are some guards here, huddled together against the cold. They look up, see Farii, who nods at them once, and they look away. They do not glance at me, do not question my presence. There is an electric car charging off a portable battery by the gate; I wonder where they had to drag the battery from, now that the local solar panels are covered in snow and the turbines are still in the hanging air. The front of the car has a little flag stuck to it, a stiff, pointed thing depicting the seal of the Lyvodian Assembly. Yoko sits in the front, driving. I climb into the back, the narrow middle seat separating me from Farii as the doors lock shut.

We slither away in an electric hum, wheels drifting a little on settled black ice, crawling no faster than walking pace for the first few streets as we slip and slide towards the broader, gritted cyclists' roads.

It is starting to snow again. The shutters are down against the cold, and very little light peeks out through the slats. Every other street lamp has been extinguished to save electricity in this end-less, deadening winter. We pass a shrine, the gate chained shut, a scorch mark up one wall where someone tried to start a fire. I do not remember the city being so big, so tall, so dark and deep. I do not remember it being so quiet.

We do not talk until we reach the wider streets, where finally enough ice has been cleared for us to pick up speed. We pass a military convoy heading the other way, and I feel nauseous, and Farii doesn't turn her head, doesn't blink, doesn't seem to see anything at all.

A line of conifers, fat triangles rising to a bent-tipped point where the weight of ice has begun to drag the branches down. The shape of bicycles buried together beneath a mound of snow; who knows when someone will come to dig them out? A single restaurant, the lights somehow burning by a cleared rectangle of pavement, a sign on the door telling customers that if they want beer, they must bring their own.

A checkpoint, set up beneath a bridge to protect the soldiers guarding it from the worst of the wind. There are three bicycles waiting to be cleared, and for a moment I remember fleeing the city with two novices, back when the bells rang across the water. That escapade didn't end well; right now, it is impossible to imagine this one will be any better.

Yoko wound down her window as the soldiers approached, torchlight flashing onto our faces. She handed over three sets of papers and, with a little incline of her head towards Farii, said: "Chief Minister, on business."

Farii did not look at the soldiers who nodded and saluted her. One of the papers had my photo on it. I didn't know where Yoko had found it, or what it claimed. An officer said: "Good trip, Minister," and pulled off an awkward salute in the style of Maze, a gesture he still wasn't quite used to yet. Yoko smiled and, slipping the papers back into her pocket, wound the window up as we accelerated away.

On the fast road, heading east. The snow is heavier now, and we are one of only a tiny number of vehicles braving the night. All I can see through the front windscreen is falling white, picked out in cones of headlight, and the barrier of the road to our left, which we follow through a nowhere nothingland of black. The internal lights of the car are few – a couple of diodes on the dashboard, and the occasional sweep of white from a vehicle

299

attempting to travel the opposite way. The cyclists have given up, the lanes empty and bicyclesarais full as we pass, little outposts of orange light.

Yoko said: "We have enough to make the meet, but if they're not there we'll have to recharge."

"They'll be there," Farii replied, with the conviction of one who needs it to be real.

"How are we getting across the border?" I asked. "I know that Farii's face counts for a lot, but they won't let her anywhere near the front line."

Yoko answered when Farii didn't, eyes still fixed to the road. "We're going to the sea. It's all arranged."

"On both ends?"

A little intake of breath, a pause. "Council has a much stronger naval presence than either Maze or Lyvodia. They dominate the Negara Sea from the Bosphorus to Azchov. If we can get past the Brotherhood patrols, we'll be fine."

"That sounds fantastically risky. Why haven't you contacted Council already? Arranged extraction?"

"Georg has a spy in the Council."

I let out a sigh, a little nod. "Pontus."

"Georg knows everything Jia does. Everything. We can't contact Council until it's too late for Pontus to stop us; do you understand?"

"I do."

She nodded, once, sharp. "The southern army is going to defect. Merthe thinks she can bring nearly all the divisions over. We have plans, documents."

"You want to barter this for your lives."

"No." Farii had been so stiff for so long that I was almost surprised to hear her speak. For another moment she didn't turn, still regarding the darkness outside; at last, she angled her shoulders away from the window, and like the blades on top of the windmill slowly turned her head to look at Yoko, then at me. "No. It is not about our lives. I am going to be arrested as a prisoner of war; I know that. If I am lucky, Jia will see the benefit of keeping me as a figurehead, a . . . a symbol of reformation that says whatever she needs me to say. If not, she'll lock me up somewhere while she works out the best use of me. I accept that. It's the correct thing to do. We need to end this war. Kun Mi cannot accept peace. She cannot. It is impossible."

"Why?"

Now she looked at me fully, and I thought there were tears in her eyes.

"In the north, the land is burning. The river is on fire and they can't put it out. They say the kakuy are awake, they are striding from the forest in plague and ash. There are bodies in the streets in Vien, frozen in the places where they died, soot in their mouths, hands clawed, still scratching at their skin. I've seen them. Their blood is ebony. It's starting in Lyvodia too, the plague coming out of the trees like mist. We haven't seen the worst of it, but it's coming. The kakuy are coming. Georg cannot stop them, no matter how hard he tries, so he has to run. Outrun the kakuy. They cannot stop fighting, because if they stop taking land then they will be trapped between the kakuy in the north and Jia in the south, and if Jia doesn't crush them the kakuy will. The Ube is on fire. We were wrong."

I have never seen a river burn, though I remember how orange it looked in the light of the blazing forest.

I wonder whether it burns because the kakuy will it, incensed to rage by the arrogance of man, or if Georg's engineers didn't know what to do with all the waste products of their military factories. Not that it makes much difference, any more.

Farii's hand had fallen on my arm, gripping tight, the strangest human contact I had felt for months. Her eyes were wide, reflective baubles in the gloom, her fingers digging into my putty flesh as if looking for bone. I put my left hand over hers, squeezed once, and she didn't let go.

"You were inquisition. Jia will listen to you."

I sighed, and suddenly all the exhaustion that had been pushed down beneath the simple imperative of moving, of getting out alive, swelled up like the foaming tide. I slumped back into my seat, pulling my arm free of Farii's grip, pressed cold palms over aching eyes. "All right. What's to lose?"

Chapter 52

There are things which were not real, when life was lived in a kitchen, that now are.

Exhaustion, so profound and bone deep that the idea of moving my legs at more than a tree-stalk shuffle seems impossible.

The shrivelled, wrinkled, old-man hands in my lap that I hardly recognise any more.

An ache in my back that has been there for months, but which I got used to when it ached on the floor, ached by the sink. Now it aches in the soft back of a seat, and I don't know if I can handle it.

Emotions, loud as the shingle sea. They are unacceptable on the job. Farii cannot look away from the dark, in case someone glances at her with sympathy, understanding or forgiveness. Such things would break her in two, and there is no time for that now. So Georg kills Nadira, shoots Lah in the head; so the temples burn; so you run across a moonlight field and are caught. These things are facts and factually you will deal with them, because there is stuff to do. Stay alive. Hope is a trap. Sorrow is self-pity and unproductive. Watch the night; stay alive.

I can hear my heartbeat in my ears, feel it in my chest, in my back, as if bone curled like ageing paper. If I listen to my breathing, as the Medj taught, it gets faster and faster and faster, and that definitely wasn't in the manual of serene practices for stable minds. Wind and earth, I need someone to try and shoot me now. A good punch to the face. Anything to focus the mind, turn off this rising fire in my brain that is, and cannot be, spinning on the edge of hysteria.

Twenty kilometres from the sea, a checkpoint. Bored soldiers given a boring shift. We slow. Yoko hands over papers, says Farii's name, and this time, rather than scamper in deference, the men shine torches in our faces, squint at me, at Farii, until she snaps: "Are you quite done?"

"Sorry, Minister," grumbles one. "Restricted area and that."

"I understand." Prim, tolerant; a hint of annoyance. "If it will make you more comfortable, please call ahead to the general. He knows I'm coming."

The soldier is a little older than his peers. He has the face of one who knows the language of wolves, and loves them, and has no illusions that they might ever love him back. In Temple, there were often men and women such as he, people of the deepest mountains, who would stop to eat and drink at the shrine, where no one troubled them much for conversation. I wonder what dragged him to this midnight road.

The snowfall has slowed, just the occasional white flake that could be stirred-up powder shook from the ground below rather than falling from the sky. Boots crunch like breaking bones; Yoko idles out the inspection by scraping ice from the wind-screen, scratching away tight curves of crystal, the motion hiding how close her other hand rests to her gun.

The soldier compares our documents with a colleague. They nod, flick through photos, nod again. Return them to Yoko, who smiles without a word, slips them into her pocket, climbs back into the driver's seat.

"Go slow," says the man who ran with wolves. "It's a treacherous road."

The battery is nearly empty, a little warning light flashing on the car's dashboard.

Yoko checks her watch, then checks it again. On the third time checking it, less than five minutes have passed, and she is clicking her teeth, jaw popping back and forth like a hungry eel.

The restricted zone runs all the way from checkpoint to sea. Signs along the road warn: permits must be shown at all times. A few watchtowers have been erected, staring down to the water. Perhaps the Council will attempt an amphibious assault; perhaps they will bring the fleet in from the Middle Sea up the Golden Straits and try to land an army behind Brotherhood lines. Such things have been considered in great depth, it seems, but no one really believes Jia could pull it off. She is far too tepid for such things, the generals say. Perhaps.

Pontus would know, and therefore so does Georg. These towers are for people fleeing, not an army come to invade.

Four kilometres from the water's edge, we pulled into the open doors of an empty barn by a small hearth. One lamp shone in a round, storm-scarred window, a crown of icicles hanging down the edge of the roof, tinged blue where the light shaved the ice. We slithered into the gloom, cut the engine. Yoko murmured: "Wait here," and got out, pulling the wind-up torch from her pocket to shine weakly round the space. A flurry of movement, a slap of heavy foot, then a mumble of recognition, a hug, perhaps, in the darkness; the doors were drawn shut behind us, another torch flickered on, flashing across the interior of the car before pointing to Yoko's chest. She called: "It's clear."

My legs were so stiff I had to lean on the roof of the car for a moment while blood shuffled back into them. My eyes hurt from sleepless blinking. Farii squinted round the gloom of the barn, then, turning to the man who'd greeted Yoko, put both hands together in front of her and bowed. "Sea-kin," she said, and there was a weariness in her voice, a bone-deep exhaustion that ran deeper than anything I could imagine. "Thank you for your shelter."

A man in a dark blue domed hat with padded wool over his ears and a hanging oilskin down the back of his neck, heavy beige coat puffed up to a fluffy ball around his frame, returned Farii's bow. His face was deep olive stained pink by years of sun bouncing off the reflective sea; his eyes were heavy and

305

his smile long. "You lot look miserable," he blurted. "Can't be having that."

His name was Khasimav, and he kept a messy hearth.

"Yes, just move that – oh, put it on the floor – yes, don't mind – no, careful, there's – yes under that, if you just – sorry – we don't get many visitors."

The hearth usually held ten or eleven people who worked the scrubby fields that rolled down to the sea, or rode the fishing boats when the weather was calm. But the war had changed that, turned the edge of the ocean into a mess of wire and permits, patrols and passports. In the end, it had been easier to leave than stay – some joining the army, others slouching off to friendly hearths further from the front lines, where they didn't have to account for their every movement to the midnight men with guns.

Only Khasimav and his wife had stayed, and, finding them-selves with sudden space, they had taken the attitude that they could fill it. Strewn across the pantry floor were half-mended nets and broken crab pots, clogged engines and vats of stinking algae oil, buckets still reeking of fish gut and shredded scale, boots discarded by the door and torn trousers with needle and thread hanging from the half-finished patches around the knee. Khasimav dug out a few cushions from amongst the debris, slapped them hard against his thighs in clouds of dust until he felt they were suitably plumped, gestured us to sit. "Please, please!"

In the centre of the room he boiled tea, black as seaweed, slightly salty on the tongue, and added a splash of something dubbed "a little helper", which burned on the way down, tingled hot in the stomach.

Outside, a single bell jangled, disturbed by unheard footsteps in the snow. A patrol car chuntered by, the smell of petrol suffocated by the still, frozen air. Dawn was lost behind a bank of cloud, an obscure greying out of black, smothered in a blanket sky.

Yoko said: "When do—"

He silenced her with a flap of a huge, starfish hand. "The tide, the tide. We are scheduled with the tide. You can sleep a little now, if you want. Sleep a little."

Farii was already half-nodding, chin jerking in short, electric pops. I found a corner near the stove, dug myself out a little nook as I had so often done in the kitchen, unashamed. Yoko did not move but held her empty cup between two hands as if its lingering heat were the last embers of a dying star. I lay on my back, staring upwards, heart in my ears.

Above my head was a sign, ancient rusted metal polished into something sacred. Written on it were words in an archaic tongue – not one I knew fluently, but with bits and pieces I could grasp. Khasimav caught me staring, blurted: "Ah, my relic! It has been in the family for generations. It brings us fortune. Do you know what it says?"

"'No parking, 8 p.m. – 6 a.m. Fine of 6000 hryvnia.' I can't read the rest."

Khasimav stared at me, eyes so wide I thought he had choked on his own tea. Then he laughed loud enough to bring an army down, and held his chest tight in case he burst with it, and spluttered: "You're funny! Isn't he – that's so – you're so funny!" and kept on laughing until he cried.

In the middle of the night, I dream of fire without end and wake to see Farii, eyes wide next to me, gripping my arm tight. There are pins and needles in my fingers; how long has she been lying next to me, short of breath?

"The bomb," she whispers. "The bomb. The bomb that killed Ull. The bomb."

I prise my arm free of her fingers, wrap her hands in mine. But she is half-awake, half-asleep, eyes still staring at nothing. I try to find words to comfort her, and cannot, and eventually roll over to sleep and dream again.

Chapter 53

Khasimav roused us a little before midday, arms heavy with clothes.

"Yes, no – yes that will – try this one!"

We changed, sluggish and weary, into the garments he offered. Farii vanished behind a huge green hat, peaked to a cone above her coiled-up hair. Yoko wrapped the cord of a slick brown apron around her waist three times, tying it so tight I thought her eyes might pop. I swam in trousers far too big for me, pinched and wriggled into a shirt a little too tight. When we were assembled, we were three utterly misshapen sailors, as natural on the ocean as a whale to the mountain.

"You look perfect!" Khasimav exclaimed, and none of us believed him. "Just do as I say and everything will be fine. Easy easy!"

He slung nets over our backs, loading up Farii with so many buckets and bags she was less woman than walking luggage rack. "If anyone stops us, I'll do the talking," he chirruped, opening the door of the hearth into a day of crystal white and smoke-drenched grey. "Ah, see, we are blessed! The kakuy gave us fog!"

I shuddered, unsure if it was at the sudden cold or the brightness of his voice, only slightly muffled in winter weight, and followed him out the door.

The path from the hearth to the sea was a little track, impossible to see beneath its fresh covering of snow save by the spindle-black thorns of half-buried shrubs sticking out either side of it, like a saluting line of skeletons, guiding us to the water's edge. The fog thinned as we approached the shore, blasted into licking smoke by the wind off the ocean . Cracked slabs of thin ice had formed at the top of the beach, creating a shattered skin of dirty mirror above black stone, and where the soldiers had laid barricades against a potential invasion a second wall of frozen foam had grown like fingers from the earth.

Towards the water's edge, the pounding of the sea had kept the ice from forming in more than tiny, quickly made, instantly broken salty lumps. The fishing boats of the village lay just above the high-tide line, most covered in oiled cloth and listing to one side, untouched and smothered in caverns of snow. Khasimav's was one of the few that still stood propped up above its wooden tracks, mast tipped back onto the deck, propeller hooded and still. It seemed, to my uneducated eye, little more than a skiff for catching the occasional tiny shad from a school of summer fish. I looked from it to the waves as they crashed into the shore. The sea popped with white, hissed and grumbled as if some hidden city were trying to rise from its depths, only for the raging water to smother it down again. I wondered what the kakuy of this place might be; black, perhaps, as its ancient namesake, with the shining body of a jellyfish that, when it reared up, revealed teeth of basalt beneath its belly, stinging tendrils longer than a city street with barbs flecked bloody. Temple had always taught that the kakuy of the sea had been the first to rise in anger during the Burning Age. The cataract-eyed spirits of the deep were less patient than their kin of earth and stone.

"Up, up, yes, come on now!" chanted Khasimav, hoicking Farii up the side of the balancing little vessel with the dignity of an errant pup. "You, priest, and you, soldier! We push!"

I followed his flapping directions, pressing both hands to the ice-crackling, salt-crusted, sea-bitten timber of the boat, and made to push when a voice called out: "Khasimav! Good neighbour!"

It was not an unpleasant voice, young and familiar, but I saw Khasimav tense, smile locked and eyes tight as if stung on the leg by stingray barbs. He glanced up to Farii, on the higher deck of the boat, and half-nodded. She returned the gesture, then vanished from sight, slipping down into the interior. Then he turned, waved at the approaching figures coming through the thin shore mist, called their names, hollered: "And greetings to you too, kin of sky and sea!"

There were two of them, both dressed in mismatched, over-sized military uniforms, as if the quartermaster who'd bartered for their gear had turned up drunk to the storehouse and come away with the dregs of some other war. Neither could be older than twenty-one, and though both had pistols on their hips, only one carried a rifle, the barrel glistening with frost. The boy who'd called out Khasimav's name approached, smiling brightly – a neighbour, perhaps, who'd joined the army for something to do, a bit of a laugh. Behind him, a woman with a young face that looked already like the older woman she would become, picked with furrows between her brow and curls around the corner of her mouth, managed the barest quiver of a smile to Khasimav before her eyes swept, grey as the ocean, to Yoko and me.

"Heading out?" asked the boy. "Got the authority?"

"When don't I?" demanded Khasimav, in the voice of one who had played this game before. He started patting his jacket, his pockets, fumbling around with exaggerated deliberation, while the boy smiled – a familiar ritual between them.

"Who's this?" the woman barked, and I looked away from her moon-rock stare.

"Oskar and Lin; my new crew. Oskar, Lin – say hello."

"Hi," I mumbled, as Yoko tilted her chin in greeting, and for a moment I thought she was going to betray us with her sheer bearing, one military woman greeting another. But Khasimav interjected with a cry of "Ah, here!" and pulled out a tatty piece of much-fumbled laminated paper. "Wouldn't catch me going to do my job without *au-thor-is-ation*, would you?" he drawled, the grin of a troublemaker still yearning to make trouble.

The boy read it and, still playing the game, laughed and waved it in Khasimav's face. "I don't see any mention of your friends here."

Yoko had a gun, hidden somewhere in her clothes. It would take her a while to get to it, of course; I'd probably be expected to tackle the woman with the rifle. If I was lucky, the cold would lead to a misfire, but even then I'd need to get to her before she had time to react and just hope Khasimav had the good sense to hit the boy before he could draw his gun. The odds were even, I concluded, given the distance between us.

"Of course they is – look, there. Two crew."

"Ahul and Pree are your licensed crew, not these two."

"Come on, it says two crew – two crew! I've got two crew."

"Khasimav . . . "

"You know what it's like. Ahul's gone done a bunk to be with his family, may skies rain upon him, and Pree's still holed up with his leg. I gotta go out with someone – or do you want to explain to my missus why you let me drown alone?"

The mention of Khasimav's missus clearly had a stronger effect on the boy than any imprecation or threat of thunder. He glanced at his colleague, who was perhaps less aware of the wrath of Khasimav's wife, then with a sigh passed the tattered authorisation back. "Get them registered," he barked, trying to infuse his voice with an authority that had already been lost. "Next time I can't look the other way."

Yoko's shoulders rolled down like the last curl of a breaking wave against a rocky shore. I realised I'd been leaning my weight into my left leg, ready to spring across the distance between myself and the soldiers. "You were always such a nice boy, when you weren't a little shit," Khasimav cackled gleefully, which was the closest I imagine he ever came to saying thank you.

Chapter 54

I was a terrible sailor. I had grown up far from the sea and couldn't work out what was worse: huddling inside in the black depths of the ship as it rocked from one imminent disaster to the next, straps straining to hold the buckets and nets tight against the swaying, sure-to-kill-us-all hull of the boat, or clinging to the side on deck, both arms wrapped around the railing as the horizon dipped below my feet, then rolled up to tower above my head like the sky itself would fall. Only Khasimav's utter disregard for our obvious imminent doom convinced me that we weren't, in fact, about to be drowned in a hurricane. Seeing my foam-drained, burning face as I leaned over the side unable to puke, he guffawed, "Nice day for it, priest!"

"I'm a spy, not a priest," I growled, but he couldn't hear me over the slapping of the sea.

A little boat on a big ocean need not meet a storm for the experience to be thoroughly vile. I drank the ginger tea that Farii brought me from the gloomy cabin below and wished that the salt would freeze on my face to take away some of the blazing nausea prickling over my skin. When I finally did throw up, Khasimav gave a great cry of victory, as if some glorious rite had been accomplished akin to the first prayers at a newly raised shrine, and I felt a little better.

We sailed south into the night. The sun did not set as a visible orb; the horizon was an endless curve of bruised grey-brown, smeared with muddy blue. The cloud was so complete that it diffused everything into one formless monoculture, hard to tell where sea met sky. For a while, it was the grey of the pale flagstones of the Temple of the River; then it was the grey of the dry pebble shore; then, it was a thick, boundless slate; and finally, a starless, shapeless, worldless void.

Lost in a forest, Lah would say, you are not alone. All around you is life, living.

This doesn't play well with my ego, I'd reply, and Lah would laugh.

That, they'd say, is precisely the point.

In the middle of the sea, the only sounds are the water and the wind – endless, gobbling, slurping hunger of sucking and spitting, slapping and slithering against the side of the boat. Khasimav has turned off all illumination but a little red light in the pilot's cabin. Farii sleeps below, Yoko keeping watch at the prow as if she might still be able to do something against some invisible threat, as if the gun buried in her clothes has any power against the ocean. With no light, no distinction between sky and sea, we are floating to some deathly land, cut off from the rest of the world, and it is terrifying, and, in a way, it is perfect peace.

For a moment, I am not afraid, and Georg is not inside my head. I had forgotten how good it felt to be free.

Beneath us, there is life. Schools of silver fish feasting on white-fleshed critters that forage amongst the clawed scuttling things of the shallow sea floor that hide from the bug-eyed creatures of the darker depths. The giant squid, flushed crimson, care nothing for the deeds of men; neither do the kakuy that lurk, tentacles spooled around some volcanic vent, at the very bottoms of the great oceans of the world. They only cared when the world was burning, and their wrath was as disinterested, amoral, potent and inescapable as the tsunami upon the gentle shore.

Instinctively, I offer them a blurted prayer. Not for blessing or safe passage – these words have no meaning to the great spirits

313

of the deep – but for my own peace of mind, and in wonder at what it is to sail across the surface of a forest.

Then Yoko was by my side, shaking me, and I must have dozed, and she was whispering: "A light."

I followed her finger, and didn't see it at first, then it flashed, tiny and white, and we both turned to look at the red glow of the pilot's cabin, and Khasimav's face was drawn and tight.

"A ship?" Yoko asked, as we slid into the relative warmth of the little square of buttons and wheel that was Khasimav's domain.

"Yeah."

"Another fishing boat?"

"Maybe. Probably not."

We watched it a while longer. I imagined it getting bigger, nearer, knew I was imagining it, that paranoia was seeped into every part of my being. Then it was definitely bigger, nearer, not paranoia at all, a true thing, and Khasimav barked: "You, hold the wheel steady," and I did, while he and Yoko scurried to raise the triangular sail, the boat lurching to the side as it caught the wind as if stung by a wasp. This done, Khasimav scuttled back into the cabin, took the wheel from me and turned so we caught the wind, deck creaking and fabric snapping taut. "Check the fuel," he murmured to Yoko, who nodded once and vanished below decks. I waited, back pressed to the wall of the cabin, smelling the sudden stench of processed algae as Yoko pulled back canisters and peered into pipes, before she returned and said, "We're full now." Khasimav grunted an acknowledgement.

From below, Farii emerged, blinking and weary, her face an alien thing in the eye-aching glow. "Problem?"

"Maybe not."

Yoko prodded one finger towards the light on the horizon, perhaps a little nearer than before, perhaps no. Farii licked her lips, inclined her head and watched, the fear deep in her too.

"Wind's in our favour," murmured Khasimav, an attempt at brightness that his voice couldn't quite carry off. "And she's not exactly a racer."

For nearly half an hour, we four stood pressed tight in the cabin, sea-sickness forgotten as engine and sail ploughed us through the dark. Then Khasimav, the only one with the right to say it, said what we all knew: "She's coming for us."

"Patrol ship?" asked Yoko, sharp, hard.

"Maybe."

"How long do you think until they reach us?"

"Maybe an hour."

"How close to shore can we be in an hour?"

"Not far. But we're still a long way north."

"Can we call for help?"

"Sure – if you want every ship on the sea to know who you are."

"Ever been stopped by a patrol boat before?" I asked.

"Only once, random check."

"Did they search the ship?"

"Yes."

Farii said: "Send out the call."

Khasimav sighed, tutted, reached for his radio with a muttered "My missus is going to kill me."

"Wait." I caught his hand. "Don't mention Farii."

"Why not?" snapped Yoko. "You know they're looking for her."

"Yes, but they probably don't know she's on this boat. If you say her name out loud, every Brotherhood vessel in a hundred miles will come crashing down on us."

"And every Council ship too, no? We're in contested waters, and they have the stronger fleet."

"Even so – we want Council ships in force, not Brotherhood."

"That's a fine trick if you can do it," muttered Farii, a flicker of her hand to the radio. "I'd love to see you try."

I took the microphone from a sceptical Khasimav and intoned, at his command, the distress call, a call for help across all frequencies, Council fleet help us, help us, sounding far too calm for anyone to take us seriously, I felt. Then I added: "Yue Taaq. This is a message for Yue Taaq. It's Ven. It's me. Help me."

Chapter 55

A chase at sea is a slow affair.

I hunched over the radio as Yoko and Farii watched the light growing nearer, highlighting form. A patrol vessel for certain, a huge kite sail unfurled above its prow, its engines growling, the scars of bio-resin glistening in jagged lines across the hull. We ran before the wind, but the bigger ship was faster, the pinpoint shards of a dozen smaller lights visible along its hull and deck as it drew nearer. It hollered at us over the radio, then by loudspeakers, sound blasted to semi-incomprehensible gibberish by the sea, and we ignored it. It flashed lamps at us in a dizzying pattern of ons and offs, which Khasimav roughly translated as a command to halt and the sailors' equivalent of cussing.

When it fired the first flare, I was astonished to see the ocean revealed in pale red beneath us, to find that we were still on the surface of this planet, not spinning through some endless void but bound by the laws of common nature. Khasimav clicked his teeth, sighed: "Warning shot next," and barely were the words out of his mouth than an unseen explosion smacked into the night, and a hundred metres to our right the water slapped up in a gout of white, reflective crimson and black.

"59mm gun," mused Yoko in the voice of one who had sat exams on the topic and not particularly enjoyed the experience. "Probably a Kraken-class cutter."

"Is that good?" I asked, and she did not answer.

Another shot broke the sea to our right, the retort quickly

swallowed by the rolling water. Behind us, the host of little red lights rose up from the deck, swerving in the wind like battered seagulls before regaining a little stability as the ship launched its drones towards us.

"It's all right," Yoko murmured, as they rose around us. "They're mostly just for surveillance."

"Mostly?"

"Bet you wish you were a proper priest now," rattled Khasimav, all grin and no humour. The next warning shot hit so close to the prow that we bucked above the shockwave it sent out like riders on a wild horse, and Khasimav uttered a curse of ancient foulness between gritted teeth.

"They're launching inflatables," murmured Yoko, head turned to the ship behind us.

"Oh good – they're not going to blow us up, just shoot us."

"I don't know if they'd rather arrest me for a public trial or shoot me and lose my body," mused Farii, with the stiffness of a critic discussing a show of dubious quality. "That decision may be above their pay grade, of course, which makes it more likely they'll at least arrest me first."

"They don't know you're here," I offered brightly, "so they'll probably just shoot you by mistake." Yoko glowered, but Farii gave a single burst of laughter, that died as soon as it had lived. I shrugged. "Sorry. Just saying the obvious."

"Why would you do that?" scowled Yoko.

Outside the cabin, a drone was bumping against the turning side of the boat, its red lights flickering as it buzzed up and down like a curious bird. Farii flapped one hand at it instinctively, a leader used to the world obeying her every whim, then scowled when it managed to settle on the deck, a squat, hunkered thing, blinking at us with its salt-scoured camera. Behind us, the two boats lowered from the larger ship hit the water, rising high on a wave before dropping so fast one soldier nearly lost their seat in the churning acceleration of the moment. They cast off from their tie lines almost together, rushing towards us low in the water, a single headlamp on each prow, vanishing and reappearing with

317

each swell of the sea. "Inflatable" seemed an odd description for the speeding vessels tearing down on us. A resin hull on a black carbon weave, the only part that appeared inflatable was a band of soft padding around its rim. Everything else was spotlight, soldier, gun and carbon.

Yoko had her weapon drawn, but Farii put a hand on her arm, shook her head. "There's still a chance," she breathed. "I'll talk to them, I'll . . . there's still a chance."

No one in the cabin believed it, and no one said a word.

As the first inflatable drew level, Farii stepped out of the cabin, hands raised. I don't know what she called out to them, but her words were lost across the water. She called again; again, the words were snatched away. A bump on our right announced that the other inflatable was against us, reaching up with hooks to snag onto the side. Khasimav throttled down the engine, shaking his head. "Well," he sighed. "I was hoping to die better."

"How better?" I asked.

"You know when you fall asleep after sex?"

"Seems harsh on your sexual partner."

A head popped above the railing on the right, followed a second later by the barrel of a gun, lugged up awkwardly by someone barely holding onto the hooked ladder that swayed and bounced against the tug of the sea.

"At least the fishes will be well fed!" chuckled Khasimav as the soldier rose a little higher over the side, struggling to hoick their gun into a more threatening pose.

I heard the whistling of the shell a second before it struck – or perhaps I imagined it, my mind retrospectively seeking to make sense of chaos. The quality of its impact was different from the warning shots that had been blasted our way – less of the sea tearing apart, and more fire and air compressing and expanding in a crimson rush. The flash of light was bright enough for me to briefly pick out the inside of the cabin, and it took me a moment to realise that the shell had fallen not on us but behind, a few metres off the prow of the closing cutter.

"Mother of—" began Khasimav. He didn't have time to say

anything more before the next shot landed, now to the right of the enemy ship, which lurched as if shoved by a playground bully, lights flickering, several going out. The one soldier who'd nearly made it onto the deck slid as Khasimav slammed his hand against the throttle, jumping us back into motion, the hooked-on ladder slipping along nearly the whole length of the railing as we chugged away from the stalled boats by our side. Farii, having perhaps thought twice about negotiation, launched herself back into the cabin as we accelerated, blurting: "Who is firing, who is firing, *who is* . . ."

Either side, the inflatables revved up, easily matching pace, and finally from the left came gunfire, rattling down the side of the ship. Khasimav let go of the wheel, grabbed Farii by the top of her head and dragged her down to the low cabin floor in a bundle. I lurched to one side, grabbed the door on the opposite side of the cabin as glass crackled and smashed, and tumbled out onto the deck. Yoko was a few feet in front of me, crawling on her belly, eyes fixed on the ladder still attached to our right-hand railing.

For a moment, I thought the marine who'd been clinging on so desperately had let go, dropped back into the water. Then a hand crawled its way over the side of the ship, scrambling for purchase, and Yoko had her gun drawn. She waited, until the top of the head was visible, and emptied out three shots. One of them missed, and I don't know if the second hit or if the shock of sudden motion and violence was enough, but with a gasp and a splash, the marine let go, tumbling backwards into the ice-black water below.

Another burst of gunfire to our left, ripping along the side of the boat, smashing out the thin red light of the cabin and raining glass and splinters across the deck. The drone that had managed to land crawled a little to one side, curious as a cat, the camera turning to examine the scene, before Yoko kicked out hard and caught something that cracked and crunched. The drone wheezed and tried to take off, but one of its four blades wouldn't spin, and it tipped itself onto the side and spun, an upturned beetle bouncing on the deck.

Another smack in the night, another whistle and thump of cannon. I peered up, tried to see its source, thought I saw the flash of something far-off and huge, spitting pinkish-sodium fire. A cloud of little red lights was drawing near from the same direction — more drones — a sudden burst of motion above us as the cutter's drones detected the incoming swarm. This time I heard the crack as the distant ship fired, the shell striking something on the patrol vessel behind. I half-expected an explosion, the rupture of a tank or some profound sign of desperation. Instead, I heard the creak of carbon bending out of form, the crack of resins popping and the sharp, hard snicker-snacker of the biopolymer frame ripping like ribs shattering along the spine.

Then the little cloud of cutter drones rose higher, and I saw something yellow flash in the belly of a half-dozen of the buzzing machines.

The bombs they dropped were tiny — little more than marbled grenades — but they were enough. Some fell on the deck, some fell in the water around, picking apart the dark in yellow-white, tearing through the hull of Khasimav's boat like bolts through tissue. The world rocked, lurched to the left, tipped down hard. I tucked my knees under my chest and wrapped my hands over my head as the world around crunched and spat sizzling salt, heard cries below and the creak of resin tearing apart.

Then the new batch of approaching drones was on us, and suddenly the air above was full of little machines smashing head first into each other like drunken wasps, of blades caught on blades and swirling, whining, messy flight. I smelt burning algae oil and resin-coated timber, tasted acrid smoke and heard a high-pitched scream in my left ear that drowned out even the sea. I moved one hand, and it seemed to travel incredibly slow. Tried to move it faster and knew that, though I had the physical capacity, the connections between mind and fingers weren't having any of it, that my mind couldn't conceive of motion.

Another smack of light, another crump of something striking the cutter behind, and this time I knew it had hit something flammable because there was a rising mirrored glow across the ocean, picking out the shape of the drones falling like spring blossoms from the sky. Yoko's head emerged in the reflected darkness of a world turned to fire, and she was dragging Farii behind her by the armpits, hissing something at me which I couldn't hear over the singing in my ears and the tearing of the sea. I wrapped one arm around Farii's chest and heaved, and was surprised to feel how wet and cold Farii was, catching in the light of a rising flame behind us a smear of blood across Yoko's face as she mouthed more inaudible commands.

The inflatables either side of the ship had stopped firing, and as I dragged Farii further up I felt the boat tip, a little at first, and then irrefutable, nose-first, and thought for a moment we were being sucked down beneath some great wave. Now the shape of Yoko's mouth had some meaning to it, and I dragged Farii backwards, hooking one loose arm across my shoulders and hauling her towards the stern, which began to rise like a closing drawbridge. Glass tinkled all around, and I managed to gasp: "Khasimav? Where's Khasimav?" but Yoko just grabbed Farii's other arm and pulled her, nearly climbing now over the wreckage of the cabin, away from the sinking prow. I looked down into the blackness of the stairwell at our backs and thought I glimpsed a face turned up to me, eyes closed, something dark smeared across its skin. The water rose from beneath it, through the shattered hull, briefly floating it a little nearer to me, or perhaps I was descending as the ship did, all things in motion. I wondered if the fish gave thanks for the food they ate. I wondered if there was a place at the bottom of the sea where the creatures of the deep sucked on the white flesh of the kakuy as it flaked away like dust in sunlight.

Then the water was rising, pricking at my toes, and I scrambled hand-over-hand up the sloping deck of the ship towards the stern, where the motor had lifted from beneath the sea, blades still spinning on loose momentum, flopping in the air. I crawled onto the hull of the boat itself as we began to tip over, grabbing the limp form of Farii and hauling as Yoko crawled up with me. A drone fell into the water a few metres away, sending up a splash

321

that shivered through my sodden clothing. In the distance, the patrol cutter was now thoroughly on fire, the two inflatables rushing back towards it to rescue the sailors jumping from its blazing decks.

I didn't know how we would fall, what it was like to be on a ship that was drowning. Yoko was shaking Farii, snarling, wake up, wake up, and I saw Farii begin to blink, fingers tightening around her loyal guard's arms – perhaps too late. The boat jutted upwards, stern tipped to the sky like a spire, and balanced there for a moment. Perhaps we would stay like this, bobbling like a bottle through the sea. Then it began to roll to the side, and I jumped, hurling myself as far as I could as the broken vessel slammed into the water, hull stuck up into the sky and the flat, shattered deck below, flinging us into the darkness of the sea.

Chapter 56

In the winter wood, the kakuy makes no sound as it moves across the snow, nor leaves any trace.

Tseonom is buried beneath a mudslide, and in Tinics the forest burned, and the kakuy too.

The forest will return, of course, one day. One day, there will be nothing but forest on the earth, when humankind is gone. The forest was always better at co-operation than man.

In the middle of a sea that is a forest, teeming with life, I felt the boat lurch beneath me and jumped as far as I could away from it, into the frozen water. It hit like stone, slamming the breath out of me, flushing up my nose and straight into my brain, as if the fluid sac that cushioned my skull would pop. I pawed at the surface of the water as I fell and kept on sinking. I had not imagined it was possible to be colder than the deepest ice of the winter wood, but in this place my arms were wet sand, everything so slow. To drown starts as a constriction in the throat, a closing in of the chest, a popping of final breath from nose and mouth, as heaving, heaving, heaving as you swallow down the need to swallow for air, a gasping, gasping, gasping, each moment this will be the one where you inhale the sea and fall like a stone, fingers of blue, eyes of red, at least this will only be a moment, only a little, terrible moment.

I hit the surface, hauled in air, bobbed down, water rushing up my nose, brain sloshing in salt, surfaced again, tried to swing my legs up, to float, saw the sky lit up in silver-white as something burst in the night, and in that instant understood the need to scream, not in fear or hysteria but pure frustration, pure inexpressible grief that this was it, this was how it ended, a thing without words, all the things I'd never do, never be. Managed to surface again, tilted my head back so that water sloshed into my ears, choked out water and felt my back begin to bend upwards, every breath shivering fast as a mouse's racing heart.

There were no stars above. The waves pitched me side to side, constantly tipping a mask over my face so I spat salt and blinked fire, unable to predict their motion, arms floating like flotsam, dead in the water. The burning patrol ship was a pyre in the dark, bright enough to cast a glow on the low sky. Somewhere nearby, there was the ship that had destroyed it, coming for us, but whether it was five minutes or five hours away I couldn't tell.

I tried to fight the sea, to find stability in its motion, and couldn't. I tried to relax into it, to let it carry me, to trust that I was still here, still breathing, still alive, and for a little while that was easier, and I could focus on shivering, shivering, shivering, until I wasn't shivering any more. I felt my shoulders roll down from my ears, as Lah had taught us back in the temple – let go, let go. These stories you hold in your body, these stories you hold in your mind – let go. Every time my ears rose and fell between water and air, a roaring, then a silence – so much easier to listen to the roaring than the silence, but listen, listen, here it is, that quiet place that is inside as well as outside. I felt the salt seep into the raw skin of my scrubbed red hands, and for a while the fire was pleasant, cleansing, and I knew that I would heal, if I did not die, and I didn't want to die, and I knew as surely as anything I had ever known that I might, and I might not. Both these knowings seemed so certain, so absolute, it was almost impossible to imagine they could live together, and yet like the turning of the sea they rolled over me. Now I breathe and will live; now I do not and will die.

Around the wreckage of the cutter, the inflatables circled, their mission of murder now one of rescue. The pilots had their orders, but a higher order prevailed on the ocean: you saved your friends. The sea would take care of the rest. The sea did not care for prayers.

A light shone in my eyes. I tried to swat at it, irritated, and found that my left hand could move, a little, a limb far away, belonging to another nation state. The light blinked at me, then swung to my right, then swung back, then swung once more to my right, like a hungry gull circling the smell of snacks. I looked where its light flickered and saw a shape, stable and black in the moving world. The drone danced towards it, bright across the water, picking out the upside-down hull of the fishing boat. It stayed there, hovering, light flashing, waiting. I tried to kick, on my back, a little, and didn't go anywhere. I rolled onto my front and tried to swim, the head-spinning, shoulder-slapping crawl of a creature not used to water. That took me a little closer, but so slow, so slow. The distance could not have been fifteen metres, and it was swimming through tar, swimming with the great kakuy of the deep already half-entangled round my legs, her tentacles embedded through the tears in my skin, running all the way into my veins, the two of us already one, like the roots of the tree in the soil of the earth. My arms smacked the water like falling sacks, fingers spreading and wrists buckling beneath the waves, and it occurred to me that if I didn't make it to the hull of the broken ship I would drown for sure. Five metres, and a wave tipped my head under, and when I surfaced again I didn't know where I was, couldn't see, couldn't make my legs kick, arms drag, then saw the light of the drone again, bright white to my right, and threw myself towards it, fingers stretched, as if I could bridge the gap by will alone. A turn of water picked me up from behind and pushed me, sudden, hard, towards the inverted vessel, and my fingers scrambled and scratched against the scars of old, scrubbed-off barnacle, ancient algae and newer resin.

I lunged to find a grip, nails cracking as I slid, the same water that had flung me forward trying to haul me back. Lost my hold, fell into the water, swallowed salt and felt my eyes tear as ice filled my nostrils and every tiny tube and empty corner of my skull, then was pushed forward again, grabbing for the thin ridge of the hull, right hand missing, left catching by a few curled fingers as I clung on. I felt every muscle in my arm stretching, could feel the tiny tendons where they joined, the full length of each fibre and the shape it made as my fingers began to give way, sliding back like a broken lock. I began to fall, for the last time, and as I did a hand, an arm, a shoulder flung itself up from the other side of the hull and caught me by my forearm as I slid backwards, holding me tight.

I looked up, saw the pallor of Yoko's face as she draped herself, bent almost double over the ridge of the hull, bringing her left arm round to join her right and snatching me before I could fall. I swung my right arm round, held her tight, and for a moment the two of us hung in precarious balance on the slippery, tossing curve of the boat, her feet braced as I slithered and slipped to some sort of purchase. Her eyes were wide, black in the brightness of the drone's light, her hair riddled across her face like seaweed. Somewhere, once, she had perhaps seen images of drowning women returned as demons, flesh bloated and skin shining, swollen, liquid things, and in her face now was a determination that bordered on fury – not her. Not today. I did not know when I had last seen – if I had ever seen – such a will to live. I tried to remember what that might have felt like, to steal a little of her fire for my own, and as she pulled me in I let myself flop beside her, our grips changing as we locked tight into a woven fortress of hand and arm, sprawled across the tipping hull of the boat.

There was a ship. It was a destroyer of some kind, low in the water, hull textured like the skin of the shark. It launched inflatables, as the cutter that pursued us had, two points of bright white rushing towards us across the sea. Above, drones zipped back and forth over the water, one staying bright above us, catching us in a fountain of light. Another hovered some twenty metres away, and I thought I saw a glimpse of someone in the water, and couldn't be sure, and didn't know, and held onto Yoko like a child in the forest.

Don't let go

Vae

Don't let go

Behind us, the cutter burned. In the past, the fires would have been of gasoline, yellow and black. Today, it is the pop-pop-popping of biomatter resin straight from the vats, flares of pale pink and flashes of spring-soft green, bursts of lithium white and blue when the batteries burst, the stink of silica, black puffs of carbon from melting fibres and withering corn as the cellulose bonds in the hull started hissing and breaking apart in the flaming, turning air.

Yoko, I whispered. Yoko, listen to me.

Listen to me.

If I die here—

Don't you die, priest.

If I die – I know who Pontus is.

I know who

I know

I know why Georg never killed me.

If I die—

You're not going to die, shut up!

You need to remember this.

You need to tell them.

I leant in and whispered a name in Yoko's ear. And it was the breaking apart of a world, and it was the great rain that follows the endless burning fire, and she nodded once, and we held on tight to each other's arms in the burning dark, and she said: don't let go.

The rescue boats went to the first pool of light before they came to us. Then they motored over, so slow, the cold a moment-to-moment discovery in our bones. Voices spoke words, hands reached up for our legs, hips, and I didn't let go until Yoko nodded, until even she believed it would be okay. Then I did, and slid backwards onto the rigid deck of the inflatable, saw faces that seemed barely human, felt someone wrap something that was meant to be warm and felt cold around me, heard commands, questions, didn't answer. Floated a little while in the dark and watched the burning remains of the ship that had pursued us tearing apart. Tried to say a prayer for the dead. Thought of Khasimav's corpse, perhaps only a hull's width away from me. Perhaps there was still air inside, perhaps he wasn't dead at all but screaming for help. I leaned over to press my ear against the hull to listen, but someone stopped me, pulled me back, said something polite, or maybe rude, and probably had a point. Yoko watched me as we pulled away from the wreck, as if looking at a dead man.

Chapter 57

The destroyer was called the *Shearwater*. They dropped planks on rope for us to sit on rather than ask us to climb the net slung over its side. On deck, two sailors in thick, padded jackets and dark woolly hats hustled myself and Yoko towards a door, all the while asking us questions: are you bleeding, what's your name, can you tell me what day it is?

I couldn't. I had no idea. I hadn't known for a very long time.

A larger crowd stood round a more complex assembly of pulleys that had hauled up an orange stretcher, scampering to the bark of a woman's voice. A man ran past holding a yellow box slathered with warning signs; someone else pulled their gloves off with their teeth so they could load a syringe from a small, transparent bottle. Yoko stopped and stared while the sailors tried to hustle us inside.

"Farii," she said flatly, and when no one seemed to respond, she raised her voice, one arm out to lean on the wall of the ship as if her legs might finally go. "Farii. Chief Minister of Lyvodia. If she dies, you lose the war."

"Sea-kin," murmured the sailor with the most common sense, "I need you to be clear. You are saying that woman is Chief Minister?"

"Yes. We are defecting."

"Who are 'we'?"

"I am her head of security, Yoko Blagha. This is Ven of the Temple of the Lake. We are defecting. We didn't broadcast Farii's name because it would have brought the entire Brotherhood on

329

us. We only broadcast Ven's because ... " Her voice trailed off, and she looked at me, and there was something in her gaze that made me feel ashamed. Then she turned away, eyes fixed on the gaggle of sailors. "We have vital information for Jia. Only Jia."

"Sea-kin, I need you to go inside now. We need to get you warm." Yoko didn't move. "We will give the Minister the best possible medical attention."

"I am her head of security." A mantra, intoned, as Yoko did not move.

"She's safe. Please, come inside."

Yoko stood a moment longer, then nodded once, and I followed her into the warm.

There was a medical bay.

We sat in it, watched by a sailor at the door.

The doctor and nurse were nowhere to be seen. Cupboards stood open, their contents ripped out as medics ran onto deck. We were given tea, wrapped in blankets. My teeth clattered like castanets, but the sailor said we couldn't be warmed up too fast, that it would be dangerous. Drink your tea; stay here. You're safe. You're safe.

After a while, an officer, dark skin tinged with the deepest blue as if something of the ocean had grown within her, came to our beds. Tell it to me again, she said. Who are you? How did you come to be here?

I am Yoko Blagha; this is Ven of the Temple of the Lake. We are defecting.

           And the woman?

Farii of Lyvodia. How is she?

                She has a heartbeat. She is not awake.

        I need to see her.

     The doctor will bring her here soon.

                I need to see her. I am her ... her friend.

                My name is Yoko Blagha.

                    She's getting the best possible care.

                    And who are you, Ven?

There is another question here, far more interesting to this young officer. The question is: why in the name of sun and sky did we come to rescue you, shivering man, when someone much more important was on your boat? Why did we race across the sea to save your body from the deep?

I'm a spy, I replied. I have information of vital importance for the Council.

What kind of information?

I know how to win the war.

Chapter 58

Here: land. We arrived mid-afternoon, overcast, grey, thin snowy slush on the shore, a bobbing, sulky sea. My legs did not quite know how to walk for the first few steps, teetering like a baby deer.

Here: a small delegation of military types and one civic dignitary to meet us, scrambled from who knew where to say they knew not what, awkwardly assembled in haste to deal with a problem beyond their expertise or authority. An ambulance waited by the quay, charging off one of the electrical posts fuelled by the tidal turbines beneath the water. Yoko walked next to Farii's stretcher as they carried it into the back, one hand gripping Farii's. Farii did not grip back, half a dozen lines and tubes running from her flesh to a small scaffolding of bamboo that a nurse pushed alongside her.

I looked, and did not see Yue. Instead, a man who introduced himself as Nkasogi and smelt faintly of menthol and mint stood before me, pressed both his hands together and bowed. I bowed in reply, awkward, fumbling and slow, a thing almost forgotten, mumbling some half-apology. "Sea-kin," he announced, taking my arm by the elbow as if I were a dry flower about to crumble, "I have been sent by the Council to bring you home."

Home is a thousand kilometres away, inaccessible to me. Perhaps he saw this in my eyes because he pressed his hands together again and bowed a little deeper. "I have been sent," he corrected, "to bring you to Yue Taaq."

*

Farii and Yoko rode in the ambulance. Nkagosi and I rode with eight others on the back of a navy truck, heading inland. Low hills of needle-dark winter green stepped in long undulations away from the sea, hard mountains blasted to a soft bulwark by millennia of salty wind. A few cargo bicycles passed us by, heading towards the sea, and one fish truck, coasting down the side of a hill with the casual familiarity of a driver who knows every ridge and switchback and doesn't care if no one else does.

I thought I saw the lights burning in a hilly shrine up an icy path and felt a momentary stab of fear – the soldiers would come, they would shut it down, beat the Medj who guarded this place – and then no. That was in Maze and Lyvodia, where Kun Mi was queen and Georg sat behind his mausoleum desk. Here, the Medj gave thanks to the kakuy of the hill and pine, without consequence.

The truck took us as far as Safaan, a one-track town of red-roofed hearths overhung with heavy cypress trees. Bicycles were lined up outside the communal bathhouse, steam and the scent of thick, foaming white soap spinning from the upper pipes. Across the way, the lights were on in the bakery, flatbreads folding around spinach and nuts for the teenagers in ear-muffling hats and heavy gloves. One station guard huddled inside her office by the railway track, reading something on her inkstone, booted feet up and chin tucked.

"Half an hour," said Nkagosi, as I watched the truck drive away. "You must be hungry."

"Where are they taking Farii?"

"There is a hospital twenty minutes from here. The ambulance will take her there first; then, if she is well enough to move, they will bring her on to Isdanbul. We will go ahead." He waited for me to reply and, when I didn't, bent his head bird-like towards me, as if wondering whether I too hadn't been struck a little too hard by the sea. "Earth-kin?"

Across the way from the station, the wooden gate of a small shrine stood open. A single white lantern hung outside it, swinging erratically in the wind. Nkagosi followed my gaze, let out a little breath, patted me on the shoulder. "I'll get something to eat for the train. You take your time."

The shrine smelt of wet timber. Incense burned in the little ceramic holder. Three rooms clustered tight around a flagstone yard, barely large enough to hold the schoolchildren who came to sing songs and learn the mysteries of the ancient spirits, the great kakuy and the nitrogen cycle. The lights burned in only one window, which I took to be both the office and sleeping quarters of the resident Medj. Another room was raised up a few feet above the earth on wooden legs, open to the elements down one side, woven straw mats on the floor and the trunk of a living silver birch rising up through the middle. Its roots spread out beneath the building itself into the earth below, while its crown reached up through a round hole in the ceiling to plume its branches overhead. Around the hole in the floor through which it descended were offerings. There were a few bags of grain, and a lidded pot containing something that was still warm and smelt of pumpkin, clearly left by someone who knew the Medj's tastes and was willing to occasionally indulge them. There was the shrine's watering can, with a little note on it inviting visitors to water the tree that was at the building's heart, and a scrawled reminder that this month's theme was "renewal" and to please not feed Moonshine the cat. There were a few sticks of incense and bottles of scented oil, an old inkstone, perhaps loaded with suitably contemplative texts – or perhaps not; perhaps it was rich with the kind of scintillating fiction that an honourable Medj might feel a little self-conscious about downloading on their own account but would love to read when the lights were low and no one was looking. There was a woven bracelet of stones and beads, threaded with ancient plastic strings mined from the old landfill sites. A mirror of scrubbed bronze around which were pressed multicoloured shards of more plastic flakes, arranged in a mosaic of ancient and new. A packet of tea. A carved dog, tail wagging and face anthropomorphically split into a friendly grin. A little box of ancient rusted pieces of metal, oiled and scrubbed back into some sort of sacrificial state. Nuts and bolts, an old spoon,

334

a collection of ancient lids in faded green and red. The nib of a pen, and the flaking remains of a circuit board, its use long since lost to time and decay.

A cat meowed, brushing against my legs. I squatted down, held out my hand for him to sniff. "You must be Moonshine." The overweight blue-grey feline contemplated my fingers, found no trace of anything worth licking on them, and, having got my attention, decided that was enough and slunk away. I watched him as he followed an easy familiar path of hop and jump until he was happily on top of the roof of the Medj's small office, curling into a shadow near a hot pipe, a ring of melted snow around it revealing deep red tiles below.

I turned back to the tree, tried to pray, couldn't. I looked for old words, the familiar sounds of the temple, made it a few syllables, stopped. Felt eyes on the back of my neck. Georg would know if I prayed, of course. He'd always know.

I thought of knocking on the office door, asking to see the priest who looked after this shrine. Maybe a cup of tea, a friendly conversation? In Tinics and Bukarest, the Medj had always been horrendous gossips, thrilling in the notion that the drinking of tea and sharing of biscuits could be considered, in its way, a religious duty. "Why I joined Temple!" Lah would say. "Tea, nice music, decent architecture!"

"And the devotion of your life to awe, gratitude, compassion and respect?"

"Yes yes yes – all that stuff too."

I put my hands together and managed the first few words of the prayer for the dead. We had sung it when we'd given Vae's body to the earth and the sky. The tune had been different from the one chanted in Bukarest, which was itself deeper and simpler than the songs sung in Vien, before the temples burned. I tried to hold to Vae's version, to catch at some loose memory of it, but the notes got tangled as I tried to fit word to note, so I stopped, and thought I was going to cry, and couldn't quite believe it. What would Georg say? It would be unacceptable, immediate dismissal. There's no time for such things; utter absurdity. Don't you dare let go!

335

Then Nkagosi was there, a small bag of hot pastries in his hands and a flask of something tucked under one arm, a precarious juggling act waiting to fall. He made a little sound that was the beginning of words, and when I turned he stopped himself and simply smiled. Perhaps the sea had washed something false from my face because he looked and seemed to see someone real. Not Pityr, scrubbing in the kitchens, nor Kadri Tarrad, beaten by Pontus to the chase. He looked at me with kindness, compassion, and for a moment I thought all the things I could not express and did not understand were suddenly present in him, and he had no qualms about naming them, feeling them, even if he didn't know what it was that now burned inside his heart. His empathy was a slap of seawater in my mouth, and I turned away, staring at my feet, rubbed my face to scrunch away salt and fatigue, looked back up and blurted, "Right, yes. The train. Yes."

For a moment, I thought he'd ruin everything and say something thoughtful, or generous, or kind. When was the last time I had heard these sentiments from a stranger's mouth? I would not be able to cope if he did; all my training had been for the opposite – I had no defences against compassion. But he smiled and said: "There's spinach and cheese and nuts and pickles and cardamom tea."

"Thank you."

"Do you need . . . "

"No. No – I mean . . . no. Thank you. Let's . . . let's get this done."

He nodded once more and walked in silence by my side to the train.

Chapter 59

I had never been to Isdanbul.

We arrived at night, by the little four-coach train that wove down along the edge of the water into the city through clinging hill and tight-sliced cutting. The stations we stopped at were quiet: snatches of lone travellers framed in pools of light; a single guard waving us on our way. When the doors opened, I thought I smelt forest through the cold air, heard the steps of the kakuy waiting just outside the light, silver eyes gleaming in darkness, imagined I heard its call in the screeching of the brakes.

Then Isdanbul rose around us, in clinging rows of pinpoint light huddled around the track. Gardens of vegetables and leaf-less winter fruit trees ran away from the line to the hearths and their low yellow lights, growing taller and thicker as we drew into the city. Little wind turbines whooshed busy on top of the highest blocks, and banks of batteries clunked and ticked and whirred in tight coppices of trees between the zig-zagging streets. We rode on bridges cut above the busiest roads of black pressed polypropylene mined from the ancient landfill sites, lined with market stalls and little cafes where the locals drank coffee so thick you could stand a spoon in it, and the cyclists swore and cursed and wove around each other to the jingling of bells and cries of "Move, idiot!" and reproofs of other locals who knew that there was no place for rudeness on their streets and would shout obscenities at you until you understood that fact.

On the edges of the city, I saw regular blocks of buildings

337

laid out in modular stacks, with space between each one like a moat so that when the earthquakes came, the whole thing might shake side to side and not fall, let alone fall on a neighbour. Wide boulevards with trees down the middle; lamps shining above the temple gates and signs at the local stations advertising student shows or concerts at a nearby venue. And yet, here: a knot of soldiers, coming home or returning to the front lines – it was hard to tell – their heads down and eyes up, as if they cannot quite believe that there is peace anywhere they go. Here: guardia on the station steps, watching all who pass by as if they might sniff out subversion like the scent of jasmine on the air. Here: a recruitment sign, defaced, and on one platform a Medj who stands stiff in grey, folded robes and looks lost and utterly alone.

In the centre of the city, the old and new mixed together. Narrow streets ruled by fierce stray cats that curl and rub themselves round the legs of strangers and bite at those who do anything other than try to feed them. The domes of ancient mosques and the tight black stubs of hidden churches where the followers of the old faiths still come to pray, raising up their songs to some creator more benevolent, more caring than the kakuy – or at least, more willing to promise a heaven, as well as a hell.

Some have been converted over the years, turned into community halls or repurposed as museums where you may inspect the ancient texts and artefacts of a long-lost age. Temple built its own premises elsewhere, nestling in between the ancient wooden abodes of centuries-old peoples who clung together through the great burning to build their city again from the fire, as it had been rebuilt so many times before. On the slopes beneath the cracked and teetering tower of Peara, a stepped complex of shrines and halls running up from the sea, where travellers could give thanks to every kakuy of sea and city, of sky and earth you could name. Above the grand bazaar, revellers huddled between the solar tiles, drinking throat-burning alcohol mixed with coffee and breaking bread to the sound of midnight bartering in the maze-tangled streets below. In the quiet streets that staggered and started down to the river, shutters were pulled down against the night and electric trucks groaned as they tried to scale the hills to the first-thing groceries, while cargo bicycles gave up altogether and unloaded in a messy tangle at the wide mouth of the bridge that linked one side of the horn to the other, men and women with sack barrows standing by, arms folded and eyebrows raised at the laziness of their pedalling colleagues.

It was a city that made winter feel like summer, buzzing as the pollen-hunting bees, the sound of war nothing more than an edge to that hum that you thought you caught before some other noise knocked it away.

And then, at the station, was Yue.

She said: All this drama. One day we should just meet for lunch like normal people.

I tried to think of something witty to say, but it had been so long since I opened my mouth to say anything human that nothing came out.

I think she saw that dumbness in me, that mute place where words should have been. Then she held me, in full sight of everyone there, arms wrapped tight; and I held her too, and wondered who this person was who was so unafraid of showing affection, what had happened to Yue Taaq, servant of the Council.

She held on, and I put my arms around her like she was a kitten with a broken bone, terrified of doing the wrong thing. And when it seemed fine, I held a little more tightly and then held her like she was real and this thing between us was true, and never wanted to let go; and there, for a while, we stayed.

When she finally stepped back, she cleared her throat and there was a look in her eye that might have been happiness, or relief, or something else entirely, and I wondered for a moment if she'd finally forgiven me for the day Vae died, or if perhaps she'd forgiven me years ago and I'd just imagined that there had always been this broken thing between us, and never quite forgiven myself.

There was still salt in my hair. She said: Come with me. You're safe now. He can't get you here. Come with me.

*

339

Yue lived in a hearth a few streets up the hill from the hastily re-occupied Council chambers that pressed to the water's edge. It was a place for civil servants from every department, she explained – quiet, most of the time, especially with the war – too much work for more than the lowest conversations around the table or in the bathhouse as they scrubbed each other's backs and ran soap through their neighbours' hair. Occasionally they partied, incredibly loud and incredibly drunk, and in the mornings after would wake, diagonal across their beds or the beds of their hearth-kin, and pad tip-toe across the hall to their own rooms, and find each other's socks in their washing for weeks to come.

The floors in the downstairs living quarters were pressed crimson earth, still smelling of fresh wax recently laid. The staircase was ancient stone, each step smoothed to a dip in the middle by centuries of footsteps. At the top, it opened to a high skylight, and banks of sage, tarragon, rosemary and mosquito-repellent marigold ran up the wall, padded with green moss. What building the stairs had once served, I couldn't tell, for the corridors that split off from it were panelled wood and bamboo, pressed earth and thin solar glass; the new slid into the frame of the old like the mushroom sprouting from the fallen tree.

Yue led me to a room that seemed to be for a guest: a double futon on the floor, folded; a low portable writing desk beneath a little lamp; a cushion to sit before it and fresh straw mats that still smelt of autumn rain. A sliding door opened to a balcony on which grew crocuses, tulips and mint; another, presumably to a wardrobe, stood closed on the opposite wall. On one shelf, I could see a solar torch, two ceramic soup bowls, two sets of cutlery, two white cups without handles – the fingerprints of the potter visible in the clay – and an unlit yellow beeswax candle. It all reminded me of a moderately priced guestroom in a bicycle-sarai until Yue opened the wardrobe door to reveal clothes that could only be hers. There were only two types: long-sleeved, warm tops and trousers for winter, and short-sleeved tops and light trousers for summer. They had no marks on them or signs of character, and came in sky blue or dark blue. She had two pairs of shoes, apart from the thick winter boots she had left by the door of the hearth, which again conformed to the requirements of either sun or rain and were both dark brown. She had one scarf that shimmered like real silk, grown from the cocoon of the worm itself rather than woven in the bio-labs, dazzling yellow; a gift, perhaps – a token of someone else's idea of her character – whether kept for good manners or fond memories, I couldn't tell. It was a flash of incongruous vibrancy in the austere stiffness of her room.

"I've asked them to give us the bathhouse for twenty minutes," she said, pulling a towel from the top of the wardrobe. "Nkagosi has gone to fetch you clean clothes; he will return soon. I hope that is appropriate? That this ... this is appropriate?"

I mumbled some thanks, suddenly awkward, bumbling, too big for my skin and too small for this place. "I thought I would stay in a temple."

"Of course – of course. I can make that arrangement. Forgive me, I didn't think. All of this is so ... I wasn't ... "

"But I'd rather stay here, if you'd have me."

She nodded once, chewing her bottom lip in a sudden, childish anxiety. Then she straightened up, gestured towards the door. I followed her downstairs, and then down again, to the hollowed-earth cellar where the hearth kept its bath. Damp footprints led away from the cold pool. There was the smell of soap, suds around the greywater drain, hot water ready in the communal tub. Yue dipped her fingers in it as I undressed, testing the temperature, seemed satisfied, rolled up her sleeves and trouser hems and waited for me to climb in. I did so gingerly, not sure whether the touch of water would be a threat, a trauma, a memory of the sea, and instead gasped as the heat broke through every cut and tear, every salt-baked frozen inch of skin and bone, shuddering through me like a train over loose tracks.

"Is it too hot?"

"No. I just need a moment."

She nodded, and as I slowly sank deeper, she scooped up a bar of shampoo and rubbed it into my hair, digging hard with fingertips and occasionally giving an order – rinse – head back – head down – rinse – until every inch of my scalp was pummelled and new.

When she was satisfied, she ordered me out of the tub and splashed warm, clean water over me before murmuring: "Cold tub?" I looked at it with trepidation, warmth still such an alien friend that the idea of losing it seemed suddenly unkind. She smiled, shook her head. "Next time."

She scrubbed me dry with the fat towel from upstairs, then examined my cracked, crimson hands, rubbed something waxy and smelling of spring into them, caressing the thin webbing between each finger and rolling her thumb into the creaking bones of my palms, all in silence, save the tick-tick-ticking of the pipes.

Nkagosi had returned with clean clothes. They were cut in the same severe, brisk style as Yue's own – from the very same market, perhaps – but were warm and smelt of vanilla freshness. I dressed while she cleaned the floor around the tub and pumped water from the greywater tanks into the thin pipes that fed the walls of herbs and moss that ran up the stairs. By the time we emerged, the hearth was sleeping, and even the midnight cats of the city had found some hot pipe to curl up by, a truce declared in their constant bickering as they huddled into the thin heat of each other's bodies. I was exhausted, elated, so tired that it seemed as though I had detached from my own self, become the wind, the breath of the kakuy, floating above human events.

We ate in silence sat opposite each other, cross-legged on floor cushions, leftovers of re-heated beans and grains, thick white yoghurt and hot red spice. I finished first, and when I put my bowl down she took it without a word and refilled it to the top, and I gobbled it up in an instant, and she poured clear water into a cup by my side, and I drank it down, and had never been so thirsty, so hungry, or so full.

When at last I stopped, aching with bloated satisfaction and still feeling a strange hunger – the hunger of not knowing if this feast would ever come again – we sat in the low dark of the kitchen, bowls scraped clean between us.

"Yue . . . " I began, and she shook her head.

"Not now."

"You don't know what I was going to say."

"You were going to say that you have vital intelligence for the Council. You were going to tell me about Farii's defection and the things that needed to be done. You were going to talk about Georg Mestri and the war. Am I wrong?"

"No."

"Not now. Tomorrow. Georg can wait until tomorrow."

I nodded, and thought perhaps Yue was just as tired as me, that she too had left her body behind and was watching this as the kakuy do, apart from it all, just moving air that hummed and shuddered in strange noises.

She twined her fingers in mine as we went back upstairs in the half-dark of the skylight. The hall smelt of moss and linseed oil. The door to the balcony of her room stood a little ajar, letting in a slither of winter air. Her back beneath the blankets was warm; her fingers were cold. I did not think I would sleep, and was dreaming in an instant of the sea, and was strangely unafraid. I do not know if Yue slept, or, if she did, what she dreamed.

Chapter 60

I woke, I thought, from a nightmare, and did not know where I was, or whether I was drowning.

The mind can find reason, calm, a place of safety, but the body still rushes on. In that grey hour before dawn, a thing beats against your skull and says lies, lies, lies. All this reason, all this rationality, this repeated safe thing, these words, lies, lies, lies. Listen to the pounding of your heart; listen to the rushing of your breath and know this civilised safety you have talked yourself into – it lies.

You will never be safe. You will always pretend, when the sun comes up, that it will not set again.

The mattress next to me was cold where Yue should have been. There were birds calling to the morning, and in the distance human voices raised from the high minarets, summoning the faithful of the old religions to prayer. The kakuy are angels, or devils, guardian voi or djinn of fire and sea – all the oldest stories survive because they find their place in the new. There is but one God, sang the chorus to the dawn, and all of us are one. There at least, Temple and the old faiths find a point of agreement, though they will still bicker over the nuance until the tea has gone cold.

The single light by Yue's desk glowed low, but the rising grey through the half-open shutter would soon outshine its dim illumination. A bicycle clattered by in the street below, cargo bouncing on uneven cobbles. A door closed; a shutter slid back. Yue's inkstone was plugged into a hard-wired dataport, the kind we used to queue to use at the Tinics post office when we were children, always discovering as soon as our downloads had finished that someone else had downloaded something better. Someone else would always have something better, when we were young.

I shuffled to my feet, feeling the need to be silent without knowing why. Dressed in the clothes Nkagosi had left me, bare feet on woven straw. Folded back the mattress, laid the pillows on top, heard a temple bell ringing, the voice of a novice calling a prayer for the dawn. In Bukarest, the novices kept such prayers inside the temple courts to rouse only sleeping Medj. In Isdanbul, where the last of the Burning Age minarets still stared proudly down at the sea, the temple felt perhaps a certain need to disturb its neighbours with the best of them, insecurity fluttering in the chilled lungs of the boy in the street.

Yue stood on the little balcony outside, a steaming cup in her hand, the smell of cinnamon and liquorice rising from within. She glanced at me as I emerged, then looked away, as if waiting to see the first lick of sunlight rise above the black-timbered buildings opposite, pushing through the heavy night. I ran my fingers over the wooden rail of the balcony, listened for the ticking of the batteries and the water pipes, heard someone shout at a passing cyclist, another morning of abuse in the ting-a-linging, chain-crunching streets of the city. Said nothing at all.

She did not drink her tea. The temple bells stopped ringing; the faithful scurried to prayer.

All things went in cycles, the inquisition liked to teach. Day and night; summer and winter. Human behaviour too. Lah is an eyeless corpse, swaddled in their infinite robes, laughing like a prophet's bones thrown onto sea-scoured stone. We forget how it felt to suffer, they say. The capacity to forget is how we carry on living. It is our happiness. It is much easier than asking why we had to suffer at all. Round and round and round it goes.

"Farii is awake," Yue said, and any chance we had to continue saying nothing to each other was gone. I watched it vanish with the morning mist, and was grateful she'd spoken before I did, and wished she hadn't said a word.

"Good."

"Weak, but awake. We're going to release her image – an interview, perhaps, the tyranny of Maze, the cruelty of Kun Mi, rebellion, that kind of thing. It will be more effective to do it while she's still in a hospital bed. More valiant, you see."

"Sounds very practical. Cynical, even."

"That," she replied primly, "is war."

Nadira is kicking autumn leaves. She tells her agents that the only thing you can't lie about is how you feel. Lie about anything you need to, do whatever you need to do to get the job done; lie about why you're scared, of course, lie to save your life. But don't pretend you're not afraid.

"It might be worth holding off on Farii's announcement for a few hours."

"Why?"

"There is an order in which things need to happen, I think."

"Do you have a plan?"

"Maybe." Words on the tip of my tongue; they taste like bile and emptiness. "I had a lot of time cleaning dishes to think things through."

"I'm sorry. For that. For what Georg did to you. I tried . . . I had hoped to negotiate . . . but it was just another game he played."

"It's fine. Georg mostly did it to himself. Priests of old would listen to your sins and forgive them. He is in many ways an old-fashioned kind of man. Thank you for trying to get me out."

She watched the light, squinting up into the sky as if trying to spot the sun. I stayed with her a little bit longer, until it hurt to look any more.

Chapter 61

A day of being not human. Or perhaps too human to bear. These things are growing harder to distinguish.

Close my eyes and here it is, here it is . . .

Khasimav, drowning. I did not see him drown and yet I cannot shake it from my mind: the sea, the night, the cold. He is drowning and so am I, reliving, replaying, reliving.

I sit in front of Medj of the inquisition in someone else's clothes and I talk, and they listen. I sit and watch myself speak, and for a little while I am not myself but the wind, drifting in and out of my breath, and the earth, pressed beneath me, and the water in my eyes and the sea in my blood, and it is impossible that I might drown, being made already of the world that will take me into it; it is impossible I should die while crows may feast on me and insects clean translucent wings in the moisture of my lungs. I am a machine for condensing and expiring, a perambulating gas exchange; matter enters my body in one state, leaves it in another. I convert energy to heat, and one day my heat will leave me and other creatures will convert my energy for themselves.

One of the inquisitors asks: "Who do you think Pontus is?"

And in that moment, I am something else instead. A tiny, fleshy thing, a scrambling organism scuttling across the dirt, blind to the forest around, seeing only danger and fearing the things that come in the dark. "I will tell Jia," I reply.

"We are Temple. You are one of us."

347

We are the same ecosystem. We are the same breath. Sometimes I forget this, and then I remember.

"Yes. And I will only tell Jia."

"May we know why?"

"No. Call it trauma. Call it madness. Call it whatever you want. I will only tell Jia."

"Are you mad, Ven?"

"I think so. I think it's very likely. Don't you?"

The Medj mutter amongst themselves. I had not seemed mad – not until this moment. What smile should I give them? I try to remember how it felt to smile. When was the last time I laughed at anything other than the dark? I think, perhaps, it was with Georg. I think, perhaps, he said something that I found genuinely very funny. Now I'm not so sure. Things that seemed real are only stories, when I try to remember them.

Just in case, the Medj send me to see an emergency counsellor before I am taken to report to the Council. They are a priest called Jaqcs, who adjusts their robes a little tighter against the cold, leans forward over a flask of water to pour me a cup, sits up straight, runs one pink hand over a silver scalp and says at last: "So, tell me why you're here."

"I was a spy, I was betrayed, I escaped, I was captured again, held as a prisoner of war, forced to work for my captors, escaped, nearly drowned, and am now going to destroy it all. The inquisition wants to make sure I'm not insane before I make my report."

Jaqcs clicked their tongue in the roof of their mouth. "Insane is a strong word. Is it theirs or yours?"

"I think I need to commit heresy."

"Why?"

"Might be the only way."

"Well. Always nice to have lots to talk about."

After, inevitably, I am sent to meet the Council.

The building in Isdanbul was not as grand as Budapesht's, a symptom of Council's hurried flight. The street around was cleared of bicycle and pedestrian alike, creating an urban moat of empty space where guardia in heavy hats and gloves like bear paws paced, as much for warmth as duty. The entrance gate was busy with security who didn't have quite enough room to do the tasks they were set to. Bags were searched by two men with elbows tucked in close so they didn't knock against each other; visitors patted down by a woman who'd managed to squeeze a stool, which she rarely got to sit on, into the furthest corner by the door. Nothing electronic came in or out. Even the cables hastily slung down the corridors were guarded by patrols with batons and radios at their belts, as if the technicians who'd installed them weren't quite convinced the whole infrastructure wasn't about to start singing its secrets in operatic binary.

"Do you have a shrine?" I asked Yue.

"What?"

"A shrine. Is there a shrine in this building?"

"Yes."

"May I see it? I would like . . . a moment, before we do this."

Doubt flickered through Yue's eyes, but she nodded and led the way. I felt a little of Kadri Tarrad stir as we prowled through the corridors, counting doors, watching faces, until we reached the small room set aside for prayer and contemplation, sandwiched between a cleaning cupboard and an overflowing office. I stepped inside, removed my shoes and left them on the shelf beneath a line of hooks for coat and bag, bowed to the kakuy stone on its little plinth, took a cushion from its shelf, sat, pressed my hands in prayer, did not pray.

There was room on the straw mats for no more than ten people to sit in contemplation. Only two others sat there now, and the incense stick someone had lit earlier in the day was already burned down in its little ceramic jar. I watched the others shamelessly, their eyes closed, a violation of their privacy in my gaze, an insult they would never know, then rose, bowed again, retrieved my shoes and said to Yue, who waited by the door: "Thank you. I am ready now."

*

They meet me in a room with thick timber walls and a heavy, soundproof door that takes a shoulder's weight to seal properly.

Antoni Witt, who can't quite reconcile his desperate desire for victory with Jia's refusal to start pumping oil from the earth or blast iron from the mountain. No one has seen the kakuy, he whispers, no one has seen them for centuries, we have a war to win — by sky and sea, we have a war to win!

He should have turned traitor, an Anglaes heretic with a one-track mind — but he loves Jia too much.

Krima vaMiyani. No one really knows how much she knows, or precisely what she does with her days. When they told her that her agents had been wiped out in Vien, every Council mole and spy she'd ever snuck into the heart of the Brotherhood, they say one eyebrow twitched, but she still left the office at her usual hour.

Pav Krillovko, chief of staff. He could have been sacked years ago for calling Shahd of the Delta a self-important little bleeder, but for all it was terribly impolitic, there was enough truth in it that Jia kept him on. He is pious in the mornings, outrageous in the afternoon, repentant in the evenings, and what he does at night is his own business, for better or worse.

"I would like Yue to be here," I say.

"She is not cleared for this debriefing."

"I am an inquisitor, not a Council agent. I answer to none of you, yet I am here. And I would like Yue to stay."

Witt looks ready to argue. Pav looks small and tired, skin hanging loose beneath his jaw where he's lost weight. They let Yue stay. She sits cross-legged behind me, a little to the left, where I would sit sometimes when Georg made his pronouncements.

Jia is late. She is often late to things, these days — meetings seem to endlessly overrun. No one can reach consensus.

They have already interviewed Yoko; she swears that Merthe's army is ready to turn, stab Georg in the back. If they strike now, they can have Bukarest before spring, turn the tide. Now is the time, mutters Antoni Witt, for decisive action. If only we'd built our own tanks.

Witt demands: Can we trust Farii? Why has she turned? She seemed loyal enough before.

That was when she thought Jia killed Ull, I reply. That was before she realised who really benefited from the bomb on Kirrk. Her sin has been stupidity and grief, nothing more.

Who is Pontus? Krima doesn't ask the question with much interest. It is a passing thought, barely worth her time. But her eyes are bright moons in a triangle face.

I would like to speak to Jia, I reply.

We are her Council.

Yes. But this is her fight.

Krima huffs in incredulity – her scorn, at least, she is willing to show. Georg sits next to me, right leg folded over left, as he used to before I stuck a knife in him. He's smiling too. I think he is interested to see what I'm going to do next. I close my eyes, try to will him away, but he's still there, in the swimming darkness behind my eyelids. It makes me angry that he got into my skull instead of Nadira or Lah or Yue.

Jia is even smaller than I remember when she arrives. She, who holds the remaining Provinces together by sheer will and clawed fingers, now walks with her neck sticking out in front of her like a pecking bird. Her smile, as she sits at the centre of the table, is like mine – a thing of habit, a half-remembered art folded out of paper. She isn't sure if it's the right smile any more. What will people think of it? Will they see that she is an alien, that she's pretending? Perhaps it would be better not to smile at all, but that doesn't feel right either. I want to talk to her about it, more than anything. Perhaps we can work out something together, some mimicry of humanity that will allow us to pass, accepted and acceptable through the day, without anyone stopping to ask if we feel all right or expressing concern for our sanities.

Someone moves to pour her tea, which she waves away. She leans back far enough to tilt her head up, and her eyes are still alive, glistening, framed in sagging grey folds. "Ven, yes? We met on Kirrk."

"Yes, honoured kin."

"They tell me you've been busy."

"Not really."

"No – you have. You have. They tell me you have things you need to say but will only say them when I'm here."

"That's right."

"May I know why?"

"I need to discuss Pontus and heresy."

"And heresy too? How lovely." She speaks like she's discussing a burnt slice of cake. Will someone fetch her a new one? She won't make a fuss if it's impossible, but a war leader in her own capital can dream sometimes. "Well, you have my attention, for the few minutes I can give it. But please be concise. The only reason we're not all hiding in bomb shelters is that winter has slowed even Kun Mi to a halt. But the spring will come and the snow will melt and we will not be able to hold the roads when it does, and time is short."

"Winter is not the only reason the war has slowed – but I will try to be concise. When I was an active agent in Vien, Temple contrived an operation to ascertain the identity of Pontus. Documents were distributed to the prime suspects, ostensibly containing military heresies. They were false. Each file we sent contained a unique error that marked out who had received what – a spelling mistake, for example, nothing that would stand out. It was a fishing exercise. Who would take our bait? It took a while, but eventually the doctored document was given to me in Vien, by Georg Mestri, to verify whether it was genuine. I photographed it, returned it to my handler, Nadira, who concluded that the version I was seeing came from Pav Krillovko. He was Pontus.

"Temple shared this intelligence with Krima, Krima drew up an arrest warrant, but before it could be enacted, it emerged that Pav was not in Budapesht when the document was distributed. He could not have seen it nor have forwarded it to Georg. He could not be Pontus.

"Our failure to determine Pontus' identity at that time was a disappointment, of course. It contributed to my exposure and the

352

death of my handler. It has led to many of your defeats during the war as Pontus continues to transmit vital intelligence to Georg. However that only made the search more urgent.

"Two questions remained: was there any way in which Pav could be Pontus, despite his apparent alibi, and, if not, how could someone else get the document from Pav's system to Georg? Krima vaMiyani was aware of this mystery and pursued it, causing I have no doubt deep discomfort to any and all on Pav's staff who might have had access to his inkstone and the more classified materials within Council premises. But she found nothing."

Krima is stone, her long fingers poised to drum on the tabletop, without moving.

"This, of course, put the suspicion on Krima herself. How hard can it be to catch a spy? And if she were Pontus, she would have access to the intelligence that was being fed to Georg, as well as regular access to Pav. There was also her attempt to recruit me in Vien – presumably for Council purposes, but the crudeness of the approach also raised the question of whether this was a counter-intelligence move by Pontus against the inquisition, to sound out whether I was capable of turning traitor. No evidence emerged conclusively either way.

"It is an error for a spy to assume their opposite number is in any way like them. It is a presumption that only clouds investigation. But I had a lot of time in Bukarest to think about how I would go about being Pontus.

"First, consider Council security. Much like Georg, each of you has an inkstone and a fixed terminal secured with biometrics and a passcode. These things are not impossible to break into, of course, but doing so takes time and skill. Nothing electronic is permitted to leave or enter Council buildings unless it has been cleared in advance through a torturous bureaucratic process, which means if you are being hacked, it must happen on site. None of you are able to remove your inkstones, with classified material, from Council premises, and at night they are locked away in a secure charging port. Your networks are isolated from other servers, and your offices regularly inspected. Again, all this would point the finger of blame at Krima, as hers is the department responsible for counter-intelligence and thus the most likely source of any failure in the system; but, then again, insufficiency is not evidence of betrayal. So I ask myself: how would I beat the system?

"The first step is to use analogue technology, rather than attempt a hack. I used it in Vien myself to take photographs of documents using chemically developed microfilm, which I would leave in capsules at dead drops for Nadira to collect. The camera need be no bigger than the end of a spoon, and may be manufactured from mechanical moving parts, rather than electronic ones. I found capsules in Bukarest that resembled the photographic capsules I myself used to conduct my espionage. I also found the microdrone that Pontus uses to send their packages to Georg. They can fly by night and recharge in the morning – a perfectly discreet tool, so long as the weather's not too bad.

"Both these items support the hypothesis that Pontus is using microfilm to smuggle intelligence out from Council buildings – film that would not be detected by your electronic or manual searches – and sending it in drones, rather than transmitted over any network, to Georg.

"We know that Pontus transmits highly classified intelligence, but how did they specifically access intelligence on Pav's ink-stone, when he himself was not in the building? Let us eliminate, for now, the notion that Pontus is somehow ... shimmying through the window to access Pav's office and rifle through his private things. And let us eliminate from our list of suspects those staff of Pav's who may have had access to his files while he was on retreat, given that Krima has already investigated them. If Krima herself were Pontus, that same investigation would be a good opportunity to find a scapegoat, so we will cautiously accept its veracity for now. Yet the fact remains that someone must be accessing Pav's inkstone – an item which is either secured and guarded when he leaves or which he carries with him at all times, full of classified material."

"My inkstone never leaves my sight." Pav's voice rises

sharply, bristling with something of the old pride. "From the moment I check into the building to the moment I leave, it is attached to me."

I half-nod, raising a hand in placation. "Of course. I have seen your security. Nothing in, nothing out. And you are all experienced – none of you would just . . . leave classified material lying around. Yet there *is* a weakness. Something that makes Pav in particular vulnerable to attack. On Kirrk, I saw you praying to the dawn. Repentance, the gossips say – nothing quite as pious as the man who has repented of past sins. How do you pray?"

"I beg your pardon?" blurts Pav.

"When you pray. How do you pray?"

"That is a very personal question, especially coming from a priest."

"Do you put your hands together, like this?" I raise my hands, palm to palm, touch the fingertips to my lips. "Do you listen to the sky above you, and feel the earth below?" I bow my head in thanks to the breath in my lungs and the ground beneath my feet. "Do you close your eyes?"

I close my eyes, and in my mind Lah whispers: *We give thanks. We give thanks.*

There you are, Lah. There you are.

I open my eyes again, look up to see the whole room staring at me, Pav's eyes so wide they must have ached in his narrow face.

"Council and Temple have always been . . . close. Perhaps too much. In every Assembly and every Council building I have ever been to, there is a room set aside – a shrine – where people go to pray. There's one here, in this building. I imagine, Pav, that when you come to work you pass through security, collect your inkstone, head to your office – but before you reach it you stop. You enter the shrine. You take off your shoes, put your bag down by the wall – not exactly out of reach, but not in your grasp either – kneel before the kakuy stone and close your eyes to pray. I imagine it is a comforting ritual. I imagine you arrive early to ensure you have enough time to catch those few minutes when the shrine is quiet, without singing or the ringing of bells. Just a few people around in the morning, hands clasped, eyes closed, like you. You may only be in there for a few minutes, but it is enough. For those brief moments, your inkstone is not in your hands. It is unwatched."

For a moment, I think Pav is going to splutter, mock, deride the whole idea. His eyes flicker to his colleagues, but Krima is stone, Witt a bastion of folded arm and crossed leg, Jia leaning forward with that same automatic smile locked on her lips, curious and polite. "All right," he exclaims at last. "So for maybe three minutes my inkstone is not in my actual hand. So what? It has never been stolen, and no one can unlock it without my code and fingerprint. Three minutes is not enough to hack a stone. What do you propose?"

"I agree – it would be impossible to hack your inkstone in that time, and you have never noticed its absence. But you do pray in the morning, yes? And in the evening too?"

"A few minutes. A brief ritual. What of it? My inkstone is neither accessed nor stolen."

"The problem with theft is not the stealing of the object – it's that someone almost immediately notices that it's happened. Three minutes of prayer is not long enough to bypass your inkstone's security and photograph classified documents. To do that, Pontus needs several hours at least. My theory is that Pontus steals your inkstone in the evening, as you are on your way out. When you stop to pray, or are in the bathroom or the last meeting of the day – a momentary lapse of attention, a few seconds for Pontus to slip a hand into your bag. That's when they swipe your stone, knowing you aren't going to check it again before securing it away under guard and key."

"How precisely does Pontus do that? I *do* secure my inkstone, every night. Every night it is locked away, and every morning I recover it. You're saying I have been robbed and not noticed?"

"That is precisely what I'm saying. Pontus doesn't just steal – they swap. They replace your inkstone, the real inkstone, with a copy that to all intents and purposes looks the same, which, if you turned it on, would show perhaps an unexpectedly low battery – ah, I see that's happened to you before. You return this inkstone to its dock to charge, and in the morning collect it, and go to pray, and when you are praying, that is when Pontus completes the switch, returning your real inkstone to your bag while you sit in devotion. It is risky, of course. A rare, dangerous risk. Pontus has to stay late, three or four hours to hack the inkstone and leave it downloading its material overnight. They'll have to photograph everything they steal, of course, since they can't smuggle out any digital device containing your archives – that also slows down the process. But for the wealth of material, it's entirely worth the risk. What makes it feasible is your piety. Your piety makes you predictable. It makes you weak. That is how Pontus steals from Pav Krillovko."

Silence in the room. I half-expect a slow hand-clap from Krima, but none comes. In the end, it is Witt who speaks. "If we accept this . . . somewhat fanciful hypothesis . . . explain this: There are no electronics in and out which are not logged. So how has Pontus managed to smuggle in some . . . dummy inkstone, some unauthorised device to swap with Krillovko's own?"

"That's simple," I reply. "Inkstones are modular, made for easy repair. Each component is small enough that you could hide it in a shoe or at the bottom of a purse. Sky and earth, you probably even have a technical department in this building that has boxes of the larger, more difficult parts you might need to assemble a stone. All you need to do is gather each component one at a time, over the course of a few months, maybe a year, and put them together. She builds it."

There is a silence in which even dust in the air dares not ripple.

There is a silence where the forest grows; listen, and you can hear the leaves unfurl.

"The rest is simple," I say, and it is not, and it is the hardest thing in the world. "Temple has every report I ever sent as Kadri Tarrad. These include the times and dates when I was given classified material by Georg – stolen documents sent to him by Pontus. We know the model of drone that is used by Pontus to send Georg information. We know it's likely flight time from Budapesht to

357

Vien. This is enough for you to begin to build a picture of when Pontus stole Pav's inkstone. Prayer is private, but entry and exit times to the building are not. Pontus does not need to have a high security clearance – just high enough that she is regularly seen in the same place as Pav, at the back of meetings or popping into the shrine now and then for a moment of peace. The list of suspects writes itself. On the nights Pontus stole Pav's inkstone, she would have had to stay late to work, those dangerous few hours in which she was hacking his device. Perhaps she couldn't smuggle in the larger components with which to build an inkstone entirely, which means there will be maintenance records of her requesting them – a spare battery, perhaps, or a new screen cover – harmless repairs. Nothing to arouse suspicion, unless you're looking. Line these up and you're done. You have Pontus. It is over. The only question remaining is – what are you going to do with her?"

What does the mountain feel, when the seasons turn? Rain, sun, snow, wind, the slow indentation of the river down its back, the patter-patter-patter of a thousand creatures scuttling across its chest, the moon rises and sets, the shadows turn and turn and turn again, and only the mountain remains.

Do not make me a mountain, I pray. I think I would go mad.

Jia stands, and she is not looking at me. Forgive me stars, forgive me the water that we share, Jia is looking at the woman sat behind me.

She is looking at Yue.

So is Krima, and now Pav too. Only Witt hasn't lifted his gaze from the table, but he'll come round in time. With Jia on her feet, the rest of us rise, Yue last, and for a moment the old woman sways as if this little breath, this room of exhaling people, were a storm too great for her to bear.

Then she says: "Krima. Do you accept what this priest has to say?"

Krima is quiet a long, long time. Then: "Yes."

"Pav?"

"I . . . it merits consideration. It is . . . but it merits . . . it would be worth considering more."

358

Jia's eyes have not left Yue's face. "Is there something you would like to add, Taaq? Is there ... a reason your friend has brought you here, today?"

Yue is silent. I cannot turn to see her face. Even the mountain would break.

"I think," she says at last, "that I would like to negotiate."

Chapter 62

There is a time after.

After everything.

They send me back to Temple.

I think I am escorted, but it is hard to say.

Yue does not look at me as she is led away.

Here, said Jaqcs, here. I find this a lovely spot to sit, beneath the cherry tree.

You can take one of the hot stones we keep by the stove and stick it under your robes, such a lovely sensation, when I was a novice I would put one behind my back and curl over it like a cat, chest to the sky, it was the most wonderful feeling.

Here.

Have some tea.

When the snow falls all around, but you are warm, there is something in the silence, in the way the light is different in winter, it is quite . . .

You probably are insane – your word, not mine – but you've got a few more weeks of good use in you before you crack completely.

Do you want to talk about it?

Maybe later.

Jia has asked that you stay in temple grounds, and I wanted to show you my favourite spot, my favourite . . .

You've really done your best.

I think you need to know that.

Everyone thinks you've done ... very well.
Really made a difference.
I'll ...
... leave you to it.
... we've prepared a room ...
... all spick and span ...
Well.

       Well.

              I will see you at the ringing of the bell.

When the dinner bell rings I do not hear it, and a novice comes to bring me to the hall. My fingers and toes have gone blue. Jaqcs was right – it is a very nice cherry tree. There are early spring buds, tiny and crimson, on the ends of the matt-grey twigs.

There are prayers, which I mouth.

There are bowls of soup, steamed dumplings, roasted vegetables and thick yoghurt to take away the heat of some of the more liberally deployed smoked spices. Whoever has decided to claim the kitchen as their domain would not have been contested in their mastery. My room is slightly smaller than the attic where I slept on the floor in Bukarest, and clean. The walls are paper bricks lined with bamboo. There is a spider-silk woven tapestry on one side depicting kakuy representing patience, generosity, balance, compassion and so on. It is a bit of a metaphorical stretch, but then, as Lah would say – bums on seats. No point preaching the oneness of the universe, the inter-connectedness of all things and the harmony of being if no one turns up to hear the sermon. Nice bit of singing, biscuits straight from the oven. That joke you know, Ven – the one about the anemone – it's so lame it's almost funny again, yes?

Lah is decaying in a corner, smiling as the maggots wriggle from out their eyes. They'd hoped for crows – lovely creature, a crow, carrion are always so much smarter than your standard herbivore, count to seven, bring its friends, always know which Medj had a soft spot for feeding it leftovers – love a crow. Be eaten by a crow. Couldn't ask for a better end. Not that they have anything against maggots. Whatever gets the job done.

361

The midnight bell rings, and will not ring again until dawn.

This is an hour to pray.

How hard can it be?

The kakuy don't listen, there is no god who cares – gods are human things – but that's never really been the point.

Pray for yourself.

Pray for something worthwhile.

Pray for good things to happen.

Pray for it to be all right.

Pray for hope.

Pray for forgiveness.

Pray for yourself.

Be someone worth praying for.

Useless bastard, pray.

Empty little eggshell, pray.

Well.

Maybe tomorrow.

Chapter 63

Tomorrow came, and the day after, and the day after that, and on the fourth day they called me back.

Not to Council halls.

To a small house on the edge of the city, pressed behind straw-bale walls, a garden of winter vines, security dressed in civilian clothes and the shutters locked on the low windows. They asked me to wait in the pantry, near the stove, brought me dark brown tea and a honey cake served with a petal on top. Krima came down first, saw my food and drink untouched, didn't bother to sit, barked: "She says she'll talk to you."

I rose without a word, followed Krima up the creaking stairs to a door with a bolt across it, a woman guarding it with a set of keys. Waited for it to be unlocked. Followed Krima inside.

Yue sat on the rolled-up cylinder of her mattress, elbows on knees, head turned towards the thin light that drifted down from the single window. There was a stool opposite her, unoccupied, an empty plate by her side, and a clay cup and beaker of water. She wore clothes of thick winter grey and had no shoes. Her head didn't turn from its contemplation of the light until the door clicked shut, and when she at last looked to see me there was a flicker of surprise.

"Ven. I wasn't sure they'd bring you. I hope it wasn't too far to come."

I folded myself down onto the stool, adjusted it a little so I faced her, pulled my inquisitor robes a bit tighter around my neck for warmth, let my hands hang loose. Krima stood by the door, leant against it with arms folded, a weary bend in the curve of her spine. "Yue," I said. "They are treating you well?"

"Oh yes, fine. It's all pretty procedural."

"Good. I'm glad." And when she said no more: "They said you wanted to talk to me."

"Yes. Of course. You are Kadri Tarrad. I am Pontus. Of course."

These words said out loud were the hard thump of the winter gale that fills your lungs too fast, too deep for breath. I half-closed my eyes, felt the blood in my fingertips. Remembered standing in front of the mirror, learning to meet my own reflection while Vae's hand slipped from mine again, and again, and again. Looked up, and met her gaze.

"What would you like to talk about?"

"I was wondering when you knew."

"Knew?"

"About me. Pontus."

"I see." She waited for me to answer, but I was slow, so slow, trying to fish the words from some distant, crumbling part of myself, memory slipping like dust. Finally: "I suspected you when I was in Vien. Right at the beginning. As a matter of course, you understand. When I first saw you, trailing along behind Jia, I was excited, terrified. Someone I knew – someone who could know me. A single word from you would blow my cover, but at the same time, it was ... I wanted to reach out to you, so of course had to question my own assumptions, practise the paranoia that the inquisition taught. Had to be safe. Then Nadira told me that your clearance wasn't high enough, that the inquisition didn't suspect you, and I was so relieved that I didn't stop to check the obvious assumptions – that my clearance wasn't high enough either, and I was still tearing Georg to pieces.

"I wanted you not to be Pontus. And then when you told me how you knew Georg, it was so damning, such a compromising thing to say that I thought, well, there you go. She can't be Pontus. Pontus would never have said something like that. And

364

besides, if you were stealing intelligence, you would have stolen from Krima, the person nearest you, not Pav. Pav seemed out of your reach – until I saw his devotions on Kirrk. Then everything went wrong, and I didn't have much time to think about these things. I should have been executed in Bukarest. Georg should have executed me. I couldn't understand why he didn't. Vanity, of course. His ... need for power, a playmate, a confessor. All of that, perhaps. But still. He is also a pragmatist, at the end of the day.

"Then I saw you, that night you came to negotiate, and the thought crossed my mind: for Yue. He's keeping me alive for Yue. I am leverage. It seemed inconceivable, but then why had he dragged me to Kirrk? A display of power, of course, game-playing, time-wasting, but what else? Why were you responsible for me on the island? And why had you of all people come to find me in the forest, alone, your military escort still shuffling around in the snow? I thought perhaps you had come for friendship, that you'd seen something in my file, seen my real name – but no. You didn't know it was me until the moment you saw my face. Georg sent you. You had come for Pontus. You were meant to kill me, out of sight, a quiet ending to this little dance. And you didn't."

A little shrug, a little nod. "Georg didn't understand why you were still alive. Why I hadn't put you down. He wanted you on Kirrk to show off – always showing off – but he mainly dragged you there for me. To see how I'd react when he put you in danger. To work out why I hadn't killed the man who had tried so very hard to destroy me. It didn't take much for him to solve it. When he realised that he could use you against me, hold your life over mine, he did. He didn't need to. He already owned my every breath and bone – but he does enjoy power."

"How did Georg recruit you?"

"We met when I was eighteen – I think I said? The same university – he was a little older, on the sprinting team; a brilliant runner. He had interesting friends, with lots of opinions. They talked the usual revolutions. How Temple was bloated, blind and old. How it existed to make sure that nothing changed. No one

365

had seen the kakuy for years. What he said wasn't attractive, but how he said it – that was hypnotic. The first time we made love I couldn't believe someone this remarkable might be interested in me, might take the time to care for me. Nothing he ever does is casual. But when his course ended he went back to Vien, and we drifted apart. We tried to make it work for a few months, but you know how these things are. He encouraged me to go for Council work. He was supportive. Believed in me. I trusted him. I joined security; things fell into place. Georg was working for the Brotherhood, watching me rise – helping me, even. He would feed me titbits from Maze, bits of gossip and things he called "secrets" to make me feel like we were part of some mutual exchange.

"The first time I betrayed Council, I thought I was doing the right thing. Greasing the wheels. Solving a problem. Then I did it again. And again. And one day Georg laughed and said, 'Good thing no one knows about this, otherwise they'd arrest you on the spot,' and it was a joke, a silly little joke; and just like that, I was his. I understood in that moment what I had done, how deep I'd gone. He owned me. He laughed, one arm round my shoulder, chatted about nothing – some sport, perhaps – said, 'Same thing next month?' and it was done. I had become a traitor without even noticing. After a while, he stopped pretending. We stopped having our little dinners. Stopped with the smiles and the solicitations. He would ask me for information and I would do it. Like a dog trained to fetch, I fetched. Fetch, puppy, fetch. Go fetch. He's always seen the animal in people."

"Did you ever believe? In what he said – the kakuy, humanism?"

"Believe? I never really thought about it in those terms. But this I know: one day, the kakuy will wake. They will come from the forest again, some day, and when they do, we have to know how to kill them. It is the only way humanity will ever be safe. Georg was right about that, at least."

She was not looking at me, at anything, not moving, her face a barely living thing, blood turned to crystal ice.

366

"Why did you sleep with me on Kirrk?" I asked, and at my question Krima stirred, and Yue did not.

"Because I wanted to. Because it was nice. You were available and I knew . . . well, perhaps this is the last time. When Jia is dead and Georg has won, when he no longer has any use for Pontus, he'll put me in some apartment somewhere with guards to watch over me, and sometimes we'll have sex and dinner because he has me. He has my mind and he has my body and that's all there is to it. That is what my future holds. I had spent so long looking for Kadri Tarrad, so long trying to find you, I could feel you, see the shape of you without knowing your face. And when I found you, I already knew you. All such a mess. I was meant to kill you, and even before I knew you were Ven, I didn't think I could. I don't know which you I spared – Kadri or Ven – but I couldn't do it. What mercy would there be for Pontus? What mercy for me? What would Vae say, if she saw what I had become?"

"Who's Vae?" Krima's voice, hard from the door.

I ignored her. "Why did you come to Bukarest?"

"Jia sent me – peace talks. Nothing would ever come of them, of course, but Georg does like to string the old woman along. And he always insists that they send me."

"Why did you really come?"

"To see you, idiot. To make sure Georg had kept his promise. Kept you alive. He asked me, Why does this man matter? Why do you care? I told him we were lovers once; he likes it when it's about sex. He understands that sex – love – these things make people vulnerable. It is much easier for him to comprehend than the truth. I tried to get you out. I did. But he would never let you go." She smiled, held out her hands. I took them. Her fingers were cold, tipped with blue. I squeezed them tight, pressing a little warmth into her. "What a mess!" She nearly laughed, eyes shining, chin twisted high. "What a stinking mess."

"If I asked you, would you help me destroy Georg?" Her eyes lowered back to me, and there was a smile on her lips, tears on her cheeks. "In Maze, the kakuy are waking. The rivers carry plague, swarms of black flies that sit in the corner of the eye and

367

lay their larvae in pink flesh. Fires leap from the furnaces to the schools, the streets, the forests. This war can never end, because the Brotherhood cannot turn back. They have burned everything they have to take what was never theirs."

She looked away and did not answer. I sighed, spoke to the sky, to the earth, to her bare toes pressed to clay. "Temple teaches that the kakuy wake not because they are angry at humanity and the things it has done but because the cycle must not be broken. Anger, shame, guilt — such human things. It is hard to teach that the sky doesn't care. Destroy ourselves, or live in peace — all this will someday end, and the earth will endure, in one form or another, whether humans breathe or not. In Tinics, the forest burned, and then the forest grew, and we were taught to give thanks that we lived in a world where that which is lost can grow again. Give thanks, they said. We are of the forest. We are of the earth and of the sky, boundless and eternal. So give thanks." I pressed my hands around hers, tighter. "Yue — sister of earth and sky; kin of sun and moon. Thank you for saving my life."

Her smile broke into a grin, a laugh that dislodged the tears that ran down her face. "Ven — I've made a total mess of mine."

"On that point in particular, we have something in common. Will you help me?"

Chapter 64

Three days before the end of everything, Jia came to the temple to pray.

They sent me to the main hall a little after breakfast bell, and there she was.

They'd brought out a chair for her to sit in before the altar. The altar carried images of a hundred kakuy, spirits of the cypress tree and the fish creatures that still played in the darkness of the cistern beneath the streets when no humans were there to see them. But the largest image, moulded from ancient sea-smoothed plastic pulled from the deeps, was the kakuy of the water, the place where two seas meet. It had tentacles woven in plastic bags, a crown of metal shards dug from the landfills, eyes of black opal. It was neither beautiful nor ugly, kind nor vengeful. It had clearly been created by someone with a great deal of piety.

The Medj slipped from the hall as I settled down on a wobbly pile of cushions stacked up next to Jia. She prayed a little longer, or pretended to pray – a woman of her profession must be supremely skilled at demonstrating piety while wanting to pee. Finally she said: "I suppose it's sacrilegious to discuss war in a place of contemplation?"

"When I last checked, the falcon didn't care about the scenery if there was something to eat."

A little nod; she found this satisfactory. "Farii is up and about and has done us a lovely little speech about the tyranny of the Brotherhood. We're releasing it this afternoon, and have established contact with Merthe in the north. As soon as the message goes out, she is bringing her divisions over and Kun Mi will have a hostile army in her backside. It has all the hallmarks of a bloodbath. I trust you're satisfied."

"Not really."

She nodded; neither was she. "I had a long chat with my advisers. They are, disappointingly, desperate. We are all desperate. None of us have slept enough. None of us have time to sleep. It makes for terrible judgement." A slight bristling; a tilting of her chin at an unwelcome thought. "How does Mestri do it? You were his assistant for months – does he drink a lot of coffee? Stimulants and hard drugs? How does he run his war?"

"He likes washing in icy water."

"As if I didn't despise him enough."

For a while we sat in silence as the smell of incense drifted on the air with the out-of-tune calling of a novice new to the sacred songs. At length, Jia said: "When this is over, there will be a trial. Quiet, of course – it would be embarrassing to have to admit in public how far Pontus got. But it will be imprisonment, parole at fifteen years if she keeps her nose clean, shows remorse. Five years' probation, never hold any meaningful position ever again and so on. If she co-operates. If your little scheme works."

"I understand."

"She betrayed you. She betrayed your handler. She is directly responsible for the deaths of countless people. She can't argue ignorance. She knew what she did and understood its consequences. Would you forgive her?"

"My forgiveness is mine to deal with on my own terms. You cannot mandate it or enforce it with a court order. That's not what justice is for. I'll deal with it when I'm ready, in my own way."

A little sigh, a little shrug. She's heard more laughable things, in her time. "Why did you join the inquisition, Ven of the Temple of the Lake?"

"Why do you ask?"

"You could have worked for Council."

"Council is too political. You come, you go. You have short

370

memories and short-term goals. It's all necessary, of course. Society, culture, all evolve far faster than our genes do. But Temple measures its objectives in the erosion of the valleys and the churning of the glaciers. It is fantastically dull, very hard to emotionally engage in and entirely necessary. I saw the forest burn, when I was young. I would like to see it grow, before I die."

She thought about it, nodded. "Bit self-important, but not completely inane."

"I was taught that when you thought people were talking absolute nonsense, you should always say, 'You are partially right.' It allows everyone to feel that their views are valid and worth consideration, even when they're categorically wrong."

Jia laughed. It was such an unexpected sound that I nearly jumped, held onto my knees and wondered if this was a cackle too far, whether someone so frail should be allowed so much merriment. Found that I was smiling, didn't quite know what to make of the feeling. She patted me on the shoulder, stood up slowly, still beaming, exclaimed: "I like that. I will use that in meetings. So much for the end of the world!" and hobbled away, chuckling as she went.

Chapter 65

All things ended in a place called Martyza Eztok.

It lies at the bottom of a valley of terraced steps, an unnatural hollow in the earth. No river had carved its lines; no great ice age scratched it from the earth. It was as if the talon of some mighty kakuy had descended from the sky to just pick, pick, pick at the land like some yellow spot, ripping out nearly ten kilometres of blackened dust from the flatlands to create an indent through the rock.

The first inquisitors who ventured into it could see chimneys still sticking up from the earth, the buildings beneath them long since collapsed or buried beneath black. Their smooth stacks were shattered, but the rusted remains of some still lay where they'd fallen like clawing fingers. Closer still, and the smell of festering eggs grew, a throat-closing tingle at the back of the mouth, and concrete blocks rose from the shaggy ground, empty windows and cracked walls, pools of brackish water and signs in archaic script. Previous travellers had tied signs of their passage to the fallen lampposts or broken, bleeding pipes that zig-zagged across the ground. Scraps of cloth and woven patches of plastic; bits of ancient fishing line and crumbling wire turning to orange flakes. They were the only living things in this place, catching and snatching at the wind. The walkways of the refineries had tumbled down, nosing into dirt. The great cooling tanks had shattered; the acid in the pipes had eaten everything they'd touched until there was nothing left but hollows and dust.

There was no shrine in this place, no monument to the spirit of rust and the pit. The Medj had argued over whether to build one, to try to re-sanctify the blasted earth, but had eventually agreed that there were some things best left profane. Nothing grew from the yellow muck save brown, scraggy grass that lived only long enough to die. Even the crows kept away.

Nadira had been one of the first inquisitors to risk diving into the abandoned coal mines below, swimming through collapsed tunnel and flooded shaft, unable to see her hand in front of her face as she twisted and wormed her way to the archives the burning ones had hidden within. It had taken the inquisition nearly six years to dig new passages down to the surviving chambers of hidden knowledge, and what a surprise they'd had when the first translations of recovered material started to emerge.

Lignite mining and the great toothed engines that could carve out the belly of the earth.

Essays on storage of radioactive waste; lessons on slag heaps and acid rain.

This is our knowledge, our gift to you, wrote the last of the archivists who had died when the world burned. *Everything we did, everything we made, we made so our children could live better than the ones who went before.*

After fifteen years, the tunnels beneath Martyza Eztok were re-sealed by inquisition order, the recovered material distributed to the anthropological and historical working groups for analysis and classification.

Sometimes, when the wind was right, black clouds of coal dust still spun on the edges of the valley, and the few inquisitors left to guard the mines swore that there were things which groaned beneath the earth that had in their sound something living.

Nine days after Yue was arrested
and Merthe turned her guns against the Brotherhood
I got on the train heading north
towards the mines.

Chapter 66

By the time I reached Martyza, the Council had moved a small army in.

They spread themselves into the villages to the south of the torn-up land, camped in clumps of forest and little knots of wood between the thin, dusty fields that clung to the edge of the hollowed-out, blackened valley. Blood-red bricks and a cracked roof were patched over with sheets of waxed fabric. Portable solar arrays were lined up towards the noonday sun, pickets of mounded earth dug out in the scrappy, broken land beyond. To the north I could see the last standing remains of two ancient cooling towers, their curves tumbled in on themselves like broken smiles. A few signs still lined the muddy borders where fences had once separated the old factory lands from the farms, written in archaic script.

PPE must be

Beware the dog

a better future for

I wasn't sure what "PPE" meant, tried to turn over the ancient dialects to find words that fit, and came up with nothing. Georg would not have been impressed.

An army Medj, head shaven and uniform indistinguishable from anyone else's, met me at the edge of the camp as I pedalled up on my borrowed bicycle. "Inquisitor!" they exclaimed, bowing low. "Welcome to Martyza Eztok."

"Temple-kin," I replied, slipping off my muddy vehicle and returning the bow. "I had no idea there'd be so many soldiers here."

"Brotherhood troops have been seen heading south towards the mines, bypassing Plovdiq altogether. The assumption is they're going for the archives – more heresy, I assume."

"You assume wisely. What is your role?"

"Me?" they answered. "I'm here for sermons and hugs."

In the evening, I shared dinner in a tent with the Medj and a bustle of soldiers, knees stained with dust and coal. They led the prayers. We thank you, earth, for the food we eat. We thank you, night, for the safety you give. We thank you, dawn, for all that will follow.

I wondered where this soldier-priest had been, and what they'd seen in this war, and didn't have the courage to ask.

An hour before sunrise, I woke, freezing cold on the thin mat between my body and the earth, legs stiff inside the barrel of my sleeping bag. I uncurled, wound up the little torch that lay beside my head, fumbled out in the night, trying not to step on too many slumbering bodies, looked to the east and saw a hint of grey that might have been the approaching sun, and tried to remember where the toilet was.

A guard sat hunched like a raven on the broken roof of the little farmhouse, weapon tucked into chest. A low light burned from the makeshift kitchen, where breakfast was already being prepared. I sat on the broken wall on the edge of the compound and looked towards the skeletal valley beyond, wondering what it had been like when the cracked towers and toppled chimneys of this place were living, powerful things. The people of the past had made their own kakuy, spirits of metal and steam, great gods that, for a little while, challenged the thunder itself. They had seeded the clouds and put machines into space. Perhaps Georg was right;

perhaps with steel and oil they could have tamed the earth. Those who survived, at least. Those with the will to survive.

Something moved overhead. I glanced up, tried to pick it out in the darkness, strained my ears for the telltale whine of the rotors, couldn't hear it. The sky was streaked with scudding clouds that opened and closed like tired eyes. Sometimes I saw stars behind them, a promise of infinity – a busy, beaming void. Then it vanished again, and again I looked and thought a tiny point of darkness moved, but when I looked one last time it was gone.

"Brotherhood drone," explained a sergeant in the breakfast queue. "They say the main force will be here by tomorrow."

"Aren't you . . . a little concerned by that?"

He shrugged. "Witt's good at rearguard actions. Didn't think it'd be over some stinking archive, but still . . . " But still, but still. What's a soldier to do, when the inevitable calls?

By daylight, I drift through the camp, half-listening to the soldiers talk. They glance to the north, the flat, broken plain between us and the wide horizon. They do not talk about the approaching Brotherhood forces. One drops his pants to stick his buttocks up at a passing drone, until a colleague hisses that it's one of theirs. They wonder where Merthe is; rumours and gossip from Lyvodia. A few wonder where they will be when the day is done, and are hushed, and go back to talking of little, idle things.

There are muddy crates stamped with the mark of the inquisition being loaded into a truck. They look crudely out of place, each one designed to fit a rack of ancient hard drives or chipsets preserved from static, moisture and time. They should not be slathered in mud or thrown from soldier to soldier like a toy box. There should be Medj here, protecting the history of our ancestors, of the burning ones who died wishing us well.

Old Lah walks beside me and reminisces about the ancient hard drives they've unlocked, piecing together the code of our history. Pornography; bank statements; computer games full of slathering demons and sexy aliens. Family photos. Endless pictures of food on white, round plates with captions full of yellow smiley faces and exclamation marks. Infants beaming up at a camera, at the parent that wielded it. Children running through autumn leaves in red rubber boots, being pushed on swings by cobweb Grandma, come alive again. Lovers, puckered lips, cheek-to-cheek, black background, overlit, over-bright faces and black-rimmed eyes. Friends dancing in the summer streets, drinks in hand; holiday shots across monuments even more ancient than the fires that ended the last great age. Lounging in sunlight on a golden beach. Running, sweaty and out of breath across the victory line. Waving goodbye at an airport, bags packed and guidebook in hand. Thumbs up and big grins. A father who cannot find his child in the ruins of war. A glimpse of someone famous on a bright red carpet, the shot out of focus against the hordes of fans trying to get in close. Wedding photos, confetti, tears; the kind of beauty that can only be born of joy. A woman sleeping in afternoon sun.

It is strange to imagine that the dead were ever young, children covered in cream, teenagers falling in and out of love.

I want to go back to Georg.

I want to sit him down and tell him: You never find what you expect when you dig through the archives. You want nuclear fission and geoengineering. You want oil refineries and investment banking prime-mortgage re-packaged bonds. You want pesticides and herbicides and humanicides and a way to kill the kakuy.

But look, look. Here's what you get.

Three pictures of different kinds of food shared between friends, an out-of-focus shot of two lovers sticking their tongues out at the camera, a screenshot of an ex-boyfriend's stupid text message to share with friends, because you can't *believe* he'd say that shit.

Here's the history of the world for you.

Here's what the burning left behind.

You want gods, and all you get are people.

*

I see Krima vaMiyani.

She nods at me once, from the passenger side of the heavy truck she rides in, then turns away.

In the morning, the truck of crates marked with the badge of the inquisition is gone, and on the other side of the gouged-out valley there are black fumes in the air as an army approaches.

Chapter 67

Once, on the edge of Martyza, there was a church.

It was far older than the coal mines, than the black claw raked through the earth. It did not make itself especially denominational, having at some point in its history been a place of worship for nearly every flavour of monotheism imaginable. Its yellow stones had cracked and fallen away in places, and the roof was long since tumbled down. Moss grew on the piled mounds of fallen masonry, glistening in the morning frost. A hollow stair led to a soggy black below, perhaps a place of corpses and snakes, of ankle-deep fetid water and ancient bones with wet hair on bare skulls, and sometimes children dared each other to go inside, and sometimes they did, and usually they did not, because some darknesses were a little too conclusive.

I cycled there on a borrowed bike as two armies lined up across the scarred field of Martyza. They told me it was far enough away from the main battle lines that I probably wouldn't be mortared to death, that the worst of the crossfire would pass me by. They told me, if it didn't, if the battle raged out of control and soldiers with guns descended upon me, to surrender immediately and grovel for mercy. They seemed fairly sanguine about the whole affair.

"How does a battle begin?" I asked one.

"Oh — they'll probably start shelling us when they've had a bite to eat, and if they don't, we might try shelling them. There's a lot more of them than there are of us, of course, but they've had to travel a long way so they might not be feeling too frisky."

I wondered what "frisky" could possibly mean when two armies faced each other over the black-dust belly of the earth, and decided not to ask.

In the church on the edge of the field, I left my bicycle by the dry mouth of a little bowl where worshippers had once dipped their fingers by the broken door, and sat inside on a stone near a place where once an altar had been, swathed in my priest's robes, and closed my eyes, and waited for the end of all things.

I did not pray, since there are no gods with interests in human things.

But, for a little while, I let my mind be in the cold morning air, and my toes be in the cold morning earth, and my heart beat with the fluttering of the wings of the crow on the wall overhead, and my mind grow slowly, so slowly, with the moss unfolding over fallen stones. And for a little while, that was enough, and I was nothing, and everywhere, and everything, and I was the kakuy.

All around: nothing.

No forest, no hills, no mounds of slagged chemical sewage belched from the belly of a machine. Nowhere to hide, nowhere to run. Just the flatland before the fall into the pits and the dry rasping of brown grass rubbing against the dead stems of its nearest neighbour.

A little snow fell, crystals melting slowly on my sleeve. I watched each one, determined to spot a pair, and soon lost interest. Drew myself a little tighter into my robes, drank tea from a hot flask, felt the knife buried in my boot, listened.

I heard the armies move before I heard him.

They didn't open with shelling, as had been promised. Everyone was in too. much of a rush to get the artillery out. I had imagined the belching roar of the Brotherhood's tanks to be an offensive shuddering in the land, a tumour in the ear. But the morning was kind, and the faint snow muffled the rumble of their movement to a distant animal growling as they revved their engines and charged forward. Drones buzzed high overhead, impossible to tell which was on whose side, sweeping back and forth across the field. I wondered where Antoni Witt was now, and what his soldiers thought of the lumbering death shuffling towards them. I waited for the sound of artillery, and the odd big gun fired desultorily into the sky, and no more. The sound of small arms fire when it began was an erratic, far-off thing, odd units skirmishing in strange places, the constant dance of fire-withdraw-fire that was Witt's calling card. I wondered if his troops could outrun a tank. I wondered how much fuel a tank needed to mow down men. I waited, checked my watch, waited.

Put my fingers on the earth and felt the hum of the vehicles moving across it, far away.

Listened for the sound of birds; heard none.

For the crack of animals moving across frost; heard none.

Only the distant thump of unseen shadows, inhuman things, busy about killing.

Understood, for a little while, why Yue wanted to go to prison. Missed for one startling moment my cell in Bukarest. Decided I was, indeed, finally, mad. Drank some more tea.

When he came, he did so on foot, and that surprised me. I heard his stick on stone, striking hard as he approached the church, near enough to cut through the chunking, thumping, rumbling growl of the Brotherhood soldiers pouring across the ruined land to the west. Was Witt even bothering to fight back? Perhaps not. Say what you will of the general, he liked his troops to live.

The man approached at the pace of one out for a hearty constitutional, a pleasant early morning walk. There should have been mist on the ground and bells ringing in the air; he should have nodded politely at people who owed him favours as he passed, a grand fellow about his business.

Instead, he stopped on the edge of the church, listened to a sudden swell of distant gunfire, knocked once with the tip of his cane on the broken porch, stepped across the threshold, a smile on his lips.

"Hello, Georg," I said.

He was surprised enough for the smile to freeze, for the stick to hang in the air for an instant. Then his smile changed; he nodded, beamed, tucked the stick under one arm and straightened a little, as if he could hide his limp from me. "Kadri. Congratulations – I am surprised. Goodness, indeed yes. Well done."

"Tea?" I held out my steaming flask.

"What is it?"

"Jasmine."

"Thank you, no. Are you alone?"

"Regrettably, yes. With so many of your drones flitting about, it didn't seem prudent to bring a whole military convoy with me, however much I would have liked the cover."

"I didn't expect to see a priest so close to the battlefield."

"I don't think anyone expected to see you so close to one either. Not Georg Mestri – not sticking his neck out. But then you expected Yue."

His smile widened, a flicker of something real, something familiar. His eyes roamed round the ruined place, he paced a little forward, a little back, saw no threat as he talked. "Ah. Yes. I did. I do believe this is what it's like to feel . . . flustered. How novel. Are you armed?"

"With more than tea? Are you sure you won't drink?"

A hesitation; a memory in his eye, perhaps, of hours spent in each other's company, playing games, drinking wine, talking of nothing much. He gestured towards a little mound of stone slightly lower and less comfortable than mine, tried to find a comfortable way to perch on it, found it impossible, tried for the sake of the illusion anyway, one leg high, one leg low, smiled again, hands folded, stick tucked into the bend of his hip, watched me, watching him. Finally, he said: "I've never seen you in priest's robes before."

"That would have somewhat blown my cover."

"You look like an ugly duckling, all fluff and a tiny head."

"They're not really cut for style. The sexy Medj with gleaming torso was always something of a myth. How are you doing?"

"Oh, fine, fine – you know. Fine. Busy as ever. You may have spotted the little ruckus happening a few thousand metres from here. Yourself?"

"Could be worse. I mean – significantly better than in recent months. Keeping busy, and so on. I've been reliably informed that I'm going insane. But I'm not of any strategic significance, so it probably doesn't matter."

"Probably not. Where is Yue, out of curiosity?"

"Under close arrest, behind the lines."

"And she's turned, presumably? Her message told me to meet her here, but it showed none of the duress protocols we established."

"She is no longer your agent, as you can see. But then again, all we asked her to do was bring you here – that's hardly so much, given that you brought an army with you."

"What? Oh, yes. Technically I brought the army for Martyza Eztok, for the archives. Yue's message suggested they would be heavily defended. I am beginning to suspect that was also a lie, yes?"

I've left the lid off the flask of tea. It'll be getting cold, ruined soon. Never mind.

In the distance, someone opens up with a high-speed kind of gun, nothing I've ever heard before; they must have dug the designs out of some sealed archive, a hundred bullets a minute, two hundred, pop pop pop, you're dead and you're dead and you're dead, so easy, so much easier if you do it right, just like a game, really, a short story on a winter's morning.

"Witt has brought in a few divisions – enough to make a scene worthy of your attention. It was . . . nice of you to come for Yue personally, when she asked. I wasn't sure you would. Wasn't sure if you cared so much for your assets."

"Yue was more than an asset. She was . . . she is . . . special. She has done more for my cause than you'll ever know. And I'm fond of her. We were friends, when we were young, did you know that? We lived together for a few months, argued about all sorts of things – we had some serious fallings out, in the way you only really can do when you're that naïve and pig-headed. I can still make her favourite dinner. Do you know what her favourite dinner is?"

"What would you offer, in exchange for her?"

"Is that what this is? You've asked me here to negotiate a prisoner exchange? Really? Not a special operations team – not an assassin?"

"You would have spotted an armed bunch of bastards with big guns a kilometre off. And killing you isn't Jia's preferred outcome. But seriously – what would you give for Yue?"

"Oh ... some of the politicals we've got in Bukarest, perhaps? Now that Farii has betrayed us, I imagine she'll be keen to get a few of her last surviving allies out before we shoot the lot of them."

"I didn't know there were any you hadn't shot."

"That's because you're middle management, if that. Secretarial – that's more accurate, isn't it? A competent secretary."

"I imagine you burn through staff at a terrible rate."

He smiled, shifted his position on his uncomfortable seat, found it too much, stood, walked a little back and forth, hiding the limp now, hiding the pain as the weight fell on his injured leg, swinging his stick side to side as if it were just an ornament he carried for fun. I closed my eyes, heard gunfire but nothing human behind it – no screams, no cries on the wind, just the tearing of broken air.

"Do you know this place?" he asked, sweeping his stick towards Martyza. "Do you know what it was?"

"Coal mines. Power stations. A relic of the burning. Nothing grows here, any more."

"Coal mines and power stations," he mused, half-nodding into the grey morning gloom. "The burning lifted people out of poverty in numbers never seen before. It extended the life of man to nearly a hundred years – a century of living. It made it possible to travel the world, to change the face of the planet. It changed what it meant to be human. Our minds expanded as our potential did; we could conceive so big, so far, of so much. Ability was rewarded. We were not afraid of consequences; there was nothing that could hold us back. It breaks my heart to see what we have become. So scared of the kakuy, we barely dare tread on a dandelion for fear it brings down the thundercloud."

"We've understood very different things from the past. All I see are a few people getting rich in paradise, while everyone else chokes and burns. An age of economic tyrants with too much power and not enough care. One man may burn a forest, but he can't make it grow again."

Georg rolled his eyes. "Do the robes make you more pompous, or have you always been like this? There will always be a top and a bottom of society, but at least it will be one of merit. War teaches us that there are generals and there are soldiers, but you too could be rewarded, if you are strong enough."

"To be honest, at this stage all I really want is to go home and have a nervous breakdown. It's not very meritorious, but it'll probably help in the long run."

He scowled, a sudden flare of anger bursting from behind his smile. "Don't you know there's a fucking war on?" he snapped, and I recoiled a little, curling up tighter on my rock, but then the smile was back again in a moment, bright and merry as if we were discussing butterflies or the first buds of spring. "Anyway. All this is academic until Jia's deposed. We'll take Isdanbul then negotiate a settlement with whoever's left standing. Give everyone a chance to calm down a bit, reconsider their positions. In time, the remaining Provinces will see the power of our argument; the strength of it. I do believe in something, you see."

He talked light and easy, but his eyes were to the west, to the rumbling of his army as it growled across Martyza Eztok. Too far now. Too late – all of it, far, far too late.

"All this would be an even more stupid waste of life if you didn't believe." I raised my voice a little, to cut through the barrage of his thoughts. "But I imagine the wrathful kakuy currently poisoning the land in your wake might be a bit distracting – not to mention Farii's rebellion." Not a flicker in his smile, not a flinch, but neither did he reply. "You are worried. About the archives in the coal mines, yes?"

"It's my job to be worried. While it is always . . . nice to see you, the thought that Yue lied to me about the level of defence Jia would dedicate to this region is naturally perturbing. It suggests, in the worst case, a trap."

"What do you think is down there?" I asked, following his gaze. "Nuclear? Biowarfare? Cluster munitions? What are you hoping for?"

He shrugged. "I will take what I can get. We can extrapolate a lot from a little. Look at the advances we've made already."

"Perhaps you hope there's a way to kill the kakuy. The great ones, I mean. The ones that come in thunder."

"As I said – I make do with whatever I find."

I sighed, checked my watch, clicked my tongue in the roof of my mouth. Georg stopped pacing, half-turned, looked at me and seemed for a moment to see me, myself. I smiled, put the lid back on the flask of tea, sealed it up tight, creaked side to side, felt the little muscles down my back ache.

"It is a trap, of course," I said, and finally he turned to face me full-on, one eyebrow raised. "Oh, there's an archive down there, full of frightening, terrible things. Even without Yue's invitation, you should have left it alone. You talk about ingenuity, but your mindset is so stuck in the past you can't see the extraordinary advances of the present. You are incapable of appreciating the wonders around you, incapable of ever just being . . . all right. Satisfied. Under other circumstances, you could have been an astonishing human being. You could have achieved wonders. But you are not. Instead you are remarkably easy to manipulate."

I checked my watch again, watched the second hand ticking down.

"I wish you'd got here on time," I sighed. "We could have done this differently." He didn't speak, didn't blink. I couldn't remember the last time he'd listened to me so intently. "I am here to commit a terrible heresy. When it is done – if there is anything left – your army will be destroyed and you will lose Bukarest, probably Budapesht too. It's going to be hideous for everyone. But you have a choice. You came here for Yue. That was good of you. That suggests consideration for the life of an agent. I'm here to return the courtesy. Krima vaMiyani would love to talk to you; she is as close to thrilled at the prospect as I think she can physiologically be. Defect now, and you'll have a perfectly comfortable war in a nice hearth somewhere by the sea. Or don't, and watch everything you've built tumble down, and eventually be arrested as a war criminal, perhaps by our side, most likely by your own. Kun Mi strikes me as fond of a scapegoat."

He turned, took a step away, stopped, turned again, rubbed his leg – an unconscious movement, a little leaning – seemed to realise what he was doing, straightened, stiff as a tree. "All right," he murmured. "You've surprised me. Thoroughly and actually surprised me. I'm impressed. You've given me a great deal to think about. Thank you for that."

"I fear that in moments we'll both have a great deal more."

"Even if you did have some sort of trap to spring, I've seen your troops, Jia's little armies. You could bring every soldier she has from every corner of the Provinces here and all you'd do is speed your demise."

"Yes. She knows that. She's old, Georg, but there's a reason she's in charge. Winning was never the plan."

He looked directly at me, his chest square, shoulders back, stick rammed into the dirt between his feet like a flagpole. "Fascinating. I can still see you – some of you – some of Kadri. But only pieces of you; of him, rather. Little parts you used to be Kadri – or perhaps little parts of Kadri that you have used now that you are trying to be Ven. I have always prided myself on being better than people – at knowing them better than they know themselves. You force me to rethink this position. Thank you."

I sighed, stood, stretched, checked my watch one last time. "Too late," I said. "But for what it's worth, you're welcome."

"You know that this can never be a—"

I raised one hand to silence him, and he stiffened, astonished, utterly unprepared for the gesture. "To be clear. There is an archive under Martyza. It was buried in the mines. All the way under the valley, stretching on beneath the earth all around. Tunnels which your army are currently running – in the case of the tanks, driving – directly above."

Here it is.

Here is the moment that Georg's world falls apart.

I thought I would enjoy it.

I thought it would make everything all right. That I would punch the air, laugh, cackle, say something pithy. I thought I would watch him collapse into an old, broken man, and I would feel somehow young again, feel that I had clawed back some piece of myself that had vanished so far into Kadri, into Pityr, into the air and the earth and the forest and into him.

Instead, he took in a single breath, and let it out slow, because even he had to breathe again.

I felt tired.

I wanted to take his hand, tell him it would be okay.

I wanted to apologise – maybe not to him, but to anyone who'd listen.

I opened my mouth to try and find words, and there was nothing.

We stood, frozen in that place, and there would be a part of us always frozen in that place, a shadow of ourselves left behind that we could never find again.

I wanted to say: Georg. Please defect.

Please.

It will just be . . .

. . . it's the sensible . . .

. . . maybe even the right . . .

. . . we can work something out, it'll be . . .

Sorry.

Sorry.

It wasn't ever a game, but in the end that was the story we told to make it . . .

Sorry.

You weren't ever really human in my eyes either. You were always just . . . something else.

Sorry.

Instead, I stared at my boots, and then up at him, and wondered what words he'd find, if it would be kindest to speak, or if he needed a little space. When I was Kadri, I had always known these things, but that was another man, another time.

I thought he'd say the obvious – you wouldn't dare, you never would, the inquisition would never allow it! But Georg was not one for obvious falsehoods. He nodded, tilted his head to one side. Nodded again. Didn't meet my eyes. Then he straightened up and, looking a little past my head, said: "So, are you armed?"

I went for my knife, which is why his stick whipped just above my head as he swung it with both hands, before he turned and, stepping to the side, brought it down across my shoulders. I crumpled beneath it, rolled onto the earth and away from his kick, tangled now in robes – stupid bloody robes for a stupid bloody priest – tried to crawl away from another swipe, couldn't quite make the distance and deflected the weight of his stick across my arm. The pain of it cracked down into my spine, salivated in my mouth, more than just bruising, but the adrenaline kept me moving away as I tried to grab at the weapon, over-swung on its arc, and hold on with one hand while fumbling for my blade with the other. My fingers slipped on the waxed wood, and Georg stepped sideways again, using the weight of his body to pull the cane from my grasp, landed a kick, a little awkward, across my ribs, stumbling back off balance from his own efforts as I rolled away from it, gasping for air. In the moment it took him to steady himself on his feet I scurried onto mine, hands up, and as he swung again I barrelled towards him, fingers aiming for his face, trying to close the distance before the full force of the strike could reach me. The heavy handle of the cane flew past my head, but the tip of it bounced into my skull behind my ear. By then my momentum was too great to slow; I slammed into him, fingers clawing at his face, his eyes, trying to get pur-chase on something soft and squelchy. Georg dropped the stick to flail at my hands, strength against strength, before some more intelligent instinct kicked in and, reaching through my arms, he tried to ram his thumb into the ridged length of my windpipe, pushing me back as I curled away from the choking pain of it.

I let go of his face, dropped myself to his left, went to grab his stick as I rolled away, got one hand round one end, but he had caught the other and for a moment we were tugging on it with all the grace of two muddy, yapping pups fighting over a chewed twig. He pulled a little too hard and I let go, fast, his own strength knocking him onto his backside as the energy between us was released. As he fell, I fumbled for my knife again, felt the warmth of the handle against my calf and looked up to see him swinging for my right eye.

It was somewhere around then that the mines blew.

It wasn't one coherent blast. First one chamber beneath the earth, then another, then another, like a string of beads falling from a necklace and clattering to the floor. The roar – the coherent, concerted roar – was a thing that grew over a few seconds as the separate pops joined together, as the clouds of black coal dust and yellow dust broiled and rolled together and upwards, feeding each other, seemingly propelled by the noise of their own explosion. From the church I could see it rise, and an instant later could see nothing at all as a sideways wall of dust choked in off the flatlands. I squeezed my eyes shut and curled up into a ball, covering my ears, trying to breathe only through my robes, the heat and the scratching, suffocating blackness of it a spider's jaw; nothing but this devouring, this coming apart. The ground bounced and buckled like it was a liquid thing, back on the sea again, drowning again, don't let go, don't let go, I had not realised until this moment that the earth was nothing but broken dirt hemmed in by water and air, we would sink, we would be swallowed whole. I couldn't see Georg, couldn't open my eyes for more than a moment to try and peer through the blackness, had never tasted coal before – is this what coal tastes like? The taste of the past, of a dryness that prickles your tongue, of red tissue burning raw and breath with stones in it. Medj should taste coal, before their ordinations; they should swim through the flooded caves of Martyza and learn the songs of the old gods too, the ones who made people special.

After the first roaring, a falling rain. The earth as it falls sounds like hail on metal. It has notes to it, discordant percussions and

390

strange chords. It bounces on your back, runs fingers through your hair. The dust moves like a living thing as you blink and try to rise, shielding your face from the fog of black and grey, blood thick, greased with yellow, melting the soft whites of your eyes. I coughed and spluttered and choked, staggered a few paces, ears singing; tried to shake the singing out, tilting my head side to side, but the note didn't change. I stumbled to the broken door of the church, half-fell, black lumps of broken world falling all around me, slow, fluttering down like feathers or slamming hard in wet splotches of heavy clay. I coughed, spat the colour of slate from my lungs, staggered a few more paces over the buckled earth, distorted like dunes at the beach, saw only blackness rising from Martyza, heard no guns firing, could not see the hollow, empty place we had ripped through the earth beneath what was left of Georg's army. Could not see the bodies they would find there in the months to come, even their eyes turned black by the dust that caked them when the world had caved in.

I thought I heard something behind me, but it was hard to tell through the ringing of my ears, looked up, up through the dust and the black, to where the cloud of coal blown into the sky was still billowing overhead.

I saw something ripple in it, and it was just the wind.

I saw something spark within it, red like fire, and it was just the light.

Then Georg, face turned to soot, caught my shoulder and tried to hit me, but his weight was off, his ears as bloody as mine, and he missed the punch, and I caught him as he half-fell, sinking with him onto the crackling earth. I grabbed his arm before he could swing again, his stick nowhere in sight, and pointed to the cloud, didn't think I could speak, didn't think he could hear me.

He blinked, not understanding, tracks of thinner grey around the corners of his eyes where moisture was trying to form. He followed my finger, pointing to the heavens, saw the dust, saw the coal.

Saw it catch on fire.

The flame started at its root, where the black cloud still clung

391

to the earth, and spread up like a blooming flower. It leapt through the dust and through the fog, a rippling wall of crimson, spilling in all directions across the battlefield, curling in and rolling out like the all-consuming wave of the tsunami. The earth boiled beneath it, fused to stone; the clouds parted overhead as if frightened by a predatory beast, and still the inferno rushed outwards, tumbled down, tumbled towards us.

And for a moment, in the light that was too bright to look at, the fire igniting in every mote of dancing coal spinning on the air, I saw a creature drenched in blood, and its eyes were the hollow voids of an endless death, and its jaw was a waterfall of dripping oil, set alight. It had no wings, no talons or claws of prey, but it beat vengeance across the sky in crimson and black, dimming the sun as it roared across the field. It consumed the ancient chimneys, boiled the water in the abandoned lake. It melted the tanks of Kun Mi, charred the lungs of Antoni Witt and all who followed him. It ignited the grass in tiny spears of spitting yellow, turned the few standing walls of ancient metal into pools of burnt-silver slag. It roared, and roared again, and its voice was the fire, the storm and the earth. The kakuy of Martyza Eztok was as old as the first iron rod driven into the earth, with a heart of coal and a skin of oil. It knew only how to burn.

I crawled to my feet, called: Georg, Georg!

Georg, come with me!

Stumbled towards the hollow open dark that plunged down to the crypt, broken stairs and broken stones.

Georg!

He didn't move.

Kneeling in the peeling ground, staring up at the firestorm.

And I wondered if he saw it too, the great kakuy of the mines, vengeance set aflame. I wondered if he saw it reach out as if it would set the whole world ablaze, as if it could tear down the stars, boil the moon.

Perhaps not. Perhaps, even then, all he saw was the fire.

I tumbled into the darkness of the crypt, as the world burned.

Chapter 68

After a great fire, rain.

The rain was not the rain of the falling forest. It was the winter rain, sucked in by the air being burned away, a tumult of clouds spinning into the eye of the storm. It was cold, melted ice that sizzled and steamed when it hit the ebony earth. It fell for nearly a day, which is why it finally roused me, the thin stream of slime-ochre water at the bottom of the crypt rising to tickle my nose where I'd fallen. Choking woke me. Then I thought perhaps I slept again, and was awake again, back pressed up against a broken sarcophagus, and wondered if this was me awake at all.

I moved my fingers, and the skin was leather.

I listened to the world, and all I could hear was ringing in my ears.

I looked up, and there was night above me, which seemed a lot like being entombed for ever. But if I was entombed, how was the rain getting in, drizzling sideways into my face? My clothes were sodden, black, singed at the hem.

I unwound myself from some of them, tried to tear off a strip, couldn't get enough grip on the tough, wet fabric, wound myself back up again.

It hurt to breathe.

My tongue tasted of ash.

I sat a while.

Someone would come and rescue me, I decided.

Then I decided that the world was dead.

The sky had caught on fire and the world was going to start again from the ashes. The deep-sea creatures would have their time at last, those that barely needed a sip of oxygen to endure. The cave sprouts of impossible green, the crimson algae that lived beneath frozen lakes – they would come into their own and start gorging on the burnt ashes of this new world, exhaling oxygen as they slithered across the earth. Cockroaches would be fine, they always were, and probably form the basis of new life. I wondered what monuments they would make, and what they would make of the ruins of ours.

I sat a little longer, and no one came.

I started to feel cold.

The sensation was astonishing. I had not imagined I could feel cold ever again.

I coughed, and the pain was like bones puncturing flesh. Our lungs are terribly soft, squishy things.

I tried not coughing, and the cold, which had been my friend, became a dull ache, a restless, heavy thing.

It occurred to me that it wouldn't be so hard to die here.

I didn't have much of an emotional relationship with this outcome, but, resting with it for a little while, I felt a growing conviction that to die in this place would be insufferably dumb. It would have been easier to drown, or freeze in the forest, or get shot in the head, or burn alive. All of these would have been quicker and almost entirely someone else's fault. Still, there were plenty of little insects down here – shiny-carapaced millipedes and green-bellied beetles that got tangled in my hair. They'd probably make something worthwhile from my corpse.

I think I slept a little again, couldn't be sure, woke, angry at myself for sleeping, felt the edge of snoozing, raged and cursed and fought against it, found that I had one hand braced against a broken stair.

Climbed.

It was all right to stop every few metres.

It was all right to lie down and try not to cough, to burn, to vanish into this pain.

Reached the top.

Lay down in the rain.

Listened to the earth, hissing, uncoiling from fire to ice.

Crawled towards the broken door of the tumbled-down church, realised it wasn't a door but just a hollow where walls should have been. Pressed my fingers over stone and found it warm, warmer even than my body, was amazed, and clung a little bit longer, revelling in this strange sensation.

Made it all the way out into the ash beyond. Lay on my back to drink down the grey sludge of feathered soot and water falling from the sky.

Slept again, but felt much better about how far I'd come.

Dawn, the colour of an iceberg.

My bicycle was a melted, shrivelled thing, turned in on itself as if ashamed.

I discovered I was incredibly hungry, and that amazed me. I had no idea that hunger could make itself known over so many other unpleasant sensations.

There was a tickle at the back of my throat, a single delicate hair tickling my epiglottis, but I could neither cough nor swallow it down.

I made it to my feet, walked a few paces, crawled a few, walked a few more. If I could walk more than ten, that made the next ten easier. Then I would stop a while, then walk twenty, twenty-five, then rest again. This was how exercise worked, I seemed to recall. You do a little, then a little bit more. It was hard to find a direction and keep to it. The sun swung, a pendulum, back and forth across the sky. I did not aim for the heart of Martyza, for the place riddled with ancient tunnels. But I supposed it was where I needed to be.

There was no clean cliff where the earth had collapsed. Rather, the land caved in towards the valley in slippery, sodden sheets. Nor was it the black of the fire that had burned away the yellow grass but rather the charcoal, coal-burnt, dust-blazed black of an ancient fuel that had nothing left to give. The rain had liquefied much of the broken soil, creating a sea of dust and mud that stretched to the horizon. Those who had not been crushed when the world gave out beneath them, had suffocated. Those who had not suffocated burned. There were no hands reaching up to the sky; no last pictures of pain. Most had been blasted apart when the sky ignited, and only around the very edges of the broken land were there bodies, black, their moisture boiled away so that, mummified, their limbs had curled in, knees to chest, arms laid across their hearts as if peacefully slumbering as every ligament shrivelled and contracted in the heat. I had expected something more. A scarlet morning over which good people might weep. Carrion, pulling at bare flesh. Survivors howling in their agony. There was none of that. Death was too absolute for human drama.

I walked south, towards where there had once been a camp.

The land beneath me squelched and crackled as the rain fell. Sometimes I slipped, half-tumbling into soft earth up to my knee, my thigh, and crawled out hand-over-hand, and then rested a while, drank down air. My breath was wheezing in my chest. A tank was still burning, near the edge of the field. I stared at it, amazed, wondering how there was still fire left in it. Then I smelt the petrol from its broken engine, and it made a little more sense, and either side of it were the foetal, blackened bodies of its crew, ringing it like flowers round a monument.

I found the first trenches that Jia's soldiers had dug. Some lay empty; in others, bodies were still hunched, wrapped around their guns, suffocated as the oxygen burned away. I kept going. There were no bodies in the forward station, but the ceiling was black, the floor too, all the way across the room – not collapsed, but rather a tongue of scarring as if some timber-licking ghost has wet its lips at the window frames. There was no sign of life. The turbines had melted, the solar panels cracked into a greenish, liquid stain.

I walked on as the sun set, and did not hear them over the ringing of my ears but merely stumbled into their camp because it was on the side of the road, and the road was what I was vaguely following. The tents were untouched by char, sagging under the weight of rain, the waxed fabric bowing and bending in pools that the nurses tried to splatter clear with broomsticks from beneath. For a moment I wasn't sure whose side I was looking at, or what I saw. Stretchers were laid out across the floor, faces without eyes, without skin; the less injured sat in rows, knees hunched up, squinting as if the fire still burned in front of them. No one called for the doctors – there seemed a consensus that this would achieve nothing – and in a buzz of orders and ticking compression batteries alone the camp scuttled on.

I thought of asking someone for help, but there didn't seem much point.

Instead, I found what looked like the end of a line and sat down in the mud.

The woman next to me didn't look up, didn't ask me any questions, didn't blink. She held her knees to her chest, arms wrapped tight, and watched sights only she could see.

There was soup.

I ate too fast, and someone snapped at me to stop.

There was clean water.

I choked as I drank it.

Someone said, "His breathing doesn't sound too great ... "

Someone told me to lie down on something that bounced.

Someone else shoved something up my nose that tickled. I tried to swat it away, but hands caught mine and tutted and said, "Leave it – leave it!"

I think they gave me something that felt nice, like cherry blossom, but inside.

Sometime later, someone asked: "How are you feeling, earth-kin?"

I tried to speak, couldn't. They gave me water. I tried again. "Terrible."

"I'm going to do some tests, okay? I just need you to ... "

A little later, someone else leant over, white rags turned black with the soot from my face, my hands, my skin. They'd taken off my robes and manhandled me into some sort of sterile gown that tied at the side. I wasn't sure if I'd participated in the process or not. They said: "What's your name?"

"Ven. My name is Ven."

Chapter 69

There was time in a hospital.

Then there was time in a temple room.

Jaqcs came to me and said: "The fires have burned out now. The rain has stopped. The Brotherhood is in full retreat."

I didn't answer, lay curled on my side, staring at the wall.

A delegation of inquisitors came to me and said: "It was heresy. It was. It was heresy. Blowing the archive at Martyza Eztok . . . we meant it for the best. The longer the war goes on, the more angry the kakuy become. We had to end the war. We have to keep the peace."

Someone turned on the radio, and there was music playing, and it hurt my head.

Someone gave me an inkstone, and the news showed an artist's impression of the great kakuy of the pit, and it looked human, it looked like the kind of creature that cared how humans looked.

I threw the inkstone across the room, and no one asked why.

Then, one unremarkable day, Jaqcs came to me and said, "Merthe has taken Bukarest," and asked me if I wanted to light a lantern at the spring festival, and I smelt the cool damp of unfolding green after rain, and held the thin, painted paper between my hands, and that was when I cried.

So ridiculous, I thought, to cry for the lighting of a lamp. Of all the things to get messed up over, this little, absurd thing, this tiny point of light – it made no sense at all.

They put one hand awkwardly on my shoulder while I wept, and murmured, there there, it's all right, it's all right. You're all right now.

In the evening, we processed down to the water's edge, all the Medj of the city, the temples great and small, and some people came to watch the procession and eat sticky cakes of nuts and honey, and others joined in, dancing and ringing bells, for the spring festival of Isdanbul was meant to be a party, not a serious, chanting affair. There were stalls selling sticks of fruit and piles of hot, steaming bread; competing bands trying to out-blare each other, flags flying from the branches of the newly budding trees. The Medj of the Blue Temple lit their lamp first, from a taper they'd carried down the hill, and that fire was then passed to the next lamp, and the next, and the next, until the flame reached me. I cupped it carefully as the wick caught, then passed it on, until at last the lamps of every priest and novice were lit, and the youngest went into the crowd to pass the fire to the waiting tapers and lamps of the hearth-kin waiting there, and I wasn't sure if I would get through the business in one piece, and Jaqcs stood nearby to say nice things in case I didn't, and they helped me push my lantern out onto the still waters of the strait, to join the others, swimming in light.

In the morning after Bukarest fell, Jia went on the radio and said: This is the beginning of the end. We have suffered, we have endured, but now the tide is turning. The tide always turns.

She sounded tired, but who didn't these days?

Kun Mi's entire second army was gone, along with large parts of the third. The lucky ones would have died too quickly to know how it ended. Council did not report the losses on its side or speak of the tongues of flame that had melted the railway tracks and ripped the nearby villages from the earth.

The kakuy of Martyza had not cared who it killed, the day the sky caught fire.

If, that is, there had been a kakuy at all. All you need to start

400

a fire is fuel, oxygen and a spark. And who was there left alive to report on the details of what they'd seen? Not Georg. Not anyone whose report could really be trusted.

Do you think you saw the kakuy of Martyza? asked Jaqcs as we drank cool water by the temple stream. Do you think you saw the spirit of the flame?

They had found a few ashen bones from Georg's body and the metal head of his stick, wolfen, grinning still, its snarl a little twisted at the edges where it had started to melt, turning from a leer to a sobbing scowl.

Coal dust in the air, I said at last.

Sparks from a gun.

Does it make a difference, when the day is done?

Krima vaMiyani sits, cross-legged, on a cushion by the door of the shrine reading from her inkstone. There is a guard nearby, examining the wall of little prayers inked onto bamboo by the door. I do not know if he is impressed by what he reads. One day, he may be thinking, our civilisation will fall and when people find our prayers they will discover it's all "please let her love me again" or "I lost my favourite necklace" or "just no morning sickness this time round".

I want to take him down, down, to the cold archives beneath the temple, to the tunnels where we keep the past, to show him selfies and pictures of food, jokes and terrible puns in dead, archaic scripts, tell him, look, look – look at people living. Look at how beautiful it is to be alive.

Instead, I follow the jerk of Krima's chin into the shrine, where Yue sits, back to the wall, hands loose by her sides. I ease down next to her, bump my shoulder against hers, mutter, "Hi."

"Hi."

"You heading out?"

"Uh-huh."

"Got everything you need? Toothbrush, spare change of pants?"

"I believe the system provides all that when I get there."

"Take it from someone who was a political prisoner: you'll want your own toothpaste. It makes such a difference."

"I'll be fine."

She has shaved her hair down to a buzz, perhaps unwilling to trust a prison barber. It makes her look younger, a child with tired eyes.

"They let you have an inkstone?"

"They believe that busy, occupied minds are safer than bored, unstimulated ones. So yes, I have an inkstone, and there is a library."

"I'll send you books."

"That's hardly necessary."

"I have eclectic taste."

She smiled, quickly turning her chin away from me to grimace at the painted ceiling of the shrine, where kakuy of sky and star danced in blue above us. "Nothing too philosophical, please. I think I'll get enough of that anyway."

"Trashy romance?"

"If you absolutely must."

"There are some fascinating old-world texts. Girl meets boy, boy is a dickhead, girl falls for boy, girl meets different boy who isn't a dickhead, but in her infatuation can't see the merits of new boy because the first boy is pretty . . ."

"Did you study this? Is this what inquisition training involved?"

"Eclectic tastes," I repeated. "Good for insomnia."

She nodded, unfolded, rose, stretched. I rose too, facing her, a breath apart. She looked past me for a moment, then said: "Don't wait. It's very important to me that you don't wait."

"That's my choice to make, isn't it?"

"You can take good advice."

"I can find no evidence whatsoever to support that hypothesis."

Her eyes flickered to my face as if they would stay there, then danced away again. "According to the priests, everything changes. They say it's the only thing you can rely on."

"Please. I am a professional deliverer of pithy contradictory-yet-demonstrable nuggets of wisdom. And what Temple says is

402

true. The world is vast and everything changes; but that doesn't mean we don't try."

She nodded again, harder, brisk. Smiled at her shoes, smiled at the painted roof of the shrine and finally smiled at me. "Be well, Ven, kin of earth and sky."

"See you around, Yue."

One last nod, an ending of all things. She pressed her hands together, and bowed, and so did I. Then Yue walked away, and in the shrine I prayed for her, and felt that she would probably be okay, and that if she wasn't there were things people could do about it, and that made praying much, much easier.

Later, the forest grew.

About the author

Claire North is a pseudonym for Catherine Webb, a Carnegie Medal-nominated author whose debut novel was written when she was just fourteen years old. She has fast established herself as one of the most powerful and imaginative voices in modern fiction. Her first book published under the Claire North pen name was *The First Fifteen Lives of Harry August*, which became a word-of-mouth bestseller and won the John W. Campbell Memorial Award. Her follow-up, *Touch*, was described by the Independent as "little short of a masterpiece". Her next novel, *The Sudden Appearance of Hope*, won the 2017 World Fantasy Award for Best Novel, and *The End of the Day* was shortlisted for the 2017 *Sunday Times*/PFD Young Writer of the Year Award. Her 2018 novel, 84K, received a special citation at the Philip K. Dick Awards, and her latest novel, *The Pursuit of William Abbey*, has been shortlisted for a Locus award. Claire lives in London.

Find out more about Claire North and other Orbit authors by registering for the free monthly newsletter at orbitbook.net.

Help us make the next generation of readers

We – both author and publisher – hope you enjoyed this book.
We believe that you can become a reader at any time in your life,
but we'd love your help to give the next generation a head start.

Did you know that 9% of children don't have a book of their
own in their home, rising to 12% in disadvantaged families*?
We'd like to try to change that by asking you to consider the role
you could play in helping to build readers of the future.

We'd love you to think of sharing, borrowing, reading, buying or talking
about a book with a child in your life and spreading the love of reading.
We want to make sure the next generation continue to have access
to books, wherever they come from.

And if you would like to consider donating to charities that help
fund literacy projects, find out more at www.literacytrust.org.uk
and www.booktrust.org.uk.

Thank you.

little, brown
BOOK GROUP

*As reported by the National Literacy Trust

The Self-Preservation Society

KATE HARRISON

ISIS
LARGE PRINT
Oxford

First published in Great Britain 2007
by
Orion Books,
an imprint of The Orion Publishing Group Ltd

Published in Large Print 2007 by ISIS Publishing Ltd.,
7 Centremead, Osney Mead, Oxford OX2 0ES
by arrangement with
The Orion Publishing Group Ltd

British Library Cataloguing in Publication Data
Harrison, Kate
    The self-preservation society. – Large print ed.
    1. Fear – Fiction
    2. Life change events – Fiction
    3. Large type books
    I. Title
    823.9'2 [F]

ISBN 978–0–7531–7898–0 (hb)
ISBN 978–0–7531–7899–7 (pb)

Printed and bound in Great Britain by
T. J. International Ltd., Padstow, Cornwall

Fear is the prison of the heart
Anonymous

Acknowledgements

The world is definitely a dangerous place, but it feels much safer thanks to the following special people . . .

Tessa Carey was a great help when I was researching the earliest stages of the book. I'm also indebted to the information provided by Headway, the national charity assisting those recovering from brain injury (http://www.headway.org.uk/). Many patients face far greater challenges than Jo, and Headway is a lifeline for them and their families.

My own memories of living near Greenham Common were supplemented by *Greenham Common: Women at the Wire* (edited by Barbara Harford & Sarah Hopkins), which gives a terrific picture of life at the Peace Camp. I watched numerous terrifying 1980s Cold War programmes, including the brilliantly clinical *QED: A Guide to Armageddon*, and the chilling *Threads*. The accident statistics have been collated from a variety of government, newspaper, and web sources (though any errors are undoubtedly mine).

On the writing front, thank you to Araminta, Lizzie and Peta, for helping me reign in my tendency to give every second character bad skin (and for doing so much more besides.) Thank you to all at Orion, including the brilliant sales reps and Sidonie Beresford-Browne and Robyn Neild for the gorgeous cover. Special thanks to Juliet Ewers, Susan Lamb, Lisa

Milton, Angela McMahon and Emma Noble. And of course to Kate Mills and Genevieve Pegg for helping me to see the wood for the trees.

My former colleagues in development (especially Lillie, Lucy, Richard and Samia) showed admirable restraint in putting up with my authorly ways. Now that I work from home, I rely on other writers to provide the fourth emergency service when confidence fails: the Romantic Novelists' Association, the Novel Racers, the Bloggers with Book Deals, everyone on The Board and, of course, the Girly Writers (Jacqui H, Jacqui L, Linda, Louise and Stephanie). Thank you too to all the brilliant authors who agreed to read advance copies of this book!

My own scaredy-cat tendencies are kept firmly in check by friends and family: You're all stars. Big hugs to Geri and Jenny, Pat and Pete, Toni, Mum, Dad and Rich . . .

Finally, many thanks to everyone who reads this novel, and especially to all who've taken the trouble to email me about my books: you can get in touch via my website, www.kateharrison.com

Kate Harrison, March 2007

Prologue:

GREENHAM COMMON HIGH SCHOOL, 1982

Nucleomituphobia —
Fear of Nuclear Weapons

This is how fear feels.

". . . now, the theory of fight or flight originates from studies of animal behaviour."

I don't mean the fizzy fear you get from things that go bump in the night, or watching *Halloween II* and *Friday the 13th.* Or even the moment in a dream when your feet turn to lead and the flame-throwing monster is catching up.

No, this is a nightmare I can't wake up from, because everything familiar in this world — from biology lessons to Adam Ant and pregnant giant pandas — is under threat. One day, maybe today even, it'll happen. And it'll kill anyone who hasn't prepared, and change life for ever for the lucky few who make it. And the really nightmarish bit? No one else seems to care.

1

"The term describes the physiological response to extreme stress, priming the body to attack or to run away, both responses which reflect the ultimate instinct for self-preservation."

Lorraine has drawn a picture of a willy in the back of her exercise book, and is folding up the sheet of paper to pass to Steven Chubb. I suppose there are worse things to draw in a biology lesson. She's added pubic hairs with curly pen strokes. The only willy I've seen is my little brother's but Lorraine has seen a real one ("OK, one in a dirty magazine, but it was on a real man. It was ginormous.") so her picture must be pretty accurate.

The probability that I'll die before seeing an erect penis is high, but it's not top of my worry list. I'd like to have kissed a boy, maybe, but I'm not too bothered about missing out on *intercourse*. It sounds like the most embarrassing thing in the world.

The second most embarrasing thing in the world will be having to use the toilet in front of my parents, but that's the price of survival. At least it'll be dark in the shelter.

"The body responds to stress by stopping non-essential functions. A human being may experience a dry mouth as salivation ceases, along with sudden evacuation of the bowels or bladder as gastro-intestinal function shuts down . . ."

Something hard hits the back of my head, like an air pellet. I reach under the wooden bench, and discover Steven's reply to Lorraine, screwed into a tight ball.

2

". . . and the inability to sustain an erection." Mr Jones, our biology teacher, is careful not to meet anyone's eye when he says "erection". "These changes prepare the body for fight or flight."

Lorraine unravels Steven's note. It says, "Suck on mine".

"As if I would," she whispers to me.

"The body instinctively prioritises muscle function to allow a rapid . . ."

And then it happens. A sound that would chill the blood even if you didn't know what it meant. But I do. That wavy wail is saying *take cover, the bomb's on its way.*

Mr Jones flinches, then begins to wave his arms around. His mouth is moving but all I can hear is a rushing noise, like the sound of a thousand seashells held against your ear. More urgent, my stomach contents feel like they're on a one-way trip out of my body.

This can't be happening. I should be at home, where the stockpile is hidden in the garage. Sixteen weeks' worth of pocket money spent on baked beans and evaporated milk and plasters and Dettol.

It'll take twelve minutes to run home. We only have four.

Mr Jones is lining everyone up by the door. I still hear nothing except whooshing but sweat has chilled my skin, and it feels like a huge fist is squeezing my heart.

There's meant to be a build-up, a two-week "escalation of hostilities".

I cast around the room, trying to remember the guidelines from *Protect and Survive*. You're safest in a downstairs room, with no outside walls.

Lorraine is pulling at my arm but I can't move. Or breathe. The science department is on the ground floor but there are draughty metal windows from floor to ceiling in place of two walls. They'll shatter in the first few seconds of the blast wave.

Oh my God. We're going to die. I told Dad we should have moved to Wales or New Zealand. I've survived a near-death experience involving a poncho and a slide, *and* a hundred childhood illnesses, only to be split into a million atoms and turned into a mushroom cloud.

Keep calm, Jo, remember to breathe. I stare ahead, try to think straight. And then I spot it.

Yes! The science prep room. The dizziness stops, though I'm still not at all confident I can hang on to the contents of my bowels. I let Lorraine pull me from behind the bench — we're the last to leave the classroom — and at the very last moment, I grab her blazer sleeve and drag her into the prep room. I take the key from outside the lock and then pull the door shut behind us, locking it from the inside. The cramped space stinks of iodine and mouse feed.

I grope for the light switch on the wall. "Lorrie, put the plug in the sink and run the water. We don't have much time."

My hearing is returning now: the siren's still sounding and Lorraine shouts above it, "What the bloody hell are you doing, Joey? If there *is* a fire, we'll be burned to death in here, you nut-job."

"It's not the fire bell. It's a *siren*. An air attack siren. There's a bomb on its way."

Now her face is less certain. If anyone in school is an expert on the bomb it's me. And our fire bell has a reassuring ring, like a phone in a public call box. Not like this.

I hide the key in my pocket — I won't let her out, she's my best friend. I'm not going to think about Mum or Dad or Timmy or Misty. "The water, quickly." I spot a grey metal bin. Oh God, that's going to have to be our loo. On the bare brick wall, dog-eared posters show photosynthesis, native trees and the inner workings of the human body: maybe all three will be history, not biology, once the nuclear winter comes, and our organs mutate, thanks to radiation. The open wooden shelves are stacked with Pyrex flasks and disposable gloves and plastic bags big enough for corpses. The first aid kit is serious and satchel-sized. It's not a bad shelter, under the circumstances.

"You're wrong. You have to be." But Lorraine begins to fill the sink. I push stacks of green paper towels against the bottom of the door and into the lock, to keep out fall-out. What will we eat? Lab mice? Humans can survive for weeks, so long as they have water.

The sink is almost full now. "How long, Lorrie? Since the alarm started?"

"Buggered if I know." She always swears when she wants to seem cockier than she's actually feeling. Her eyes are dark and wide, as if her Miners Special Effects black kohl has run. "Three or four minutes."

The fist tightens around my heart. "Right. Switch off the tap. I'm going to have to put out the light." My finger hovers over the switch. What if the gas supply for the Bunsen burners causes a fire? Shouldn't I have released the mice? I cut the light, and reach out for Lorraine. "Shut your eyes and put your fingers in your ears."

Oh God, I hope this isn't going to hurt. If we're going to die, let it be quick . . .

It begins, not with a flash, but with a rumble, and I wonder if the first missile has fallen somewhere far away, London or Oxford. Lorraine wriggles and I try to hold her still until she pulls my hands away from my ears and I realise that someone's pummelling on the door.

"JOANNA MORGAN! UNLOCK THAT DOOR THIS INSTANT!" It's Mr Jones.

"We can't let him in, Lorrie. There's no room and the bomb could be about to —"

"I said, open the door." The banging continues. "I don't know what you think you're playing at but you're holding up the entire fire drill and the whole school will have to stay outside in the freezing cold until you come out. And you're not going to be very popular."

"Fire drill?" Lorraine finds the light switch. "You wally. You complete and utter Joey. I knew it wasn't a bomb. We'll be in detention for a month now. Or on litter duty."

6

She fumbles in my blazer pocket for the key and unlocks the door. Mr Jones stands on the other side, his left eye twitching in fury. "What the hell were you thinking?"

My hands are shaking as I emerge into daylight, and I feel colder than ever, the sweat gluing my skin to my nylon blouse. I'm desperate for the toilet, because my insides seem to be made of water, but instead Mr Jones marches us down the corridor.

"I'm flabbergasted at this behaviour from you, Joanna. What was that about?"

"The siren . . ." I say. "It wasn't a fire alarm. It was an air raid siren."

He stops. "No, Joanna. The alarm was upgraded this weekend. This is a test."

"But Mr Blake says . . ."

"But nothing." He sighs. "So you're in Mr Blake's class, are you? Bloody English teachers. There is such a thing as too vivid an imagination."

And then we walk out of the main entrance to the field where 700 kids and sixty teachers are standing in shivering lines. My knees bend like Olive Oyl's as I stumble down the steps. Some fifth-formers start jeering and within seconds everyone is laughing and pointing, and I want to run for it, but Lorraine grabs my hand and we walk towards our tutor group.

As I pass Steven Chubb, he begins to whisper, "Chicken, cowardy custard, scaredy-cat. Chicken, cowardy custard, scaredy-cat!"

And I know that I've just earned a nickname that I'll never shake off. But at least I'm still alive. Until the Bomb drops for real.

CHAPTER
ONE

Tyrannophobia —
Fear of Tyrants

"Of course, the Tudors had it easy."

The dead eyes of Anne Boleyn stare at me from behind the velvet rope as Dennis, my soul mate, warms to his theme.

"Think about it. No electricity, therefore no ineptly wired sockets capable of delivering hundreds of fatal volts. No gas, therefore no danger of leaks which could blow your house . . . or, in this case, your castle, to smithereens."

He's only *half* joking.

Soggy families gather around us, forced indoors by a January downpour. They jostle for position alongside seen-better-days mannequins dressed as Henry the Eighth and his unfortunate wives. They clearly think Dennis is an official tour guide.

He looks the part. He took his anorak off before entering the Great Hall ("wouldn't want the rainwater to damage the historic tapestries, would I, Jo?"). Underneath, he's wearing a check shirt and chinos, as sported by younger Oxford dons in TV documentaries, an artfully casual uniform that proves they have weightier matters on their enormous minds than mere fashion. Quantum physics, maybe, or the preservation of relics of ancient civilisations.

Or, in Dennis's case, the preservation of civilisation in the small corner of southern England we call home.

Dennis couldn't care less about colour or pattern (unless the patterns are on the side of a lorry, warning of corrosive or explosive chemicals). But I do care, and I buy his clothes, so I chose a blue check that matches his eyes, and chinos the same sandy brown as his curly hair. He reminds me of an ageing cherub, the curls shot with grey, and the eyes wrinkled by forty years of trying to save people from themselves. A kind of suburban Superman.

He smiles at me. "And no motor cars, so therefore no speeding accidents, no road pollution and no greenhouse effect. Those were the days, eh, Jo?"

"Utter bollocks!"

Disapproving eyes focus on the impertinent member of the tour party. Except it's not a member of any tour party. It's my dad.

"What about the dangers of bloody horses and carts?" my father says, delighted to have a captive audience. "Toxic manure fumes. Crazed carriage drivers with road rage. Dick Turpin and his Merry Men lurking behind every tree to rob your gold bullion. Not to mention Jack the Ripper *and* the bubonic plague." What he lacks in historical accuracy, he makes up for in enthusiasm.

10

Women are meant to fancy men who remind them of their dads, aren't they? No danger of that with me. My father thinks he's Michael Caine, but while his hero has grown old gracefully, Dad has not. He sports a year-round golf-club tan, and would rather die than countenance casual clothes. So apart from the security staff, he's the only man here in a navy blazer, but because it's a Sunday his bright white shirt is unbuttoned to reveal a wisp of chest hair, suspiciously dark for a man in his sixties.

What Dennis and my dad do have in common is a conviction that they're always right. In my boyfriend's case, that's true. He's incredibly well read, and shares my love of statistics: in a dangerous world, statistics keep you safe.

Whereas my dad is a dinosaur. Albeit quite a charming one.

"No drug-induced soaring crime rates," Dennis counters. "No hoodies. No crackheads. No nuclear, chemical or biological weapons of mass destruction."

"What about those cannon things that propelled great balls of fire across the battlements? They were pretty destructive."

Anne Boleyn holds out her tiny plastic hands, which are peeling as if she's contracted some nasty Tudor skin disease. Alongside her, Anne of Cleves stares into the middle distance. Her wary expression seems familiar and it's only when I turn around that I realise why: my mother's face is composed in the same mask of careful neutrality.

11

Whenever life gets awkward, her eyes glaze over, as if she's teleported herself back home to her "babies", the three Maine Coon cats that are Mum's reason for living. But she doesn't fool me. Every time Dad says something daft (i.e. pretty much every time he speaks), her pale lips purse, fleetingly, a dozen new lines of disappointment appearing like tiny needles around her mouth. Then they're gone: no one notices but me.

"A few cannons are nothing compared to the Ebola virus. Or sarin gas. Or DIY. Did you know that a thousand people a year end up in casualty from sandpaper alone?" Dennis considers this a killer blow.

My father shakes his head pityingly. "I'm delighted to say that I didn't know that. And if I did, I wouldn't be showing off about it."

The other tourists have finally realised that Dennis and Dad aren't an English Heritage-sponsored sideshow, but just two blokes having the kind of spat you could see in your local pub any night of the week. "Torture chamber's this way," a weary mother tells her ginger-haired twin sons. "Whips and branding irons and a rack where they used to stretch little boys who refused to eat their greens."

Dennis whispers, under his breath, "There's a word for people who think ignorance is bliss."

"And there's a word for people like you," Dad says, not under his breath at all. "Smart-arse."

OK, so maybe today wasn't the best idea. It's Dennis's fault: his mother's idea of an outing for her eight-year-old son was to send him on a "treasure hunt" around the local shops until he found one willing

12

to sell him twenty Benson and Hedges to bring home. So he's never realised that wintry day trips to damp, draughty castles are simply the modern version of thumbscrews: torture for all the family.

Thank God for out-of-town superstores with Sunday opening: shopping beats heritage every time when it comes to domestic harmony.

Mum's lip needles appear again and I think it's time to change the subject. "Maybe life wasn't too bad if you were King but somehow I doubt Henry's wives felt all that safe."

My mother looks at me gratefully, her face relaxing enough to remind me how pretty she was, once. "That's true. What was it we learned at school? Divorced, beheaded, *died*, divorced, beheaded, *survived!*" She nods in satisfaction. "Funny the things you remember."

I haven't exactly lightened the mood. We turn to stare at the crash-test-dummy wives, who surround the fat king, his codpiece obscenely prominent. Dad only agreed to come as research for his forthcoming role in the Operatic Society's production of *Henry — The Musical!* but the part of a womanising, gluttonous patriarch fits him like a glove.

I remember studying the Tudors at school, sitting at the back of the history lesson with my best friend Lorraine, trying to work out which queen we most resembled. I saw her eyes narrow and braced myself: to this day, Lorraine combines ruthless honesty with a bitchy streak. I kept my fingers crossed as she considered my Tudor *doppelgänger*. *Please, please don't let her say poor plain Anne of Cleves with her long nose and pointy chin, or sour-faced old Catherine Parr with her sulky lips.*

But she must have been in a generous mood, because she chose Catherine of Aragon. It wasn't a bad likeness: Henry's first wife and I share the same round face, big eyes and flushed cheeks (I wonder if hers, like mine, went red at the slightest provocation). And while neither of us could be described as skinny, we both got a decent cleavage as a consolation prize.

Lorraine wanted to be Jane Seymour, until she turned the page in *Kings and Queens for Secondary Schools* and realised Henry's third wife was distinctly beaky, had a double chin and looked nothing like the actress who did the ads for Le Jardin de Max Factor. In the end she settled for Anne Boleyn, "because Henry the Eighth dumped Catherine of Aragon for her as Anne was prettier. Like me and you!" And then she giggled.

". . . but what I don't understand," my father is saying, "is how come the most powerful man in the country had to keep getting *married*. One wife is enough for anyone surely?"

Mum's lips purse so hard that even Dennis notices, but Dad ploughs on regardless. "I mean, sow his regal oats, sure, but wouldn't he get a nightly smorgasbord of ladies-in-waiting dying to lie back and think of England? Perk of the job and all that —"

"Talking of smorgasbords . . ." I interrupt, spotting my chance, "all this talk of death is making me hungry. It must be tea-time by now?"

14

★ ★ ★

While more sensible families are tucking into IKEA smorgasbords, their kids safely immersed in the children's ball pool, we're being royally ripped off. Dennis has paid £20 for four teas and four "authentic Elizabethan cakes". I love all cakes, but these taste as if they were authentically baked the same week poor Katherine Howard lost her head.

Rain thuds down on the corrugated iron roof of the King's Buttery (which my father keeps repeating in a silly, high-pitched voice, "The king's buttery, he's covered in the stuff, that's why he's such a lard-arse," and then laughing at himself). It's a modern building, if a Second World War Nissen hut counts as modern, and inside, you can see your breath in front of your face. The beige fan heaters produce very little warmth, but make the air smell scorched.

We've found a seat by the tiny window, and I wipe away the condensation with my fingers. Framed by the glass, the castle's like a drawing from a child's picture book, with stone walls washed grey by the rain, and a perfect ring of a moat to keep enemies out . . . or the women in. The castle windows are even smaller than the one I'm peering through and I wonder whether the occupants felt lucky to be there, or trapped.

Dad's fallen silent, and Mum's stirring her tea with the little plastic stick: the grey liquid whirls like filthy bathwater going down the plughole.

"Tuesday will officially be the most depressing day of the year," I say, to break the silence. "According to the statistics."

Oddly enough, this doesn't seem to cheer anyone up, but Dennis tries to join in. "Don't tell me . . . let me guess why. Is it because it's the beginning of the week?"

I shake my head. "It's part of it, but not the main thing. Anyone else?"

Mum begins to fiddle with a knot-effect gold button on her pink fluffy cardigan, so she's obviously not playing.

Dad shrugs. "The weather in January is the worst of the year. So is it to do with seasonal depressive pre-menstrual tension or whatever hypochondriacs get?"

"That's another contributory factor," I say. "But there's something more obvious. Dad, you definitely ought to get it, it's your specialist subject."

My boyfriend and my father exchange looks of undisguised rivalry. Dennis tugs at the kiss-curl in his fringe, a sure sign of irritation. I'm already regretting the remark about specialist subjects, as Dad's main areas of expertise are: a) women young enough to be his daughter; b) the best tailors for bespoke suits in Bangkok; and c) the love songs of Rogers and Hammerstein. Whereas the area of expertise I was referring to was . . .

"Got it!" Dennis claps his hands together. "It's credit card bills, isn't it? This is the week when the wages of Christmas sin come back to haunt us, in the shape of huge bills. Well, I say, us. I mean, anyone daft enough to rely on credit in the first place."

Dennis has never had a credit card, or an overdraft facility. He even got through university (BA Hons,

Social Policy) without going into the red and prefers the certainty of standing orders to fickle direct debits. Lorraine thinks that makes him "the dullest man in the known universe, worse than Tim Henman or Prince Charles". But I love his utter dependability. Surprises are seriously overrated.

Dad tuts and chews his cake with grim determination. After forty years as a bank manager, he's used to being in the right. "Yes, January is dismal. Which is why we're taking the Caribbean cruise next month. What about you two? Any holiday plans?"

He folds his arms across his chest in triumph. He knows the answer to this one already. We don't *do* holidays. Not abroad, anyway.

"We might take a cottage in Cornwall at Easter," Dennis says. His lazy mother never took him to the seaside, so he imagines *Famous Five*-style picnics on sunny beaches, rather than entire days spent in the car, chasing clouds from coast to coast, in the vain hope that it might stop raining for ten minutes.

"Far East's unbeatable at this time of year," Dad says, sensing victory.

I sigh. "Dad, stop it."

Dennis takes my hand. "The Foreign Office website is very insistent that no part of South East Asia is 100 per cent safe for British tourists."

"As if *anywhere* is 100 per cent safe," Dad mutters.

"Tenerife's lovely at this time of year," Mum says.

"OK, OK," I say, holding up my hand. "Dad, you won't be happy till you've taken the piss so why don't I do it for you? I know I'm safer in the air than I am walking down the street. I know there's a whole world out there waiting to be discovered. I know I'm a great big cowardy-custard chicken scaredy-cat. But it's just the way I am, all right?"

Dad looks sheepish and I realise I must have been talking rather loudly as people are staring. "Now, now, Bean. That's a bit harsh. What's wrong with wanting my only daughter to live a little?"

Dennis grips my hand more firmly. "We like staying at home," he says, "and if other people followed our lead, the polar ice-caps wouldn't be melting, would they?"

It's not that I don't *want* to fly. I did it reluctantly when I was little, but the older I get, the more terrifying it seems. And however reassuring the safety statistics, I can't bring myself to travel in a tin box with no visible means of staying airborne. Not that it hasn't been frustrating. After university, I got endless postcards from backpacking college friends who'd been celebrating Christmas on the beach in Fiji, or swimming in Iceland's Blue Lagoon. Dad offered to pay for a course he'd seen advertised in the *Daily Mail* called "Get High: Overcoming your Fear of Flying". But then I met Dennis and he told me that fear was nature's way of preserving the human race, and that I didn't need to turn myself into someone else because he loved me exactly as I was.

That's when I knew we were made for each other.

"I doubt one trip to the bloody Canaries would be responsible for the end of the world," Dad mumbles, but he knows he's defeated. We sit listening to the rain on the roof.

"Ought to start heading back," Dennis says eventually, "before the Sunday traffic gets too heavy."

I look at my watch. It's two thirty in the afternoon.

In the car park Dennis averts his eyes from Dad's gas-guzzling 4x4, and Dad can't resist a sly chuckle at our mauve super-mini (chosen by Dennis because it tops the European NCAP safety league tables). As I kiss my parents goodbye, I realise I'm rather looking forward to the most depressing day of the year: at least at work, you don't have to pretend to be enjoying yourself.

CHAPTER
TWO

Ephebiphobia — Fear of Teenagers

"Keep it safe, keep it real, stay well cool, do what ya feel . . ."

There is nothing more cringe-worthy than adults trying to relate to the younger generation.

"We is safe . . . and we is sound."

Especially when the adults in question all work in local government and would probably class the misuse of an apostrophe as the ultimate rebellion.

"We belong to da underground."

There's a pause in the rap music and we hold our breath. I'm hoping that's the end of the Courtbridge Schools' Safety Group Young Person's Safe 'n' Sound Project hip-hop presentation. We wait, just to be certain it's over, before Mikey — the only member of council staff who could *ever* qualify as cool — starts applauding, then we all join in.

We're a pretty sorry line-up, the kind of people the tabloids love to hate for banning daisy-chains, or conker competitions, or coins in your Christmas pudding. I'm a foot soldier in the Killjoys' Army, as

Community Liaison Officer (Accident Prevention, Public Protection and Civil Defence). Not that I've got the power to ban *anything*. The real clout lies with slutty Sheila Fothergill (mayor and chairwoman of the Civil Protection Committee), and Dennis Diffley (Deputy Director, Public Protection and Civil Defence. And my soul mate).

Dennis winks at me and I hope the teenagers don't see, because they'd be horrified. To them, I'm sure he seems ancient, but he's only just turned forty. Our clothes don't help: he's in the suit he wears for photo-opportunities, the one that makes him look a dead cert for the Director's job. I'm wearing my grey suit. OK, the tailored jacket barely fastens across my chest, but once I've done it up, it seems to make my boobs disappear, which is just the way I like it.

Mikey high-fives the teenage lead rapper so hard that the boy has to clutch his palm to stop it stinging. Because Mikey has a tattoo (a rather small black Celtic pattern on his upper arm), one piercing (that we know of, in his eyebrow), and has been through rehab, the powers-that-be let him do precisely what he likes. He's spent an entire term on this peer safety project for the socially excluded, though the kids he's targeted with his workshops don't look particularly socially excluded to me. They have neat fringes and clean nails, and seem almost as embarrassed as the adults.

Mrs Fothergill gets to her feet, swaying slightly in her banana-yellow kitten heels. She steadies herself on the enormous oak table, her polished black talons leaving eight crescent-shaped dents in the Doomsday-old wood. I booked the council chamber for this special occasion, and the burghers of Courtbridge stare down at us from their gilt frames. They were moved from the Georgian town hall into the new-build council HQ in the 1970s, and they still look perplexed at their surroundings. Mrs Fothergill's portrait will join them before long, as the first female mayor in the town's history. No one stands in her way. She'd pierce their feet with her pointy shoes if they dared.

"Girls . . . and *boys*." She lingers on the word boys, smiling at the lead rapper, who blushes so violently his spots look fit to burst. "What a performance! As your democratic representative, and more importantly, as a person, I know what a terrible trial growing up can be. All those uncontrollable hormones . . . No wonder accidents are so common among you youngsters."

I catch Dennis's eye and we exchange sly smiles. Though menopausal, Mrs Fothergill is famously awash with uncontrollable hormones, and not shy of acting on them. Though I can't believe she'd take advantage of a teenager.

"That's why we're so grateful to Mikey. I have never met a man able to express himself so powerfully. He is willing to risk life and limb to engage the disaffected, and yet he bears this burden so lightly on those broad . . . *capable* shoulders." She pauses, licks her Juicy Tubed lips and winks in Mikey's direction.

I don't know whether to be scandalised at her cradle-snatching (she must be fifty-five, and Mikey's twenty-six), or relieved that she isn't targeting the students.

"So without further ado, that buffet's looking rather inviting so I think it's time to — what would you say, rap-style, Mikey? — ditch da bitch and get stuck into the food, yeh, mother-suckers?"

There's a pause as the kids look at each other, unable to believe what this old woman has just said, before Mikey steps in. "Hey, Mrs F, we'd never diss you. But no messing, man, that grub's on borrowed time. Go, go, go!"

This time, they don't need any persuasion, and two dozen teenagers fall on the refreshments like a meeting of the Young Bulimics' Federation. They won't be disappointed: our subsidised canteen is one of the very few fringe benefits of working for Courtbridge Borough Council. The jam roly-poly won the traditional pudding category of the South-East Local Authority Catering Awards three years in a row.

"So, Mikey and Sheila, who'd have thought it?" Dennis whispers, creeping up behind me. "Don't they make a charming couple?"

"Well, they would if she wasn't married."

Dennis has a satisfied smile on his face. He loves knowing people's secrets. "Never stopped her before has it? She even tried it on with me before we got together . . ."

"You never told me that!"

"Oh, yes, she used to play footsie with me under the table during cabinet meetings . . . though thankfully our vandalism and accident rates in the borough are beginning to diminish in line with our Strategic Objectives."

I'm just wondering whether the stress of his job has turned Dennis quite mad, when I turn and realise the *Gazette* reporter is earwigging.

I try to think of something supportive to add. "Yes, I agree, it's a real achievement to engage all those troubled young —"

But my boyfriend cuts across me. "Hi, Dennis Diffley, Deputy Director, Public Protection. I don't think we've met?" he says, addressing the reporter.

"No. I d-don't think we have, no," the journalist stutters. He looks like the trainee, podgy and uncomfortable in his cheap jacket. The *Gazette* would hardly send their star reporter to this event. "I wasn't quite sure who to interview."

I smile reassuringly. "I'm sure the kids will talk to you, once their noses are out of the trough."

"Right. Better wait a mo then. And are you involved, too?"

"Well, I organise the schools programme so I suppose —"

But Dennis holds up his hand. "Oh, Jo's one of the backroom girls. I'm sure you'd get a better quote from Councillor Fothergill." He pushes the reporter a little too forcefully on the back, towards the fragrant Sheila. "You don't mind, do you?" he mouths to me, but even if I did, I know he wouldn't turn back.

At first, when we started dating, it used to hurt like crazy when he ignored me at work or used my ideas in meetings, but when he explained why, it did make perfect sense. "The thing is, Jo, your ideas are brilliant, but you're so quiet that if I didn't tell people about them, they'd never be heard and never be acted on. We're a team, now, aren't we? If I get promoted, we both see the benefits."

I never dreamed I'd end up with a high-flier like Dennis. Fifty per cent of people do meet their partners at work, but I've always been rubbish at flirting, and he seemed so out of reach. Until the Strategic Safety Partnership Christmas Dinner Dance, where my colleagues pulled snap-free, child-safe crackers (2350 Britons are injured every year by Christmas trees, lights and decorations) and congaed round the ballroom, while Dennis told me I was beautiful.

It's not as if he doesn't help me out too. He's banned from discussions about my pay rises or promotion, but he's nominated me for three different assertiveness courses (surely one day I'll get the hang of it?), given me new responsibilities (including the all-important Seasonal Safety Bulletin) and he agreed to come to the event today as a special favour — usually he's far too busy planning for major disasters to come to tinpot stuff like this. He came because he loves me.

There, I don't feel hurt at all. Except . . .

I stand in the centre of the council chamber and when I look down, my hands have formed fists. Chit-chat bounces off the walls, louder and louder, and I feel like there's a huge red arrow above my head, pointing to the loser who's so inconsequential that not even her boyfriend wants to talk to her. I'm considering bolting to the toilet when Mikey appears with a plate of crab pinwheel sandwiches. I could kiss him, except Mikey's such a tart, he might kiss me back.

"You look cheesed off," he says, slipping out of street slang. "Boyfriend's hob-nobbing I see."

Dennis is already posing for a photograph with Sheila, who has snaked her arm around his back . . . no, hang on, it's lingering on his hips now. I turn away. "I wish I could do all that schmoozing stuff."

"Nothing to it. You've got to believe in yourself."

"Hmm. Easier said than done."

He raises his pierced eyebrow: the ring trembles for three seconds afterwards. "Why? I mean, look at Dennis. He doesn't let his obvious shortcomings hold him back."

"Oi! That's the love of my life you're talking about," I protest, but not too strongly.

"Only kidding. All right, look at the teens. Seething masses of puppy fat and rampant oily t-zones, and yet there's no stopping them."

I study the students in their little cliques alongside the buffet: there's a lot of pony-tail flicking going on, and that's just the boys. "I wouldn't want to be that age again."

Mikey raises his eyebrows. "God, I would. Imagine all that sex to look forward to."

"I was terrified of sex when I was a teenager. And adolescent girls are *horrible* to each other."

Mikey frowns. "But I bet you had the boys flocking round you when you were at school. What with your natural assests!" And he nods towards my cleavage.

I feel my face turn purple, and I pull the lapels of my jacket together. "I'd have done anything to make them shrink when I was thirteen years old."

26

"Really? What a waste."

"It was like my boobs were the only thing about me the boys were interested in."

"Don't be so hard on them. The boys, I mean. I bet they didn't know how to approach you. Shy girls are so forbidding. Such a shame. Harmless flitation is what makes life worth living."

"Like you and Mrs Fothergill," I say, desperate to change the subject.

He cringes. "Oh God. I hope no one reads anything into that old bag's fantasies."

"Now who's being judgemental, Mikey?"

"Fair point." He scratches the stubble on his chin. "Maybe I should give her one. To show willing. After all, Courtbridge Borough Council never discriminates on the grounds of age, gender, race, religion, sexual orientation . . . or wrinkles."

I giggle. "Or grey hairs."

"Or receding hairlines."

"Or support tights." I am laughing out loud now.

"Stretch marks . . ."

Tears are rolling down my cheeks now. "Liver spots."

"Saggy boobs, varicose veins or haemorrhoids."

I shake my head. "You win. I can't think of any more."

He nods over at Sheila, who is still lingering round my boyfriend, though the photographer has moved on. "Oh, I've got the right horn now. She's such a temptress."

"Stop it," I say, feeling almost sorry for Mrs Fothergill. "We'll end up that way, sooner or later."

27

Mikey snaffles the final pinwheel, chewing it thoughtfully before declaring, "All the more reason to make the most of our youth while it lasts, eh, Jo? I don't think you appreciate how special you are."

And he smiles at me so kindly that for a moment I really believe I can change; joke, flirt and misbehave like I've always wanted to. Remembering a magazine "party confidence trick" that recommended circulating with a bowl of nuts, I head for the buffet, grab a bowl of unflavoured corn snacks (Courtbridge is officially a Peanut-Free Anaphylaxis-Aware Zone) and scan the room for the least intimidating group of people.

Aha! The teachers are bound to be patient with me. I force my mouth into a confident yet friendly expression, and propel myself towards the corner, holding the bowl in front of me, like a Wise Man bearing myrrh.

"Corn snack, anyone?" My voice doesn't match the smile: it's more of a bleat. The teachers — two women nearing retirement, and a younger man with body odour — look a lot less friendly close up.

"No thank you." The man's halitosis forces me to take a step back.

I try again. "So what did you think of the performance?"

They sigh, clearly desperate to resume their discussion of detentions or the teachers' pension scheme or whatever is the topic *du jour* in staffrooms. The older woman eventually says, "Bloody awful, of course. But on the plus side, that idiot Mike did agree to take our most irritating students, so what do you expect?"

The others nod agreement, then stare at me, waiting for me to go. I want to be assertive, stand up for my friend, but I can't remember any of the techniques properly: should I be using the "broken record", or is this a good time for "fogging"? I shuffle backwards until I am in the corner of the chamber, trying to merge with the wall. I was *stupid* to try.

I am a scaredy-cat. This is what I know. No gain but no pain either. Safe 'n' sound.

I peer at my flat Clarks shoes resting on the blue carpet, and wish I could disappear into the thick municipal pile. *Get a grip, Jo. Make yourself useful.* I look around for something to do. Hurrah! The remains of the buffet looks like a landfill site. I take my bowl of corn snacks — I seem to have eaten most of them without realising — and begin to stack stray plates and cutlery. No one pays me the slightest attention now they think I am a clearer-upper.

After all, isn't that what backroom girls are for?

From:	Joanna Morgan [mailto:JMorgan@courtbridge.gov.uk]
Sent:	Wednesday 14 February
To:	Dennis Diffley
CC:	Courtbridge Accident Prevention, Public Protection and Civil Defence Team
BCC:	LusciousLorraine@tramp.net
Subject:	**Valentine Safety Bulletin: Beware of Cupid's Arrows**

Dear colleagues,

Here, as promised, is my latest research on seasonal health and safety risks. This month, as Dennis Diffley is giving the keynote speech to the Round Table Valentine's Day Lunch today, I've focused on affairs of the heart. Feel free to use these as you see fit! And remember, love is a dangerous business.

- Watch out for anonymous e-Valentines, which security experts say are more likely to come from hackers who are targeting your hard drive than from suitors targeting your heart (if you do fall victim, remember IT are on extension 34567).
- Roses are red, but they also have thorns which harbour deadly tetanus and several types of fungus that can cause severe damage to the body.
- 2.3 million Britons are allergic to perfume, so if you must *splash it all over*, keep an inhaler handy in case your paramour suffers an asthma attack.
- Sex-related injuries cost Britain £358 million a year in days off sick and insurance claims. Apparently, one

in ten of us have claimed for damage to soft furnishings, and the most common injury is a carpet burn.
Keep safe, everyone,
Jo "The Scaredy-cat" Morgan

CHAPTER
THREE

Gamophobia — Fear of Marriage

I'm late for Dennis's special Valentine treat.

It's all Lorraine's fault. I always copy her in on my safety bulletins, though she takes the piss out of them. She printed off the email and took it with her to work on the maternity ward, to keep her ladies entertained between their contractions. Though if anyone appreciates the hidden risks of romance and sex, then surely it's a woman in labour.

"I ONCE THGT ID BRKN A PENIS IN HALF ON A 1 NT STAND," her first text informed me. "BLOOD EVRYWHRE. ID ONLY BROKN SKIN BUT IT FREAKD ME OUT. MY TOP TIP 4 YR NEXT SAFETY BULLETIN — BEWARE OF OVERDOING THE FRCTION WHN WNKING A BLOKE OFF."

The next text contained a list of the things her colleagues had retrieved from orifices while working in casualty, including "PLICEMEN'S TORCH, PENKNIFE & A PRIMUS STOVE."

I texted back: "THAT MUST HV BEEN SOME CAMPING TRIP!"

Lorraine has always been my expert on matters sexual but I'm not sure that spending her working hours at the sharp end of the birthing business, and her time off prowling the streets for men, has given her the most balanced approach to love.

The texts made me forget the time and when I get down to the foyer Dennis is pacing up and down, wearing a hole in the monogrammed Courtbridge Borough Council royal blue carpet custom-made in 1972. The council architects must have come fresh from designing Eastern bloc airport lounges, because they completely ignored the beautiful mottled-honey Bath stone buildings that feature in all the local guidebooks. Instead they created a civic centre that looks like a stack of concrete shoeboxes.

"You're late," he says.

"Only ten minutes," I protest, though for Dennis ten minutes might as well be ten hours.

"I managed to be on time. I cut short my meeting with Wessex Water." He pulls at the kiss-curl on his fringe.

"Let's hope no one decides to poison the rivers overnight, then, I wouldn't want dead fish on my conscience," I say and he frowns back, as disapproving as a sitcom dad. I try again. "So where are you taking me?"

"It wouldn't be a surprise if I told you." He's striding ahead now, past the raised flower-beds which are

33

dotted here and there with purple crocuses. Climate change has reached Courtbridge, no doubt about it.

I struggle to catch up in my heels. I'm normally a flatties girl, for safety reasons, but thought I'd make the effort for a special occasion. When I first moved in with Dennis, Lorraine warned me I'd have to put more work into keeping things *fresh*, that sharing a bathroom could prove the death of romance. "Make an effort," she advised, "and I don't mean baking cakes."

But two years on, I haven't yet had to buy a peephole bra and crotchless knickers, or greet him at the door wearing only a smile and a fur coat. Then again he's never needed any encouragement on that front. No one at work would guess that mild-mannered Dennis is a tiger in the bedroom. And the kitchen, the hallway, the living-room and the bathroom. Even the patio, though not at this time of year. Global warming hasn't quite penetrated his flagstones.

We cross the road, leaving behind the brutalist building, and darting down a cobbled alleyway that challenges my heels still further. I try not to guess where we're headed but the options for a Valentine's dinner in Courtbridge are limited.

There's the Pony and Trap, the town's oldest pub, now run by a national chain: the romantic menu will have been cook-chilled months ago in an Eastern European warehouse, and the red fabric roses on every table taken out of storage for their annual night of glory, before being packed away again, still in their little silver vases.

I'd have put my money on the Trap, but Dennis walks straight past and I catch a glimpse of the packed dining room, couples blinking under the fluorescent lights.

The Golden Orchid has a more intimate (i.e. pitch dark) ambience, mainly to conceal the food. The main source of lighting is the turquoise glow from the fish tanks, where doomed lobsters drift from one glass wall to the other. The Golden Orchid offers Chinese and English cuisine side by side, both loaded with monosodium glutamate, and neither remotely appetising. I know Dennis won't be taking us there. He is uncompromising on the topic of MSG.

He strides past as though there's a nasty smell. Well, actually there *is* a nasty smell, of chicken fried in old oil. Then he crosses the road.

He wouldn't be taking me to Matches, would he? Now that would be a surprise. Matches is the closest Courtbridge gets to trendy: it has Spanish-Bulgarian-Korean fusion tapas, a purple frosted-glass bar that runs the length of the room, and the most expensive cocktail menu in the county. In the year it's been open, I haven't ventured through its smoked glass doors, but the thought of a Slow Comfortable Screw is oddly tempting right now.

We don't mix drinks at home because *it makes it almost impossible to keep track of alcohol units*. I never exceed fourteen units in a week, and Dennis always stays the right side of twenty-one.

He marches past Matches without a glance.

"Slow down, please, Dennis."

He turns, his forehead creased with impatience. "Well, if you will wear ridiculous shoes . . . You know there are 8000 casualty admissions from high heels every year."

I smile. "Yes, I do know, because I was the one who compiled the footwear hazards bulletin. But if you remember, trainers cause 290,000 accidents, so surely stilettos are the wiser choice, statistically speaking?"

He gives me a dismissive look, unsure whether I'm teasing him, before turning down Canal Path.

I definitely know where we're going now. Courtbridge's very own floating restaurant: the Romantica, the number one location for illicit trysts and indecent proposals. But it has its legitimate side, too. I'd lay bets that nine out of ten couples within a ten-mile radius got engaged in the bobbing barge.

I stop in my tracks.

No. He couldn't be . . . not Dennis. Dennis isn't the marrying kind. He's too practical, too realistic. Moving in together is one thing — the bills are split, the chores are halved and the sex is on tap — but marriage is altogether too risky for the professionally cautious. A tiara, a vicar and a finger buffet don't exactly come with a money-back lifetime guarantee.

I shake the thought from my head and follow Dennis towards the gangplank. The Romantica looks charming in darkness: unlike in daylight, when you can't miss the rusty-brown stains on the hull, and the filler that's holding the windows in place. It feels like the boat's been here for ever, but apparently she began life on the Continent, perhaps cruising along the Seine occupied by elegant French couples, or floating past naked ladies in the red-light district of Amsterdam. Life in Courtbridge must be a let-down.

Through the window, I can see eight candlelit tables for two, most already occupied. Because of the date, these couples all fall into the legitimate category: you can tell by the bored way they're playing with the lettuce on their plates when they'd prefer to be playing footsie with the flirt from accounts.

Stop it, Jo.

It's dark inside the boat, and the smells of garlic and damp are competing with each other. Garlic is winning. My feet feel unsteady as I adjust to the movement of the water. "Herr Diffley?" The owner appears from behind the fly-strips that conceal the galley from view. The Romantica is run by a spooky couple from somewhere behind the old Iron Curtain. I've never been inside the Romantica before, but everyone knows Karl and Kristina. They're always taking out ads in the *Courtbridge Gazette* to showcase their vampire-unfriendly menus.

The man who must be Karl looks like Wee Jimmy from *The Krankies*, dressed in full *maître d'* regalia. He shows us to the best table in the boat, at the back, facing the medieval bridge which gives our town its name. My eyes are adjusting to the gloom now, taking in the lacy tablecloths and the scratched crystal glassware. Our place-settings are an arsenal of dulled cutlery. Fish knives, butter knives, odd little pastry forks. Whatever's on the menu, I have a strong suspicion that every course, including dessert, is going to taste of garlic.

He hands the wine list to Dennis — "is no choice of food, is set dinner we create to made ze heart and other parts leap" — and negotiates his way between the tables, flashing lascivious smiles at the women diners and raising his bushy eyebrow at the men.

"This is a nice surprise," I say. Well, it's definitely a surprise.

"I thought it would fit the bill," he replies, and gives me a meaningful look. "It's a special night."

He disappears behind the drinks list and I wish I had a menu to hide me. Could he *really* be about to propose? Dennis plans everything, with the exception of sex. Actually, I wonder if he even plans that during public protection meetings, mapping out the exact positions in his head to relieve the monotony of avoiding Armageddon.

I peer out of the window at the bridge: two teenagers are chasing each other. Their hoodies are black, and they wear drainpipe jeans that make their legs look as skinny as toothpicks. They weave in and out of parked cars, before the shorter one leaps up on to the narrow stone wall, placing trainered feet one in front of the other, like a wirewalker. The taller boy runs alongside, and I feel flushed with fear that Hoodie One might tumble off the side, into the water.

"Stupid little bugger," Dennis whispers, following my gaze. "Probably been sniffing glue. The canal's so shallow he'll break his neck if he falls."

As he says it, the shorter teenager wobbles and I gasp, as he seems to hover in mid-air for seconds . . . it can't possibly be that long but that's how it feels, and then his friend reaches out and they both tumble back on to the bridge, the friend breaking his fall.

God, what a relief! But he fell from quite a height. What if the weight has injured him? I crane my neck, my nose so close to the cold glass that it gives me goosebumps, trying to see through the gaps between the stone balustrades. Nothing happens. I don't breathe. The clink of cutlery stops or, at least, I stop hearing it. I can see the two figures flat out on the bridge, there's no sign of movement at all, and I replay that fall in my mind. That boy could have broken his back.

"Dennis?" I'm about to suggest calling an ambulance when I see them, Hoodie One and Two, scrambling to their feet, unsteady enough for me to worry that they might be injured. But then I wipe the condensation from the glass and see that Hoodie One's hoodie has slipped off, revealing a great mane of long blonde hair . . . and now Hoodie Two reaches down, his head hidden by fabric, and the two Hoodies are snogging.

"Oh. It's a girl."

Dennis pulls a face. "Even more reason for her not to be out after dark. Kids like that are the reason Anti-Social Behaviour Orders were invented."

I'm about to protest when Karl arrives at the table bearing a round white plate covered in . . . oh no . . .

"Snails in garlic butter," Karl says triumphantly. "Nothing better for putting ze lead in the pencil."

Snails are more likely to make me throw up but at least Dennis likes them. As he orders the wine — something French and expensive sounding — I wonder who on earth first decided that these flaccid rubbery creatures, which retreat into their shells at the slightest provocation, could be an aphrodisiac.

After three snails (cut into pieces small enough to gulp without chewing or tasting), one French onion soup, and half a chicken with 40 cloves of garlic, my tastebuds are screaming in surrender.

The booze and the gossip distract me from the food, though. Dennis is on form, telling tales from the disaster planning committee. He's surprisingly indiscreet when he's had a glass of wine, and now we're well into the second bottle, there's no stopping him. He seems to be on a mission to consume all our allotted units on one night.

Mrs Fothergill is apparently having affairs with both the fire chief *and* the ambulance control room supervisor, and the speculation's rife over which senior policeman she'll choose to complete her 999 hat trick.

Outside, incredibly, the Hoodies are still at it. Their lips must be numb but they only manage to detach from each other for long enough to take a few steps, before they're compelled to kiss again.

"They're not *that* fascinating, are they?" Dennis asks, sounding amused rather than annoyed.

"Do you think it's their first kiss?"

He smiles. "And their second, third, fourth, fifth, sixth . . ." he counts off on his fingers, "ooh, they must be up to their thirtieth by now."

"Novelty's not wearing off yet, though."

"I should hope not," he says. "I've been at it twenty-seven years and it hasn't worn off for me."

It's true: Dennis kisses like a teenager. Fervent and passionate. OK, and a tiny bit sloppy. But in a good way.

For a while, we stare at the couple, who're still joined at the lips. They're not even groping. They're clutching each other's hands, down by their sides, as if the kisses are so tumultuous that they need to hang on for balance.

Dennis reaches over to take my hand and grasps it hard. "I wanted this to be a special night. A memorable night."

Now my mouth is dry. Is this going to be *my* moment? My first proposal of marriage? From the only person in the world who is ever likely to offer?

"I was bloody nervous about us living together, Jo, I'll admit it." He blushes, as he rarely admits to weakness. "I'm not exactly a spring chicken, after all, stuck in my ways and with who knows what kind of bad habits. And as for your habits . . ." He chuckles.

I try not to think about his bad habits: the way he scratches inside his ears and then inspects the wax on the end of his finger. The way he monitors my toilet roll consumption, and bites his lip over my excesses when we have to buy "yet another family pack". But compared to my dad, he's a paragon.

"No, to be fair, Jo, I have to say you're pretty house-trained. And the benefits of having you around — well, the bed's always nice and warm — do outweigh the disadvantages."

"Dennis Diffley, last of the great romantics!"

He takes a sip of wine, then refills both our glasses. They are *enormous* glasses and we must be on ten units each by now.

"Now I never claim to be a New Man. It's taken me a long time to get my life *just so*. Well, you know how important being settled is to me, after my childhood. I like my own company. But I don't think I could ever go back to living alone."

He's right: we did make the transition without any of the fireworks Lorraine had prediced. No arguments over cleaning the bath, or putting the rubbish out. "Me neither," I say. Though I do miss my little studio flat. Now and then. It's only natural to feel nostalgic occasionally.

"I've been thinking about it a lot. You know I'm not a man to rush into things, but there comes a time when one needs to think about the future and . . . Oh, *good* timing."

Karl is carrying a large spiky pudding which, as it looms closer, I realise is a heart made from meringue. None of the other diners have had a heart-shaped meringue. We've been earmarked for special treatment.

"Shall I do ze honours?" Karl asks, his alarmingly large kitchen knife poised above the meringue.

"No, no, leave it to me," Dennis says, waving him away. "Now where was I? Oh yes. Commitment."

There are pointy brown peaks on the meringue, where the heat has toasted the sugar. It looks delicious: meringue is one of my favourite things. But I can't imagine ever eating again. Because Dennis is about to propose marriage.

He gives me a special lingering look, one that's usually a prelude to sex. I feel ever so slightly queasy. Must be all that garlic, because this is the happiest moment of any girl's life, surely, even now we're liberated and assertive. I love Dennis. He's a good man, the nearest to my twin on earth, the only bloke I've ever found who will tolerate my warped view of the world.

It's definitely the garlic.

I take a deep breath. OK. Maybe I feel a teeny bit nervous. Perfectly natural. It's not like I've ever been one for impulsive leaps in the dark. I was scared when we agreed to move in together, after all. If it hadn't been for the lease on my studio running out and the landlord wanting to flog the building to a developer, I'd have stayed there till my dotage.

"Jo," he says. "I know you won't be expecting this, but . . ."

I look down, avoiding his sincere gaze because I don't want him to notice my queasiness when he pops the question. I *knew* I should have passed on those bloody snails.

By the bridge, the Hoodies are no longer kissing. There we are. Nothing lasts for ever, not even hormonal teenage passion. Other things matter more. Compatibility. Attitudes.

Fear of being alone.

Where did *that* come from?

The Hoodies are coming towards us now, not realising we can see them. They stop a few yards from the boat, and Girl Hoodie stops and traces her finger down the side of Boy Hoodie's face, as though he's made of marble.

There's a dragging feeling in my stomach, like lust, but then I recognise it. Envy. I don't want Boy Hoodie, but I want the feeling Girl Hoodie has, whatever it is that's transforming her face — glowing under the street lamp — into radiance.

"Jo . . .? Oh bloody hell, I don't see what's so fascinating about snogging teenagers. When did they come back?"

"They were there all the time."

"Idiots. They must be frozen. Anyway . . . what I wanted to ask . . ."

I prepare myself for my big moment.

"Jo, would you like to get a joint bank account?"

I snort with laughter — it comes out before I can stop myself. He stares at me, with the same irritated expression he gets when our Head of Department talks over him in a meeting. "Sorry, Dennis! But . . ." I can't tell him that I'm laughing out of relief. "I just wasn't expecting it."

"Well, I think it's time. And it's also the fairest way of doing it. Of splitting the bills. And I know we both want everything to be fair."

"Hmmm, yes," I say, nodding until my neck's sore. A bank account! Hooray. "Great idea. But the thing is, Dennis . . ."

He's raising his knife to pierce the meringue and down it comes, in the centre of the heart, and there's a hiss and out pours a pool of blood-red sauce, followed by a melted pool of egg-yolk-yellow vanilla ice cream. Baked Alaska. I've always wanted to try it. He slices right through the meringue, adjusting his knife carefully so our portions are of identical size, exactly half a heart each. "The thing is, what?"

"Nothing," I say. The Hoodies have gone. "So long as we can have one of those cheque books with animals on them. Otters and badgers and stuff."

He raises his eyebrows. "Well . . . it's not what I'd choose but if that's the deal . . ." and he reaches out to shake my hand, as though we're business partners. But then he reaches across and whispers in my ear, "We'll ratify the merger later, eh?" before kissing me briefly on the lips.

I *do* fancy him. I really, really do. And I'm excited about spending the rest of my life with Dennis. We're made for each other. It's just odd that when I transfer the meringue and the ice cream and the raspberry sauce from my spoon to my mouth, all I can feel is the heat and the cold.

It doesn't taste of anything at all.

CHAPTER
FOUR

Alliumphobia —
Fear of Garlic

This morning I feel new empathy with the chicken cooked with forty cloves of garlic. Our bedroom is hot thanks to the early sunshine and Dennis's energy efficient central heating. As a result, our garlic-infused sweat has soaked into the bedding and the curtains and the walls, and I know that however many showers I have, the stink will linger for days.

But I do need to make at least a token effort to banish the miasma of garlic, so I clatter into the bathroom, making as much noise as I like because Dennis left an hour ago. I climb into the shower using the grip handles, avoiding the emergency pull-cord. The water is on the chilly side, so at least there's no danger of getting scalded, but I wish the Man of the House would turn the temperature up a few degrees, like he keeps promising. I think he secetly likes the icicle effect. He's a little bit strange that way.

I don't mean that he likes to dress in giant nappies or craves six of the best with a garden cane. Or at least, if he does, he hasn't asked me yet. Maybe that comes once we've set up the joint account, and are bound together by standing orders . . .

I take the loofah (fairly traded of course) and scrub away at my garlicky body. The last time I put this much effort into exfoliating was when I was eight and Lorraine told me everyone was born with freckles and I wasn't washing hard enough to get rid of them. I ended up taking the top layer of skin off my arms and legs, but when it grew back — painfully — the freckles were still there. A couple of years after that, I grew breasts and Lorraine didn't, and she stopped going on about my freckles. She's been much happier since she bought herself double-Ds for her twenty-fifth birthday present.

Dennis likes my boobs. And my bottom is "nicely proportioned and entirely lacking in cellulite". My legs are "well toned, if very slightly too short". Might not sound like the most generous compliments, but he's scrupulously honest, so I couldn't really ask for higher praise. And in bed, he's as ardent as any Hollywood lover. Last night our clothes were off before we'd got out of the entrance hall (though Dennis folded them away after we'd finished).

He's quite bossy in bed: not in a pervy way, just making all the decisions about, well, you know, what we do. Suits me. Sometimes sex is so daft that you need at least one of you to be taking it seriously or you'd get a fit of the giggles and that wouldn't be the right thing at all.

He's also *deadly* serious on the topic of contraception, with a belt-and-braces approach, involving ultra-safe condoms, spermicidal jelly and his uncanny knowledge of the safest phases of my menstrual cycle. The condom failure rate (up to fourteen pregnancies per one hundred users) gives him sleepless nights.

The shower goes cold, so I leap out. I brush my teeth and then use the special water pump that jets away food debris like a high-pressure car wash (though I'll confess I don't use the safety goggles that Dennis insists upon in case the water hits my eyes). I aim the jet at my tongue, too, but the garlic's burned into my mouth, so I can't taste my coffee or my hurriedly buttered toast. All the scrubbing's made me seriously late for work.

Outside, the sharp winter sun makes my head ache, and my poisonous breath forms a thick mist that follows me as I leave our bungalow, number 64 Salzburg Avenue, and head towards real life. That'll teach me to consume all my alcohol units in one go (hangovers cost the UK £2 billion in lost wages every year).

As usual, the wide road is deserted, an asphalt river with bungalow-tugboats evenly spaced along its curves. All the bungalows have a nautical feel. Number 64's side walls curve gently like the bow of a ship, the downstairs toilet window is a porthole of stained glass and inside every surface is panelled and polished, awash with mahogany and oak.

When I first moved here, I couldn't get used to the quiet. I didn't miss my studio flat, which always made me feel like Gulliver, thanks to its miniaturised kitchenette and its three-quarter-sized bath. But its location was great, right in town, near the marketplace and a paper shop and late-night convenience store. I've never had the wildest of social lives, but I loved sitting in the big Parker Knoll granny chair, looking out of the window. At Christmas I'd watch families weaving around the stalls looking for the gaudiest decorations, eating the oily fresh doughnuts I could smell from two floors up. Or in the summer, I'd wait for darkness to tempt out the skateboarders, all in black like bats. And I'd gawp at the impossible manoeuvres that became more daring with every bottle of strong cider.

Lorraine used to laugh at me. "Life isn't a bloody spectator sport, Jo. Let's get down there and join in."

But she didn't understand: I'm no good at joining in. You can divide people in this life into doers and spectators — and Lorraine, of all people, should know that the doers need an appreciative audience.

There's nothing to see in Salzburg Avenue. Estate agents call our area Little Austria, but everyone else knows it as the blue-rinse ghetto. The neighbours are friendly enough: the weekend I moved, Mrs Cronin from next door came round with a bottle of sherry which she obviously hoped to share with us. Dennis took it before she could take a step over the threshold.

"I had my fill of snooping neighbours as a kid," he said. Dennis doesn't talk much about his childhood, but it's left him with a pathological hatred of prying eyes. I knew I couldn't argue. But, whenever I see Mrs Cronin through the kitchen window, clods of soap suds dropping from her pink flowery rubber gloves, she looks away. And I can't say I blame her.

I walk out of Salzburg Avenue, down Vienna Way, and towards the Old Town. I move slowly because of the hangover: my pupils are slow to respond to light, so when the sun emerges from behind a cloud, my surroundings seem bleached out. And when I step into the shade, it's like there's been an eclipse and I'm falling . . .

I get as far as the cobbled pedestian area, where the street is so steep I need to lean on a postbox for support. I watch the people who pass by. There's not exactly a rush hour in Courtbridge. That's for city folk. We have a bustle hour. Imagine Women's Institute stall-holders trying to secure the best tables in the church hall, sharp elbows at the ready. *Oh, excuse me. No, excuse ME, I'm so sorry*, they say, almost always meaning the exact opposite.

Today people seem as weary as me, moving more languidly than usual, yawning from lack of sleep and wincing from muscle strain after spending last night in traditional style, i.e. getting pissed enough to sleep with their partners. I wonder if Lorraine went home with the cross-dressing barman from the hospital social club at the end of her shift.

I look down and realise I've forgotten my fluorescent bib: Dennis gave it to me when the clocks went back in October. It's the same design the rescue services wear on the hard shoulder after an accident. I remember what Dennis told me about Mrs Fothergill and wonder if she likes her 999 boys to put theirs on in bed. Or perhaps she keeps them as trophies.

The thought makes me giggle, and the giggle turns into a laugh, and then as I cross the road my eyes seem to be playing tricks because there's a flash of fluorescent green and it's the same shade as my bib and I wonder whether I haven't somehow put it on after all, and then the flash gets brighter and that lime green is all I can see and then I feel myself falling and my face is reflected in the time-polished mirrors of the cobblestones, my mouth in a ragged "O" and then . . .

CHAPTER
FIVE

Gnosiophobia —
Fear of Knowledge

"Jo . . . Joooo?"

Disinfectant catches in my throat and stings the inside of my nose. But however much the cleaners use, it still never disguises the twin smells of the school toilets: Impulse — men just can't help acting on it, or so the girls in the fifth form say — and drains.

"You're bloody miles away again," Lorraine calls from outside the cubicle. "Come on, you moron, we'll be late." Her insults echo round the room, bouncing off the tiles.

I straighten my skirt over my goosebumpy legs, and try to get the loo to flush. Always a high-risk activity in this cubicle, but the one next door is worse, a bubbling volcano of dark blue toilet roll and urine that's spilled across the brown floor. Parents are impressed by the pristine paintwork and modern signs welcoming them to Greenham Common High School ("Working with Common Purpose") but after three months here, I know it's more a case of "Common as Muck". Not one of the toilets has escaped some form of vandalism.

Broken seats, cracked cisterns, handles repaired with yellowing Sellotape and metal coat hangers. I don't need any persuasion to Now Wash Your Hands. Except the water's always freezing and the liquid soap dried up circa 1976. As it's now 1981, this place must be germ heaven.

"Jo. We'll be late. I'm not waiting no more."

I open the door in time to see Lorraine wiping the back of her hand across her mouth, to remove ninety per cent of the Rimmel Toffee Apple lipstick she's applied so she doesn't get detention for wearing make-up. She coloured her hair at the weekend with a Shaders & Toners so the brown lipstick clashes with her plum-coloured fringe, but I'm not saying anything. Wouldn't dare.

Alongside her in the age-mottled mirror, I frown. Why can't I be pretty too? My fingers sting under the running water where I've bitten them, while Lorraine's fingers are long and perfect, like a hand model's.

"Oi, grumpy. Come on."

Lorraine pokes out her tongue at me in the mirror and I smile. I pick up my khaki schoolbag, with its Biro-ed graffiti promising devotion to bands I'm not allowed to listen to: the Sex Pistols and the Boomtown Rats. In the other hand, I'm carrying wellies in a green St Michael bag.

The corridor's already empty as we run upstairs to the English department, pushing past prefects to race into Mr Blake's classroom.

He's not there yet, but the rest of my tutor group is more hyper than usual: Harriet the class bitch is spitting chewed balls of paper at Steven Chubb, the heart-throb. Everyone's carrying wellies. Some have already put them on, and are stomping about, leaving footprints of dried mud on the lino.

"Good morning, IG!"

That voice makes me blush and I hope no one's noticed. It's like dark chocolate and crumpets dripping with butter. Melty and rich but edgy too.

I dare to look up, then away again as the blush spreads. He's wearing a brown suit and brown penny loafers and his black hair is uncombed, with soft sleepy peaks. I wonder if he slept alone.

I've gone bright red. Lorraine nudges me. "Reckon it's all off. Wouldn't be wearing a suit if we was off to the farm, would he? Dragged the bloody wellies in for nothing."

"Settle down, IG. I have bad news, and good news . . ."

He waits for this to sink in. He comes from Liverpool, like the Beatles and Kenny Everett and Keith Chegwin. On our first day, he explained that people from Liverpool were either known as Liverpudlians or Scousers, and that seemed so sophisticated. There's not a single special name if you come from West Berkshire.

"The bad news is . . . the farming project has been brought to a rather unexpected halt. And that means we won't be going on the field trip."

The farming project is nothing to do with geography: no crop rotation or "compare and contrast the benefits of arable over dairy herds".

There's a moan, and he nods back at us. "I know. I think you can draw your own conclusions about why Mrs Henderson decided to stop us going to the abattoir. Censorship is never a positive step. But I think the quality of work you produced after our visit to the cattle market is a powerful statement in itself."

I'm sure he's talking to me: he read out my poem to the whole class. I called it "Bite to Eat" and it was about the journey to market of a calf taken from its mother and the meadow where it eats fresh grass. I showed my dad my exercise book, with the comment Mr Blake had scribbled in the margin: "Remarkably moving and insightful, A-minus". Dad read the poem several times, but all he said was, "So we've got your bloody English teacher to thank for this vegetarian fad then? Just what we need — some lefty teacher filling your head with mad ideas. Not like you haven't got enough of your own to begin with."

I didn't think that was very fair. Yes, Mr Blake is a vegetarian, the first I've ever met, and yes, he explained about factory farming and battery hens. I hadn't known what an abattoir was before then. It sounds too nice a word for something so horrible.

But these are the things people *should* tell children. We're the ones who can change the world.

Not that the boys were going to the abattoir to change the world. They wanted to see lots of blood, so now they're annoyed. But most of the girls look relieved. I know I am: I'd hate to break down in front of my favourite teacher. And I bet abattoirs are freezing in November.

"I understand you're disappointed — but it simply means we'll be moving on to the next project that bit faster . . . I hope you're ready, because this is the big one."

We wait. There are stories that Mr Blake's been in trouble with the head teacher before after parents complained, but at least it means English is never boring. He pauses again, his face — which is usually moody and pale, even in the summer — is pink, and I can see he's excited, so I feel excited too.

"It's war."

He lets the reaction ripple around the room — nudging and jostling by the lads at the back, nervous giggles from the nail varnish wearing mob immediately behind me. Lorraine pulls a face. "Bor-ing . . . I get enough about the war from me nan."

The room has gone quiet again. "Leave your wellies here, but bring your exercise books. We're off to the hall to see a movie."

We drift out in crocodile formation, with that giddy feeling that always bubbles up when we're allowed out of the classroom in lesson time.

We find our seats as the scent of baking gingerbread comes through in waves from the school kitchen.

It's my least favourite of all the cakes the dinner ladies mangle. As it cooks, it smells boggy, too much flour dragging down too little stale ginger. When you stick your spoon in it, it smells of damp laundry.

Lorraine and I sit next to each other in the front row. Mr Blake has already set up the projector — this is a real *reel*, not a flickering Betamax video in the cramped TV room.

"There's no sound on this, so I am going to play some music. I want you to concentrate on the images, and jot down your first reactions."

He presses "play" on his Alba cassette recorder. The clunk and settle of the needle into the vinyl groove echoes round the speakers: I imagine Mr Blake at home, in frayed denims, kneeling at the side of a turntable, making the tape for us.

The first notes on the piano make me wince as I realise what it is. "Imagine".

I scowl. *How could he?* I took against The Beatles last December, when Mum and Dad went into mourning over the death of John Lennon. They played the records so loudly that the house seemed to shiver from the waves of guitar music. And Mum kept singing along, while Dad grasped her hand, more affectionate than I'd ever seen him. "We've lost more than John. We've lost . . . our youth."

It takes Mr Blake a while to get the reel loaded, but finally, the film is sucked up into the projector. The screen fills with light, and then shades of darkness, as a title appears: "Hiroshima, 6 August, 1945".

I've heard of Hiroshima, of course. A big bomb in Japan. Didn't it mean the end of the war?

"It was a clear morning," says Mr Blake, in the deadpan voice he usually saves for poetry. At primary school, Mrs Fitzpatrick spoke like a xylophone, veering from high shrieks to low growls to keep our attention. But Mr Blake speaks as though he doesn't understand what he's saying, no emotion, just words. Except somehow that means you can't stop listening.

"A perfect morning for flying." A plane in black and white cuts across a grey sky. I wonder if the sky was blue in real life. On the tail of the aircraft, the stars and stripes, again in black and white.

"The *Enola Gay* left the Tinian airbase at 2.45 a.m. Its mission was straightforward — to drop a single bomb."

The plane rumbles silently through the grey-blue. I can hear the clanging of tins from the kitchen, one of the dinner ladies has heard the record and is singing "Imagine".

"La-la-la . . . all the people . . ."

"The bomb was called Little Boy."

Lorraine starts to fidget. They're catching, fidgets, like hiccups, so I sit on my hands to stop myself. She reaches into her bag to pull out a tube of Spangles and offers me one. Its fizzy orange flavour makes me feel sick.

"Whoay-whoay-whoay . . ."

The screen goes white again, and I turn round, expecting the tail-end of the film to be spinning off the reel, as it does when something goes wrong with the projector. But it's still whirring, and Mr Blake is staring at the screen. "The bomb exploded at 8.15 a.m., in the air above Hiroshima."

The screen is still white. Then a picture begins to melt through, like a photograph appearing in a tray of developing fluid. At first it looks like fabric rags hanging in strips off a football. It's being held by a woman in a cap with a cross on the front, a nurse's cap.

"La la la today . . ."

And then I realise: the ball with rags attached is a person's head, on a body with skin peeling away. A moment later, there's an odd noise from Lorraine, not a word, but a croak from her throat. She begins to cough and I think her Spangle's gone down the wrong way.

Mr Blake says, "The people who survived said the bomb was like a second sun. The people in the centre of Hiroshima died instantly. They were the lucky ones."

The picture changes, to a silhouette of a houseplant. My eyes stretch open, trying to process what they're seeing.

"The explosion caused a light so bright that for miles around, the patterns of objects in its way were burned into stone . . . you can see the shadow of the leaves on the pillar . . ."

He pauses, and another image replaces the plant. A child, wearing a patterned kimono.

"It had the same effect on skin."

The child is naked. The patterns are burns. I've seen enough. The smell of ginger is in my nose like sneezing powder.

"Imagine . . . la la la . . ."

"The people who could run, couldn't see. The flash had blinded them. The ruined city was an obstacle course."

The film shows a dome, its tattered roof now open to the sky. What colour was the sky now?

"But they had to run. Because what was left of the city was going up in flames, and so they tried to find their way to safety by sensing the heat on their skin."

I can't take my eyes off the screen, but I want to run too. The middle of my Spangle has dissolved, and I stick the tip of my tongue into the sharp gap to stop myself crying out.

Pictures of people with no clothes on, streetcars reduced to metal skeletons.

"Some of them tried to find their way to the river, where they could bathe their wounds, where the water might act as a break between the flames and safety . . ."

His voice is slower now.

"But when they got there, the water was boiling. They had a choice. Wait for the flames, or jump in."

"Lah lah lah a dreamer . . ."

"Oh, belt up singing, Glenda, you're not exactly Sheena-bloody-Easton."

I drag my eyes from the screen, but the pictures are burned in, like the flowers on the kimono, the leaves on the pillar.

I blink as the lights come on, my hands wedged between my legs and the underside of the chair. When I pull them out they're red and the dimpled pattern of the plastic is imprinted on my palms.

"And that, IG, is what war will be like for us. Or rather, much worse, because the bombs that are trained on Newbury, *right now*, are hundreds of times more powerful than the one used on Hiroshima. Shortly to be joined, literally in our backyard, by American weapons at the airbase, aimed at Russia. You might have seen it on the news, the women who arrived at the beginning of the month, on a peace march?"

I do remember. Dad laughed at them. "Deluded fools. As if the Soviets care about a bunch of hairy-legged women!"

Mr Blake's not laughing. "This is a threat to all of us. To the survival of the human race. Our parents and our grandparents had it easy, with battles where you could be a hero, or could get lucky. Well, our luck has run out."

He flicks his eyes up at the hall clock, as the second hand counts the last moments before midday. "Thank you for your attention, IG. A little food for thought before lunch. We'll talk more of war tomorrow afternoon. Meanwhile, isn't that spaghetti bolognese I can smell from the canteen?"

He stops speaking one second before the bell sounds, jolting me into reality. My classmates are subdued as they file out, but once they're in the corridor, queuing for dinner, the chatter starts up again. For them, Hiroshima is a long time ago and a long way away . . .

But I can't move. Mr Blake fusses with his precious reels of film, and the caretaker is wheeling tables into position for the dinner sitting.

"Jo," Lorraine punches my arm, "you're behaving like a right dipstick. I'm starving and if we get in the dinner queue now we might get chips before the fifth years nab them all."

I look up, but I can still see the pattern of that kimono.

"Come on, Jo. You're being weird. Jo. Jo . . ."

CHAPTER
SIX

Nosocomephobia — Fear of Hospitals

"Jo . . . Jo . . ."

I'm falling, but before I hit the ground, it melts away. Everything's bright white and I feel like I'm outside, cold and dazzled by sunlight and there's a crunch as I hit cobbles. I don't feel anything but I *know* it's my bones making that noise and then all I see is rubies and diamonds . . .

"Come *on*, Jo. I bet you can hear us."

It isn't Lorraine any more. It's a man's voice, a Welsh voice, the vowels soft as double cream and the consonants brittle as toffee.

Rubies and diamonds glitter in the sunlight, tiny fragments against the cobbles, but more rubies than diamonds now, a wash of red spreading, changing colour . . .

"It's a crucial time," the voice continues, more matter-of-fact now, "the sooner a patient emerges from this stage, the better the long-term prognosis."

Someone's sweeping the diamonds away, but the red wash is still spreading.

"Is she going to be brain damaged?"

My father . . .

My father's voice is dragging me to a place where I don't feel weightless and where nothing sparkles. Gradually my mind reacquaints itself with my body, part by part, each area mapped by a different sensation: throbbing down my left side, as though someone is twisting my hip-bone slowly in its socket. My torso feels scrambled, nothing quite where it should be, churning as lost organs try to find their way home. Stinging in my groin. Heaviness in my hand, like I'm tethered.

"It's always a waiting game, I'm afraid. I don't think we're going to have to operate to reduce the cranial pressure, which is good news. And she's young. Do you hear me, Jo? Fancy trying to open those eyes?"

My head pulses, as though my brain is too big and trying to escape the confines of my ridiculously small skull, but the skull is like a vice and . . . shit, that *hurts* . . .

"Was . . . was that a blink?" My mother. Not daring to trust her own eyes. I wish I could reach out to her, but even if I could work out how to raise these leaden eyelids, I'm too scared it'd trigger new waves of pain.

"You probably imagined it," my father says.

"If she did blink, it might only be a reflex," the warm voice says. "We still know very little about what triggers a patient's emergence from coma."

Coma? Is that where I am? My body's definitely here, feeling a thousand years old, yet moments ago I was at school. And twelve again. With bitten nails and a monster crush on my English teacher.

"And whatever you've seen on TV, if . . . *when* she begins to respond again, it's rarely a miraculous overnight recovery. Two steps forward, one step back, is the mantra with brain injury."

"Could I hold her hand?" It's Dennis.

Please don't, Dennis. Don't touch me, touch equals pain . . .

"That's fine, but be gentle. And don't be too disappointed if she doesn't respond."

No, *don't*. I want to shout out but I can't and the words of protest reverberate in my brain like howl-round on speakers and I tense in anticipation of the agony of Dennis's hand on mine and everything begins to fade away . . .

"Tell you what, I didn't fancy her chances one bit when they dragged her in."

Where am I now?

"Right dent she had in her scalp, measured it on my fingers, three centimetres deep, even though it hadn't hardly broke the skin." The voice is gossipy and female, belonging to someone who is used to being listened to. A teacher? But I'm not back at school. And I can't open my eyes which means I must be . . .

"You *didn't* stick your fingers in there?" The other voice is little-girly, enjoying being scandalised.

"Course I *didn't*! But you could see. Like a boiled egg when you tap it with your spoon and it caves in. Only time I seen a head that bashed before, we lost 'im."

64

"Oooh," says the scandalised voice. They must be nurses. God help me. "Doesn't look too bad now, does it?"

"You never can tell what's going to happen next, Kylie, you just can't. But still I wouldn't be betting my bingo money on this one regaining all her marbles, put it that way."

You're wrong. Anger makes the pressure in my brain hum because I can't tell her she's wrong. *Isn't she?*

"Such a shame," says little-girl. "Can't be much older than me."

"Shoulda looked both ways, shouldn't she, eh? You all right to wash her? Last thing she needs is bedsores."

"OK."

Rubies and diamonds flash before my eyes again. And I sense a familiar taste in my mouth. It feels gritty and dirty . . . Is this what fear tastes like? Because I ought to be afraid, surely? I ought to be terrified.

"Leave you to it, then."

But I'm not. Floaty, yes. Muddled, definitely. But frightened . . . for the first time I can remember, I'm not afraid.

"One more thing. Am I meant to talk to her, like the doctors tell us to? In case she can hear us?"

The other woman tuts. "Not sure there's much point. Mind you, if it got me into Dr Williams' good books, I'd sing her the entire Take That back catalogue."

I feel a cold breeze as someone lifts the sheets away from my body, followed by a hesitant hand on my leg. "Shoulda looked both ways." But I *always* look both ways. What the hell's happened to me?

"H . . . hello, Jo," the girl says. "Um . . . I'm going to clean you up a bit, OK?" And I hear a trickle of water followed by a wet stroke, like our old dog Misty licking me. As exhaustion descends like a heavy, scratchy blanket, I taste that taste again and I *know* that on some level that taste is connected to what I am doing here. And then I work out what the taste is.

Garlic.

". . . I would have expected better of the police, given my connections."

Dennis. And other people. I can hear their breathing. My mother's doll-sized intakes of breath, as if she's frightened someone will tell her off for taking more than her rightful share of oxygen. My father's deep inhalations more than making up for it. And a fourth pair of lungs, producing a whiny wheeze so high-pitched that perhaps only the comatose and dogs can hear it. Surely it can't be . . .

"Well, let's face it, mate. Courtbridge's finest plods are hardly Inspector Morse, are they?"

My brother. That voice, complete with the estuary drawl he's adopoted to get ahead in advertising, is unmistakable.

So I'm still in the hospital. I check for pain but my body feels as insubstantial as cotton wool. Maybe it's the drugs. And then I check for fear: *nothing*.

"I'm sure they've been trying their best, Timmy." Mum, the human emollient, tries to keep things nice. Dennis's breaths become more laboured.

I don't need to open my eyes to picture the gathering: my dad pacing the room, wondering how long before he can go and flirt with the nurses. His face will be creased with just enough lines to show deep concern, without making him look his age. Occasionally he might run his fingers through his thick hair, blonder and shinier now than it was in his twenties, thanks to fortnightly dye-jobs at the caressing hands of Savannah, the hairdresser to whom he's entrusted his locks for twenty coiffed years.

As you'd expect of the perpetually leading man of Newbury Amateur Operatic Society, he'll have agonised over his costume for the role of anguished father. I'd guess at a sober black suit, *Love Story* meets *The Godfather*. Or smart and dignified like his idol, Michael Caine. Ted Morgan, the ultimate chameleon.

Dennis will be in casuals: a garish rugby shirt bought from a Sunday supplement, and . . . God forbid he's come out in jogging pants. I can only hope they're not the ones with the hole in the crotch, because the more defensive he's feeling, the more inclined he is to spread his legs wide, like men on trains.

My mother in a size 8 baby-blue twinset, the uniform all women pensioners wore in the 1970s, before they began shopping in Gap and going on superannuated hippie trails to smoke hash in Marrakesh and Goa. Poor Mum. She hasn't quite caught up. And no doubt my condition has added a dozen new wrinkles of disappointment to her face.

And then Timmy. He's inherited my father's awareness of the dash he cuts, but he'll have aimed for "grief casual". Good jeans from a label too trendy for me to have heard of, hugging his ridiculously skinny frame. Perhaps a preppy Henry Winkler zip-up cardigan, but with some kind of twist, like a Serbo-Croat swear-word knitted into the back. Handmade shoes. A gold ring. Hair tousled with £25 styling gel, to suggest sleep disturbed by his elder sister's plight. A look designed to get tongues wagging at the nurses' station: hetero, metro, homo or bi? My little brother likes to keep them guessing.

"I can't help feeling that a spate of thefts of penny chews from a newsagent would have your local bobbies calling for reinforcements."

"And I suppose London policemen are all masters in the art of detection?" Dennis says, instantly switching sides from criticising the local bobbies to defending them.

"How masterful do you need to be, exactly, to solve a hit-and-run perpetrated by a Lycra-clad individual on a *pushbike*?"

I hear *another* person's breathing then, speeding up, and wonder who's joined us before I realise: that's *my* breathing. And the hit-and-run . . . that's *me* they're talking about. I search for a scrap of a memory to make sense of it.

Nothing.

"It's not as if bikes have registration plates," Dennis says, "though I'm planning to lobby our MP to present a motion arguing the case for them."

"What? Would you have them for tricycles, too?" My brother's enquiry is deadpan.

"There'd be an exemption for three-wheelers or child-specific models."

I must remember something. But all I can summon up is that revolting taste of garlic. Don't nurses brush the teeth of people in comas? Or is my injured brain producing a mirage in my mouth?

"Ah, but how will you define a child? I reckon most street crime is committed by under-sixteens on Raleigh Choppers anyway," Timmy sneers. "Hey, I know. What about licensing clothes? Lycra licences only issued after a body scan to ensure no unsightly wobbly bits. And no hoodies permitted unless the wearer has been cleared by local magistrates."

Hoodies? I grasp on to a fragmentary image, of two kids wearing hooded jumpers on Court Bridge. But it doesn't seem to connect to push-bikes or accidents, and the effort makes my head ache. It's exhausting.

". . . and I hardly think that making jokes as your sister lies critically injured is appropriate." Dennis's lecturing tone is so familiar, it's almost reassuring.

"What do you suggest, Herr Commandant? That we sit here miserable as sin waiting for her to flatline?"

"Timmy!" My mother's warning is whispered, as if she doesn't really mean it.

"Or maybe you're expecting some emotional scene where she wakes up, we all cry, and suddenly she's able to recite Shakespeare's sonnets or see visions of the Virgin Mary?"

"You're upsetting your mother," Dad says.

"As if that's ever bothered *you*," my brother spits back.

Well, don't mind me, chaps. I'm only the one who's hovering on the edge of life here.

"Bloody hell, Tim, you've been here five minutes and you've started," Dad snaps. "You're not helping. Why don't you bugger off back to London where you're needed for your oh-so *vital* work? Because we don't need you here."

"Ted," Mum bleats, on the edge of tears.

This is beyond a joke. Aren't they meant to be wafting aromatherapy oils under my nose? Playing compilations of my favourite songs, or a tape from a pop star begging me to return to consciousness? Since when have coma patients been tempted to come round by a full-blown domestic?

". . . Lynda, don't defend him. He's taken two bloody days to get here and now he's lording it all over us as usual. Can't he ever learn to put someone else first?"

Huh. Like Dad would know anything about that.

Enough's enough. I concentrate hard on remembering where my eyes are, on trying to recall what it feels like to open them, how each little muscle works to lift a millimetre of skin on my lids. It feels like lifting up a double-decker bus.

"Um . . . I don't know if you remember, but the doctor did say that even if we don't think she's fully here, Jo might be able to hear us," Dennis says.

No kidding, buster. Remember me? The patient you're all here to help? Now I'm determined to shift these sodding eyelids just to show 'em.

My brother sniffs ferociously. He's been doing it since childhood, and I'm sure his outstanding nasal control comes in extremely handy at ad agency parties. "Well, it'd probably be more of a shock to her if we were all getting on like a house on fire. Eh, sis? If you can hear me, give me a dirty look like you always do . . ."

My eyes are still weighed down, but lifting them feels achievable now, somehow. I try to remember what they taught me when I joined a gym (for precisely one session). Are you meant to push on the in-breath, or the out-breath?

Pop.

The weight shifts and I feel cold air on the whites of my eyes. For a moment I can't see a thing, and just as I'm panicking that I've gone blind, my family swim before my eyes. They're bleached out at first as though I've been staring at a lightbulb, but gradually the scene settles, the colours return. Dad in his navy suit, aggressively flicking through a magazine. Timmy languid on the edge of the bed, picking at an imaginary spot of dirt on his laundry-fresh jeans. Mum, in rose-pink knitwear (I was nearly right), peering down at her hands, tightly coiled in her lap.

And Dennis in his rugby shirt and — thank God — decent cords, looking back at me, more tired than I've ever seen him, my clean-shaven boyfriend covered in whiskers that make him look like Captain Birds Eye.

"Jo?" he sounds hesitant at first and I try hard to widen my eyes in response, but I don't think it works. "Look, her eyes. She's waking up."

71

"Typical Jo," my brother turns quickly, and his face is so uncharacteristically soft that it makes me want to cry. "Just in time for dinner."

I've been focusing so hard on my eyes that it's only now that I smell food.

Mum and Dad turn to stare, but already the tiredness is weighing down my eyelids and I begin to drift to a place scented with roast dinner and overcooked vegetables and overripe oranges . . .

CHAPTER
SEVEN

Russophobia — Fear of Russians

Gravy and bacon and the bitter scent of Brussels sprouts boiled into submission. The sickly sweetness of clove studded oranges, already going rotten. And the farmyard tang of wet Labrador.

The perfume of Christmas at 17 Greenham Lane, Newbury. If you bottled it, you'd have to call it Eau de Desperation.

"There was no hot turkey and crackers on offer at the camp today, but the protestors, almost all of whom are women, insisted that missing out on Christmas dinner was a small price to pay."

"Ruddy lesbians," my father says, enjoying his outrage.

"Ted!" my mother scolds, but it's too late.

"Mummee, what's a lesbian?"

"It's another word for a kind of lady, Timmy. But not a very polite one," Mum says, then whispers to my dad, "Now look what you've done."

I try to zone out. I'm sitting on the floor, leaning on the radiator, which is so hot it stings my skin, although

I'm wearing a T-shirt under my new dog's-tooth batwing jumper. I trace the pattern of the carpet with my finger: thick golden rope against an emerald green background. If I focus hard enough, maybe I can forget where I am.

"The pastry's *soggy*, Mummy, I can't eat nothing *soggy*."

"I know, darling." Mum and Timmy are wedged together on the sofa, sharing a plate of cold sausage rolls. She begins to remove every speck of pastry so that the bare sausages resemble the babies' willies we saw in the RE module on religious rituals. Timmy won't touch them uncircumcised.

Dad is fiddling with the huge remote control for the new TV, which is his present to himself, though he claims it's "for all the family". It comes with a new invention, Teletext, and we're the first people in our street to get it. Dad is a bank manager, after all, so must always be one step ahead of the neighbours.

He presses some buttons and the image of tired, dirty women disappears from the screen, replaced by coloured electronic squares.

"Look, it's an advent calendar," Dad says, before Timmy can ask about lesbians again.

It doesn't look much like an advent calendar to me. I try to decipher the picture on the screen: crude blocks of green and red in a primitive cone-shape . . . "It's a Christmas tree!" I say, pleased I worked it out faster than my brother.

The TV sound is still playing behind the advent calendar, and a woman is being interviewed: "We'll definitely be here past new year into 1982. We'll stay till 1992, 2002, if the world's not been blown up by then. This is deadly serious. We won't let them bring in the missiles. It's a matter of life or death."

I realise it's the peace camp down the road at Greenham. "Dad —" I wave my hands, trying to get him to flick back to the news.

"And look what happens when I press 'reveal'," he says. The tree lights up with yellow cubes, flashing on and off like cursors on the two ZX Spectrums in the computer room at school.

"Dad, let me watch the news."

"For God's sake, Jo, not that again. It's Christmas."

"But it's important . . ." My news fixation is the latest family joke; hot on the heels of my hilarious crush on the footman in *Upstairs, Downstairs*, and my craze for collecting gonks (which I now see are ugly as sin), I am officially obsessed with doom and gloom.

Mum looks up from the plate of naked sausages. "Let her watch it, Ted."

He sighs then points the remote at the TV. The black background disappears, but the green tree remains, like the Cheshire cat's smile, hovering over footage of enormous warheads.

"That's the mix function," Dad explains, before pressing another button.

"Meanwhile, government ministers insist that Cruise is an essential part of allied defence strategy. They point to the situation in Afghanistan, still unresolved two years after the Russian invasion, as evidence that the threat of nuclear aggression is as acute as ever."

75

"Nuclear aggression?" I feel shivery, so I push my body against the radiator, before realising I'm not really cold. I'm scared. Since Mr Blake's movie, I see flower-patterned burns whenever I close my eyes. And sometimes I dream I'm standing by that super-heated river, trying to choose whether to be roasted or boiled alive.

A look passes between my parents, a kind of shutting down, and Dad rearranges his face into the relaxed expression of Terry Wogan interviewing Shakin' Stevens, while Mum takes refuge in the kitchen.

"Load of fuss about nothing," Dad says.

"But they said —"

"It's the news," he insists tetchily, "that's their job, making everything sound as bad as possible. It's not bloody *Jackanory*. They're hardly going to say, 'The Ruskies are welcome to wander through some country none of us have heard of, we're all going to live happily ever after.' But that's the truth, Jo. We've lived through much, much worse."

"But . . ." I stare at the ceiling now, counting the cracks in the Artex, knowing Dad's wrong, that this is the most dangerous time in history, but unable to find the right words to persuade him.

"But nothing . . . you need to grow up, Jelly Bean," he says, and his voice softens as he uses my nickname. "Having daft crazes for toys or pop stars is one thing. Even that bloody vegetarian phase was better than this. It's abnormal for a twelve-year-old to be into current affairs. No boy is ever going to fancy a girl who likes warheads, you know."

I bite the inside of my cheek to stop myself crying from frustration. I know I should be more like Lorraine, worrying about whether it's cooler to fancy Andrew Ridgeley or George Michael. But how can I do that, when my parents have their heads buried in the sand? We're one nuclear button away from annihilation and all Dad cares about is the auditions for the Operatic Society's production of *My Fair Lady*. And all Mum cares about is Timmy.

The dog waddles in from the kitchen. She nuzzles my face with her nose and her eyes meet mine. We called her Misty because of those eyes: even though she's *only* a dog, when I look into the blackness, it makes me think of infinity, of staring into the sky and wondering what exists beyond the stars and our galaxy. I asked Dad once and he couldn't explain what was beyond infinity. Or what happens when we die. Whenever I think of either of those questions, it makes me dizzy.

"Hey, daydreamer? Wakey wakey?" It's Mum, holding out an extra large slice of chocolate yule log. "This should take your mind off the end of the world."

CHAPTER
EIGHT

Nostophobia —
Fear of Returning Home

They don't know much, doctors.

After three weeks and six days in hospital, that's my staggering conclusion. Not that I remember much of the first week, except fragments of eavesdropped conversations that I shouldn't have heard (it's amazing what people say when they think you're half-dead).

Dr Williams is right about one thing: coma isn't like it is in the movies. There's been just one Tinseltown moment: my miraculous awakening after forty-nine hours of absence. I've heard four different accounts of this touching scene now, from Dennis ("I was the first one to notice you'd come round!"), from Mum ("Your eyes were shining, it was like you'd been reborn."), from Dad ("I've got to be honest, Jelly Bean, I thought you looked like you weren't all there! Sandwich short of a picnic or something.") and from Timmy ("All very moving, but don't go getting a taste for the limelight, sis, it's not you."). I've no way of knowing which version is nearest to the truth, but I think there's been a fair bit of rewriting history, in true Hollywood style.

The rest is pretty un-showbiz. The catheter to drain my bladder and the itching sensation I can't quite shake off although it's been gone two weeks. The bird-like legs where my plump thighs used to be. The scaly patches wherever my skin met starched NHS sheets.

My face is now the colour of those sheets. But looking on the bright side, my features are sharper, because hospital food is inedible and Dennis's food parcels — health-enhancing, will-to-live draining dinners, full of Omega-3 oils, to assist brain function — are even worse. The bruising on my face took for ever to disappear, but now all that's left is a grey shadow on my temple and, above it, a dent I can't stop touching. Oh, and a bald patch.

Yep, I have gone bald before my dad.

I've always known that the human body is vulnerable. I hadn't understood quite *how* vulnerable.

"You all set, Bean?" My father smells of cologne and wears a spiv-sharp grey suit (very *Alfie*). He takes my holdall while I carry the movie-star bouquet of pink roses and gerbera that Timmy had couriered over from his favourite Notting Hill florist yesterday. He's kept up an ambush of impressive floral arrangements in lieu of visits, and I think he forgot I was going home.

"Whatever," I mutter. *Going home*. Nearly four weeks in hospital, yet I haven't had my kidneys removed for sale on the international organs black market. I haven't been suffocated by a murderous medic with Munchausen's. I've even escaped the superbug (well, I won't quite believe I'm out of the woods till I've checked the incubation period for MRSA on the internet).

"Shall I have them bring you a wheelchair?" Mum suggests.

"I'm perfectly *fine*. Can't you lot ever stop fussing?" I snap back, and the guilt kicks in instantly. Pills and physio sessions in the chilly hospital gym have begun to unfurl my locked limbs and restore some muscle tone, but my brain . . . let's just say I'm not myself. I seem to have developed temporary Tourette's: time after time, my mouth responds before I have time to censor it.

My parents exchange glances that say *we're lucky to have her at all* and *we need to give her time*.

They don't know the half of it. The confusion. The sentences I start and can't finish, because I lose my thread.

And the flashbacks.

The only person who knows about my flashbacks is Dr Williams. I steeled myself to mention them a few days ago, when he called me in to talk about what happens when I leave hospital, i.e. what to expect from the rest of my life. Sitting in his shabby office, I felt underdressed: it's hard to pull off a grown-up conversation when you're in your nightie.

"What I really want to know is, will I ever return to *normal*?"

"Normal! Now why on earth would you want to be that?" He leaned back in his chair, feet on the desk.

I was shocked the first time I saw Dr Williams. His mellow voice suggested a beefy rugby player with a cauliflower ear. Instead he's what Lorraine would call "a lanky streak of piss": tall and wiry, like a medical Morrissey. He has floppy brown hair and his face is a network of lines, though I'd guess he's younger than Dennis. But he also has the gentlest brown eyes I've ever seen and a sense of humour that makes brain injury seem almost bearable: no wonder the nurses swoon. The unluckiest pedestrian in Courtbridge has somehow landed the best doctor in the world.

"OK, I grant you that I probably never was all that normal in the first place. But will the moods ever go?"

"Moody's normal, too, remember. Let me find those statistics I dug out for you . . ." He rifled through his in-tray. I told him early on that statistics make me feel better, however grim they are. I like to know what I'm up against. "Here we are. Twelve months after a moderate head injury, forty-eight per cent of patients report problems with anxiety, pressure, depression, irritability or temper." He paused to let this sink in.

"So I've a one in two chance of staying this way?"

"Yeah, but then again," he turned the page, searching for another figure, ". . . ninety-eight per cent of women without a head injury are moody."

"You made that one up, didn't you?"

He grinned. "I like to call it extensive field research with the female gender."

"Can't you ever be serious?"

"In this job? No way." He scratched his head. "Look, Jo, I appreciate that the lack of answers is irritating."

"You mean maddening."

"Could we compromise on *a little trying*?"

"Absolutely totally bloody exasperating is my final offer," I said, arms folded.

"No problem with your vocabulary, then. OK. I'll confess, I get frustrated too sometimes. But it's so fascinating: the brain is the world's last uncharted territory. My job is all cliffhangers. Why would a blow to the head turn a sweet girl like you bad-tempered? Will the old personality ever reassert itself?" He frowned. "Would you want it to?"

"Of course I . . ." I stopped. There were benefits to being permitted to snarl, though I wished I could discriminate more: Dad and Timmy were definitely overdue for the odd tongue-lashing, but Mum and Dennis didn't deserve it. "It's not just the moods."

"Go on."

I blushed. "I know it sounds crazy . . ."

"Nothing you can say to me will sound crazy, Jo. I love symptoms. Clues to what's going on up here." And he knocked his knuckles against his head.

"I keep . . . going back. In time." I looked up, waiting for him to press the secret panic button that would summon the men in white coats.

"How far back in time, exactly?" he asked, evenly.

"Eh? I don't follow."

"Second World War? Stone Age? I've had a few French Revolutions. Marie Antoinette's very popular with women who're fond of cake."

"Oh." I giggled. "No, not like that. In my own time, my own memories . . . Things that have happened to me. Flashbacks, as though I'm back, in the past, watching myself."

82

"Watching yourself? Like an out-of-body experience?"

"Sort of." I felt relieved that he was taking me seriously. "Not that I'd mind having that body again. Not a trace of cellulite. Didn't know I was born." Then I blushed. He'd already seen my body, cellulite and all.

"I'll ignore that," he says, "though it's my duty to point out I've seen more cellulite on a supermodel. So how often do the flashbacks happen?"

"I know it's definitely happened twice, though I suppose it's possible I've forgotten some other ones. But those two flashbacks are so clear. So detailed. Flicked fringes, high-necked frilly blouses, the works."

"Were you the same age, in the flashbacks?" He'd begun to take notes. "And you don't have to tell me this, Jo, but were they traumatic occasions?"

"Hmmm. I was eleven, twelve. And I suppose, well, they weren't traumatic as such but . . ." To my surprise, I realised tears were running down my face.

"But not very happy either?" he said, passing me a tissue.

"No . . . sorry." I gulped, really crying now and feeling the pressure of more tears behind my eyes. It didn't used to hurt to cry. "I used to feel *frightened* a lot of the time. Sounds silly, doesn't it? I mean what does a kid have to be afraid of?"

"It's OK, Jo. There's no hurry, we can take our time with this. You can make a follow-up appointment, whenever you need one."

"I . . . Is it bad? What I've told you?"

"Not really. Everyone responds differently to head injury. An out-of-body feeling, floating above yourself, that's a commonly reported experience. Often people who've been in a coma have . . ." he hesitated, "what laymen call Near Death Experiences. Some surveys say it's as high as thirty-seven per cent."

I smiled at his statistic, though my throat had tightened. "Thanks for that." My voice was croaky: the word death hadn't been spoken by anyone I'd met in hospital. When Mum or Dennis alluded to the times they'd been most afraid, they tended to trail off or talk in euphemisms about "slipping away" or "fading". But I had the haziest memory of nurses standing at my bedside, rating my chances in more down-to-earth language.

"Typically patients imagine themselves on the cusp of this world and another."

"Another world. Like heaven?"

"Mainly heaven, yes. Hell's not popular at all. Generally people report bright lights and clouds and soft voices behind them, offering them a choice between following the voice or returning home. Sometimes it's a river, with the patient on one bank and their loved ones across the water."

"Sounds . . . nice. Peaceful. Trust me to get the smelly girls' loos at school."

"I've always wondered what females talk about in the toilets."

I ignored his distraction attempt. "So . . . does that mean I've officially been *near death*?"

He hesitated again. "The visions don't, in themselves. Personally I think the bright lights may be produced by coma-specific brain activity." He took a breath. "But you *were* near death, Jo. We don't dwell on this when patients are recovering, but as you've mentioned it, well, I wouldn't have staked my car on your chances of emerging. And *pretty much* unscathed."

"Right." I made no sense. The original glass-half-empty girl had a stroke of luck. Jo Morgan, ultimate scaredy-cat, an against-all-odds *survivor*?

"You're in bloody good shape, Jo. I mean it. I can see why the flashbacks are disturbing, but there were only two. Maybe you won't have any more."

I sighed. "There's nothing you can do to make sure?"

"We could try medication, but it'd be a sledgehammer to crack a nut. I'd pefer to let you heal in your own time. Hey, don't look so sad. Not many of us get a second go at adolescence."

"I'd have preferred the angels and harps and flouncy nightie stuff."

"You're a one-off, Jo. Too smart for angels and all that bollocks," he said, then tapped the side of his nose. "But don't you dare tell anyone I said that. You'd get me struck off."

If I wasn't a whey-faced invalid, I could have sworn he was flirting with me. "I'm going to miss having you to make me feel sane," I said. "And safe." That was the strangest thing about hospital: despite the monitors and the smells and the sounds, I never once felt afraid. For a while I hoped perhaps I'd put my fears behind me, that the knock on the head had turned me into a bionic woman, fearless and feisty. But as soon as I thought about life *outside*, I realised I was the same old cowardy-custard.

"Aha. That's another thing I wanted to talk to you about. It doesn't have to be goodbye . . ."

I blushed again. Surely Dr Williams wasn't going to ask me out? After he'd seen my devoted Dennis visiting me twice-daily (boring me rigid by reading out Sudoku hints, but at least he was there). "You know I've got a boyfriend but if I didn't . . ."

He shook his head, blushing himself now. "Oh no, no, not like that. Not that you aren't my loveliest patient, of course, but . . . I know you'll be coming in for physio and occupational therapy, but I wondered if you'd also like to come to my rehab group?"

I stared at him.

"Listen, it's a laugh. You'll love the Monday Club. Bingo. Board games. Free drinks. Well, free Ribena and decaffeinated tea, anyhow. And the best company you'll find this side of Swindon."

"I . . . the others, are they very disabled?" I whispered the last word, already feeling guilty at my seemingly lucky escape.

"They're just *people*, Jo. Nothing to be afraid of. Maybe you'd call them . . . eccentric, some of them." He spread his fingers. "OK, I won't fib. Some of my patients are never going to enjoy the quality of life they had before. They can be difficult and unpredictable. But so can I. I think it could help you. Give it a go, Jo!" He winked.

I know patients always fall in love with their doctors, and maybe I have, a little bit, with mine. So I must have said yes to keep him happy, because I don't have *any* intention of hanging out with a bunch of head-cases.

"I had to park miles away," Dennis says, puffed from his walk. As he kisses me briefly, hot panting breaths on my neck, I remember the last time we made love. Valentine's night. Garlicky sweat forming wherever our bodies met. His weight, his passionate clumsiness, had felt as reassuring as usual. Even his slight selfishness — coming before I did, as he tends to after a few drinks — made me feel irresistible and alive. Yet hours later, I nearly wasn't alive at all.

They've told me the story now, what they know of it. I was in the wrong place at the wrong time, as a cyclist ploughed down the hill. A racing bike, a flash of Lycra (most witnesses agreed lime green, though one insisted it was more of an acid yellow), and I hit the deck, my head taking the force of the impact on the hard cobbles, my body sliding after it. The bike went down too, briefly, but its rider wasn't hanging around: as the Good Samaritans of Courtbridge came to my rescue, Lycra-man was back in the saddle and steaming off like Lance Armstrong. All he left behind was a pile of broken plastic from the light on the front of his bike.

Rubies and diamonds . . .

That's what I remember: shards of plastic in a pool of my own blood. They said it was pouring from my head, though it was only a shallow flesh wound. What was going on inside that would cause me *much* more trouble.

Eight people called an ambulance. That's the kind of place Courtbridge is. As I was being strapped onto a stretcher in case of spinal injuries, the speculation was beginning: was the cyclist blinded by sunlight? In such a state of shock that he'd fled without thinking? Or in the wrong place at the wrong time, perhaps an adulterer on his way home from a Valentine's tryst.

He still hasn't been found and the smog mask he was wearing means it's becoming less and less likely that he will. Dennis seems more aggrieved about that than anything else, "A smog mask? In Courtbridge? Didn't he know we've made greater strides towards improved air quality than any other local authority in the south of England?"

Apparently my case provoked endless headlines about the "Tragic Valentine Coma Girl", "Lycra Louts" and "Cycle-Ogical Warfare" (nine pedestrians killed and 1000 injured by cyclists in the last five years). Dennis has saved the cuttings but I am in no hurry to read them. Yes, the bloke was stupid to run away, but I was stupid to cross the road without looking. I don't think I've ever done that before, I'm like one of those teenagers who fall pregnant the first time they have sex.

Accidents will happen. Even to me.

"You off then, Jo?" says the Sister, in that irritating way of stating the obvious that seems to pass for chit-chat on the ward. I'm sure she's the one who was writing me off when she didn't think I was listening.

"You take care of her!" she tells the others. "She might not be so lucky next time."

That word again. *Lucky* Jo.

Dennis cups his hand round my elbow, like a solicitous grandson leading his elderly nan across the road. "Will you stop pawing me, please, I *can* walk on my own," I snarl and his eyes narrow before he gives me a tight smile.

"Of course you can." His voice is tolerant and I feel like a total bitch.

Once we're out of the ward, turning left towards the car park rather than the familiar route I've taken for weeks towards physio, I wish I hadn't been so fast to brush him off. The corridor is long and low, with lights that make my hands look like a corpse's. The smell of lukewarm beef stew and disinfectant is stronger than it ever seemed on the ward. Grey lino stretches ahead of me and it begins to swim before my eyes and I have to lean on the wall.

"You OK?" Behind me, three anxious faces are lined up, watching for the signs of mental meltdown.

"Never felt better," I lie.

They don't look convinced. Something tells me that my accident might have turned them into scaredy-cats too.

CHAPTER
NINE

Soteriophobia — Fear of Dependence on Others

According to breakfast TV this morning, the secret of happiness is counting your blessings, ideally six a day. After two long weeks of miserable house arrest, I'm willing to try anything. So . . . blessings. Um.

Got it!

Blessing number one: we live in a bungalow.

When I announced I was moving into Dennis's place two years ago, Lorraine thought it was the funniest thing in the world: in her eyes, single-storey dwellings are strictly for the over-seventies.

The first night Dennis brought me here, after the legendary Strategic Safety Partnership Christmas dinner dance, I was unusually giggly and made some remark about how at least he'd never have to put in one of those Stannah stairlifts.

"That's why you're different, Jo," he whispered to me, "no one else but me has ever thought ahead like that, planning for inevitable infirmity, but *you* understand." I was about to protest, to explain I was joking, but then he kissed me for the first time. And after that, it no longer seemed important.

Now, like the other residents of Salzburg Avenue, I'm finding our one-level living a blessing. No stairs to topple down if I have a funny turn. Who'd have guessed infirmity was so imminent?

The net curtains twitched when I came home from hospital, but now they're still again. I suppose I could try to bond with the neighbours, but my family aren't keen for me to go out on my own just yet. They've tried to lock down every moment of my day, no room for accidents. Lorraine is banned from visiting because she might over-excite me, like a toddler exposed to preservatives and trashy cartoons.

It seems strange, but I think my head injury has affected them more than me. If you are a scaredy-cat, you always expect to become a statistic one day. But they were unprepared for the worst and it's hit them hard.

Whereas in my case . . . it makes no sense at all, but now that the worst *has* happened, a newly hatched reckless streak keeps telling me, *you've beaten the odds once, Jo, maybe you could do it again. Why not take a risk or two?*

I ignore it, of course. That way madness lies.

Blessing number two: every day is a duvet day.

Though actually my life now is more timetabled than when I was twelve. At 07:00 hours, Dennis gets up, accidentally on purpose brushing against me to make sure I'm still warm to the touch. Some mornings — and I know this isn't nice — I stay still, like a child playing statues. Not because I want to frighten him but because . . . actually, I don't know why I do it. I used to be such a good girl.

07:49 Dennis leaves the house, but not before he's stood for a full minute at the foot of the bed, watching me. He doesn't say anything but I know he's there, I can hear his breathing. I became very good at reading noise in hospital: you can learn so much when you're feigning sleep. Eventually he'll lean over and plant a kiss on my lips, like the prince in the fairytale. It's a solicitous kiss, the kind you'd give a hairy-cheeked granny on visiting Sunday, when you don't know whether she'll still be there the next time you come. He hasn't kissed me *properly* since we came back from hospital.

Sometimes I wonder if he ever will again.

08:30 The phone will ring: either my mother or my father at the other end. I daren't ignore it as that would cause a 110mph Berkshire — Wiltshire mercy dash. Dad drives like he's in *The Italian Job* under normal circumstances and he can't afford any more penalty points on his licence.

I prefer it when Dad rings. I always answer with the sprightliness of an actress in a cereal commercial. He'll ask how I am and I will say I feel great. He'll give me a weather report from the electronic monitoring station in his shed, along with an account of what the pretty weather woman on *Breakfast News* was wearing. Then, occasionally, he'll forget to put my mother on and hang up and *then* I can ignore the phone because I can pretend I was in the shower.

Of course, four out of five times it's Mum on the line, her hesitant voice expecting the worst.

I crank up the *joie de vivre*, in the hope that they might decide to leave me alone for *one bloody day* but it never happens. Tuesdays and Thursdays are unavoidable, because I need ferrying to physio and occupational therapy sessions and, of course, I can't drive since my injury. But on the other days, her excuses are increasingly imaginative. "I need some upholstery fabric I can only get from that lovely shop near you," she'll say, though she's shown no previous interest in soft furnishings. Or, "the cats need their space", which is equally unconvincing, as she mollycoddles them more than she ever did Timmy.

08:45 I shower. The best time of day. When I first came home, I was terrified of getting my head wet (in hospital I'd survived on strip washes and the occasional excruciating bathtime supervised by a nurse) so for four days I pretended to shower, running the water, and splashing shower gel around so the room smelled Ocean Fresh.

I did this until I realised I was no longer smelling Ocean Fresh myself and my latest craziness was bound to be discovered. I looked up phobias on the internet and found a site saying that if you sing at the top of your voice whenever you're terrified, it blocks the bit of the brain that produces fear and — three verses and choruses of "My Favourite Things" later — I was clean.

Now I look forward to the only moment in my day when I can guarantee to be alone. And I sing my little heart out, adding rude words as I go . . .

"When the bike hits, when my head splits, when I'm feeling shit . . . I simply remember the booze and the fags, And then I feel less of a tit!"

09:00 Breakfast. The accident's taken away my appetite, but I force something down before Mum arrives, otherwise she'll insist on watching me eat, mumbling, "Oh, you must have more, Jo. Keep your strength up," as I struggle to swallow a few mouthfuls. Things don't taste the same; I used to hate coffee, but now I crave it, because the bitterness masks the tinfoil-flavoured jam on my cardboard toast. Not that I'm allowed the real thing, of course: Dennis thinks I haven't noticed that he's swapped our normal brand for the organic fairly traded, single bean, decaffeinated variety (the caffeine removed by the water method, rather than noxious chemicals, of course).

10:00 Typically, Mum, Dad or, worst-case scenario, both, will arrive just after the Courtbridge bustle hour is over. If there's an OT or physio sesion, then it's easy: I zone out of Mum's chatter on the way there, and on the way back I pretend to sleep again, as a result of all of my "hard work" in the therapy room.

In truth, it's a doddle. The OT woman who did my assessments seemed almost disappointed at my competence. Of course, I didn't tell her about my showerphobia, because I knew she'd adopt this caring-sharing Cabbage Patch Doll expression, tell me it's normal and then try to "devise some strategies for adapting and managing the challenge".

I don't want to adapt! I don't want to manage the challenge — we're talking about a bloody shower, not climbing Everest.

I did try to convince her that there must be *truly* sick people who were more deserving of her valuable time. And she smiled at me, oh so bloody patiently, and told me that, "Physical progress is certainly easier to map, but the mind needs time to heal, too."

"I don't see why," I whined, "everyone says I've been so lucky."

"Well, that's great," she said, still saintly. "And are you feeling lucky?"

It was strange, but when she said that, I was hit by this awful urge to wail. Not a delicate dab at the eyes with a tissue, but a full-on, ear-busting wail that would echo through the clinic. Hoping she wouldn't notice my eyes bulging with kept-back tears, I managed to say, "Of course. I had a miraculous recovery."

She didn't smile that time. Instead she said, "Yes. You have done well. But what looks like a miracle from the outside doesn't always feel like one on the inside, Joanna."

I pouted. "It's not Joanna, it's Jo."

Physio's easier. The woman knows I don't want chit-chat, and I'll let her know if anything hurts. I'm a good girl, I do my exercises, and I can see I'm getting stronger. Sit-ups haven't put any hairs on my bald patch, though.

Blessing number three: my newly toned thighs now fit into size ten jeans.

13:00 Lunchtime. *Bad* time. It's like being three years old, except I don't have a highchair. And if they did them in my size, I'm sure Mum would have bought one. She tries so hard to pretend we're having a "girls' lunch" (though we never had them before), or that she's "dying to try this recipe", but we both know that there's only one objective, and that's to get me to consume calories, preferably wholemeal organic ones but, failing that, empty calories will do. Even Dad's in on the act. He takes me to non-smoking gastro pubs and orders real ale that he forgets to drink because he's too busy monitoring what I leave on my plate.

14:30 Afternoons are the worst. No comedy emails doing the rounds in the office, no nodding off at your keyboard when no one's looking. I suppose it'll be different when I go back. *If* I go back. No one's talked dates yet. I'll need a medical and there'll doubtless be more counselling than was offered to an entire battalion of shell-shocked Second World War veterans. "But don't worry about rushing back, we'll muddle by without you," Dennis says, which is a nice way of saying, "your job is so inconsequential that it barely matters whether you're there or not".

Usually I sit in the living-room, playing Monopoly or Cluedo with my parents. Mum never suggests Scrabble, because she's read all the booklets, and knows brain-injured patients sometimes have trouble with words and self-expression.

Last week, she arrived with a carrier bag full of crusts.

"You're not *seriously* going to suggest we feed the ducks, are you, Mother?"

She blushed. "I thought it would be nice to get out of the house. Fresh air."

"I am not a *bloody toddler*, Mother. I had *an accident*." I jabbed my finger in her face and the more she recoiled, the louder my voice grew. "I haven't entered my *second childhood*. And the last thing I want in the whole bloody world is to *feed the bloody ducks! I hate ducks. Creepy fat buggers!*"

Blessing number four: evidently I'm not having too much trouble with self-expression.

I felt so guilty afterwards that I threw everything I had into feeding those lucky ducks, for her sake. I stood at the edge of the pond, a giant among small children in Boden rainwear, trying to make sure every bird, regardless of size, had at least one crust. I engaged in sophisticated decoy activity to stop the geese demanding bread with menaces from the moorhens. I grinned manically at Mum, pretending I was enjoying myself and, after a while, I almost was.

"Where's *your* child?" A small boy in crocodile wellies, who had tired of kicking water at his younger brother, poked me in the knee.

"She must have swum off," I said, without thinking. The boy stared harder.

"I didn't see anyone swimming," he mumbled. "I'm not *stupid*."

"She's awfully fast," I told him. "And she has her own diving suit, so she can stay underwater for ages and ages."

He began to back away from me. "*Not* true."

"And then, right at the last minute she will jump up out of the water, grab any boys wearing crocodile wellies — which she hates — and push them over, head first, into the mud. And then the ducks will peck at them. Quack, quack! Quack, quack!"

He ran off so fast that he tripped over his own feet and for a moment, I felt terrible. At least the wet earth made for a soft landing. I heard him whispering to his mother, but she ignored him, irritated at having to abandon her gossip and take him home to change.

I couldn't stop quacking under my breath all the way home. If Mum noticed — and I can't see how she wouldn't have — then she was discreet enough not to say anything.

Blessing number five: these days, I can get away with anything.

16:20 Peace. Mum doesn't like driving in traffic, so she leaves after *Countdown*, urging me to get some sleep, as Dr Williams insisted it was *the* most important factor in my recovery. I comfort myself with the knowledge that, according to statistics, 4.20p.m. is *the* peak time for nervous breakdowns in the UK. Although of all the figures I've researched in my time, this is the one I find hardest to believe. Surely it's the wind-down time of day: only an hour or so before you and your neuroses can skip off home to hit the bottle or watch snuff movies or whatever keeps you sane. 4.20p.m. is when I'd most like to be back at work. Our office was directly above the canteen, so our afternoons were punctuated by the sounds and smells of institutional catering: the clattering and sloshing of the post-lunch clear-up, followed by the first sensory clues in our daily guessing game: what was Bella, the canteen's expert baker, making for tea? If it was lemon drizzle cake (my favourite), the acidic citrus aroma always gave the game away early, as Bella and her ladies pulverised enough fruit to satisfy 400 hungry council staff. But most of the other bakes began with a vague, warm waft of sugar and butter and flour, before one of us took a first wild guess. *Macaroons!* No, no, caramel crunch, I can smell burned sugar. *Aha but how do you know that isn't just one of the cakes left in the oven too long?*

No sugar-loaded cake for me at home, though. Just one hundred minutes of surfing the net for weird statistics (well, it passes the time) before . . .

18:00 Dennis returns. I usually spray on some perfume and apply lipstick, in the manner of a 1950s' housewife (amount of lipstick consumed by average woman in a lifetime: six pounds). But he never notices; instead, he inspects me for *symptoms*. He works his way down my body, checking for twitching or odd rashes or tremors or paralysis. Then he instigates some pointless conversation and I can tell he's not listening to my words, but to my speech. Am I slurring? The lights are on, but is anybody home?

He used to eye up my body like a hungry wolf about to devour me. Now he's like an anxious farmer, convinced his prize cow is about to succumb to a bout of foot-and-mouth.

I told him exactly that last week.

"Don't be so daft, Jo. What a stupid thing to say."

"I've watched *All Creatures Great and Small*, Dennis. I've seen the look on Christopher Timothy's face just before he went to his car to fetch the shotgun."

"Oh for God's sake! If I'm getting a shotgun it'll be to shoot myself," he said, storming out. But within a few seconds he was back, that social-worker expression on his face. "Let's sit down, Jo," he said, and led me gently towards the sofa.

"I *can* manage!"

"Yes, yes, you can, I know that," he soothed. "And I'm sorry for being short-tempered with you. This isn't your fault. It's what they said might happen."

"What is?" I hissed back.

"Well . . ." he pulled on his kiss-curl, "the irritability. The irrational thoughts. It's all to be expected and sometimes I forget that. The report I read in *BMJ Online* said that both patients and relatives underestimate the time it takes for the brain to heal fully."

"Fucking hell!" I shouted, and it felt good, so I shouted it again.

"*Please*, Jo. The neighbours." He placed a firm hand on my arm.

"Sod the sodding neighbours. They'll understand. Of course they will, because everybody bloody sodding fucking understands, don't they? I don't want to be sodding understood! I want to be normal!"

And then I did the worst thing possible. I burst into tears. Instantly Dennis switched back into sympathy mode, all soft murmurs and strokes to the head, like you'd comfort a baby, and half of me wanted to wriggle out of his arms, but the other half made me bury my

100

face in the long-hard-day-at-the-office crumples of his shirt, sobbing until he was soaked to the skin.

"There there, Jo Jo," he repeated over and over, until the words no longer made sense. "It's all going to be all right."

That night, I fell asleep there, in his arms, and only woke up when he was putting me to bed.

I seem to be short of a sixth blessing. But all I need to do is remember the figures Dr Williams gave me: fewer than fifty per cent of people who've been in a coma survive. I might be a bit eccentric, but I'm alive . . . even a scaredy-cat can see that blessings don't get much bigger than that.

CHAPTER
TEN

Phengophobia — Fear of Daylight or Sunshine

Today, Mum's call never came. I waited by the hall table (Dennis is not a fan of cordless handsets, due to the potential health risk of all those signals bouncing round the house), willing the phone to ring, so I could get on. Not that I really have anything to get on *with*, but even so . . .

I amused myself by flicking through the *Civil Protection Chronicle*. I'd got all the way to the classifieds — some poor bloke is trying to flog a load of Cold War era prefabricated fall-out shelters, suggesting they're "ideal for storage or as a den for children and stressed-out dads" — and Mum still hadn't rung. 08.51. My body felt itchy because my shower was overdue.

I made myself a cup of tea. It's the key task the occupational therapy woman asked me to perform on the first session, and now I wonder if I made some basic error that proved I required months of intensive rehab. Did I put the milk in before the water? I could never remember the "right" order *before* the accident.

Though, uselessly, I have no problem remembering that thirty-seven people a year are injured by tea cosies.

09.04 and I was starting to panic, which couldn't be good for my neurological health. My imagination, fired up by tannin, pictured Mum and Dad suffocated in their beds by the over-affectionate Maine Coons. Or murdered by one of Dad's many bits on the side: beaten with a putter by Mindy the golf club receptionist, or snipped to death by Savannah from the salon.

09:12. I was about to call Dennis in a panic when the phone *did* ring.

"What time do you call this?" I said.

"Oh, Jo," Mum said feebly, "we've come down with a bug."

"Bug?" I computed the implications of this sentence. If the bug was bad enough to interfere with phone-call timings, surely a half-hour car journey was out of the question.

"Only a twenty-four-hour thing, I'm sure. We've certainly had a good clear-out, if you know what I mean."

"Yes, thanks, Mum —"

"It's been both ends at the same time, half the night. Your father took the en suite, of course, so I've been on my knees in the main bathroom, and he never did get round to fixing the radiator in there. I've nothing but bile left, now, I swear, but still it keeps on coming."

"Right. Thanks. Really wanted to know that. Have you taken a pill to stop it?"

"No, let it all out, is what I say. But it does mean . . . Jo, I can't see how we can possibly come over."

"Ah. No, I understand. I'm sure I'll cope," I said, trying to sound sad.

"Why don't I ring Dennis? Couldn't he work from home?"

"I'm a grown woman, Mum. I can be left Home Alone for a few hours without burning the house down or having a wild party."

"Hmmm." She sounded doubtful.

"Anyway, Dennis is on a Nuclear, Biological and Chemical Threats awayday at a five-star hotel in Hampshire," I said. It was only a little white lie. "I can't interrupt that. It could put everyone in Courtbridge at risk."

"I suppose so. And you'll definitely be OK?" There was an urgency in her voice now that suggested she needed to bring our chat to a swift conclusion.

"Yes, Mum. Now why don't you ring off now? Don't you have an appointment with the big white telephone?"

"The big white . . .? Oh, I see what you mean. Yes. In fact, now you mention it . . . bye, Jo. Ring later, I promise." And she hung up.

I walked into the kitchen and peered out at the daffodil-filled garden, which seemed, like the day ahead, to shimmer with freedom and opportunity.

But the shimmer was a mirage. So far I've made and consumed three teas and two decaff coffees; polished off an entire packet of plain chocolate digestives; and watched several makeover shows and a schools programme about the fight or flight response.

I've also answered the phone to three cold-callers and had fascinating chats about no-step bath cubicles, panic buttons mounted on a tasteful necklace that will give me the confidence to live independently for longer, and the free Scandinavian cruise I've won (all they need from me is my credit card number).

As I don't have a card — the woman from the cruise company couldn't believe I survive without one — I then went on to Dennis's laptop and applied for one. Well, more than one. Six, actually. It's all very well for him to say that credit is the last resort of the financially incontinent but as my jailers, sorry, parents, haven't been dishing out pocket money, I don't have much alternative.

I also sent some emails to the sites run by personal injury solicitors, after the woman from the panic button company mentioned that I could probably get compensation for my accident (I'd told her all about it and she'd ooohed very gratifyingly in all the right places). I wasn't sure, what with it being a hit-and-run, but she thought it was worth a go.

But I haven't gone outside.

My courage failed me. It's been seven weeks since I went anywhere on my own, and though I loathe being watched all the time, *out there* now seems impossibly dangerous . . . So much for the new adventurous me.

I've moved the net curtain aside in the lounge so I can watch the comings and goings in Salzburg Avenue, logically the most unthreatening "outside" in the world.

A tortoiseshell cat lies in the middle of the road, its body splayed out to capture as many rays of weak April sunshine as possible. A turquoise blur whizzes past the window — it's the woman opposite, a retired whirlwind who lives with her sister. Today she's been jogging: as she turns up her path, her tight-fitting vest top has rings of sweat around the armpits. The cat, intimidated by her sense of purpose, lolls away.

After that flurry of activity, nothing happens. Not a single car enters the cul-de-sac. The postman and milkman have already delivered. There's no breeze so even the leaves on the trees are motionless.

Still life.

Oh dear. I'm Sleeping Beauty, trapped in Dennis's bungalow for ever. In the kitchen, making myself yet another cup of tea, I remember Dr Williams' club. He's written to me since I was discharged, reminding me of the times and dates, but I threw the letter in the bin. It's bad enough being an invalid without sitting around drinking endless cups of tea and achieving nothing.

Oh.

The heavy panting of a diesel engine breaks the hush. I cradle my hot mug and tiptoe back into the lounge, which has gone quite dark. A dirty great lorry is parked right outside.

What starts as a niggle about the way it's reduced my right to sunlight turns rapidly into full-blown irritation, and I fly out of the front door in my bare feet to give the driver a piece of my mind. Only when I get out there do I notice the lettering on the side of the lorry, "Courtbridge District Council Neighbourhood Cultural

Resource — Working for U, with U and in UR Community."

It takes me a moment to realise that this is the mobile library. And one more moment to feel the cold on my soles, and remember I don't like *outside*. Just as I turn to go back inside, the little door on the side of the truck opens, and a stout woman in a gaping red wrap-dress pokes her head out.

"Oooh, a non-member!" she cries. "Can I sign you up?"

"No, you're all right," I say without slowing down, "I thought you might have been delivering something."

"But we are! We're delivering cultural resources, the joy of learning and some surprisingly explicit romantic novels!" She's out of the truck now and heading towards me.

"I'm not much of a reader, to be honest."

"Oh, go on! I get brownie points for signing people up, especially if they're from a disadvantaged group. Are you?"

"I don't think so."

"Didn't think so. Shame. What about kiddies?" Her smile, I notice, is on the hungry side.

"Nope."

"Disability?"

I glare at her. "Don't you think it's rather intrusive to ask all these questions?"

She narrows her eyes. "Sorry . . . It's ME isn't it? I can always spot it. I've got a great title on alternative remedies come back in. Woman in Venice Grove had the book for a fortnight, could barely get out of her bed

107

except to see me, and since she's been growing her own wheatgrass, she's training for a half-marathon."

"I don't have ME."

"But by the look of things, you don't have much to do either. And you really ought to put something on your feet, at least," she says, and this time she's got a point. Bare feet, uncombed hair, unironed clothes. "Listen, why don't you sign up anyway, see if there's anything you fancy? That way I get those brownie points, and I promise I'll leave you alone after that."

I can tell she's not giving up. "All right. I'll join. Let me get something on my feet."

By the time I comb my hair and force my feet into some old trainers, the library has filled up. Not that it takes much. The pushy librarian, whose name is Penny, only just fits into the narrow aisle running the length of the truck, so the decision to move from Sci-Fi to Misery Memoir is not one to be taken lightly.

"Got a great one in," Penny calls across to a very elderly woman who is browsing the Noir Crime shelf, her neck sunken into her shoulders. "Woman was born in Stoke-on-Trent, sold as a sex slave to a Russian mafia boss and now runs her own porn studio in California. Won the Godalming Book Club's best non-fiction of the year."

"Lovely," says the woman, reaching out a gnarled hand to take the book for a closer look.

"Not a word of it's true, but that's never bothered anyone," Penny whispers to me. "Now then, what do you fancy? Nice bit of fluffy chick lit, take your mind off your troubles?"

"What troubles?" I snarl back.

"Now, now, don't fret. Mrs Hastings here —" she nods at the hunchback — "was telling me all about your accident. Goodness me, you could write a book yourself. Miraculous recoveries always go down well. Though you do still look a bit peaky."

I frown at the old woman in the corner. How the hell does she know about the accident? Must have read about me in the paper, I suppose.

"What about this one?" Penny continues, " 'Fifi's life as a PA to dashing concert pianist Christophe is every girl's dream — until she's accused of stealing his earnings. Left with only the Manolos she stands up in, Fifi must clear her name and try to win the heart of her man in a million'."

"I'd rather read the phone book." It's very hot in the library now; the tiny windows above the tall bookshelves barely let in any light.

"Yes, it does sound awful, doesn't it? All those books with pink covers, I'm sure they're written by trained monkeys. What about something a bit heavyweight then? This one's surprisingly interesting: *Greased Lightning: How Lard Changed the World*."

She holds out the book and her perfume hits me: a Gothic scent like tropical flowers dying in a cave, blending with the musty smell of books that have been pored over by thousands of sweaty fingers.

"I'm sorry but I feel a bit . . ."

I'm swaying and it feels as though the shelves are going to topple on top of me, like Alice, and then . . .

CHAPTER
ELEVEN

Bibliophobia — Fear of Books

"I heard . . ." the girl behind the counter lowers her voice, "that they're testing them for the bubonic plague."

"Never!"

The queue isn't moving and I look nervously over at Dad and Timmy, in the corner of the library that's reserved for Little Readers (or Little Bleeders as my father calls them). Dad's chatting to Charmaine from the Operatic Society, and she's giggling a lot as usual, flicking her stupid ginger hair.

Every Saturday, Mum does the washing, while Dad drags Timmy and me round town to do the shopping. The library is always the last stop before we go home to spend the evening working out Ted Rogers' stupid clues on *3-2-1*, and inventing disgusting new fillings for our Breville Cut 'n' Seal sandwich toaster.

Timmy is sitting in the corner with a stack of Smurf cartoon books and "practical jokes to play on your big sister" manuals, while Charmaine's five-year-old daughter Crystal stares at him as though he's the most beautiful person on the planet. He ignores her completely.

I always hide in the Teen Fiction section. I won't be a teen for six more months, but I've had it with stories about ballet and ponies. I like proper novels, about hostage-taking and weird ageing diseases that wipe out the entire population except a couple of fourteen-year-olds who will snog on the last page. The girl who stamps the books is only sixteen herself and recommends the gorier ones, turning a blind eye to the age limit.

"It's *true*. It's because the women are so filthy. Did you know it's apparently against their feminist rules to actually wash?" She flicks back her Lady Di fringe in disgust. She's getting into her stride now and showing no sign at all of stamping the borrower's Jilly Coopers.

I wish she'd hurry up. Today my illicit borrowing is riskier, because between my Robert Cormier and my John Wyndham, I have three adult books. And even if she lets me take them out on a child's ticket, I need her to do it before Dad comes over because he definitely won't let me borrow these.

"I didn't know they had a set of camp rules," says the Jilly Cooper reader. "My Tony was thrilled to bits when they arrested some of them the other day. Send 'em to bloody Russia, see how they like it in the salt mines, that's what he says."

You can't go anywhere in Newbury these days without *Them Women* coming up in conversation. No one sticks up for them, even though they're the most exciting thing to happen round here since I was born.

112

They've been here seven months now and there's no sign of them leaving.

"Russia wouldn't have 'em," the girl says, finally lining up the books. "Because they're smelly —" stamp "— weirdo —" stamp "— perverts!" Stamp. "There you go. Oh, I like that one. I swear it's the raunchiest one of hers I've read."

The borrower leaves happily, anticipating a night of posh rumpy-pumpy. I approach the counter nonchalantly, checking that Dad and Charmaine are still lost in discussion about their roles in *My Fair Lady*, before I hand over my five choices. She stamps the Cormier, then stops.

"Oh, now, *Joanna*," she says disapprovingly. "What do you think you're doing with these?"

I blush. "I'm doing some research. For school."

"Come on. We never did this at school and I'm not that much older than you."

"Well, we do. You were never in Mr Blake's class, were you?"

"*Flaky* Blake? Well, that makes more sense. But you know I shouldn't let you take them out on these," she says, holding up my five green tickets, which mark my subhuman status as a child borrower.

I can hear the weary rumble of my father's voice from the kiddy corner: he's tugging at my brother's arm. "Time to go, Timmy."

"*Please*," I beg the girl. "I can read them in a week, and I'll make sure I return them back to you next Saturday, then no one else needs to know. It's *important*."

113

She folds her arms across her large chest. "I don't get it, I really don't. Rude books I understand. I learned everything I know from novels."

There's a howl from the corner. Timmy! My brother's always threatening tears, but rarely lets himself cry in public. Everyone in the library, including Counter Girl, looks up.

At first I wonder if he's play-acting to get noticed, but the howling continues and my father's face is white.

"Can anyone . . . is there anyone who can . . ." his voice gets louder and louder, as the head librarian races over from Large Print Historical Fiction. She's followed rapidly by Counter Girl, who can't resist a drama.

I seize my chance, scooping all my books into my carrier bag. The Cormier, the Wyndham, *Effects of Radiation on the Human Body*, *Cold War Targets in Western Europe*, and *Home Sweet Home: Fall-Out Shelters for the Armageddon Age*. If no one else will take the threat seriously, it's down to me to save our lives.

Holding the bag behind me, so Counter Girl doesn't notice, I jostle my way to the front of the crowd surrounding Timmy. "That's my brother, let me through."

When I get there, I wish I hadn't. Charmaine is quite pale, despite her mustard-coloured instant tan, and Dad seems paralysed, his mouth wide open in shock. And Timmy . . .

The first thing I notice is the blood streaming from his nose. Then the tears that are tumbling down, diluting the shockingly red blood that covers his face.

And his Muppets T-shirt. And a section of the space rocket patterned carpet.

He's had nosebleeds before — I'm sure he can bring them on, to get attention — but this is different. It's not stopping. If he carries on like this, he'll run out of blood. And human beings can't survive without blood.

Much as I hate my brother, I don't want him to die . . .

The head librarian swings into action now, pouncing on Timmy's nostrils and pinning them together, despite my brother's howls. "Will you all move away from the boy, this isn't story-time," she barks at the onlookers. Then she turns to Counter Girl, "And Jessica, stop gawping for once in your life, and call an ambulance."

CHAPTER
TWELVE

Xenophobia —
Fear of Strangers or
Foreigners

Dr Williams couldn't quite keep the satisfaction out of his voice when I rang.

"Oh, that's excellent. I knew you'd come round in the end."

"I've only said I'll give it a try. Once," I said.

"Once tried, never bettered." I pictured his sharp smile. "So what made you think again?"

"I suppose . . ." I hesitated, unsure how much to reveal about my current state of mind, "I'm surrounded by people who want to help but it feels more like being under surveillance. I thought strangers might be more laid-back company."

"My bunch are so laid back they're almost horizontal," he said. "And how are you feeling generally?"

"Better," I lied. Well, it's only a half-lie: physically I am better, in fact probably in better shape than I was before, thanks to all the exercises. But I don't mention the peculiar incident in the mobile library van, that horrible tiredness that took me back to 1982 again. Or the fact that Dennis has begun to ask questions about the avalanche of junk mail offering free holidays, free money and very expensive medical appliances, that followed my web surfing and heart-to-hearts with friendly cold-callers. Or the split personality that I've developed, which means *I want to be alone*, but get totally wobbly as soon as I am left to my own devices.

"So will you be bringing anyone with you? Only, if it helps, you can tell them that it's doctor's orders that you come alone. Part of the rehabilitation process, step towards independent living, blah blah blah."

How did he know? "That does help," I said, feeling an unfamiliar bubbling sensation in my stomach, and then remembering that this is what it's like when you have something to look forward to.

Of course, the excitement doesn't last. In fact, by the time Mum drops me off outside the hospital gates, I feel more like a shy four-year-old about to start school. And on that particular occasion, I wet my knickers before I made it into the classroom.

"I'll be back at one," Mum says bravely. "Have a lovely time."

She's wrapped me up warm against sharp April winds; I'm almost disappointed she hasn't also given me a ham sandwich and a Kia-Ora. At least clutching a packed lunch would give me something to do with my hands. But head injury patients travel light: my mother

117

wouldn't trust me with house keys, and like the Queen, I don't carry cash.

I walk through the grounds, past the redbrick Victorian ward block, past the physio and OT departments, past the brand new buttercup-yellow maternity unit, past A&E. I pass a woman in a wheelchair, snoring in her sleep as an orderly pushes her across the lumpy concrete. Then there's a man so old his clothes look fossilised, and a flushed young girl whose belly is so extended I don't know how she stays upright.

This is *my* world now. At least the pregnant girl is only a temporary member of the In-Firm, but the rest of us are going nowhere fast. Or, very slowly, in the case of the fossilised man.

I follow the signs for Brain Injury Rehabilitation: through the car park, behind ENT and Ophthalmology, past the wheelchair repair centre, and there it is. Tucked away, as if the hospital authorities are ashamed of it. Even the building looks apologetic, a slumped hut, with a balding felt roof and pockmarked pebbledash walls.

It's not quite 10.30, and I don't want to be the first in, so I take my mobile out of my pocket, to make it look as if I have a life. The phone is the only valuable Mum lets me carry, and then only because she fears I will collapse somewhere. She even conquered her lifelong technophobia to program in an ICE "In Case of Emergency" number so that kindly strangers can give her a tinkle if further disasters befall me.

I text Lorraine, "AM ABOUT TO ENTER LION'S DEN. WISH ME LUCK."

118

She's still banned from Salzburg Avenue, which I suspect suits her just fine. And the sad truth is that her phone calls exhaust me, making me dizzy with gossip and overly gory details of her recent deliveries.

She responds straight away, "U R THE SEXIEST, BRIGHTEST HEAD-CASE I NO. STAY COOL."

I smile, despite the complete uselessness of her advice. But "Head-case"? I quite like that. Makes me sound wilder, more rebellious than before: the girl who beat the odds.

"Now you *are* a vision in blue jeans."

I look around for the source of the poshest voice I have ever heard, richer than treacle tart.

At first, all I can see is a cloud of cigar smoke, condensing thickly in the cold spring air. Then a pocket of clear air appears, revealing a racing-green tweed jacket . . . then a pink shirt . . . a purple Paisley cravat . . . a lizardy neck and, finally, a pink wrinkled face with grey eyes so bright I instantly know they've seen more than I might in ten lifetimes.

He's leaning on the bicycle rack. A slow, confident smile lifts first his lips and then multiple folds in his cheeks, a concertina of skin folding all the way up to his eyes, like a fancy Austrian blind. On top of his head are vanilla-ice-cream-coloured curls. He takes another puff of his cigar before he speaks again.

"Did I startle you?"

"No. Not really."

He smiles again, raising an eyebrow. "Shame. You look a little startled. And, you know, when you're my

119

age, being able to surprise a beautiful young woman really would be something to celebrate."

I manage an embarrassed laugh. The smoke dissipates again and I dare to look more closely at his face, to attempt to carbon-date this strange figure. He's short — no more than five foot eight or nine — but not stooped. The hands that hold the cigar are mottled yet powerful, but when I catch a glimpse of the palms, they're scarred, the colour of farmed salmon.

I have never seen anyone like him before.

He takes a step forward, politely transferring the cigar to his left hand and moving it behind his back. "I'm Roger. But everyone calls me Frisky."

"Right," I say, pulling a face before I can stop myself.

He shrugs. "I *know*. The nickname seemed appropriate when I was a young man but it's faintly grotesque on a wrinkly old bugger. The trouble is, I'm rather too used to it now to change back."

"I didn't mean . . ."

"Oh, my dear, I know you didn't. You seem a very well-brought-up young lady. Although there is *one* thing."

"What?"

"It is customary to return the favour when a stranger offers his name."

"Sorry. I forgot. I'm Joanna Morgan. Jo."

He holds out his hand to shake mine and I avert my eyes: the texture of his palm is like Barbie doll plastic. He looks unimpressed at the weakness of my handshake and I sense he's already bored.

120

"And you're . . . don't tell me, let me guess. A *social* worker?" He bares his teeth — so shiny-white and straight, they must be false — in a sneer.

"God, no."

"A volunteer?" This is said with less contempt.

I blush. "No. I'm a patient."

His eyes narrow in surprise and then he beams again. "*Really.* Oh, excellent news. About time we had a little feminine influence at the Monday Club. You know," he whispers now, letting me in on a secret, "the trouble with the bloody brain injured is they tend to be male and distinctly oafish, because it's mainly men who are daft enough to end up with a blow to the head. What a refreshing change it will be to have a young *lady* in our midst."

I flinch at the implication that only stupid people end up here. "I'm coming to try it out, that's all."

His face softens now and those eyes, again, draw me in. Looking into them makes me feel understood, somehow. "Oh, that's what everyone says, Joanna. But you know, there's a camaraderie among head-bangers that can prove a hard habit to break."

"Head-bangers? Isn't that a bit offensive?"

"What would you prefer? Brain injured sounds rather feeble. Without being too presumptuous, Joanna, would I be right in assuming you're new to all this?"

"Yes. It was only two months ago."

"Right. Well, what the doctors don't tell you — even our lovely Dr Williams, who's a pretty decent sort — is that you're in a different world now. One where we tend to be direct. Speak our minds. It saves time, which is what some of us are short of."

I nod, feeling still more terrified of the people I'm about to meet. I'm tempted to run away, except I'm pretty sure this Frisky would come after me. "I have felt *odd* since it happened."

"Well, compared to the rest of them, you look *smashing*, if I might say so, Joanna Morgan." He takes a drag on the cigar, the end burning red, then orange, before producing a perfect smoke ring.

"Take no notice of this miscreant! Whatever he's said it's an outrageous lie."

"Dr Williams!" I'd recognise his warm voice anywhere. "Actually, he was singing your praises."

I turn to see him; he's in "civvies" — a black shirt and skinny jeans that make him look more like Morrissey. Outside the ward, it's easier to see that he's *very* cute.

"Jo! I am so pleased you made it. So what's the Air Vice-Marshal been telling you then?"

I turn back to Frisky. "Air Vice-Marshal?"

He blows away the last of the smoke and raises his eyebrows. "My dear, take no notice of our Welsh friend. Young people today have no concept of military ranks. A few dogfights, half a century ago, that's all."

Dr Williams winks at me. "A few dogfights? Not what I've heard, Frisky. And not like you to indulge in false modesty, especially when there's a lady present."

Frisky steps alongside me and touches my arm, to guide me towards the door. "Lady? Joanna isn't a lady. She's *one of us*."

And, as I let myself be led up the rickety steps into the rehab unit, the words repeat in my head. One of us. *One of us.*

I never thought I'd be so pleased to be labelled a head-banger.

Dr Williams unlocks the door and switches on a bank of strip lights, which flicker alarmingly. Aren't flickering lights meant to trigger fits? Not advisable in a room full of the brain injured.

The hut is ninety-nine per cent youth club, one per cent family planning clinic. There's a game of table football, a dartboard (with Velcro darts, of course, no sharp edges allowed), piles of car and motorcycle magazines and a set of foam easy chairs coated in a livid green and black print. An ancient coffee machine in the corner, one of those that also offers soup and squash so that each drink tastes more of the previous one than the flavour you asked for. Plus orange plastic stacking chairs, wood-effect laminate tables, and a tall bookcase stacked with battered boxes of Monopoly, Mousetrap and Operation. I know already each one of them will have some vital piece missing that renders the entire game redundant. Still, it's not the winning, eh?

But the rack of books and leaflets on the wall isn't fun and games. *Why Did I Have a Stroke?* nestles next to *What to Expect after Brain Injury.*

Dr Williams looks at me anxiously. "Now I know it doesn't look much . . ."

"Oh, it looks *fun*, doctor," I insist. And it definitely beats Salzburg Avenue.

"You're not still calling him doctor?" Frisky says scornfully. "Everyone is equal at the Monday Club."

Dr Williams' face flushes, redness spreading from his neck through his cheeks. "Well, yes, that is the whole idea. That there's no hierarchy. No experts." He holds out his hand. "So, in the spirit of the club, I'm Nathan." And he blushes more deeply.

"Hello, Nathan," I say and I find myself blushing too at the strangeness of saying his name.

Frisky sighs. "Don't mind me. I feel like an extra in *Dr Kildare*."

Dr Williams — Nathan — steps away quickly and switches on the radio, Classic FM, which is presumably the station of choice for patients with dodgy brains. Motorhead would be asking for trouble. The strip lights have stopped flickering, but the string quartet doesn't quite mask the hum from the bulbs.

I sit down on one of the spongy chairs. "So what *exactly* happens at the club?"

"Well, if you get here early, *Nathan*" — Frisky says the name in a slightly mocking tone — "will treat you to one of his *special* coffees, reserved for those of us he thinks are able to handle the neurological consequences of caffeine exposure."

I look over my shoulder and, sure enough, Nathan is retrieving a travel kettle from a locked cupboard. "You've spoiled the surprise, Frisky. Caff or decaff, Jo?"

"Caff, please." It'll make a nice change from the insipid stuff at home.

"Better do it fast, Nathan, or the boys will get jealous," Frisky says. "Mind you, they're going to be so distracted by our new recuit, I doubt they'll notice."

"So who else comes along?"

"There's usually about a dozen of us, plus the volunteers."

"And . . ." I hesitate, struggling to find a way to ask the question. "The others. Are they . . . well, what are they like?"

Frisky pats my hand. "They're just a bit more direct than most people. I always think a head injury magnifies your existing quirks, maybe adds a few more."

"Very well put," Nathan says, handing me my coffee.

Frisky winks at me. "Of course, there are people here I'd normally cross the street to avoid. But I think they were always like that, even without a bang on the head."

I nod nervously and suss out my escape routes. I can't help thinking that it's nice and cosy with only the three of us. Then we hear a noise like a herd of elephants on the steps outside.

"Better hide the coffee," Frisky says, "because that sounds like Monster to me."

"Monster?" I say, gripping the mug.

"Long story," Frisky says. "But don't worry, I'm sure he'll tell you himself."

Two hours later, and I do indeed know all about Monster: the fight outside a nightclub at Christmas five years ago, the drunken kicks and blows to the head that

125

made his face swell so dramatically that his then-girlfriend couldn't recognise the "monster" in ITU. By the time Monster's face had returned to its former boy-band glory, albeit with a long, neat scar along his hairline, the girlfriend had shacked up with his best friend. And in the time it's taken him to recover sufficiently to find a part-time job in a factory, the girlfriend has married and had two kids: the family Monster always wanted.

Then there's Falsie. Falsie lost his left eye and his living in an accident at the tiny under-the-arches garage he owned. His speech is difficult to decipher at first, and he knows it, so he simplifies the story into a few key phrases. His wife sits next to him at the centre, they travel everywhere together now they've sold the business. In two weeks, they're off on a Nile cruise. Frisky tells me later that when Falsie's had a couple of drinks, he takes out his eye and passes it around. It's a work of art, apparently: the hazel colours match his real eye exactly.

Slasher is an ex-Hell's Angel who came off his bike six months ago. After me, he's the newest head-banger. He made a beeline for the sofa without saying a word to anyone, picked up a *Motorcycling News*, and within seconds, tears were rolling down his tattooed cheeks. I nudged Frisky.

"Shouldn't someone go and help him?"

He shook his head. "He needs his space. At home, his parents won't leave him alone so this is his safety valve. He'll be OK in a few minutes."

Frisky introduces me to everyone, and I try to keep track of who's who. The men all have aggressive, matey nicknames, but the two women, Liz and Deidre, are called by their proper names. Liz is barely out of her teens, and nearly died in a pile-up on the M4; she sits in a corner, clutching her brown plastic cup of tea, reading magazines and looking fed up. And Deidre is in her late sixties; she had a stroke a year ago and though the only outward sign now is a slight downturn on the left-hand side of her mouth, she comes back every week to play cards. "Gives me something to look forward to, dear. Before the stroke I never used to go out, not since my husband died. Now I have quite a social life, what with this and moving into the sheltered housing. Stroke of luck, I call it."

Nathan works the room, chatting and joking like a holiday rep. I eavesdrop on a few conversations and realise that with each anecdote or casual remark, he's collecting information, without them suspecting a thing. He asks about Monster's new job and explains how his employer could get cash to make the workplace more Monster-friendly. He listens to Falsie's wife's concerns about making new friends on the cruise, and role-plays what they might say about the accident. And with Slasher, he waits until the tears have stopped, then offers him a biscuit and a chance to talk.

When he comes over to me, I'm instantly on guard. "What's the prognosis, Doc? Am I going to lose my marbles?"

He smiles. "I think the fact you've hung on to them so far is a good sign. So how are you finding the club?"

"It's . . ." I look around the room, thinking it over, "great. Not what I expected, though."

"In what way?"

"I thought the people would be, well, scarier. Does that sound awful?"

"No, not at all. Humans very quickly accept other humans with missing limbs and horrible injuries but there's something about the brain that makes us extra wary."

"What made you want to spend your life with *us*, then?" I say, surprised at the strange solidarity I feel with Slasher and Liz and Frisky: us against the world.

"Oh, I've always been contrary. And it's what I said to you in hospital: the brain is one of the last uncharted territories. As a boy I wanted to be an explorer, but let's face it, I don't have the physique. You don't need crampons to enter the dark world of the central nervous system."

"That makes you the Edmund Hillary of the mind then?"

"More like Phileas Fogg," he says.

"Around the brain in eighty days?"

"Eighty days wouldn't begin to cover it," he says, then stops. "You've got me on my hobby-horse, Jo. Sorry. This is meant to be about you."

"I'm a bit bored with me, though. Especially because me these days means illness and amnesia and paranoia and bad temper."

"That's not how you come across to me, Jo," he says, then coughs. "And bear in mind that the people here are the ones who still feel the need for some support.

There are hundreds more who've come for a short time, then moved on. So what about you? Will you be coming back? Next time there's a talk about memory tricks. And we'll decide where to go on the summer outing."

I look around the room at the nicknamed people, and the shoddy furniture, and the low-tech games, and it occurs to me that two months ago, I couldn't have imagined spending time here, never mind choosing to. But this is also the first place in two months where I have been able to relax, to stop caring what other people think.

"Well, so long as my Mum lets me out to play," I say, surprised at myself.

Nathan beams. "Terrific. I *knew* you'd like it. I knew it. That calls for a drink — can I interest you in a criminally weak cup of tea to celebrate? Daren't get the coffee out in public."

"You make it sound so tempting," I say. "Go on then."

Nathan heads for the machine, still grinning. I feel someone brush against my arm.

"Well, well, well. Haven't you made our young doctor's day?" It's Frisky, his face more wrinkled than ever in amusement.

"I expect he's on commission from the hospital, to get people to come here," I say. "Like pyramid selling."

"Hmm. If that's what you want to believe. Never mind him, what are *you* doing later?"

I giggle. "Are you propositioning me, Frisky?"

"Oh, if only, my dear. If only. The spirit is just about willing, but the body . . . however, I did wonder if you might like a spot of very late lunch? Some of the chaps go to the WRVS, but it reminds me of the NAAFI. I don't live far away, and I can guarantee you'll be quite safe. Unfortunately."

"My mother's coming to pick me up," I say, realising I sound more like a four-year-old than a grown woman. "She's not wanted to let me out of her sight since the accident."

"All the more reason to spread your wings, wouldn't you say?" And he chuckles. "There comes a time for every chick to fly the nest."

I weigh up the options. Beans on toast with Mum scrutinising my every move in case I've over-exerted myself. Or lunch with a mysterious — yet too old to be dangerous — stranger.

"Give me a minute to make a phone call."

Of course, my mother thinks I'm having some sort of brainstorm and the only way to convince her otherwise is to introduce her to Frisky. I've told him to meet us in the hospital car park, after I've had a few minutes to prepare her.

"Mum, I know it's a bit sudden, but Frisk . . . um, Roger is a total gentleman."

She folds her arms across her chest. "Is that so? I mean, how do you know he hasn't preyed on young women like you before?"

"He's not preying on anyone."

130

"Really. Well, it seems very fishy to me." She's straightened up and seems taller than usual. This is a side of my mother I barely recognise: the last time she stood up to anyone was two decades ago. But despite the mint-green trouser suit, and the pink frosted lipstick, she now looks like a force to be reckoned with.

"He's a harmless old chap who wants some company," I say, hoping Frisky can't hear me from his hiding place behind a St John's ambulance.

"Harmless? Don't you think it's rather peculiar for a man to hang around a group of people with head injuries? Waiting for someone vulnerable."

"Mum, he's not a weirdo. He's a patient himself," I say, and then regret it. This is not going to reassure her one bit. And actually, I still don't really understand why Frisky keeps coming to the club. I'm sure he'd have much more fun at a tea dance or bridge night; a man like him would be mobbed by oversexed grannies.

Mum's eyes nearly pop out of their sockets. "What, you're proposing to slope off with some potential psychopath? There's no way of telling what someone like that might do . . ." She trails off, realising what she's said.

"Really?" I say, simultaneously angry and more determined to spend time with Frisky, even if he does turn out to be an axe murderer. At least he doesn't judge me. "Well, I'm glad that's out in the open, Mum."

"Joanna, I didn't mean that *you're* like that." She's shrinking back into herself before my eyes, mortified.

"Whatever, Mum. But I want to go with Roger and I'm a grown woman and there's nothing you can —"

And then Frisky appears from behind the ambulance, more dashing that David Niven. "*Hello* there. You can't be Joanna's *mother*."

Mum stares at him.

"No," he says, shaking his head in a brilliant show of disbelief. "You must be Joanna's *sister*."

This has to be the corniest line ever, one even my father wouldn't attempt, yet my mother actually flutters her eyelashes. "No," she says, a girlish quality to her voice. "Definitely her mother and don't I know it."

"They can be such a *worry*, can't they?" Frisky says, switching into caring, sharing parent mode.

"Oh!" Mum says. "Oh, it's been quite, quite the most stressful time lately. I thought she might not make it and now . . ." her hand darts to her mouth. "Sorry. I'm usually more discreet."

But then usually no one bothers to listen to my mother.

Frisky holds out his liver-spotted hand. "Roger Freeman Van Belle. A pleasure to meet you."

Freeman Van Belle? What kind of a name is that?

"I'm Lynda," my mother says breathlessly.

"Lynda. I know it's hard to let Joanna out of your sight while she's so *delicate*, but I'd very much like to treat her to lunch. It's important, don't you think, to widen her horizons gradually?"

"Oh," she says, as if this is a surprise. "Well, I don't doubt you'll take care of her."

132

"But?" Frisky raises his curly white eyebrows, which knit together momentarily.

"But . . ." Doubt and then shame cross my mother's face: she can't bring herself to ask Frisky if he's *OK*, if he can get through an afternoon without a seizure or a naked romp up the frozen food aisle in Sainsbury's.

He steps in front of her, well inside the exclusion zone she always maintains with strangers, and touches her shoulder. "Lynda. I *promise* I won't let her come to any harm."

And I don't actually care what Mum thinks because *I* believe him. This wrinkly old man with a ridiculous name and mysterious past makes me feel completely safe.

"All right," my mother says. "You look after her, though, Mr Freeman. I'm trusting you with my baby."

He nods solemnly and waits while she clambers up into Dad's 4x4, waves at me and drives off.

"Now, Joanna," he says, smiling, "I think it's time for you and I to get roaringly, steamingly drunk!"

CHAPTER
THIRTEEN

Cibophobia — Fear of Food

Frisky's house is ten minutes' walk from the hospital, in a tree-lined avenue of tall Victorian villas. His is semi-detached and, like its owner, gently decaying. Next door has a stone façade the colour of Cornish sand, ornate detailing as sharp as the day the mason took a chisel to it, and paintwork that zings, from the black lacquered railings to the white sash window frames.

Frisky's stonework is discoloured, his masonry aged into soft focus, his railings rusty and his woodwork peeling, revealing a dozen different paint shades. But the house has a certain dignity, as a four-storey home should, and inside it smells of fresh flowers and emulsion.

"The kitchen is in the process of redecoration," he says, rather unnecessarily, as we enter a high-ceilinged room with a Belfast sink, a range cooker and a dozen doorless cupboards. The walls are bare plaster, still drying from the edges inwards. Under my feet, the original black-and-white herringbone tiles display a century's worth of wear and tear.

"And how long before it's finished?"

"Ah, now, there's a question. Not sure a house like this is ever *finished*, Joanna. Especially not when one's relying on the grandson to do it. Wonderful boy, of course, such a perfectionist, but I wouldn't bet my shirt on it being finished within my lifetime."

I look at Frisky, wondering how much longer that lifetime might last.

He catches me looking. "Since you're clearly speculating on my appalling old age, I'm eighty-five. Twenty years younger than the house."

"Sorry, I didn't mean . . ."

"Nonsense. It's natural to wonder. Frankly I wake every day utterly astonished to have been granted more than my three score years and ten. But thrilled, of course. Absolutely thrilled." He touches the bare walls tenderly. "The more time I have to see her restored to glory, the better."

"Your grandson's a builder, then?"

"More of an enthusiast, like me. Except considerably better up ladders than I am. Vertigo, you know. But Luke . . ." he pauses, looking at me intently, "is a good boy to his grandfather, all things considered. And he loves the house as much as I do, and not only because he'll inherit it one day."

Before I can reply, my stomach growls so loudly that it echoes around the room.

"My dear! I am being the most *appalling* host. Take a seat in the conservatory while I knock up a little something for lunch. We can't starve you when you're

135

still convalescing, can we?" And he shooshes me out of the kitchen.

The conservatory dates back to a time before double glazing: it's possibly the prettiest room I've ever seen. The ironwork seems organic, ornate curls and tendrils wrapping themselves around thick glass. Though many of the panes are speckled or cracked with age, they still seem to trap what little sun there is today, so that my skin feels caressed by unfamiliar warmth.

Beyond the glass, the garden is thawing after the long winter and bluebells are scattered across the lawn. Two enormous oak trees stand like ancient sentries at the far end of the plot guarding the ugliest of caravans. It is large, brown and derelict, with a hideous corrugated roof and small mean windows.

"Here we are. Not too early for a snifter?" Frisky brings in a tray with two tumblers full to the brim with ice, lemon segments and a shot of unidentified spirit. "I take it you do drink gin?" he asks, and from his tone I know the only acceptable answer is yes.

"Well, um, of course, I *used* to. But I was advised that after the accident, I ought to avoid alcohol, for the time being."

Frisky's eyes narrow. "Oh dear. Do you know, it's one of the things I loathe most about having survived into the twenty-first century. This quite ludicrous *obsession* with being sensible."

"Well, I suppose people like that are only being careful." People like that? Who am I kidding?

"Careful. Yes. And do you think we won two World Wars by being careful? Invented vaccination? Electricity? Space travel?"

"No, but this isn't really in the same category," I say, sensing the end of a beautiful friendship. "I just don't believe in taking pointless risks."

"That all depends," Frisky says, pausing to swallow an enormous slug of gin from his glass, "on whether you perceive pleasure to be pointless." He sighs. "You know, gin is distilled from juniper. So it's virtually a herbal remedy."

"Even so," I say, "I think I'd prefer water."

He sighs again. "Goodness. Have you heard the phrase, youth is wasted on the young?"

I smile, feeling rather foolish. He disappears again, and I hear loud bangs and crashes. I've made him angry now. Why can't I stop being such a coward? I've been given a second chance, but I seem incapable of taking it. Water fills my eyes so I stare fixedly at the bloody caravan, willing the tears away, and suddenly I see a face at the window.

"Oh! Frisky?"

Frisky comes through with a terracotta bowl of olives, and a crystal glass of iced water. "What's the matter?"

"I think there's someone in that deserted caravan," I whisper, though the interloper must be at least sixty feet away. "Should we call the police?"

He begins to chuckle. "Oh, dear me, no. That's just Luke."

"Your grandson?"

"Yes. He lives in the caravan, you see."

"But this house is massive."

"And a massive mess. There's only one bedroom fit for human habitation and that's mine."

"Couldn't he sleep in the kitchen? It must get freezing in the caravan."

"Ah yes but . . ." Frisky tails off slightly. "Wildlife. Yes. That's it. Luke is *awfully* into wildlife. Wiltshire's answer to St Francis of Assisi, really. Loves all creatures great and small. And there've been some terrible cases of cat-napping in the area. So he sleeps in the caravan, to keep an eye out. Wonderful boy." He chews thoughtfully on an olive, before spitting out the stone. "And do you like cats, Jo?"

"They're all right, I suppose. More of a dog person, really."

"Oh, I thought all women liked cats," he says, sounding disappointed. "There've been some dog-napping incidents too. Frightful business. But they've gone right down since Luke decided to do his pet policeman thing."

"Right . . ." The whole thing sounds unlikely. "So will Luke come over for lunch then?"

"Possibly. He's a little shy, you know, the way people so often are when they're at one with nature. All he needs is someone to bring him out of his shell. Do you know what I mean?"

"Ye-es," I say, crossing my fingers that this cat-loving hermit won't be joining us.

Frisky disappears again. I'm starving, the first time I've felt properly hungry in weeks. I hate olives but they

138

look so succulent against the terracotta dish. I reach out for a small green one and chew carefully, afraid I might break a tooth on the stone.

The sharp lemony tang hits my tongue, then makes my nose twitch. It's delicious, the first food that tastes *better* since the accident. I try a juicy purple one the size of a grape, which tastes of coriander.

I'm reaching for a black one when Frisky returns from the kitchen with another tray. There's a plate of sliced tomatoes, garnished with pink crescents of onion; a dish of feathery rocket, with Parmesan shavings curled on top; a wooden board with French bread and a huge wedge of runny cheese that's already melting on to the knife; two wishbones of red-brown marbled sausage, tethered with string; a flash of yellowy-green oil; and a carafe of wine the colour of resin.

"These olives are great." The black one is intensely herby. "What's this got in it?"

"Ah, thyme. My favourite. Reminds me of Crete, during the war. It grew wild, you know, just the thing for livening up our bloody awful rations."

"Is that where you learned to cook?" I say, my mouth watering as he spreads the plates out in front of us.

"Oh, this isn't *cooking*, Joanna. I'll show you cooking, one of these days. But I certainly learned a lot about self-sufficiency. Now are you sure I can't tempt you to wine?"

He pours himself a glass and a summery smell of cut grass wafts towards me. "I would, but . . ."

"The doctors warned you, I know. But do you always do as you're told, Joanna?"

"Ummm. Well." I can't quite bring myself to admit it. "Not *always*."

He looks at me for so long that I feel uncomfortable. Perhaps he's developed a sixth sense for when someone's fibbing.

"OK, most of the time," I admit, eventually.

"And has doing what you're told stopped you landing up in a coma? Made you cram in as much fun as you can, in case there really is no tomorrow?"

"No," I say, sulking now.

"It's not for me to tell you how to live your life, Joanna. God knows, I've mostly made a hash of my own. But at least I've enjoyed making mistakes. It strikes me you're too worried about getting things wrong to do anything at all."

My sulk is turning into full-on anger. "Don't patronise me. What am I meant to do — go without a seatbelt? Or, I don't know, go for a jog along the hard shoulder. Or maybe I should go home with strange men!"

He looks shamefaced. "You know, you're absolutely right. Sorry. The war, that's my excuse. Turned me into such a bore, telling everyone to seize the day."

His climb-down takes the wind out of my sails. "What *did* happen to you, Frisky?"

"Terribly unspectacular, alas. No heroic dogfight over the Channel defending the White Cliffs and Vera Lynn's honour. I was travelling between bases when my engine failed. Brought her down in a field, and the buggers were more worried about the bloody plane

140

than me. I took a bit of a knock, everything seemed fine and then the fits started."

That must have been how he burned his hands. "Fits? As in epilepsy?"

He shrugs, takes a bite of sausage. "Well, I called them funny turns. Less clinical. Happened all the time to begin with, pretty alarming, but then they eased off until, bingo! Last year, I woke up on the Post Office floor, surrounded by nosy parkers."

"All these years later?" I ask, shivering. Will it be the same for me?

"Well, who knows if it's connected? What the docs described as a 'cerebral accident'. But a happy accident, too, as it's how I met the charming Dr Williams. Began coming to the club because my friends were dropping like flies and a chap gets lonely at home." He sees my hesitating over the cheese. "It's very good, that one, but potent. Try a little bit if you're not sure."

"It's not that. I was wondering if it's pasteurised?" Dennis and I once went on a long weekend to a food safety conference in Ipswich and I still remember the slides . . .

"Oh I shouldn't think it's safe for a second. Absolutely teeming with bacteria, listeria and little green men from Mars, I'd imagine. A truly scary dairy product." He takes a spoon and ladles the gooey cheese on to his bread. "Luke likes that horrid plastic cheese, though, let me look in the fridge."

He leaves me alone, eyeballing the pool of cheese. A surprisingly enticing smell of ammonia rises from the plate, challenging me: if I close my eyes I can recall the microscope image, little wormy tubes of listeria dyed turquoise so they showed up better, criss-crossing the screen, longing to invade my gastro-intestinal system.

When I open my eyes again, the cheese is oozing further out of its rind and, without thinking about it, I take a slice of the bread, initially to stop the liquid running off the side of the plate. It slides unctuously into the pitted dough, and smoothes over like self-levelling concrete. It has a life of its own.

And so do my hands because they lift the slice to my lips and without really thinking, I take a bite. My teeth sink into the soft cheese and then the chewy bread, and then my brain and nose and tastebuds process the texture and the taste and the mushroom-and-perm solution smell, and as Frisky emerges from the house bearing a piece of cheese the colour and shape of a Lego brick, I sigh deeply.

"Joanna, are you all right?" He stares at the piece of bread in my hand, my toothmarks giving the game away. "By God, you've eaten the cheese."

I nod, slowly, as a smile spreads across my face. "I have eaten the cheese. Tempted by forbidden fruit. Frisky, it's *wonderful*."

He beams. "Oh I am thrilled to have led you astray, Joanna. What fun." He lifts up his wine to chink against my water glass. "I think we should drink to listeria. You know, I always thought it'd be a lovely name for a little girl."

"Hang on," I say, the cheese making me reckless. "Can I change my mind about the wine?"

Frisky looks ecstatic. "My dear, it's a woman's prerogative."

Sometimes you only realise how cold you were when you warm up again. The wine spreads through my body like a sunset and I swear I can even feel my bone marrow defrosting.

"That tastes so . . ." I take another sip. "It's beyond words, Frisky."

"Let me try." He picks up his glass and sniffs. "Pine and thyme. Olive groves. A hint of smoke and the faintest whiff of donkey doo-doo."

I giggle. "And you can get all of that from *smelling* it?"

He closes his eyes. "Well, I am cheating a little bit. It comes from the vineyard near where we were stationed in '41, before we got thrown out by the Germans. Those of us that made it out. I have a case sent over every year."

"Wouldn't you rather forget those times?"

He holds his wine up to the sun, sloshing it around, before drinking. "It's still the most beautiful place I've ever seen. And I have always been more of a glass-half-full kind of chap." He grins. "Though I can't help noticing yours is nearly empty. Top up?"

I hold my hand over the rim. "Better not, I feel quite tipsy already and I don't want to end up comatose again." Frisky chuckles and I realise it's the first time I've been able to joke about what's happened. Mum and Dennis would be horrified.

"Do you remember much about your accident, Jo?"

"No. I keep expecting the details to come back to me, but nothing."

"Maybe it never will," Frisky says. "Nature's way of protecting you from horrible memories. Good memories are the ones you need to hang on to."

"Frisky?" I hesitate, then change my mind. I don't want him to think I am a loony. "Oh, it doesn't matter."

"In my experience," he says, all serious now, "whenever a woman says 'it doesn't matter', she means the exact opposite. Out with it!"

"It's what you said about memories. Ever since the accident, well, I've been having these flashbacks. Memories from when I was little."

Frisky looks serious. "What kind of memories? Traumatic ones?"

"Not really. Though they wouldn't rate in my top ten great moments either," I say, wondering as I do whether I could name ten great moments in the Life of Joanna Morgan. "They're pretty mundane. Christmas. School. A trip to the library."

"How peculiar." Frisky nibbles contemplatively on an olive. "I did know a chap who had waking nightmares after a close shave. Tumbling to earth in the wreck of his plane, flames lapping round his ankles, that sort of thing. He bailed out, but being a glass-half-empty sort of fellow, he never remembered *that* bit."

"Poor bloke. But at least his flashbacks had a reason."

He puts his feet up on the table, wincing slightly at the creaking of his knees. "Annoying perhaps, Joanna, but I'd say you've got off pretty lightly with a few flashbacks."

I look out at the garden, where two young squirrels are putting on a show, jumping up onto the bird table and chasing the nuts around. They're not eating any, just doing it for fun. "Yes, I know. But they feel so *real*. Creepy."

"I bet there's a connection somewhere," Frisky says. "A deeper purpose."

"Maybe." The first one, the Hiroshima movie, did change the way I saw the world. I've always thought that I was born a scaredy-cat, but the flashbacks have made me wonder. And if I wasn't born a coward, could I learn to be brave all over again?

"What does the good doctor say?" Frisky asks.

"Give it time."

He rubs his hands together. "Ha! I love it when the doctors don't have a clue."

"He says I should write it all down, to help me understand what triggers them."

"Never mind that, Joanna, he probably wants the material for a piece in *The Lancet* or *Head Shrinkers' Quarterly*. Sure I can't tempt you? Only a tiny dribble left anyhow."

He holds the carafe above my glass. "Oh, all right then, Frisky."

"So . . . what the devil could be triggering the strange memories of Miss Morgan? Overdoing it, maybe? My funny turns came on when I was shattered."

145

I shake my head. "Don't think it's that. I'm tired all the time."

"Something nice then? Music? The old tunes always take me back. *Just direct your feet, to the sunny side of the street . . .*"

"No. The first flashbacks were when I was in hospital, and the only sounds in ITU were pumps and beeps and whispers."

"OK. All a case of narrowing it down. Getting closer. So let's think, what else do we get in hospitals?" Frisky says, scratching his chin.

"It's probably a wild goose chase." I'm starting to feel tired again now. Before the accident, I'd forgotten how it felt to *collide* with tiredness, the way a child does, so it almost knocks you flat.

"What if . . ." a smile begins to spread across Frisky's face, "the missing ingredient was smell?" He stands up, pacing the cracked tiles, working it through. "Think about it, Joanna. It's a powerful sense. One whiff of wine instantly conjures up a few spring days six decades ago. And they pump the smell of baking bread through the fans in supermarkets to make you feel warm inside."

I try to focus, to test Frisky's theory. The first flashback began in the toilets, didn't it, that smelled of . . . well, the obvious, but also disinfectant. Just like ITU.

Then there was Christmas and the smell of hospital roast dinner. And wasn't it the mouldy scent of old books and old lady lavender perfume that transported me back to the library? "Frisky, you're a *genius*."

146

He nods. "Maybe I am. It does make sense, doesn't it? I mean, we all respond to smell, but the accident could have made you super-sensitive."

"But . . ." the euphoria is short-lived, "it doesn't solve my problem. If anything, I'm more afraid than ever. Either I wear a clothes peg on my nose, or *anything* could set it off. A chip shop. The perfume section of a department store. It's a jungle out there."

Frisky looks hurt. "Come on now. Think how many million smells you've smelled since the accident, and you've only had three funny turns."

That I can remember. I could have forgotten a dozen more, like I've forgotten the accident itself. My memory's shot to pieces.

"You're probably right," I say, struggling to keep my eyes open. "I'd like to go home now, Frisky, if that's all right."

"Oh dear. I've upset you, haven't I?" He perches on the edge of the table.

I slump further into my chair. "It's not you. I've overdone it today, I think. That's the trouble with us head-bangers, eh? One minute we're all *normal* and the next . . ."

"The doc's right about one thing, Joanna. It takes time. It will get better, I promise."

I shrug. "Time. Yeah. Shame you can't get that on prescription."

"I'd be queuing for extra, that's for sure," he says.

"Sorry to be so whiny," I say but he flicks his hand to dismiss it.

"What's a moan between head-bangers? Now, let me see if I can get young Luke to run you home," and he hops off the table, heading out towards the garden.

"No, really, I can get a minicab," I protest, though I can hear Dennis's disapproving voice in my head, "honestly, Jo, do you know how many women are assaulted every year by bogus taxi-drivers?"

"Oh no you don't, Joanna. Besides it'll do my grandson good to talk to a woman for a change. He can talk to the animals but he's pretty hopeless when it comes to girls."

I laugh, though I'm not entirely sure he's joking. My craving for bed is uncontrollable and I close my eyes as he disappears to fetch Doctor Dolittle . . .

I must have fallen asleep because Frisky's hand on my arm makes me jump.

"Your carriage awaits, Joanna. This is Luke."

He hovers behind his grandfather like a shy toddler. If toddlers grew to six feet tall. As he steps forward, I do a double-take. Frisky must have looked like this when he was young . . . combined with the RAF uniform, and more charm than my little brother, Frisky would surely have had his pick of land girls.

Luke has hair so dark it soaks up the light. His eyes are grey like Frisky's, though in the bright conservatory, they look violet. His high cheekbones are so sharp they're almost Slavic: both these men were born to be filmed in black and white, challenging the camera with broody, moody smoulders.

But Luke is *not* Frisky Mark II. That becomes clear within seconds. He won't meet my eye, preferring to

148

run his left foot up and down the loose grout between the conservatory tiles. His trainers are mud-coated, as are his loose black trousers. This is not a man who thinks twice before getting dressed: even his T-shirt looks like the kind you'd get free with a crate of beer. He does fill it rather well, though.

"Come on, Luke. Joanna's our new friend!" Frisky says.

"Hi," Luke mutters, still not looking up.

"My grandson says he'll be happy to take you home. He's completely safe."

Luke glares at Frisky. He doesn't seem happy at all, but I have a strange sense that there's more to it than a disagreement over my transport arrangements.

"I'm parked out the front," he says, shuffling past me. His voice has a transatlantic twang to it, but none of Frisky's confidence. I half expect a whiff of body odour or, worse still, cat piss from all these pets he's supposedly guarding, but instead he smells of sleep, that biscuity aroma of duvets. He must have been woken up to play taxi-driver.

Frisky and I follow him out — this time it isn't the grand entrance hall that I notice, but the brown freckles of damp on the walls, and the enormous gaps between the floorboards that a rescued kitten could fall through. Back outside, I scan the street for Luke and his car.

"Where's he gone?"

Frisky points.

Oh shit.

Luke doesn't have a car, he has *wheels*. Unfortunately, only two wheels, attached to a motorbike. He stands next to it, proud as a member of the Pony Club with her prize-winning mount.

"No *way*," I say.

"He's never had a single accident, Joanna. And there's a spare helmet in the top-box," Frisky says, in a vain attempt to reassure me.

"He could have a spare set of limbs and I still wouldn't get on that thing." The more I look, the scarier it seems: like an insect's endoskeleton in black and chrome, a proper macho Hell's Angels bike. Funny, Luke doesn't look the sort to sacrifice virgins or bite the heads off bats.

"Are you coming or not?" Luke calls over from the other side of the road.

"Sorry, but it's not really my sort of thing." I stop myself adding, *because bikes are the biggest death-traps known to man and only someone with suicidal tendencies would go on one.* I might want more excitement in my life, but there are limits.

Luke tuts loudly, then trudges back towards the house, pausing to scowl at Frisky, then at the front garden, then back at Frisky. "Bloody cats have been at it again. Shitting everywhere." He waves vaguely at the flower-beds, and I see something very strange: he has a scar, exactly like his grandfather's, on the palm of his right hand.

I realise I've been staring, so I smile and say, "You'd think they'd be more grateful, the local cats, given all you do for them."

He stares at me as though I am quite, quite mad, then his expression changes to one of sympathy. He

150

thinks I have lost my marbles. "Yeah. Right. Got to go. Stuff to do."

And he disappears back through the splendid stucco doorway. "I think my grandson's small talk needs a bit more work, eh, Joanna? In the meantime, let's see whether we can rustle you up a taxi."

My plan was to go to bed as soon as I got home. I could imagine the squidgy vanilla smell, the same way Luke smelled when he passed me.

But when I arrive back in Salzburg Avenue, there are several obstacles in the way of my deepest desire.

A huge bunch of stinky chrysanthemums. A case of wine. And my mother.

She's waiting by the window, an anxious hand covering her mouth, and when I walk into the living-room I'm convinced she's about to faint. "Thank God you're back," she says, as though I've been trekking through the Sahara rather than sitting in a conservatory eating olives.

"But you met Frisk . . . Roger, Mum. He's hardly the type to keep me imprisoned as his sex slave, is he?"

Mum sniffs. "He seemed very charming. Too charming, perhaps. If he's not planning any funny business, why exactly is he getting you drunk?"

"Drunk?" Bugger. I meant to chew gum in the cab.

"I can smell alcohol on your breath."

"Grapes," I lie. "They were a bit ripe. They just smell like wine."

She gives me a look. "Talking of wine, these were delivered for you today. Six bottles of Rioja. From a timeshare company in Spain?"

"How bizarre," I say, deciding it might be better not to mention the chat I had with a lovely guy called Miguel last week.

"And the flowers have come from MoneyCard as a thank you for signing up for their Premier card. Jo, what's going on? I'm worried about you. About people taking advantage."

I'm too tired to get crotchety with her. "Mum, I've no intention of spending any money on the card. The timeshare thing is a mistake. And Fris . . . Roger is harmless. I enjoyed myself this afternoon. I haven't had fun in such a long time."

"That's all very nice, but will fun make you feel better? Because I can't help thinking that getting better ought to be your priority right now."

I want to explain that I've been wondering about the point of getting better if all it means is more of the same. That Frisky has made me feel normal for a few short hours. That fun seems a pretty worthwhile objective to me.

But then expecting my mother to embrace the concept of fun would be like expecting an Eskimo to see the point of a bikini. "You're probably right," I say. "And the doctor said my priority is sleep, so if you don't mind, I've an appointment with the land of Nod." I use the childhood phrase deliberately, hoping it'll make her back off.

She smiles at me but I'm sure the brightness in her eyes is caused by tears. "Oh, Jo. Things were so much simpler when you were a little girl, weren't they?"

I could tell her that, if anything, things seem simpler now. Remind her about neutron bombs and new Ice Ages, and the Yorkshire Ripper, and a million other retro anxieties.

Instead I kiss her gently on both cheeks, drag myself into the bedroom, and climb into bed fully clothed.

As I pull the duvet over my head, the air is stale and smells so powerfully of sleep that I feel that familiar dizziness, dragging me down, a long way from Salzburg Avenue . . .

CHAPTER
FOURTEEN

Frigophobia — Fear of Cold Things

"Look who's here to see you!"

My little brother opens his left eye, then closes it wearily. "Big deal."

My parents' bedroom smells of sleep and sick and Nivea face cream. It's three in the afternoon, but the thick curtains are still closed, trapping the heat of the day inside. It only takes a few seconds before I feel faint; no wonder Timmy looks ill.

I'd like to leave, as he doesn't want me here, but I know I'd get a telling off, so I force my face into a sympathetic smile. As Dad keeps reminding me, *he's not well at all, Jelly Bean. You should have seen the doctor's face.*

My mother strokes his hair, which is damp with sweat. "Poor Timmy," she whispers, "my poor baby boy." She's lying next to him in bed, Kermit the Frog sandwiched between them. Mum's face is as pink as her lacy nightie, and a single vertical furrow runs between her eyes. It appeared after Timmy's marathon

154

nosebleed yesterday and makes her look old for the first time.

"Can I get anything for the patient?" Dad asks. "Ice cream? Jammy Dodgers? Cheese on toast?"

My stomach rumbles. I haven't eaten since the Weetabix I shared with Misty in the kitchen before anyone else got up.

Mum scowls in the direction of my stomach. How dare it rumble in the sick-room? "Go on, Timmy," she says, "before Greedy Guts Jo eats everything." And Timmy giggles.

I stare out of the window. I've taught myself not to cry when she says things like that. Dad tells me she doesn't mean it, "It's the tablets that help her sleep, they make her say strange things."

It's not even fair. Most of the girls in my class are fatter than me. But the blessed Timmy doesn't get hungry the way normal people do, and uses his lack of appetite to wrap Mum round his little finger. No wonder he never seems to get any taller.

"Why don't we go and make some lunch for both of you, Jo?" Dad says, and I follow him willingly. As we leave the room, I glance back at Timmy's face.

Smug.

I don't hate my mum. But flipping heck, I do hate my brother.

In the kitchen, Dad slices cheese into perfect rectangles while I take care of the ice cream. He's no chef, but his cheese on toast is OK, when he doesn't wander off and leave it to catch fire under the grill.

"Sorry we forgot lunch, Bean," he says. He always calls me Bean when he feels bad about something. Originally it was Jo Jelly Bean. Then Jelly Bean. Now Bean, to save time. It might be odd but it's nicer than Greedy Guts.

"It's OK," I say, though it isn't, not really. His tongue sticks out slightly as he concentrates on cutting even wedges off the block of Cheddar. My mouth waters. "I'll get the ice cream."

Our chest freezer — the biggest in the street, naturally — is in the garage, through a door that always sticks. Must get Dad to fit it. Otherwise, there could be a disaster when the four-minute warning sounds.

Last night, after the long wait in casualty, I couldn't sleep so I read my library books with a torch under my quilt. And after that I wondered if I'd ever sleep again. The news for number 17 Greenham Lane couldn't have been worse. Mum and Dad bought it brand-new when I was two years old; it has huge windows and an open-plan living-room, completely different from the gloomy terrace where all my baby photos were taken.

But the gloomy terrace would have offered a much higher chance of surviving Armageddon. According to the shelter guidebook, the ideal space is a cellar or a room without outside walls. But our only room without outside walls is the under-stairs toilet and there's barely enough room for the dog in there. We need enough space for four of us so that means either the hall or the garage. But the hall leads to the glass front door (danger of flying debris). At least the garage has no windows, and I know the brickwork's strong because

Mum drove into it the second time she borrowed Dad's brand-new company Ford Sierra (I was quite pleased: it is the most horrible car in the world, like a big green jelly mould).

Actually, the book wasn't guaranteeing that anything above ground would withstand an atomic explosion, but persuading my parents to move to a house with a deep cellar (or, preferably anywhere in north Wales) is my medium-term plan. In the meantime, beggars can't be choosers.

I lift the freezer lid, and peer inside. Lumpy snow sculptures sparkle back at me under the fluorescent bulb. Chicken wings and stray peas are stuck fast in the ice that lines the edges, as though they've been there since the dawn of time. The catering-size pack of Walls Neapolitan comes out easily enough — it never lasts long. Ice cream is the one thing Timmy and I agree on. In the shelter we'll finish it in the first hour. Which I suppose is just as well. It'll be quite hot after the bomb drops.

"You OK in there, Bean?" Dad pokes his head through the door. "I'll pop this up to the patient." The cheese on toast is cut into fingers, arranged like a lattice in my Peter Rabbit baby bowl (I'm sure Timmy only pretends to like it because it's mine).

"Right." The cheese smells wonderful and my mouth waters.

He frowns. "I'll make you some in a minute. Timmy needs a bit of encouragement to eat anything at the moment and until the test results come back, we all need to give him extra treats. You do understand, don't you?"

"Yes, Daddy."

He grins, and his eyes crinkle at the sides, like Paul Newman's. My father is handsome, like the man in the gravy ad on ITV: the one where the wife comes in and sees he's making her dinner and she's so surprised that she loops her arm around his back and kisses him.

Sometimes I think Dad's waiting for Mum to do the same, but she never does.

He disappears up the stairs.

"Don't forget pudding," I hear him call from the landing.

I pull the lid off the ice cream carton: it's two-thirds full, three thick stripes of strawberry, vanilla and chocolate, like a frozen flag. I take two bowls and the ladle we use to serve up soup, and begin to scrape away at the surface. Still rock hard. Time never goes more slowly than when I am waiting for ice cream to thaw.

I ram my finger into the chocolatey stripe, and the cold spreads through my skin, before my body temperature melts a thin layer of ice cream on to my finger, which I lick clean. I do it again, and again, hooking my finger a little more each time so that more of the chilly mixture settles on to the tip . . .

"Jo-ooo . . ." my father's voice drifts down to me from upstairs. "Any sign of pudding for the patient?"

I stare down at the carton. There's a fist-shaped gap where the brown stripe was, only the pastel pink and creamy vanilla are left. I've eaten every drop of the chocolate.

Chocolate is Timmy's favourite stripe.

"Coming up," I shout. I feel sick, and not because of the ice cream. I scoop some vanilla into his bowl and wonder if I have time to run to the shop, but then I remember Sainsbury's isn't open on a Sunday. Then I have a brainwave. I open the cupboard where we keep the sauces. HP, Heinz ketchup, mustard . . . I look in vain for chocolate topping but then remember that I finished the last of it yesterday evening, when no one was looking.

I head for the bin: it hasn't been emptied, and fortunately the bottle is near the top, coated in crumbs and marmalade. It feels worryingly hollow when I pick it out but it's worth a try. I turn it upside down, bash the bottom end and pray there's enough in there . . .

A first drop of sauce dribbles out into the bowl, landing on the white ice cream like a paw-mark in snow. A second joins it, and a third, smaller each time and then I take a teaspoon and mix furiously, trying to blend it with the vanilla to produce an authentic chocolatey shade.

There's no more left now and the colour's not quite right, but then it's dark in the bedroom, and Timmy's unwell so maybe . . .

The dog shuffles in from the living-room, and cocks her head to one side, bemused. "Wish me luck, Misty."

I take a deep breath and, grasping the bowl, run up the stairs. My family look up as I enter the room, and I feel — not for the first time — like an intruder, someone who's stumbled into the wrong bedroom. The wrong house.

159

"Timmy's finished his toast already," Mum says proudly, pointing at the plate in his lap. "Except the crusts, but we'll let him off today. I bet you can fit in a little bit of ice cream, can't you, darling?"

She reaches out for the bowl, and to my delight, takes it without looking and loads the spoon with ice cream. She holds it to my brother's lips and he takes his time before opening them.

I wait now. His eyes are closed and I'm beginning to believe I've got away with it when they snap open like a puppet's, and lock on to me.

"She's done something to it," Timmy hisses.

They're all looking at me now, accusation on every face, and though I know I *am* guilty, I resent the way my parents automatically assume I'm in the wrong.

"Jo?" My father's voice is a warning. My mother tastes the ice cream and pulls a face.

"There wasn't ... any chocolate left. Only strawberry and vanilla," I begin. "And I know how much Timmy likes chocolate so I tried to make some. With chocolate sauce." It isn't a lie. It's just not quite the whole truth.

"You ate it," Timmy shouts, forgetting his invalid act for a minute. "You ate the chocolate bit because you didn't want *me* to have it."

"Is that true, Jo?" Dad asks.

I'm about to answer, to tell them it was an accident, to wait for the inevitable speech about how disappointed they are with me, when Timmy picks up my Peter Rabbit bowl, still criss-crossed with the tiny crusts of bread that he was too delicate to chew. His

160

face is neutral, but his eyes are mocking as he lifts the bowl above his head and then hurls it, crusts and all, across the room at the wall.

It shatters into quarters but I don't seem to hear the smash for several seconds.

"My bowl," I whisper. My baby bowl, a present from my dead godmother, the oldest thing I own, lies in pieces on the deep creamy carpet.

My mother looks from me, to the floor, to Timmy, and back to me. Making her mind up. It doesn't take her long. "Jo. Go to your bedroom. Now."

"But . . ."

"You know how ill your brother is and yet you put yourself first."

"But my bowl —"

"It's a *thing*, Jo. Your brother can't be mended."

I try to catch Dad's eye but he stares at the floor. I wonder whether I can get away with picking up the pieces and sneaking the crusts into my bedroom, because I'm still hungry and I know I won't be allowed out till much, much later.

"I'm waiting."

I hear the steel in my mother's voice and decide against foraging for bread. I look at Timmy and his face is surprisingly sulky. He got his way, didn't he? I'm in disgrace.

But then it occurs to me: when I'm in trouble, he's no longer the centre of attention. I fight the urge to stick my tongue out at him. It's a novelty to win, for once.

And as I leave the room, I know one day the tables will be turned again. The day the Bomb drops, I'll be the favourite. Because I'll be the one who's saved our lives.

CHAPTER
FIFTEEN

Ergophobia — Fear of Work

The incident with the double-glazing salesman, coming as it did after the free case of Rioja and the complimentary chrysanthemums, finally persuaded my well-meaning gaolers that I might need a little more freedom. It wasn't my fault that the salesman was still there when Dennis got home: we'd long-since stopped discussing thermal insulation, and were talking instead about his wayward teenage daughter. So it was out of order of Dennis to accuse the man of "preying on vulnerable members of society".

I don't know who was more insulted, the salesman or me.

So, as part of my rehabilitation, I am going back into the office today, for the first time in two months. Or I am, if I can pluck up the courage to open the door. I've now been standing here for fifteen minutes, trying to stop my hands shaking.

I know there's nothing to be afraid of. No, really, there isn't. This has to be the safest workplace in Wiltshire. The flooring is anti-slip. The edges of our desks are rounded and we have an ioniser, and fully lumber-friendly adjustable office chairs, and mesh screen-covers to protect our eyes from glare. Our council was the first in the country to insist the cleaners use only eco-friendly detergents. Even the calendars and pictures Sellotaped to the metal dividers between work-stations conform to strict equal opps guidelines so no one takes offence.

Come on, Jo. It's not as if I'm going back to work properly. This is a re-familiarisation experience, otherwise known as having a cup of tea with your old colleagues. All part of my readjustment to normal life. And let's face it, anything has to be better than playing the Elizabeth Barrett Browning of Salzburg Avenue. My life is so uneventful that some days I have to pinch myself to check I'm not still in a coma.

So, yet again, tea is the test of normality. If I pass this one, then I have weeks of meetings with the council Occupational Health department to look forward to, before I am allowed to return to the cut and thrust of civil protection.

My so-called career. As a teenager, I was desperate to do something worthwhile, like be a doctor or a dentist. Though it was less to do with vocation and more to do with wanting a guaranteed place in a nuclear fall-out shelter. I suppose that began around the time when Timmy got ill, though before my flashbacks, I couldn't have pinpointed it so accurately.

But when I fainted during a dissection of a sheep's eye in biology, I had to revise my plans. After watching a contraband copy of Threads, I decided my next best chance of a bunk in the bunker was to work in civil protection itself (even though the officials in that TV show died in their shelter, buried alive). I didn't quite know what it'd involve, except that when the four-minute warning came, I'd be able to say "open sesame" or whatever the password was, and join the others who'd rule the world, post-nuclear holocaust. I wasn't that interested in ruling the world, thanks, but I imagined myself with clipboard and an austere haircut straight out of a 1940s' war movie, relaying information about casualties and fall-out with an air of tragic dignity.

By the time I graduated, the Berliners had demolished their wall, and the whole idea of bunkers and hiding from the Bomb under your kitchen table seemed laughable. Maybe to most people, it always had. But I was already on my unstoppable path towards civil protection.

So I don't have my name down for a place in one of the "secret" shelters that dot the countryside round here (these days they're used mainly by horny adolescents looking for privacy). But before my accident I did have a perfectly pleasant existence running computer programs predicting the possible consequences of super-rats invading Courtbridge Courtyard, our main shopping centre, and answering calls from the public about everything from rabies to radon.

I'm pretty lucky. One of my monthly bulletins was about workplace injury and even the safest seeming jobs have their downside — bakers are ninety times more likely to get asthma from their work than the rest of us, typists get more back trouble, and teachers get more depressed. Rock stars risk guitar nipple. And twenty-six popes have been assassinated in office.

But still I can't go into our danger-free office. My palms are sweating now. When I wipe them on my blue silk skirt, they leave child-like handprints behind.

What am I trying to prove? I can do this some other day. No rush. That's what everyone keeps telling me. All I need to do is sneak away, no one will ever know I was here . . .

"Jo!"

Oh shit. *Mikey*. So much for making a sharp exit.

"Bloody hell. I'd hoped for a dirty great scar at least," he says, running towards me. I want a hug, but the wooden teatray he's holding is in the way, so we kiss cheeks over the top of the pile of paper bags: I catch a whiff of a familiar citrus scent.

"Lemon drizzle cake," I say.

"Yup. Cooked to order by the lovely ladies of the kitchen, specially for you. But I didn't think you'd want to brave the canteen today so I got you a takeaway."

My hands are still shaking, but now my mouth's watering in anticipation of my favourite cake. "Actually, I'm not sure I want to brave the office either."

"We've been looking forward to seeing you, Jo. Hasn't been the same without you — and we're lost without your safety bulletins."

"I'm not quite sure . . ." But he's already elbowing me towards the door marked "Accident Prevention, Public Protection and Civil Defence (APPPCD)".

When you're an invalid, people seem to think it's OK to push you around.

It's odd to see the office as an outsider would. Sharon, our admin lady, is restocking the stationery cupboard, counting everything twice to make sure no one's playing fast and loose with the Post-Its. Burt, our balding techie, is on the disaster simulation software, calculating the effects of a plague of locusts on Courtbridge Garden Centre, maybe, or an accident involving a golden syrup lorry on the bypass. New Age Donna's got her back to me and she's filling in an online quiz about her Hollywood soul mate. She'd no doubt insist this is legitimate research for her role as publications manager, which involves writing the leaflets we distribute on open days (e.g. *If You're 'APPy and you know it: a Guide to the APPPCD Department. Staying Safe in Courtbridge*).

In that instant, I wonder whether I actually *want* to come back.

"She's HERE!" Mikey announces, and they all turn to face me. Sharon abandons her padded envelopes to envelop me in a huge, unwelcome hug. She smells of chip fat and Opium perfume. I try not to breathe through my nose: ever since my conversation with Frisky, I'm convinced he's right, that smells trigger my flashbacks. I don't remember any bad experiences with chips and Opium but you can't be too careful.

"Jo! Great to see you! You look so well!" she says, clinging on for so long that I'm scared I'll faint from holding my breath.

167

Eventually I wriggle away: Donna and Burt are lined up to take their turn, as if I am a minor royal. Donna smells of henna and Burt of Lynx deodorant but at least his hug is brief and embarrassed. Our emotional reunions over with, we stand back in awkward silence.

When someone comes in with their new baby, there's something to coo over. Perhaps I should invite them to inspect my bald patch.

There's a cough from the corner. *My* corner.

It's taken me years to earn the best desk, shifting places every time someone left, like a chess grand master. My desk has a window ledge for postcards and mugs, a view of the smokers' courtyard, plus the biggest benefit of all: a wall behind me, so no one can ever sneak up on me while I'm emailing Lorraine.

My desk is my salvation.

Except . . . my desk has an interloper. I only catch a quick glance before the girl ducks back behind her screen.

Mikey gives me a nervous look. "Oh, you won't have met Ruth? She's in charge of keeping your seat warm until you come back."

Ruth's mousy head appears above the monitor, an inch at a time, as if she's scared of snipers. She gives me a babyish wave (she only looks sixteen). "Hello, Joanna," she squeaks. "It's been terribly easy taking over from you."

"Really?" I say, through gritted teeth. "Nice to know my absence hasn't caused anyone any inconvenience." Who does she think she is?

"N-n-no, its been easy because your filing system is so wonderful," she fawns. "And I've been watering your African violet. It's doing so well."

For a moment, I am speechless. These, then, are my achievements in life. A corner desk. A thriving houseplant. And a filing system so easy a child can use it. My irritation at Ruth disappears as I realise I only have myself to blame. I've avoided responsibility all my professional life, so why on earth should I resent being instantly replaceable?

Even Mikey doesn't know what to say now. Finally he remembers the cake. "Lemon drizzle! Come and get it! While stocks last."

"I'll put the kettle on," says Sharon.

"I'll help," says Donna, perhaps terrified her chakra is going to be thrown off course by my quiet fuming. Burt merely takes a slice of cake and returns to his computer. And I don't think Ruth's taking any chances: she's staying put.

Mikey hands me the largest slice of lemon drizzle. "Good to have you back," he says, then adds, in a whisper, "Ruth is a temporary measure. They only got her in to prove your job was indispensable. Otherwise they might have tried to cut numbers in the department."

"Indispensable? In what way exactly? Because I'm the only one who understands the photocopier's collate function?"

"No need to get narky with me, miss!" he says. "It's not me that got knocked over by a push-bike. The powers that be have had to work bloody hard to contain the scandal. Doesn't exactly enhance our image as safety gurus."

His teasing takes the wind out of my sails. "Sorry, Mikey. I suppose you're right. I've dedicated my life to accident prevention, so if *I* can't manage to stay safe then what hope is there for any of us . . ." I decide not to dwell on this depressing act. "Wish someone had warned me about the mini-me, though."

"I thought Dennis would have mentioned it."

"God, no. He wouldn't dare do anything that might interfere with my equilibrium."

"How boring. Well, you get your ass back in here and you'll get no mercy from me. Just the way you like it, *girlfriend*."

I feel myself blushing. "Is that what you say to the luscious Councillor Fothergill?"

"Only when she's *very* naughty!" And he winks at me. "So when do you think you might be back?"

I shrug my shoulders. "Dunno. I suppose it might be different if I thought I'd be making a difference."

He pulls a face. "One bang on the head and now you want to change the world?"

"No." I think of Frisky, fighting for his country, or Dr Williams, fighting for my life. "But I can't think of a single thing I've ever done that I'm proud of."

"Blimey. Well, neither can I. Problem you've got, Jo, is too much time to think. Sooner you're back here the better." And he punches me lightly on the arm. "And at least you're more decorative than mousy little Ruthie."

"Maybe." I look down at the cake and see that I've crushed it with my hand. "Listen, Mikey. Do you think the others would be horribly offended if I disappeared? The slightest thing tires me out these days."

He looks at me more seriously. "I'm sure we'll cope. But will you cope? Are you coping, Jo?"

I cram the bag of cake into my handbag. "Do I have a choice?"

Mikey grabs my hand. "Oh, there's always a choice, Jo. You just need to learn to work out what it is."

From:	Joanna Morgan [mailto:scaredycat@headbangers.net]
Sent:	Wednesday 12 April
To:	Dennis Diffley
CC:	Courtbridge Accident Prevention, Public Protection and Civil Defence Team
BCC:	LusciousLorraine@tramp.net
Subject:	**Easter Safety Bulletin: Death by Chocolate**

Dear colleagues,
I'm back! Yes, Deputy Diffley has given me special dispensation to work on the Safety Bulletins from home before my brain goes permanently absent without leave. So, with Lent nearly over and the Easter bunnies running for cover, here are some scary food and drink statistics.

- Countries where people eat the most chocolate have higher suicide rates, but fewer murders.
- One eighth of admissions to UK hospitals are gastric in cause.
- Seventy-eight per cent of children eat the ears off a chocolate bunny first. And a million Britons have an eating disorder.
- But take comfort from the fact that you're 100 times more likely to die in a flood than of food poisoning.
- Chip stealing is the number one cause of rows in restaurants.
- Excessive alcohol shrinks the left-hand side of your brain, and champagne corks are the second commonest cause of eye injuries (after squash balls).

- 493 injuries a year are attributable to cakes and scones.

So . . . surely it's only a matter of time before Dennis launches "Courtbridge Against Cakes", the nation's first campaign against baked-goods related accidents. You know it makes sense!

Keep safe, everyone, and just say NO to second helpings, Jo "The Scaredy-cat" Morgan

CHAPTER
SIXTEEN

Ichthyophobia — Fear of Fish

Dennis's response to my little joke wasn't quite what I'd have hoped.

"I knew I shouldn't have let you do that bulletin." He came home two hours early, specifically to tell me off.

"Come on, no one takes it seriously."

"*I* take it seriously. I can't believe you've been so disloyal. I'm a laughing stock. As if I'd ever take on something as trivial as cakes." He was pulling so hard at that kiss-curl that he risked ending up with a bald patch to match mine.

"Well, exactly, Dennis. It's daft. Silly. A joke. I had quite a few emails back saying it made people giggle," I told him. I didn't mention that Mikey had sent me a side-splitting account of Dennis's reaction when the message pinged into everyone's inbox. "You should take life less seriously."

He stared at me as if he didn't recognise me. "No. You should be taking it *more* seriously. After all you've been through."

"But . . ." He was beginning to get on my nerves. I'd never really minded Dennis's underdeveloped sense of humour, after a childhood on the receiving end of my brother's stupid "jokes". Perhaps the ability to laugh at yourself only becomes essential when the going gets tough.

"But nothing. This is exactly what's worrying me about you, Jo. Unpredictable behaviour. Sending off for endless junk mail. Treating salesmen as your new best friends. And now this. Sometimes I wonder whether that doctor of yours knows what he's doing, frankly."

"What, you think I should be booked in for a lobotomy? Or doped up on something? You know how I feel about mind-altering drugs, after the effect they had on Mum."

His face softened and he sat down on the corner of the sofa. "No, that's not what I mean. But, well, the devil makes work for idle hands and the accident seems to have affected your judgement."

He took off his tie and sighed. I joined him on the sofa: his eyes were bloodshot and hooded, and I noticed for the first time that the hair on his temples had gone completely grey. My anger turned instantly to guilt. I was turning Dennis into an old man. "I know you're worried. But rather than let the devil find me work, why not give me more to do? You always say I have great ideas. I could, I don't know, write some reports for you. Or plan the talk you're meant to be giving to the St John's Ambulance Brigade next week."

His face took on the James Herriot-about-to-euthanise-a-heifer expression. "Hmm. Not sure we can risk letting you loose on my speeches yet. No, I'm thinking more of wholesome pursuits. More fresh air, or something practical. Watercolours are meant to be very therapeutic and would do wonders for your co-ordination."

I gave up then, before I told him where to stick his paintbrush. But in the week since that email, my parents have launched a full-on programme of activities to keep me busy. Mum's day trips now start earlier, finish later and involve physical exertion or art "therapy". There can't be a visitor attraction, gallery, or "paint your own pottery" café in a thirty-mile radius that we haven't visited.

Dad let slip that the Maine Coons are feeling neglected. Their protests include hiding mortally wounded mice under the sofa until they rot, and weeing in my parents' bed.

I can almost understand now why Timmy found it so impossible to give up his status as the One Who Needs Attention. I've never had so many organic Easter eggs or been taken on so many magical mystery tours.

The one place I haven't been is the Monday Club. I can't face the unrelenting cheeriness of Dr Williams. I've got enough busybodies in my life and anyway, my mother, busybody-in-chief, is deeply suspicious of Frisky. She's just left after a wet afternoon at some wildlife park alongside the motorway. "Animals can be so healing to watch, don't you think, Jo? The way they simply exist?"

I couldn't feel much healing going on as we stood in a barn, watching a group of depressed-looking ostriches pecking at their food troughs. The "park" was really a commerical ostrich-meat farm with a few rabbits and guinea pigs crammed into an outbuilding named "Petting Paradise", which sounded seedier than they probably intended. My expectations were as low as they could be but I still felt disappointed.

Mum was so wet by the time we got home that she abandoned me at the front door. "I've got to dash, darling, or I'll miss *Deal or No Deal.*" During the long dark nights of the eighties, Mum only had eyes for Timmy and Noel Edmunds.

I didn't protest too much and now I'm safely inside, I draw the curtains to stop the neighbours seeing in. It's another deathly afternoon on Salzburg Avenue, though tongues are no doubt wagging at the newly abandoned maroon Mini on the corner. It *must* have been a joyrider as no Salzburg Avenue resident would drive a wreck like that.

My shoes make a sucking noise when I pull them off, and I can't be bothered to change my damp socks. I fill the kettle but then don't see the point in switching it on, as there's nothing I fancy drinking. My mother's stocked the cupboards with Ovaltine and camomile tea and organic hot chocolate powder; every beverage has additional benefits.

Really I'd like some booze — Frisky reignited my taste for it — but it's not even 5p.m.

My stomach rumbles so I go in search of food. Brain boost multi-seed millet mix? Tofu and alfafa casserole? Mum's used stealth tactics to turn our kitchen into a branch of Holland and Barrett. No wonder I sometimes catch a whiff of illicit chips on Dennis's breath when he gets in. Yet another thing he doesn't get at home.

I'm excavating the freezer in the hope there might be something with E numbers lurking at the back, when the doorbell goes. Perhaps it's that bloody librarian again, the books she left must be overdue by now.

I ignore it, but then the chimes are accompanied by dull thumps on the door, like a large bear in search of porridge.

I don't know why I don't feel at all frightened when I go to answer it. Apathy, perhaps. If someone really wants to break in, ransack the house, abduct me for a life of degradation and exploitation, good luck to 'em. Got to be an improvement on a life of day trips.

But it isn't a burglar.

It's Frisky's grandson.

Luke looks all wrong on the doorstep, shifting from foot to foot, his neck slightly bent so he doesn't hit his head on the rain canopy.

"Oh. It's you. Hello," I say, before something important occurs to me. "How do you know where I live?"

"Frisky ordered that taxi-cab for you, remember?" His voice is brusque, but I catch that hint of an American accent again.

I try to work out why on earth Frisky might want to contact me. "Oh God. He's not ill, or . . ."

"Gramps is fine," growls Luke, saying the childish nickname with real venom. "Well, as fine as he ever is." He stares at his feet, which are in those filthy trainers again. He badly needs a makeover. With a long bath, a decent suit and a chirpier demeanour, he'd be what Lorraine calls "top totty". Mind you, I can talk. I spotted the first hairs growing on my bald patch this morning, a soft fuzz, like hamster fur. *Irresistible*.

"Right . . . and so the reason you're here is?" I smile politely.

"He sent me to fetch you. He wants to take you out."

"Eh?" My brain isn't working fast enough to process this. "But how did he know I'd be in? Hang on. Have you been watching me?"

Two perfect crimson circles appear on Luke's cheeks. "No. Just waiting for you."

I feel like I'm in an episode of *Twin Peaks*. "I'm finding this all a bit odd, Luke, to be honest. It's very sweet of Frisky, but I've had a tiring day. Perhaps you'd be kind enough to tell him I'm . . . indisposed." Oh God, now I'm talking like a Jane Austen heroine.

Luke folds his arms. "It's easier to let him have his way, really, he always wins and it's a waste of energy to try to resist Frisky's dark powers."

It's the longest sentence I've heard him speak. His face is deadpan, so I can't tell for sure if he's joking. "You make him sound sinister."

He sneers, revealing brilliant white teeth, startling in that dark face. "No, not sinister. A charmer. But charm can be kinda dangerous."

"What an extraordinary thing to say about your grandfather."

Luke shrugs. "You don't know him yet. So you ready? Or I'll wait." He sounds determined.

"But . . . but . . ." I'm floundering. I don't doubt he will wait, and if he's still here when Dennis gets back, I'll have yet more explaining to do. "No way am I getting on a motorbike."

He smiles properly, for the first time. God, he should *so* be in the movies. "No need," he says and points outside, at the beaten-up maroon Mini. "Gramps has gone and bought us some wheels."

Half an hour later, I'm in this red peril of a car with Frisky and Luke, still not quite understanding why I'm there.

"I'm keeping up with the Joneses," Frisky says, as we speed away. "Everyone else has wheels, so I've gone one better. I've got wheels *and* a chauffeur. Vintage, too."

Luke grunts. "You mean, prehistoric." The way he drives surprises me, confident but careful, as if he has a transplant patient or a priceless statue in the back of the car.

"So where have you been in it so far?" I ask.

"Do you know what, Joanna, we haven't actually been *anywhere* yet? Saved it for you. This is our maiden voyage! Ha ha. Let's hope we bowl the maiden over, eh, Luke?" And Frisky chortles away happily for several minutes.

When we picked him up from the villa, he clambered straight into the back of the car, and when I tried to climb into the passenger seat — it seemed rude to leave Luke on his own, like a glorified cabbie — Frisky shouted from inside, "Oh no, no, come and sit with me, Joanna. We can have a catchup."

180

He immediately told me off for missing the Monday Club. "Our lovely young doctor Nathan's been quite bereft, looking at that little pocket-watch of his and sighing," Frisky said, extra loud, casting glances at his grandson in the rear-view mirror. He then treated me to his opinions on rap music and global warming. "I like to keep up, Joanna, nothing worse than an old boy who still lives in the 1940s."

But he refused to elaborate on his plans for the outing. "I just had a feeling you might need a treat."

I'm beginning to realise that Frisky lives in a different world from most of us, with so much time on his hands yet so little left. Perhaps he has a God complex. Or maybe he's lonely. Either way, his enthusiasm is so infectious that saying no to him would be like telling my mother that cats don't have souls.

"Nearly there," says Frisky, sounding more like an excited child than a megalomaniac.

We're on the outskirts of Courtbridge now, the area known as New Town. There's an ugly trading estate of buildings built entirely from rusting corrugated iron. Then there's the Courtbridge Shopping Experience, with its DIY store and furniture warehouse and gargantuan new pet store (what on earth do they sell there — genetically modified gerbils?). And finally there's the Courtbridge Leisure Experience, which holds experiences I'd rather avoid: wave machines, multi-gyms and saunas.

"Hang on, Frisky. We're not going *swimming*, are we?" I say. I cringe at the thought of the chlorine stinging my eyes, of wading through a soup of kiddie

181

wee and lost beige plasters. "Only I don't have my cossie . . ." It occurs to me then that he could buy me one, so I add, "And I've got a very bad bout of athlete's foot."

"Calm down, my dear. I don't wish to know the status of your fungal infections and anyway, who said anything about swimming?"

But Luke is driving into the car park, executing a driving-test perfect reverse into a tight spot.

"Well, I don't think I should be doing weight training either."

"Golly, we are worked up. Don't you like surprises?" Frisky rubs his hands together.

I try to smile. "No, I don't. Actually. I prefer a bit of advance warning."

He shakes his head sadly. "Yawn. But don't worry, I'm not going to make you jump through any hoops. Or perform any physical jerks whatsoever." He climbs out of the car, and I do the same.

"So what *are* we doing here?"

He turns away from the shed that constitutes the Leisure Experience towards the recreation ground. "You really do need to learn to be a touch more observant, Jo."

It's only now that I notice the tip of an orange and pink tower poking over the tall hedge. And hear a blast of distorted dance music.

Frisky pulls back his shoulders and stands up straight as if he's headed for the parade ground. "Hold on to your hat, dear child. We're going to the fair!"

★   ★   ★

We squeeze through a gap in the hedge, Frisky leading, then me, with Luke behind us like a grumpy bodyguard. The ground is muddy but at least it's finally stopped raining.

Fairgrounds look creepy in daylight, the colours too bright and the punters too shifty. Half the rides aren't working yet; men are emerging from trailers with miserable eyes and roll-ups between their lips. One pulls a masive khaki tarpaulin off the kiosk leading to the Crazee Caterpillar: a sheet of rain crashes to the floor and some of the water hits us as we pass.

"Watch out!" I grumble. The man scowls back.

Frisky gives me an odd look. "It's only water. Dear me, the youth of today."

When I was a teenager, funfairs were full of men your mum warned you about: the kind Lorraine loved. Craggy boys with tattoos and strong lager and wandering hands. We went to the fair in Newbury every spring and autumn, stalking rides until we found someone Lorraine liked the look of . . . first the waltzer ("his acne would make me *puke!*"), the ghost train ("he's a vampire"), then the dodgems ("broken nose, and not in a good way") and the octopus ("now *he's* more like it . . ."). Then we'd ride over and over until the guy noticed her, at which point I'd finally be allowed to disembark, with wobbly legs and vertigo, while Lorraine went round the back with Octopus Man. Whichever ride they came from, they all had octopus hands according to Lorraine and that suited her just fine.

Once, someone chatted *me* up: his name was Terry, and he had a gentle face and a huge tiger tattooed on his skinny upper arm. He worked on the little blue kids' train that went nowhere slowly. Lorraine and I crammed ourselves into the wooden seats, and she rang the bell with such ferocity that I thought the rope would come off in her hands. She went crazy when she worked out that he fancied me, then swore she'd never been interested in the first place.

He bought me candy floss and lukewarm Fanta Orange but I backed off before he had chance to try a kiss. I spent the next two months wondering what might have happened if I'd stayed, drawing pictures in my diary and imagining our floss-coated lips meeting in the glow of a thousand green and purple lightbulbs. No one tried to kiss me for four years after that.

"Right, Joanna. When was the last time a gentleman attempted to win you a goldfish?" Frisky interrupts my nostalgia trip.

We've reached an old-fashioned coconut shy, where hairy brown shells are stacked on top of each other. Luke still hangs back, looking bored.

"I hope there aren't goldfish here. Courtbridge Council doesn't allow the use of live animals as prizes," I say.

Frisky sighs. "Well, aren't you the life and soul of the party? If you're going to behave like this, then we might as well take you home."

I open my mouth to snap back, *I never asked to come here*, but stop myself. Putting the emancipation of goldfish to one side, is there anything worse than a

184

killjoy? When exactly did I turn from a bit of a wimp into a total wet blanket?

I try to pinpoint that moment. Maybe it was after Timmy got ill, or when I joined the council. But I was always willing to laugh at my own paranoia, and never tried to pour water on other people's ideas.

Nope. I freeze as I remember exactly when I crossed the line. My hard-liner fundamentalist super safety consciousness began in the weeks after I moved in with Dennis, as I added dozens of new precautionary measures to the ones I already followed. Nothing could be left to chance.

Frisky looks worried. "Not having one of your turns, are you, Joanna?"

"No, no. You're right, I am being stupid. I promise I'll try to be less of a misery guts."

"Oh, don't fret. Anyhow, I can't see any fish, so your conscience is clear." He hands over a two-pound coin to the thin girl who's running the stall. She gives him three balls without looking: she's too busy gawping at Luke, flicking her black hair out of her eyes and pouting. He stares resolutely at the ground.

Frisky takes aim at the display. The first time he misses so badly that even the girl notices, moving swiftly out of the danger zone. "Just getting my bearings," he assures us before throwing again . . .

The hard ball smashes into the bottom row of coconuts, a direct hit that should bring the whole display crashing down. But all it does is wobble slightly and Luke seems to wake up. He glares at the girl, and then reaches over to take the final ball from Frisky.

He squares up to the coconuts, so tall and determined that the girl jumps out of range. He stretches his arm back like a cricket fast bowler, testing the movement twice before he's ready. Then he performs a throw of such force that the sound of the ball smashing against the shells seems to reverberate around the fairground.

But the column of coconuts is still intact.

"What the hell is this?" Luke growls. That American accent is unmistakable now. "Those shells are nailed down, aren't they?"

The girl cowers.

"Cat got your tongue? I want my grandfather's money back *and* a prize for the lady." He folds his arms across his chest.

"But . . . it's my dad's stall. He'll kill me if I give prizes away."

Luke doesn't move. "Well, let me deal with your father then."

She seems to be weighing up who scares her more — Luke or her dad — and eventually fishes in her money-belt to retrieve the two-pound coin. Then she rummages around beneath the counter before handing me a small furry goldfish, with non EU-compliant plastic fins.

"Not that one," Luke says and points up at the display. "*That* one."

"It's OK, Luke," I say, "I don't mind."

But he takes the small fish from me and holds it out to the girl, who swaps it for a plush deluxe version in

186

multiple shades of orange and yellow. It's the size of a Labrador.

"Um. Thanks very much."

Frisky is trying very hard not to laugh as I wrestle the fish into the most comfortable position; holding it in front of me means I can barely see, so I settle for squashing the well-stuffed body under my arm.

"I just hope they don't try to charge us extra to take the fish on the rides," Frisky says. "Now which one shall we try first?"

CHAPTER
SEVENTEEN

Potamophobia — Fear of Rivers or Running Water

Frisky and I are crammed together in a purple fibreglass gondola, waiting for the sweaty ride-owner to press "go" on "Around the World in Eight Magical Minutes". I refused to go on anything involving unpredictable movements, which ruled out pretty much everything else.

"So are we still feeling grumpy, Miss Morgan?" Frisky asks me as the boat finally jolts forward. Sweaty Bloke has given up waiting for any other customers, so as the gondola pushes its way through the double rubber doors into the darkness, we're on our own. Luke is waiting outside, guarding the mutant goldfish.

Tinkly Chinese music plays from a speaker to our left, and as we creak along at a snail's pace, a spotlight illuminates a cluster of miniature pavilions, with a family of cross-looking Chinese puppets standing guard on top of a pile of rice. "Not quite as grumpy, Frisky. Sorry. Like I said before, I'm not good with surprises."

"But they're one of the pleasures of life, my dear. You need to *embrace* new experiences."

188

"Frisky, why are you doing this for me?"

"That's rather a direct question. I suppose a direct answer is in order. I can't bear to see people waste their lives, Joanna. I've seen it at the Monday Club, people's horizons becoming so limited that they almost cease to exist. Even my own grandson . . ." he hesitates. "But that's a different story. All I know is, I don't want it to happen to you. So when you didn't turn up at the club, I decided on direct action. But if you're coping on your own, feel free to tell me to, what would Luke say, butt out!"

The gondola has moved at least five feet when the music stops and the light goes out on the Chinese family. There's a sloshing sound through the speakers and in the dark, I try to imagine we're sailing through a Venetian lagoon, rather than clunking our way through a fibreglass tunnel on Courtbridge recreation ground.

"I wouldn't say I'm coping, exactly." On the right, Moscow appears under the glow of a red bulb: the Kremlin with its towers like Christmas tree baubles, ornate tear-drops stacked on top of each other. A dozen Russian dolls stand in a semicircle on a Red Square covered in fake snow. The largest doll wears a child-size traditional fur hat, the front half-covering her painted eyes. "In fact, sometimes life feels pretty unreal."

The music changes to a polka, as Frisky takes my hand and strokes it, softly. It's a comforting gesture. "You know, we all have times like this, Joanna. Times when we're pushed by . . . circumstances into working out who we really are. Strange as it seems, this will be the making of you."

189

I shake my head. "But it's making me worse, not better. I know I've been given a second chance. Beaten the odds. But I can't seem to shake off all my stupid fears. I want to go outside, but it makes me nervous. I want to try new things, but when I get the chance, I complain. Pathetic. Someone *else* . . . no, *anyone* else would have deserved a second chance more than me." My voice sounds bitter in the empty space.

"You know, Joanna, a man died in *my* plane. The one I crashed, that they then patched up. He had twin girls, three days old when he died. He never got to see them. Did he deserve to live more than I did?"

"Well . . . that's a question you can't ever answer."

"Exactly. Did you ever wonder why in war, people talk about bombs and bullets having their name on them? It's the only way to make sense of something so senseless."

"So maybe that bike had *my* name on it?"

"You'll never know."

The gondola runs along a particularly squeaky rail, as we pass a display of threadbare polar bears. "I don't feel like I'm making a very good job of starting over. Shouldn't I be off looking at real polar bears in the Arctic? Or is it the Antarctic? See, I don't even know that."

"Well, find out. From what I can tell, there's nothing stopping you going to either pole. Or both in fact."

"Nothing except . . . being scared of flying. Um, and of falling through ice. Of losing the tip of my nose to exposure. Not at all convinced about penguins either.

In fact, I'm not at all sure about anything with wings, including ducks, moths and aeroplanes."

Frisky chuckles; I'm aware of his body trembling. "Anything else you're scared of, Joanna?"

"Where do I begin? Explosions, dirty bombs, normal bombs, heights, nuclear missiles, fire, criminals with guns, policemen with guns . . ." It comes flooding out, much easier because we're in the dark. "Deadly diseases, anaphylactic shock, takeaways teeming with unfriendly bacteria, pizza delivery boys on unlicensed mopeds, anyone who drives too fast."

"That it?"

"Oh, and ladders. That's it."

"Not spiders?" I can hear suppressed laughter in Frisky's voice.

"No, strangely enough. If I found a tarantula in a bunch of bananas from the supermarket, I'd probably keep it as a pet."

As if on cue, our gondola takes us into a lush plastic rainforest, fronds of fern brushing against our faces from both sides. The taped cicadas are so loud, their first chirrup makes me jump. Maybe the man who runs the ride hides in the fake bushes and sprays air freshener at the passengers because I get a distinct waft of exotic flowers.

As we float by, a plastic parrot shrieks, "Pieces of eight, pieces of eight," through its closed beak.

"I wonder, Joanna, do you trust me?"

I think about it as we leave the rainforest and head into the American West, where a Spanish straw donkey is masquerading as a cowboy's horse. I'd usually weigh up the evidence logically and thoroughly before knowing the answer to a question like that, but I know instantly that I do trust him. Despite Luke's warnings about his grandfather's eccentricities, there's something fundamentally *good* about Frisky, the way daisies and rainbows are good. "Yes."

"Excellent. When I first met you, I sensed that I could help you. And now I realise why. You're living half a life. Fear does that to people. And it won't get better on its own accord. Flight is a perfectly good survival strategy but there are times when *fight* is the better approach."

As Doris Day sings "Deadwood Stage", I realise he's right. I started out with an everyday childhood fear of the dark, and my fears have simply multiplied, like bacteria, ever since. "So what's the magic cure, then?"

"I think it's to tackle fears head on. Confront them. Cut 'em down to size."

As if it's that easy, I want to snap back. But instead I take a deep breath before answering. "Might work with spiders, Frisky. But where am I going to find an atom bomb?"

"Ah, you'd be surprised what I can do, my dear. Frisky has friends in high places." And he laughs again. "OK. I'll admit a ten-megaton warhead might be a problem, but sometimes all it takes is a little imagination."

I shudder, remembering Mr Blake's Hiroshima movie and the dreams that haunt me still. "I think imagination is the one thing I've got too much of."

"Let me do the imagining, Joanna. Plus I need a project to occupy me."

"A *project?*"

"Oh golly, I've said the wrong thing again, haven't I?"

I think we're approaching the end of the ride, back on home turf: there's a model of Big Ben, and a beefeater Paddington Bear. I haven't been to London for years, for fear of carbon dioxide and terrorism and mugging. If I don't do something about my phobias, this might be the nearest I'll ever get. "No, it's not that, Frisky. I just think you're flogging a dead horse."

"It's a little early to write yourself off, isn't it?"

"I've been this way for as long as I can remember."

"And don't you wonder what life would be like if you were reborn, scared of nothing?"

Without thinking about it, I crane my neck to look behind me at the world: I've seen more in this ride than I ever will in reality at this rate. I could have died two months ago without seeing the poles or the Pyramids. I feel a lump in my throat. "This . . . project. You'd be with me?"

"Every step, Joanna. And I wouldn't do anything that would put you at risk. You have my word."

Louis Armstrong's "What a Wonderful World" — the one song guaranteed to make me sob, especially at weddings or funerals — is playing as the gondola approaches the exit. I peek back a final time, and the whole "world" is lit up with the multi-coloured bulbs. It's corny and cheap yet, in that moment, it's also painfully beautiful.

193

"All right, Frisky. You've got a deal."

"Oh, *smashing*. You won't regret it, my dear."

The front of the gondola pushes through the rubber doors and we both blink as we emerge into the dusk. And then I remember something. "Frisky. There was no Venice. We were in a gondola, but we never saw the Grand Canal or St Mark's Square or Harry's Bar."

"Perfect." He gives me one of those smiles that lifts his entire face from jowls to eyebrows. "Something to work towards. And where Venice is concerned, there's nothing like the real thing. Now," he clambers out of the gondola, then holds out his hand to help me, "I think it's time you chose a more daring ride, to show willing. Don't you?"

While Frisky "answers a call of nature", Luke and I circle the fairground, looking for a ride I can pluck up the courage to go on. Being brave is something I want to begin *tomorrow*. But I know I have to start today.

I try to distract myself by talking to Luke, but he's impossible. If I even attempt a smile, he looks down. Though that moody pout of his looks a lot less convincing now he's clutching my overgrown goldfish.

"I thought that was great, earlier," I say, gesturing vaguely at the toy. "What you did."

"I'm sorry?" He stares at me as though he'd forgotten I was there.

"Sticking up for your grandfather like that."

Still he stares. Finally he flicks his hand dismissively. "That wasn't sticking up for Frisky. He doesn't need anyone to fight his battles for him."

194

I feel riled. "So what was that about then?"

"Call it natural justice," he says. "I hate cheats." And then he turns away.

"But you clearly don't hate bad manners," I say, fed up with his rudeness. His mouth twists, but I can't tell whether it's with contempt or anger. Before he can say anything, he suddenly lurches forward and only just misses falling face down in the mud. It takes me a moment to realise he's been pushed.

"Oi! Are you the fucking bully who's been shouting at my sister?"

The teenager who pushed Luke is short but wide, seemingly free of tattoos but chock-full of menace.

"Hear what I said, fucker?" Behind the Menace is a second youth, who is taller but still built like the proverbial brick shithouse. "You've had it, mate. All for the sake of a fucking fish for your fucking girlfriend."

Luke can't deny it was him. There's no one else in the vicinity holding a three-foot orange fish. Instead he says, "She's not my girlfriend."

As if that makes any difference. The yobs move closer. The menacing one has a ring of spit around his fleshy mouth, dribbling in anticipation of the fight. I look round for Frisky, knowing we can't stick around. Yes, there's a tiny part of me feeling relieved that I now won't have to brave the dodgems. But that bit's outweighed by terror at exactly how much damage the gruesome twosome are planning to inflict on Luke. Or me.

"She's not? Why, you a queer? That why you can't pick on someone your own fucking size? Eh?"

"We need to get out of here," I whisper.

Luke doesn't move. He holds out his palms in a calming gesture. Well, as calming as it can be when you're holding a giant cuddly toy. "I don't think the discussion I had with the girl on the stall counts as picking on anyone. We would have won this, fair and square, if the entire sideshow wasn't weighted against the player."

The confidence in his voice throws the boys for a moment. Then the Menace recovers and takes a step closer. "Fair and square. Fair and square." He mimics Luke's transatlantic accent, and the sidekick giggles.

I spot Frisky walking towards us, in no hurry, like everything's right with the world.

The Menace lurches forward, jabs his stubby finger against Luke's chest. "Fair and fucking square, eh, mate? So how's this for square?"

Luke must know it's coming — bloody hell, even I know the Menace is about to do something nasty and I'm usually slow on the uptake — but he doesn't flinch. Just as the thug's fist launches itself towards that distinctively square Freeman Van Belle jaw, Luke intercepts it, effortlessly, by raising the goldfish in self-defence and trapping the thug's hand under its fin. And as the Menace's other fist snaps up in a reflex, Luke grips it and digs his fingers into the putty flesh of his attacker's wrist.

"I hope we can stay civilised," Luke says, looking over the Menace's shoulder at me. "Jo, why don't you go and take my grandfather back to the car? I wouldn't want us to outstay our welcome."

196

"But . . ." I feel torn between steering Frisky away from trouble — something tells me he would relish fisticuffs, but isn't nearly as strong as he thinks — and not leaving Luke outnumbered *and* hampered by a fish. So I reach down to unburden him of the fish.

It is, I immediately realise, the wrong thing to do. I release the fish and with it the Menace's right hand, which launches itself in a straight line towards Luke's nose. Luke moves an inch so that the fist strikes him on the side of the face, rather than the nose, but I still hear the crack and it makes me want to throw up.

There's a moment of silence that seems to last minutes, as the three men consider their next options.

Luke finally breaks the impasse.

"RUN," he instructs. So I do . . . my feet splashing muddy water up my trousers, then sinking into boggy quicksands, like running in a nightmare.

I spot Frisky pondering the snack menu hanging from the burger van. "Frisky. We're off!"

He turns towards my voice and, for a split second, his bewildered look reflects his age. Then he takes in the situation: my trousers blackened from my knees to my ankles; and his grandson running in our direction, pursued by the fat gits, who keep on catching up until Luke lashes out, like a character in a computer game.

"Righto, Jo," he says and takes my hand (the one that isn't clutching the goldfish) and we run together, trying to work out the least boggy route to the gap in the fence. Frisky's breathing heavily, and for the first time I suddenly understand that, for all his bluster and energy and strength of character, he's still eighty-five. I clutch

197

his hand hard, feeling the strange smooth texture of his palms.

Only when we reach the fence do I dare to look back and there is Luke, surprisingly close, with an elegant trickle of blood bisecting his face from cheekbone to chin. The thugs are way behind: both absolutely covered in mud. Their clothes, faces and hair are caked.

"You OK?" he asks me, without breaking his stride.

"Yes," I pant back. "Terminally unfit, though."

"I hope it's not *actually* terminal. That would be a shame," he says, and grants me a fleeting glimpse of that dazzling smile. He's incredibly calm for someone who's just been punched and chased by two men who want to do him serious damage.

We're by the Red Peril now, and somehow I force myself into the Mini's cramped back seat, while Frisky deigns to get in the front. But the faffing has cost us seconds. The men are closing in on the car. "Sitting comfortably?" Luke turns the ignition key.

The car splutters and fails.

"Oh, golly," Frisky says, sounding excited rather than frightened. "And the man we bought it from swore it always started first time."

"Have you all locked your doors?" Luke asks, almost casually. "Might be a good idea."

I do as I'm told while Luke tries the ignition again. It sounds a touch more sprightly this time, but still refuses to go all the way. I feel as though I might explode from the tension. The waltzer would be child's play compared to this.

198

I catch Luke's eye in the mirror and he mouths, "It's OK." And at that point, third time lucky, the engine fires.

Luke reverses ferociously out of his space, no longer the cautious Sunday driver. I look through the back window and see the men shaking their fists, cartoon style, as we leave them behind.

Only once we're safely on the ring road does Frisky speak again. "Well, bloody hell. What a hoot. Haven't had that much fun in years."

"Are you quite bonkers, Frisky?" I say, my breathing ragged.

"Well, yes I am, but that's not the point. You must be feeling the buzz."

I shake my head. "Don't be silly." It's true that the fear is fading now and, OK, in its place, there is, yes, all right, a slight tingle in my fingers and toes, but that's purely a physical reaction to extreme exertion.

We cross the roundabout, and I notice the daffodils, thousands of them, as if someone has dropped a vat of emulsion from a helicopter, splashing bright yellow paint everywhere. How strange that spring has arrived and I hadn't realised.

"What I can't get over," Luke says, deadpan, "is that we ended up in all that trouble over a three-foot goldfish."

"Yup," says Frisky. It's the first time they've agreed on anything. "I think the goldfish should be our new mascot. And a mascot has to have a name, after all. Jo? I think that's down to you."

"Any suggestions?"

"Let me think, my dear. It should be symbolic, don't you think? Freddy the Fearless Fish? Or . . . Goldie the Valiant?"

But then it occurs to me. There's only one thing my fish can be called. "No, I've worked it out. I hereby name this fish . . . Lucky!"

It starts as a giggle, but within seconds, the car is shaking as the three of us laugh harder than I've heard anyone laugh for years.

CHAPTER
EIGHTEEN

Cenophobia — Fear of New Things or Ideas

I seem to have taken up permanent residence in the doghouse.

The night of the fairground episode, Luke dropped me off on the main road, and as I walked up Salzburg Avenue, I noticed that the bungalow was all lit up like Santa's grotto. I realised this was unlikely to be good news.

OK, so I had stopped for a little ouzo back at Frisky's house, but I wasn't drunk. I was just excitable after our great escape. And I know Mum said . . . well, shrieked . . . that they were about to call the police, but the cops would have told them to stop panicking and wait twenty-four hours.

It's not as if I didn't leave a note. Which I pointed out to them, when they finally stopped shouting.

Dennis waved it at me. " 'Gone out, back soon'? Is it any wonder we wanted to send out a search party?"

"But it's true," I said, weakly. "I had gone out. And I was back . . ." I paused as I noticed that the clock on the mantelpiece really *did* say half past nine. No wonder it was dark. ". . . well, if not soon, then at least before it got too late. And there was no need to worry Mum and Dad."

"I think there was. Where the hell were you?"

"With Frisky," I said, forgetting that I hadn't actually told the Love of My Life about the New Man in My Life. "Don't look like that, Dennis. Frisky's a patient at the clinic. Mum's met him. It's no big deal, he's eighty-five years old."

Mum nodded. "I should have mentioned it, Dennis, sorry. I sort of thought Jo wouldn't see him again. I'm not at all sure he's a good influence."

Dennis shook his head in disbelief. "You're socialising with a *patient* in his *eighties*? Imagine what could have happened. Are you right in the head?"

I stared back. "In case you haven't noticed, no, I'm not, actually."

He frowned and bunched his fists. "Jo, you know I didn't mean it like that."

"I'm not a child, Dennis, so please stop treating me like one." At that moment, I was relieved I'd left Lucky in the Mini by accident; clutching a three-foot goldfish might have undermined my argument.

"I'll stop treating you like a child when you start behaving like an adult. Obviously."

My father coughed then, and Dennis swore under his breath, as if he'd forgotten my parents were there. I looked at each member of the welcoming committee in turn: Mum with her hand-wringing, thirty-years-of-practice doomsday demeanour; Dad and his "I'm not listening" ostrich approach to anything uncomfortable;

and Dennis, reliable righteous Dennis, with his inescapable certainty that so easily slips over into dogma.

And then I wondered what they were seeing: this unpredictable creature with a bald patch, in place of the scaredy-cat they knew and loved. I don't know whether I was buoyed up by what Frisky said, or by the ouzo, but I wanted to tell them how I felt. "I know I'm different now," I began. "But different doesn't mean mad, does it? The accident was a turning point for me. A reality check, making me re-examine whether I'm happy with the status quo."

Dennis's eyes had narrowed, but his voice was controlled. "And are you?"

Oh shit. I should have seen that coming. The big question . . . if I answered yes then I'd lose my chance to make changes. But if I answered no, then all hell would break loose. I played for time. "Oh, it's nothing *major*. More a state of mind thing. Taking a few more risks. Being a bit braver."

"You didn't answer my question," Dennis said, displaying the pedantry that got him where he is today. "Are you happy? A yes or no will do."

He didn't have to do that, did he? I mean, he could have let me off the hook. Surely the rule of thumb for Mr Cautious should be never ask a question unless you're prepared to hear the answer?

"No. I'm not." It was like waiting for the bomb to drop after the four-minute warning. My mother's lips did that cat's bottom, pursing thing and I had to fight the instinct to qualify it, backtrack, tell her it wasn't her fault; but now I'd said it, I had to stick to my guns. Dad fiddled with his Aston Martin cufflinks. And Dennis . . .

Dennis looked at me until I had to look away. Then he said, "Lynda, Ted. Thanks for coming over, but I think it's time for bed. We could all do with some sleep."

And since then, he's only spoken to me if there's no alternative. It's his way of showing that my behaviour on Wednesday night was *not* acceptable. As if I hadn't already got the message.

Unfortunately, this is also the weekend he's booked a romantic mini-break to a mystery destination. There isn't much laughter in the car with Dennis at the best of times, but today the stillness is oppressive. And if he can see the contradiction involved in giving me a treat *and* punishing me at the same time, he's not letting on.

So, sitting in the car, speeding up the M40 (is this Britain's dullest motorway?), I know that I've neither been forgiven or forgotten. But instead of feeling contrite, I feel irritated: am I meant to apologise for wanting life to be more exciting? I open my mouth to talk to him about it but he turns up the volume on *Any Answers* where some vicar from Weybridge is having a rant about litter.

Dennis . . ." I try again.

His beige-brogued foot nudges the accelerator up by two or three extra miles per hour. This is as close as he'll ever get to displaying his irritation. After all, what's Dennis's temporary annoyance compared to the threat global warming poses to the planet? Even with a scary trucker behind him, full beam blazing, Dennis refuses to go beyond an optimally fuel-efficient 56mph.

So I too focus on the road ahead, on the chevrons that mark the distance between us and the next car, trying to ignore the distance between me and my soul mate. This is a *temporary* thing, caused by my head injury. Normal service will be resumed shortly, and I will remember what it is about him that I love, and he'll realise that me getting out more isn't a threat to our relationship. We will all live happily ever after.

If I can only get to Sunday night without blowing my top, it'll be fine. And the fact that he's sent me to Coventry might be my best hope of keeping the peace.

"You've brought me to *Coventry* on a romantic weekend?"

Dennis looks at the hotel, then at me, then back at the hotel again. "But it's called the *Warwickshire* Plaza Hotel. Warwick. You know, castles and cobbled streets and Shakespeare and swans . . ." His voice fades away.

"As opposed to Coventry, with ring roads and The Specials and empty car factories?" I say.

Dennis's shoulders are slumped and if I didn't know him better, I'd swear that the stuck-out bottom lip means he's trying not to cry. His best-laid plans *never* fail. "I can't believe it."

We've spent the last forty-five minutes driving round the ring road, while Dennis refused to let me look at the print-out with the directions on it. I couldn't tell whether this was male navigational arrogance, or a reluctance to spoil my surprise. Either way, it was pretty clear that we weren't headed for anywhere that could have inspired a sonnet.

"Well, we're here now. I suppose we ought to make the best of it," I try to sound jolly. He looks so crushed.

"Are you sure?"

"Yep. After all, if you're with the right person, anywhere can be fun." After the Trappist journey we've just had, my words sound oddly hollow to me. But they seem to satisfy Dennis, who perks up immediately as he carries our bags towards the glass-and-marble entrance to the Plaza. I envy him that ability to switch moods in an instant: since the accident, my resentments linger like the smell of spilled milk on car upholstery.

The hotel is glossy in a *Dynasty* way, all polished brass and shoulder-pads. It must have been *the* place to be seen in Coventry twenty years ago. Perhaps it still is. The receptionist is so skinny that I'm surprised the overactive air conditioning doesn't blow her over. She hands us his 'n' hers plastic keycards and calls the porter, who is desperate to load our pitiful weekend bags onto his huge roller-trolley, but Dennis snatched them back and we take the lift to our floor on our own. He's too tight to tip.

"There's a leisure club," Dennis says, pointing at a colour photograph of two women in bikinis who should be on Page 3, but instead are posing next to a very small swimming pool. Judging from their flicked hair, the picture was taken around the time of the 1981 Royal Wedding. One of them either has a twitch, or she's winking provocatively as she stands next to a sign reading "Genuine Swedish Unisex Sauna".

"Dennis. You don't think this is some sort of naturist venue, do you?"

I swear his eyes light up for a second, but then he frowns. "Give me some credit, Jo. I checked this out very carefully on the internet."

Though not carefully enough to discover that it was miles from Shakespeare Country. We walk along the gloomy corridor and unlock the door to our room, which is heavy on orange and yellow wallpaper but clean enough. I walk straight to the window: thoughtfully, there's a net curtain to obscure the view of the ring road. "They didn't have any rooms overlooking the cathedral left when I booked," Dennis says, which seems strange, as ours was the only car in the car park. And, weirder still, when we were meant to be in Warwick.

The heavy fire door slams behind us and we stand there. Before the accident, Dennis would have been tearing at my clothes by this point, telling me in every detail what he planned to do to me. I catch his eye and he looks away, then begins to unpack, every movement exaggerated, like a mime artist performing a sketch.

I do the same. Arranging my toiletries in the burgundy bathroom takes me five minutes, as I experiment with different layouts, finally settling for a smallest-to-largest line-up, like the Russian dolls in the fairground ride. Back in the room, I spend ages positioning my clothes perfectly on the hangers. I place my socks in one drawer, and my knickers in another.

And when I run out of things to hang, I pick up the complimentary *Coventry Evening Telegraph* and immerse myself in stories about sewage leaks and school reunions.

"I might go exploring," Dennis says, after a while. "Do you want to come?"

"I know it sounds a bit pathetic, but the journey's really tired me out."

He hesitates, then smiles tightly. "I understand. Why don't I go and suss out the sights for an hour or two?"

"Good idea. I'll be much better after a little nap."

He nods, and leaves the room. I think he's pretending too.

The thought makes me feel hot, and I go back to the window, but I can't open it. The cars race past four storeys below, paintwork shining in the spring sunshine, on their way to Saturday things: children's birthday parties with conjurors and goody bags, trips to the DIY shop to pick dream-home paint colours, long lazy lunches in the pub with football on the big screen.

Frisky pops into my mind from nowhere. I wonder what he's doing with his Saturday afternoon. Is he sipping wine in the garden, while Luke takes his motorbike for a spin? Or maybe Luke is shirtless and, I don't know, regrouting tiles or . . . well, to be honest, I'm too preoccupied with the shirtless bit to care about the details of the renovations.

I shake my head to banish the image. Dennis. I must focus on Dennis. He is a good man. He's worried about me. He's booked a luxurious hotel, so we can spend time together, work on our relationship. Because they

208

do need work, relationships, don't they? That's what everyone says. Lorraine, the Prime Minister, all those magazine agony aunts. It's all part of the natural cycle of things, ebbing and flowing, ups and downs.

I'm lucky, aren't I? Dennis has stuck by me, despite the bald patch and the salesmen and the rest . . .

I grab my handbag and head for the door. Dennis has made an effort this weekend, so it's only fair that I should do the same.

I haven't been able to face shopping in ages, but having a makeover mission makes it easier. Coventry has all the same cloned chain stores as Courtbridge, so I manage to spend £150 without breaking a sweat. I'm just considering whether to head back to the hotel, when I bump into Dennis in the street.

"I thought you were tired," he says, then spots the shopping bags and chuckles. "Now, that's always a reliable sign that a woman's on the mend. So it was a good idea of mine to come here then?"

"Yes. Though I don't know that I would have chosen *Coventry* for a mini-break. It feels a bit *nothingy*," I say.

"Don't judge a book by its cover, Jo. Look at these," and he waves towards hoardings displaying a temporary photographic exhibition, "Phoenix from the Ashes". "You know the city was wiped out in 1940?" He leads me over to one of the boards, which shows the spot where we're standing, before and then immediately after the worst night of bombing. The first image is a postcard, the clock stopped at 12.30, the scene busy with purposeful people, a smart suited man striding across the cobbles, two women in pencil skirts running towards the edge of the frame, late for lunch perhaps. A pre-war car with bug-eyed headlamps is parked in the centre, and the shops are all pristine, their stripy awnings advertising tobacco.

The second is barely recognisable as the same place, except for the shell of a three-storey building in the background, and the clock, miraculously still attached to its metal telegraph pole. The women and the awnings have gone: in their place are men in dusty overalls, hands on hips, inspecting the damage. Rubble seems the wrong word for the piles of girders and masonry, defocused by clouds of dust and smoke. I imagine the smell of bonfires and rotting.

"It's so sad." I look around me, wondering how it felt to have to pick up the pieces.

"I've been giving myself a guided tour," Dennis says, "shall I show you?"

And I follow him around, dodging determined shoppers, looking beyond the Gap posters and the traffic signs. He shows me the ruined cathedral, its bombed-out framework retained in memory of the city's losses.

"Bloody hell. Imagine you'd been fighting abroad the whole war and you came back to a city you didn't recognise." I think of Frisky and wonder what was waiting for him when he arrived home.

"Nothing stays the same, Jo," Dennis says.

"No."

We carry on walking, up Spon Street. "They moved some of the oldest buildings from the rest of Coventry here after the war," he says, back on to safe ground.

"What a weird thing to do. Like creating a mini theme park."

"But it looks good, doesn't it?"

The street is almost *too* preserved, like a film set. "What would it do to the *souls* of the building, though, moving them from one bit of the city to another?"

He laughs. "Do you really think buildings have souls? And ghosts, maybe? I thought you were more rational than that, Jo."

"Ah but that was before . . ." and I stop, wondering whether now's the time to tell him about my flashbacks. Or the fact that my overactive memory can't seem to recall any moments that involve both Dennis *and* me having fun. But I don't want to spoil things. ". . . before the accident, and now of course I believe in Father Christmas and the Abominable Snowman."

"But you are getting back to normal, Jo, aren't you?" He says this hopefully, like a child wanting reassurance that a trip to the dentist will be filling-free.

"It's slower than I thought."

"You can't hurry these things," he pronounces, back in expert mode, though quite what makes him an authority on recovery from head injury I don't know. "And you mustn't put pressure on yourself to rush back to work, especially after the incident with that silly bulletin. I mean, it's not exactly going to bring the council to its knees if you miss a few issues."

I stop walking. After my day in the office I decided against tackling Dennis on the recruitment of the Girl who's Stolen my Desk, but his comment irritates me. "What, is the new girl more decorative?"

He tuts. "Don't be silly. She's only there to stop your workload building up. As soon as you're ready to return, she'll be out on her ear."

"What if I'm never ready to return?" Or don't want to.

"Oh, *Jo*," he says, the voice of compassion, "you mustn't worry. There'll always be a job for you *somewhere*. I mean, it might not be possible to work at the same level, but the important thing is not to feel stressed. Sometimes a change is as good as a rest . . ."

"That's something to look forward to then," I mumble.

If he hears my sarcasm, he decides not to comment. Instead, he's warming to his theme, adding grand hand gestures like a TV history presenter. "Change is nothing to be afraid of. Look at Coventry! Risen from the ashes. OK, not as picturesque as it once was, but a vibrant place that focuses on its future, not its past."

"Are you saying I'm not as picturesque as I was before?"

"Ha ha, don't be daft, Jo. You're lovely." He plants a cursory peck on my cheek, before turning back to the buildings. "But this place has such energy, can't you feel it?"

"Hmmm. Maybe."

He closes his eye and takes a deep gulp of Coventry air. "I can."

212

I wait. People look at him curiously, as he absorbs the energising aura. Eventually I nudge him. "Dennis? I'm getting a bit cold, maybe we could go back to the hotel?"

He opens his eyes. "Oh, all right then. But you are pleased you came, aren't you, Jo?" His voice is pleading now.

"Of course I am. It's great. Exactly what we needed." I wonder what Frisky's going to say when I tell him about my romantic weekend in Coventry.

And then I curse myself for my disloyalty.

Dennis dresses for dinner, occupying the shell-themed bathroom (there's a steam-wrinkled print of *The Birth of Venus* above the scallop-edged burgundy bath) while I change in the bedroom. This embarrassment about our bodies is new.

But, after all, *nothing stays the same, Jo*.

As soon as I hear the shower running, I try on my new clothes. I've never before owned a purple polyester bra and knickers set, and the colour makes my skin look cadaverous. But the underwired cups form a handy shelf, offering my boobs up like a pair of violet-iced cup-cakes. Not that Dennis ever fancies a nibble these days . . .

I banish the self-doubt and try on the rest of my shopping. The blue flowery print dress looked fresh on the hanger, but now it's more like the curtain-clothes the Von Trapps wore in *The Sound of Music*. Cute on a family of singing Austrians, but not sexy.

I pull the neck down and the shadow of my cleavage appears in the mirror. I stretch fishnet tights across my legs and ignore the goosebumps. Then I sit at the dressing table and apply Magnolia Flower foundation. It was the lightest shade I could find, but it still looks orange on my pale face. My hair is lank, despite the £15.99 Energising Fixing Mist, and I attempt an old man's comb-over across my fuzzy bald spot. Only the shoes look like they belong to a non-head-banger, and though the sky-blue leather straps look soft, they're already digging into my ankles.

The shower stops and I sit on the bed, experimenting with the most appealing position. I could dispense with the curtain-dress and pose like a lingerie model but what if he turns away? Before, I only had to utter a *double entendre*, or lick my lips, and Dennis would respond like one of Pavlov's dogs. Now . . . well, I can't shake the feeling that his reaction on seeing me semi-naked would be to fetch a fluffy dressing gown from the bathroom, "we can't risk you getting a chill".

I perch on the end of the bed, both feet on the floor in the best traditions of chaste Hollywood heroines, and reach for a magazine to flick through, so that I don't look posed. I gaze at pictures of posh people's gardens, all stripy lawns and boxhedge mazes and teams of nurserymen. Does their Capability Brown view make them happy I wonder.

Dennis hums on the other side of the door. Is *he* happy? He must miss the sex, but could his role as my protector offer a kind of consolation? There's something about the way he watches me that makes me feel like a bird in an ornate cage, with just enough room to stretch my wings, but never enough to take off.

Now I'm being silly. And anyway, hasn't it always been like that? I used to like feeling protected.

The door handle turns and Dennis emerges, dressed in black trousers and white shirt, his grey tie draped around his neck, ready to be knotted. He blinks at me.

"Is that new?" he says, waving at the curtain-dress.

"Yes. And the shoes. From my shopping spree."

He looked me up and down, his eyes opening wider when he clocks the fishnet tights. He blushes slightly. "Very nice."

I stand up and angle my head so he can kiss me. He hesitates and, finally, leans down and touches his lips against mine fleetingly, a tease of a kiss. But then he darts sideways, so his cheek brushes against mine. It's soft and still cool from the shaving water, and my own skin tingles slightly from his aftershave.

"Very nice," he says again, before pulling away. As he concentrates on tying his tie, I feel as hollow and empty as one of my mother's organic carob Easter eggs.

Dinner at the Plaza is served in the enormous ballroom. It's full of chubby middle-aged Coventry couples dressed to the nines. A pianist sits at a baby grand and pounds his way through a medley of show tunes.

We're shown to a small table near the door and Dennis scowls. The seats are upholstered in peach velour, the nap worn by thousands of pairs of buttocks, and the tablecloth is the same sickly colour. We're handed enormous parchment menus by an elderly male waiter. My copy has no prices.

"So . . ." Dennis says.

"So?"

"Here we are." He stares at the menu. "Choose exactly what you want, my treat. Of course, fish is good for the brain. Although the latest research on mercury levels is rather alarming. Honestly, it's a full-time job keeping on top of it all. Lucky it is my job, eh?" And he chuckles.

"This afternoon puts it in perspective. All those people wiped out in one night of bombing. Makes mercury seem quite a distant threat."

"Different times, Jo. Different times. Just because we're not about to be carpet-bombed doesn't mean we shouldn't take precautions."

I imagine Frisky sitting with us, nudging me under the table. "Yes, but look at all the precautions I took. And I still ended up in a coma."

"Well . . ." and he seems to be thinking something over, "if you'd been a good girl and remembered your Green Cross Code, then it wouldn't have happened."

I freeze for a moment. "So I brought it on myself?"

"That isn't what I said."

"No, but it's what you meant, isn't it?"

"Of course not. It was a joke. Could you keep your voice down, Jo?"

I look around the ballroom but can't see anyone looking in our direction. A large group of rowdy diners drowns out our bickering. "Or what?"

"Oh God," he says, putting the menu down. "You're not going to get in one of your *moods*, are you? I hoped we might have seen the last of those."

I'm about to snap something back when the waiter arrives. I haven't even looked at the menu. "You order for me," I say and Dennis looks surprised but goes ahead: two melon balls in kirsch marinade ("can we have it without the dressing?"), two salmon fillets with salsa ("salsa on the side, please?"), vegetables of the day ("but no potato"), two glasses of tap water and a half-bottle of French house red.

When the waiter leaves, Dennis asks, "Is that OK?"

"You know what's best for me, don't you?"

He sighs. "This weekend wasn't a good idea at all, was it?"

"It's not the weekend . . ." I pause while the waiter delivers bread rolls, wine and water. Shouldn't I let it go, try to enjoy the evening? We're never going to change, and even soul mates have rough times. "Listen, Dennis. What I said about not being happy. It's not to do with you. I just get frustrated with my own progress sometimes." There. Olive branch offered, all he needs to do is say something nice, then we can carry on as before.

He nods. "It's bound to be difficult. I mean, it's very difficult for me when you're like this, but I have to remember that you're not yourself. I simply keep believing that the old Jo Morgan is hiding under that rather prickly exterior —" he gives me a long-suffering smile, "and that she'll soon make a welcome reappearance."

If the olive branch wasn't metaphorical, I'd snatch it back. Why is it *always* about him? I bite my lip shut, and try to call on the limitless patience possessed by the old Jo Morgan, to fight the overwhelming urge to chuck my tap water in his face. And the bread roll. And even the side plate. Not the wine, though. God knows, I need to keep hold of that.

He lifts his glass, and hands me mine. "Cheers. Let's drink to a more even-tempered girlfriend!"

I clink my glass so hard against his that I'm amazed it doesn't shatter. "Whoops. Sorry. Sometimes I don't know my own strength."

I realise things are different when we take the lift upstairs after dinner. The food was second-rate, but the other guests didn't seem to care. The rowdy table got noisier and more raucous until I was so sure they were a group of swingers that I mentioned it to Dennis. His face took on a wistful air. Then he ordered a full-sized bottle of wine.

No sooner have the lift doors closed on us, than he reaches out to touch my dress. It's an oddly unconfident gesture, like a trainspotter touching a steam engine he's admired for decades. When I don't recoil, he moves closer and strokes the fabric. "Pretty dress," he says. "Pretty Jo."

"Thanks."

He moves towards me and his breath smells of wine and red cabbage. "Are you feeling *completely* better now?"

218

"Well, yes, I suppose so . . ." I say, thinking what a peculiar question to ask, until I see his expression alter and understand what's behind it.

He puts his arm around me and nuzzles my neck. There's a gentleness that I'm not used to: less like a horny vampire and more like an affectionate pet. It doesn't feel quite right, but after so long, maybe it's too much to expect that it should.

We let ourselves into the room and he kisses me on the lips. Is this OK the kiss seem to be asking. Are we still all right? Am I allowed to do this to you?

It's messing with my head, because I know I ought to be grateful he's so considerate, that he's taking an interest in me again.

But my body's not co-operating, the urge to turn away is so strong that I have to fight it. I wish I'd had more to drink, but tonight it was Dennis who was guzzling it down.

He's stroking my hair now and I wonder whether he can feel the sticky coating of Energising Fixing Mist. I turn my head so he won't touch my fuzzy spot. It's *normal*, isn't it, to feel odd? It's like getting back in the driving seat after a crash, profoundly off-putting at first but necessary.

As he guides me on to the bed, I close my eyes. I try to take my mind off what's happening. Think of something nice. A sunny day. A slice of lemon drizzle cake. A bunch of roses.

It's not working . . . I can't ignore what he's doing, the change in his breathing since he discovered my matching underwear.

219

What would Lorraine, my mentor in all things sexual, do in these circumstances? I remember a conversation we once had about fantasies and she couldn't believe I'd never imagined I was in bed with Pierce Brosnan or Robbie Williams or, basically, anyone other than the person I was with at the time.

"But I don't see why I would," I told her. Suddenly, the reasons are crystal clear.

I attempt to summon up a movie star to serve as Dennis's body-double in my imagination. But my casting couch is empty as Dennis divests me of my purple pants, I focus. Harrison Ford (too old) . . . Tom Cruise (too short) . . .

Nathan pops into my head, suddenly, and I let him linger there as sincerely gentle fingers run up and down my thighs. I try to imagine the heavy breaths in my ear are accented in Welsh, that those hands are the ones that cradled my injured skull.

It's all wrong.

I open my eyes and there is Dennis, his own eyelids clamped shut as he concentrates. This is wrong too: I don't want him to concentrate, to treat me like a piece of antique lace that might tear at any moment.

Who else? Who ELSE?

And then, there he is, and it seems so obvious.

Luke.

With my eyes closed again, I see his sulky pout and his black hair, then a tanned, defined chest, washboard stomach . . . I feel too prudish to imagine the next bit, skipping straight to chunky thighs, honed calves and

220

then the feet under the loathsome trainers. Outdoor feet, brown, with surprisingly white, square toenails.

I feel my cheeks flushing, embarrassed at my stupid fantasy and weirdly convinced that Dennis might be able to read my mind. But, no, he continues with his elaborate foreplay, while all I want is for it to be over, like losing my virginity all over again, a rite of passage to be endured.

I can smell his sweat, and I turn my face towards the pillow and the sweat is replaced by a scent of laundry starch, powdery and ticklish in my nose. It reminds me of Sunday afternoons: the hiss of the Robin spray starch aerosol and the metallic clunk of the iron against the ironing-board, as Mum pressed an endless pile of shirts and sheets.

I stop myself. It's ten days since my last flashback and I'm tempting fate.

Dennis is hitting all the right spots in his painstaking way, but I feel nothing. I hope he can't tell. What could be worse than *both* of us going through the motions?

Suddenly I can't bear the feeling of his body on mine. I want to push him away, grab his hair, tell him to stop, but I can't hurt him. I'd like to think it'd be over quickly, but Dennis has complete self-control in bed and judging from his efforts so far, we could be in for a command performance.

I turn my head back to the laundry smell again. Dennis is moaning softly now. Sex is meant to bring you closer, but right now he seems a million miles away, lost somewhere I'll never reach him.

I press my nose right into the pillow, breathing in that smell of scorched detergent.

"Is it OK if we . . .?" Dennis whispers.

I nod, keeping my eyes closed. I feel so alone I want to cry, so I bury my head in the pillow, as if I'm in ecstasy. It makes me want to sneeze, the itch travelling up my nose and just at the point when I think I am actually going to sneeze, it feels as if the bed is falling away and I recognise the feeling and welcome it, floating in mid-air and then . . .

CHAPTER
NINETEEN

Radiophobia — Fear of Radiation

Of all the jobs Mum makes me do, I hate this one the most. The naked duvet sits motionless on my bed, its cream fabric stained from sleep and orange juice spills. Harmless.

But the moment I try to contain it with my Snoopy cover, it'll be like wrestling a giant ball of dough. Sometimes Dad helps me, and we make a game of it, but I knew today there was no point in asking.

I unfold the cover, catching a whiff of starch. It smells so *normal*, the just washed smell of a Sunday afternoon in every other house in Newbury. Not the smell of laundry in a house where a child has a *serious disease*.

I approach the duvet slowly, as though I can take it by surprise. The press-studs on the bottom of the cover are undone, and I hold open the flap, before grasping the narrow end of the duvet with the other hand and stuffing it into the fabric envelope. It flops in OK at first and I wonder whether I might be lucky today.

"What have we done to deserve this luck, Ted?" That's what Mum keeps saying, over and over. As if luck is something you earn, like pocket money. Even I know it doesn't work like that.

Leukaemia. It sounds like a heroine from a Shakespeare play, a spirited girl who dresses up as a boy, in one of those comedies that Mr Blake can't convince me are funny.

"Get in there!" I tell the duvet. It flops over the side, droopily defiant. I cram more of it into the cover, but now it's going wrong, a lousy big lump of padding that makes Snoopy look deformed.

I looked it up in the school library. *A cancer affecting the blood and bone marrow, causing cells to multiply in an uncontrolled way and crowd the marrow, eventually spilling out and travelling round the body via the bloodstream.*

But it can't be cancer because people die of cancer. It killed Mum's mum, and the father of a girl at school. Cancer is a lump they chop off or out.

I stand on the bed now and lift the top of the duvet up above my head, shaking and shaking, but all that happens is the padding gathers at the bottom.

I slump on to the bed, with the duvet on top of me, and punch the mattress. It feels so good that I do it again, pummelling away. The relief makes me feel like giggling until I realise my face is wet with tears.

"What are you *doing*?"

I poke my head up from under the duvet. My little brother stands in the doorway, sneering.

"How long have you been there?"

224

"*Ages,*" he says, stepping into the room.

"Get out!"

He moves closer. "What are you going to do? Report me to Mummy?" And he grins, knowing that if I do, *I'll* be the one who ends up in the wrong.

I dab at my eyes with the corner of the duvet. "What do you want, Timmy?"

"Why are you crying?"

"Will you *stop doing that*?"

"Doing what?"

I groan. "Asking me flipping questions instead of answering mine."

"You swore!" He sits next to me and I spot three plasters layered like pancakes on the inside of his elbow. Mum says they took so many samples for the laboratory that she thought he was going to run out of blood. I wonder what his blood looked like under the microscope. Were the bad bits obvious, like villains in a pantomime?

"Flipping doesn't count as swearing, Timmy. Shows what a little kid you are."

"At least I'm not fat. Or a spaz!"

I turn to shout at him. The sun's shining through the window and falls on to his back, so the edges of his head and body are surrounded by light. Like an angel.

"What are you staring at, wally?"

"Are you feeling very poorly?" I am the oldest, after all. It's up to me to show an example, to be caring.

"Of course I am, stupid," he says. "I got leukaemia and my blood isn't working right so they have to take it out and put medicine in me instead. They wouldn't do that if I wasn't poorly, would they?"

Chemotherapy. The use of specific, selectively toxic chemical agents or drugs to target malignant cells. Medication may be toxic to ordinary cells as well as cancer cells. Side-effects include: fatigue, nausea and vomiting; pain, hair loss, anaemia, central nervous system problems, infection; mouth, gum and throat problems; diarrhoea, constipation, nerve and muscle effects; flu-like symptoms and fluid retention.

"No. Of course they wouldn't."

He holds his hands up to the window, and the sun shines through them so his fingers glow pinky-orange and don't seem to contain any bones. "I wonder if the medicine will make my skin change colour? If it was green, I might look like *The Incredible Hulk*."

I hate my brother and I love him too. I don't understand how I can feel both things at the same time, but I do and I also prefer him the colour he is. "I don't think they'll replace your blood altogether, Timmy."

He pulls at his eyes with his fingers, and crosses them. "Yes they will and I will be a *monster*."

"You are already."

He pokes his tongue out, then lies back on the bed, his head resting against my feet. "It won't hurt, will it, Jo?"

"I . . ." I can't remember him ever asking me a serious question before. "I suppose the needle might be a bit sore."

226

He nods. "Mummy bought me chocolate cigarettes to stop it hurting when they took out my blood and put the ginormous needle in my back."

I feel sick. "And did it work?"

He closes his eyes, weighing it up. "Nearly. The chocolate was nice. But the needle still hurt."

The book said nothing about needles in the back. What else can they do to him? Will Timmy end up like that boy in the bubble in America, touching Mum's hand through a layer of plastic? "But it'll be worth it. You'll feel wide awake again."

"Not straight away. They said I am likely to be awfully tired. And then when they've given me medicine, they might put me on the radio."

"Eh?"

"On the radio. I'd lie on a bed and then they'd put me on the radio. Or the radio on me. Or something."

Radiotherapy: the use of high energy X-rays and similar rays (such as electrons) to treat disease and destroy cancer cells.

I sit up straight, and he leans into my lap, his eyes still shut. "This is important, Timmy. What exactly did they tell you?"

He opens one eye: it looks lighter blue than usual. Could it be the illness? "They told Mum and Dad that depending on how naughty my blood is, they could give me a tiny amount of radio activities. They didn't think I was listening and then I asked them if I got to be a disc jockey like Mike Read and they all laughed."

Cancer cells will be destroyed but normal cells may also be affected. Immediate side-effects can include the

227

appearance of "sunburn" on skin: longer-term effects can be noticeable as time goes by. Radiation to the brain can have important effects on growth and development.

"Oh God, Timmy!" I can't help myself. "They mean radioactivity. The same stuff you get when an atom bomb explodes."

He opens the other eye. "A bomb?"

"A *big* bomb," I say. "Like the ones they want to keep at Greenham Common. Bombs like a thousand suns. And after they explode, that's when the radioactivity comes down, like rain that isn't wet. Fall-out, it's called, because it makes everything fall out. Your hair. Your teeth. Your insides."

"But . . ." He blinks. "But why would doctors do something that would make my teeth fall out?"

This stops me in my tracks. Why *would* they? Maybe because adults are so used to living with the risk of death that they don't see it any more. Mum and Dad and President Brezhnev and Margaret Thatcher and Ronald Reagan: they're the ones with the power, and kids have to like it or lump it. Even if it might kill us. It's like the emperor's new clothes: it took a child to see what the adults wouldn't admit to . . .

But I can't say this to Timmy. Instead I try to reassure him, "Maybe the medicine will make you better on its own and you won't need the fall-out."

He looks doubtful. "I might not let them do it."

I sigh. "You're just a kid, Timmy. No one will take any notice."

He stares at me, and for one moment, it feels like me and my brother are on the same side.

Then I hear a pop. I look down and he's pressed shut one of the plastic studs on the duvet cover. As I watch, he does another.

"Timmy!"

"What?" he asks, closing the final stud.

"I *do* that. The studs. It's the only good bit of making the bed," I shout at him, on the edge of tears.

"Big deal!" He pulls the studs apart and presses them back together again. "You can do it all over again."

I snatch that part of the duvet back from him. "No, that's not right. You can't do it twice. Something bad could happen. Get out!"

He stands up and sways, left, right, then left again before he tumbles to the floor.

"TIMMY!"

He lies on the carpet with his eyes closed and I scramble up to go to fetch Dad but then he opens one eye. "Fooled you!" Then he reaches a hand under my bed and pulls out a tin of beans. "What's this doing here?"

Oh *no*. He reaches further back and retrieves more cans: pineapple rings, fruit cocktail, pilchards in tomato sauce. As he stacks up my precious tins like alphabet bricks, I consider my options: lie, and risk him telling tales to Mum, or scare him so much he won't dare say a thing.

"You have to be very grown-up, Timmy, because we're in terrible danger," I begin, knowing the effect this awful knowledge has had on me. "The big bombs I mentioned before, well, they're coming, Timmy. Nothing we can do to stop them. But we can get ready, so that when they fall, we've got enough food. Because there won't be any shops any more. Or hospitals."

His face brightens. "I'd like no more hospitals. Because there'd be no more injections . . ." Then he frowns, a grown-up line appearing on that perfect forehead. "But won't Mummy and Daddy look after us?"

Now what do I say? "Um . . . yes, of course, they will. It's just, well, I thought I'd help them out because you know Dad's always busy at the bank and Mummy's a bit forgetful. Yes, that's it. Mummy's so forgetful that if we've nothing for tea, she might use our *special* food instead of going to the shop. That's why you mustn't tell her about it. Or Daddy."

My brother stares at me as if he doesn't believe what he's hearing, which I suppose is fair enough. "You're frightening me, Jo Bean."

"It *is* frightening, Timmy. But at least we're ready, not like all the other boys and girls. That's why you have to promise me that you won't tell anyone."

He begins to push himself up from the floor, kicking the tin tower over as he scrambles towards the door. "You're loopy," he says as he leaves the room, holding his finger up to the side of his head and twisting it, in case I don't get the message. "My loopy sister."

When he leaves, I listen for his feet on the landing, to hear his squeaky voice telling on me, and then my

230

father's heavy tread as he comes back up to investigate. It's all over.

But nothing happens. I wait one . . . two minutes and then I poke my head out of the door and all I can hear is my brother whimpering behind the door marked "Timmy's Room, No Entry Without Top Secret Password".

I bury my face in the clean duvet, sniffing the laundry smell, and wondering whether I'm crying for my brother or myself.

I'm sorry, Timmy, I'm sorry . . .

CHAPTER
TWENTY

Atychiphobia — Fear of Failure

"I'm sorry, Jo . . . sorry . . ."

Dennis's face is directly above mine and he's panting. It takes me a moment to make sense of the scene. Satin sheets. Air conditioning. Coventry.

"Really, Jo, I am. I can't believe . . ."

I don't know what Dennis is sorry for. It wouldn't take Miss Marple to work out that the apology must relate to sex, but what exactly has he done?

"It's all right, Dennis, really."

He rolls off me, sighing. "But after all that's happened . . ."

"Really, it's no problem." I carry out a surreptitious check below the sheets. No split condom leaking heat-seeking sperm. No apparent physical damage. So what could it be? Did he cry out the name of Councillor Fothergill at the worst possible moment? Suffer a bout of hair-trigger trouble after such a long gap without sex?

My flashback was chilling; I'd forgotten how it felt to be convinced Timmy might die, though at least now I know he made it. But it was almost worth it to escape from the unpleasantness of the here and now . . .

He's almost in tears. "It's never happened to me before."

Now we're getting warmer . . . surely Dennis, Courtbridge Council's secret super-stud, can't have suffered a performance problem?

"It's not the end of the world."

But the expression on his face suggests it is. He lies back in the bed, frown lines criss-crossing his forehead, eyes closed in despair. He breathes so deeply that I wonder if he's fallen asleep. I'm just edging to the side of the bed for a quick sortie to the "complimentary tea and coffee facility" (otherwise known as a travel kettle) for the sachet of hot chocolate I spotted earlier, when he says, "Of course, if I hadn't been so worried about what sex might do to you, then there wouldn't have been a problem."

I stop. "What did you say?"

He opens his eyes. "Well . . . since your accident, I haven't exactly felt like coming anywhere near you. Which has proved something of a strain."

"Hang on. So, according to you, I should have been pulling on the stockings and suspenders the minute I was discharged from the hospital? Or, I don't know, nicking a nurse's uniform to get you in the mood?"

"That's not what I meant at all. I'm simply saying it's hardly surprising that my concern about your health, not to mention your erratic behaviour, has had . . . um . . . unwelcome, *temporary* consequences." He nods at

233

the end of the sentence, as if he's convinced himself that it'll all be OK.

"In other words, it's my fault you couldn't keep it up?"

His nostrils flare. "Jo! There's no need to talk like that."

This sudden coyness, from the man whose sweet nothings used to be so blue they'd shock Lorraine, hurts me. "I don't think it's fair to blame me for your impotence."

He recoils at the last word. "I didn't say that. You're being ridiculous." Then he stands up and heads for the bathroom. "I need a shower."

"It's past midnight, Dennis. And you only had one before dinner."

"Yes. Well, I'm feeling rather grubby now," he says, slamming the door behind him.

I sit in bed for a while, before deciding I do still fancy that hot chocolate. I can't get in the bathroom so I decant the water from our complimentary bottle of still water. ("What a terrible waste!" I imagine Dennis saying. "Tap water is every bit as good and has far less environmental impact.")

As the water bubbles in the kettle, I hear him splashing aggressively on the other side of the door. Before the accident, it felt sometimes as if we were one person, with the same fears and the same thoughts. The only person I've ever known who understands.

Could it be my fault, this most pride-sapping performance issue? Maybe my strange moods and

234

unpredictable behaviour has affected him more than I realised.

And yet . . . did I ask to be mown down by a reckless cyclist? I'd never have chosen this nightmare, but I can't help what happened, or the way it's opened my eyes to the limitations of my current existence. Going back to the old Jo isn't an option.

The Von Trapp dress lies crumpled on the floor, an accident waiting to happen. When Dennis has calmed down enough, he'll pick it up, tutting, and place it back on the hanger. Blaming me again, no doubt.

The kettle clicks off and I stir powdery cocoa into the boiling water. The drink burns my tongue and my throat on its way down. But it doesn't begin to melt the chilly certainty that grips me as I understand that even if Dennis loved the old me, he may never be able to love the me I've become.

CHAPTER
TWENTY-ONE

Tachophobia — Fear of Speed

My bald patch is growing back white. I caught a glimpse of myself in the foyer as we checked out of the Plaza and it looked like a pigeon had pooed on my head. I know this is meant to be lucky, but I'm unconvinced.

The Coventry dawn made Dennis's *problem*, and my agonising, seem completely out of proportion, darkness magnifying our argument, like a shadow in candlelight. We were excessively courteous to each other over breakfast, and by the time we checked out, the row was reduced to its proper size.

During the drive home, I was distracted by the snowy fuzz on my scalp. I inspected it in the pull-down mirror, tilting my head to see whether it was the first thing a stranger would notice.

"What are you doing?" Dennis asked, irritated.

"I can't believe you didn't tell me this bit had gone white."

He shook his head. "Which bit? I hadn't noticed."

At that point, something clicked in my head: not a misplaced bit of skull slotting itself into place, but the realisation that it was no wonder Dennis hadn't been able to grasp that I'd turned into a different person, when I looked exactly the same.

Which is why I'm now standing in my bathroom, stinking of noxious chemicals, with a bright red tidemark around my hairline as if I am rusting from the scalp outwards. The plan is to cover my white blob *and* provide a semi-permanent visual reminder to Dennis that I have changed, killing two birds with one pack of Scarlet Woman dye. I might end up killing myself into the bargain (I discovered on the internet that 576,000 Britons are allergic to hair colourant), though at least DIY dyeing means I'm safe from Beauty Parlour Syndrome, which causes mini-strokes if heads are forced back too violently during hair-washing. Brings a whole new meaning to the phrase "wash and go".

I've already got a dollop in my eye, the bathroom floor looks like the aftermath of the *Texas Chainsaw Massacre*, and the state of my blood-red fingernails would instantly put me in the frame. Luckily, Mum and Dad are at the West Berkshire Cat Fancy, so I've got the place to myself.

Time's up, so I step into the shower and let the water run down my shoulders, washing away the chemicals. I've never coloured my hair before in case it went bright green, or caused cancer or multiple organ failure.

My current resemblance to a badger made me reconsider. I wrap my hair in a towel, resisting the temptation to take a look while it's wet. Instead, I begin the clear-up operation, so when Dennis notices the colour (*if* he notices the colour), I can lie and tell him it's a new 100 per cent natural organic shine-reflecting shampoo. I must remember to hide the packaging.

I nearly bought my natural shade (mud-brown) to help the fuzz blend with the rest of my hair, but the woman in the picture on the Scarlet Woman box seemed to be challenging me from her shelf in the chemist's, all flame-haired sassiness. I wanted to be *her*, but that would take plastic surgery, so I thought having her hair colour would be the next best thing.

Back in the bedroom, I dig my old hairdryer out of a suitcase, and the air smells of burned hair when I switch it on and point it at my head, eyes closed again. I run my fingers through the strands: does it *feel* red? It certainly feels thicker but the colour might be appalling. Finally I grit my teeth, turn off the dryer and prepare to face the consequences of my misguided experiment . . .

It's fantastic. The shade makes me look much more alive and the badger spot has disappeared, with a patch of soft red velvet in its place.

Goodbye, dowdy brunette scaredy-cat. Hello feisty auburn-haired vixen.

The only downside is that if Dennis believes the change is down to shampoo, he'll need his eyes *and* his brain tested.

But Dennis isn't the first person to see my transformation. Instead it's strong, silent Luke, picking me up for my latest "experience". Not that my parents would approve, but then they're too busy admiring pampered Maine Coons to find out.

Luke toots the horn on the Red Peril and I race out to the car. As I open the door, he does a cartoon double-take.

"Good hair," he says when I get into my seat, and I feel ridiculously pleased with myself, as if I'd won the Nobel Peace Prize, rather than managed a half-competent dye job.

"Do you think so?" I ask, craving more compliments.

"Yeah, I said so, didn't I?" he says, and puts the Mini into gear, revving the engine before pulling away. Well, that little burst of sociability didn't last.

As he turns out of Salzburg Avenue, I catch a flash of orange out of the corner of my eyes. I turn towards the back seat. "Oh no. Not the goldfish."

"Frisky insisted we bring Lucky along."

The creature's bulging plastic eyes glint triumphantly. "I can't help feeling it's asking for trouble. He's hardly brought us much luck so far."

Luke shrugs. "Like I said before, there's no arguing with Frisky." I'd love to ask why, and while I'm at it, find out what an American is doing in Courtbridge. But I sense that asking the man of mystery any of this would cross some invisible line.

He begins driving towards the equally mysterious destination. I'm wearing old clothes, because Frisky warned me "they might take a bit of battering". I wanted to cancel when he told me that, but now I'm a redhead, I should start acting like one. He's *promised* never to put me in any danger. If you can't trust an octogenarian ex-fighter pilot, who can you trust?

The Peril's engine sounds ugly, like a football rattle, but at least it means neither Luke nor I feel obliged to talk. Eventually he manoeuvres the car into a space round the back of a large warehouse. He reaches behind him to grab Lucky. "Come on, then," he says and I'm not sure if he's talking to me or the goldfish.

The building looks menacing, but I can't work out why . . . then I realise. It has no windows. Whatever goes on inside, they don't want anyone to see. Luke turns round. "One thing, Jo. He's very persuasive, sure. But remember, if there's something you *really* don't want to do, you can say no."

I stare at him. "Right. Thanks." If he's trying to reassure me, it's backfired. He gestures with the fish towards a set of metal steps leading to a fire door.

"Why are we coming in this way?" I ask.

"Frisky insisted. To maintain the element of surprise, is what he said. I guess it's a tactic from the war." And I think Luke is smiling, though it's too dark to be sure.

I clang up the steps and through the door, waiting for my eyes to adjust to the windowless gloom. But before that happens, I get a big, scary clue: the stench of petrol.

"Where is that smell coming from?"

"Aha," says a plummy voice to my left. "The joyous Joanna. Welcome."

I turn and Frisky comes into focus, a fluorescent orange shape topped by a tuft of white. "Why are you wearing a boiler suit, Frisky?"

240

"Oh, smashing!" he says, ignoring my question. "So young Luke managed to keep the secret? And you haven't guessed." He shakes his fists like an excited toddler. "Close your eyes."

"What? No way."

"Now you did say you trusted me, didn't you, Joanna? You know that we head-bangers look out for one another."

I sigh, feeling simultaneously guilty and stitched up. "All right." I close my eyes, trying not to remember the hundreds of times I've fallen for my brother's "little surprises" which always turned out to involve something: a) prickly, b) slimy, c) alive, or once, when he surpassed himself, all three.

Frisky takes my hand, and I feel calmer. The floor seems rubbery beneath my feet and the smell is getting stronger. He stops and guides my hand on to a metal rail at waist height.

"Now you can open your eyes."

I hesitate, afraid of what happens next. If I don't want to do what Frisky has arranged, will he stop being my friend?

I open them. Then shut them again. "Oh no, Frisky. No."

"Now, now, Joanna, my dear. It's *perfectly* safe. Go on, open your eyes again, there's a good girl."

I bristle, but do as I'm told. Second time round it doesn't look any less terrifying. We're standing on a large balcony and below us is a race track. "You cannot be serious."

"When did you turn into John McEnroe?"

"It's not funny, Frisky. I couldn't possibly race a car."

"They're not cars. They're go-karts." It's only now that I notice the crash helmet he's holding in his right hand. "And you'll be fully protected."

"I can't take control of a vehicle. In my condition!"

"Shhhh," he says, putting his finger to his lips. "Don't *tell* them. A three-year-old couldn't hurt himself down there. Look at all the tyres round the edge. Any trouble with steering and you just bounce on and off them like a rubber ball."

"And that's supposed to be reassuring?" My hands are sweating against the metal rail.

Frisky looks slightly irritated. "No one says you have to go fast, Joanna. But if you're not going to try at all, then I think we need to review our arrangement."

"So are we ready to get you all tooled up?" I turn to see a rodent-faced teenager with "CREW" emblazoned across his chest holding a folded orange jumpsuit and helmet. "You can change in the girls' bog if you're feeling shy."

The jumpsuit swamps me; the orange clashes with my new hair. I feel niggled that Frisky didn't notice, but then it was as dark as hell in that viewing gallery.

I must try to connect with my inner redhead, or perhaps with miracle coma girl. Maybe all it takes is a leap of faith. I could have an undiscovered gift for go-karting, go on to represent Courtbridge, Wiltshire, even England.

242

I pull on the helmet, which makes my scalp sweat, and as I leave the toilet, my reflection in the mirror reminds me of something deeply unpleasant that I can't quite place.

"Now, don't you look the part!" Frisky pronounces.

Luke stares at me, for longer than is polite. Then he mumbles, "Yes, if the part is a prisoner at Guantanamo Bay."

That's what my reflection reminded me of. I smile, despite the volcanic bubbling in my stomach. Frisky doesn't seem to have heard his grandson and is already heading down the steps towards the carts. Luke squeezes Lucky between the railings, as if a stuffed toy needs a ringside seat.

"But I haven't given you your safety briefing," Rat-boy says. "For the insurance."

"Dear boy, I used to fly Spitfires. My grandson took a motorbike around the world, Afghanistan to Zanzibar and everywhere in between. And this young lady is the former south-east karting champion. I hardly think we need a *safety* briefing."

The lie is effortless. I whisper to Luke, "Did you really take a motorbike around the world?"

He shrugs. "I was young and stupid."

An image of Luke on his bike, the wind ruffling his hair like a latter-day Che Guevara, distracts me momentarily from the present danger. I feel rather hot. Must be the jumpsuit.

Rat-boy seems to have realised that Frisky is stronger willed than he is. He thrusts a clipboard at us. "It's a waiver. You need to sign it to show you know you're not insured."

Frisky reaches out, and signs it. "Insurance is for bores. The best insurance is confidence that you're safe!"

"Hang on, Frisky . . ." I say, but he's already racing down the steps. I follow him: the smell of petrol is so strong now that it's all I can do not to throw up. A row of karts is lined up against the wall, like a regiment of giant insects.

"Ladies first," he says, and Rat-boy points towards one of the karts.

I approach it, unable to shake the sense that I'm in a trance. Or a nightmare. If I really concentrate, surely I can wake myself up. "How . . .?" I can't see how you're meant to climb into the thing.

Rat-boy scowls at me, then sniggers. "You're south-east champion, are you?"

"*Women's* champion," Frisky says, and winks, as if that explains everything. "Allow me, Joanna." He grips my hand and manoeuvres me into the hard moulded seat, taking each of my legs and placing them gently into position. "There!"

The machine is so flimsy: a few bent tubes of metal around an ancient-looking engine, with four boy-racer wide wheels. The average tricycle is more robust. Rat-boy manages to stop guffawing long enough to check my body is in the right position, then bends across me and presses a button.

Grrrrr . . . the engine splutters into life, then settles into a thunderous noisy roar. Rat-boy points at the wheel and the pedals but I can't hear what he's saying because of the engine and the crash helmet; the helmet seems to be shrinking, putting pressure on my poor brain.

"Did you know," Frisky shouts as Rat-boy moves over to start his engine, "that many go-karts are powered by modified lawnmower engines?"

I peer down at the vibrating motor. It's not the most heartening news I've heard recently.

"And apparently," he drones on, as Luke's engine springs into rumbling life, adding to the cacophony, "they were invented by American air force chaps twiddling their thumbs after the war. You see, it's boredom, not necessity, that's really the mother of invention."

Rat-boy gives us a final, scathing glance before running back up on to the balcony. After a few moments, the opening chords of the *Grand Prix* theme music rise above the rumble of the go-karts. Frisky gives me the thumbs-up and I grip the steering wheel.

"PRACTISE LAPS FIRST!" Frisky shouts across at me and waves for me to pull out, like a polite motorist letting an old lady out into the traffic. I hesitate for a moment, until he revs his engine at me, and then I know I have no choice: I tap the pedal with my foot and the kart doesn't move. A second tap, with a little more force, jerks me forward so violently that I almost hit my helmeted chin on the wheel.

I try again, and the same thing happens, but I keep my nerve and the leap forward is less dramatic. "Kangaroo petrol", that's what Dad called my first attempts at driving. Timmy, of course, had the smooth moves of a rally champ. Maybe Frisky would have let me off if I'd told him I failed my test five times for undue hesitancy before the examiner took pity on me and nodded me through. "After all, love," he said, "never going above third gear isn't actually a crime. But don't tell anyone I said that."

On the go-kart, there are no gears and no reverse, and the only way is forward. I edge along, trying to keep the same pressure on the pedal, but the machine's vibrations keep knocking my foot away. My bones feel like they'll crumble to dust but, far more scary, my head is definitely being squeezed by the crash helmet.

It feels like it did when I woke up from my coma.

"We haven't got all day, you know, young lady."

Frisky draws up alongside me as I creep forward. "I'm not *really* enjoying this, Frisky," I say, my voice wobbly from the intense shaking.

"What?"

"I said I'M NOT REALLY ENJOYING THIS!"

We take a bend, the first on the track, and I slow down as he surges forward then reins himself back again. "Sorry, my dear. Never could resist going full throttle. Hangover from the days when going too slowly meant falling out of the sky! Now, what was that you said?"

I sigh so hard my breath mists up the visor. "This isn't my sort of thing at all, Frisky. I'll finish the lap but —"

"You can't . . ." his voice keeps being lost under the music, ". . . rest of your life . . . in the sand like an

246

ostrich . . . in your comfort zone. The whole point . . . you take risks . . . today's session is meant . . . speed is fun . . ."

I steer my car towards the side of the track and stop, my orange fireproof arms folded across my chest and my bottom lip sticking out, though my majestic pout is wasted behind the helmet. So much for miracle coma girl.

Frisky pulls over and climbs out of the kart. "Are we in a sulk now, Joanna? Because I warn you, I can probably outsulk you. Especially when I've gone to so much trouble to organise today."

I look up to the balcony, to try to stop my eyes filling with tears. Lucky the goldfish stares down at me, unblinking.

Luke has stopped behind us, and is untangling his long legs from the impossibly narrow framework. I feel hot *and* faint now, and begin to tug at the crash helmet, but the plastic lining and my own damp, dyed hair are stuck, like a cream cracker on the roof of your mouth. The more I push, the more panicky I become. I can't faint here. Not in front of Luke.

Though I'm not sure why that of all things matters so much.

"The point is, Joanna," Frisky continues, determined to finish his speech, "you're stuck in a rut, doing only what you've done before. We agreed that I would help you out of the rut. But that won't happen if you lose your nerve at the first hurdle like some silly colt."

"Frisky, I know. I've tried. And failed. I don't think I'm quite . . ." I lean my leg against the tyre wall

247

". . . up to it. Not so much a thoroughbred, as a lame duck."

"We didn't win two wars with defeatist talk like that."

I'm struggling to stay upright, never mind form any kind of sensible response.

"But we did win wars through bullying, I guess?" It's Luke, his voice lighter than his words.

Frisky shakes his head. "As usual, Luke, you don't know what you're talking about. In those circumstances, if I were you, I would butt out. But of course, that American part of you can't help wanting to intervene in matters that don't concern you."

I wait, almost hoping Luke might take the bait and reveal the tiniest glimpse of who he is. Not because I care, really. Just that I hate unanswered questions.

But Luke isn't riled. Instead he speaks very slowly, "You never learn, do you, Frisky? I'd have thought you'd have realised by now, with all those decades of wisdom, that you don't always know what's best? That sometimes you can do more harm than good?"

Frisky's face is ninety per cent covered by the helmet, but his eyes suddenly seem so sad and empty that I have to look away.

"But Joanna agreed," he says finally.

"It doesn't give you ownership of her soul, does it? Are you all right, Jo?" Luke asks, and my name sounds different when he says it. I feel even more faint.

"I'd like to . . . get this off," I point helplessly at my head. "Ideally."

248

Luke moves towards me and tugs gently at the helmet. "Relax," he whispers. Well, it sounds like a whisper, but it must be louder, or I wouldn't be able to hear him over the twanging guitar music.

He touches the back of my neck as he tries to break the vacuum. Finally, the helmet pops away and he pulls it off in one movement. I feel literally light-headed, but suddenly self-conscious about my sweat-soaked hair. I only hope the dye hasn't run.

"All right?" he asks.

"Yep, right as rain," I say. Then I look past him to Frisky. He still hasn't taken his own helmet off, but everything about his posture — the slump of his shoulders, the hang of his hands, the half-hearted way he's kicking at the wheel of his kart — suggests resignation. And, for the only second time since I met him, he looks his age. Last time it was the fault of the yobs at the fair. This time, it's *my* fault.

"Time to go, then?" Luke says.

"OK," I say. I take a step towards Frisky. "I'm sorry I couldn't go through with it, Frisky. Thanks for trying."

He holds up a hand. "None of it matters, my dear. I'm only a silly old fool with mad ideas. I'll stay here a while, perhaps take this beast on a lap or two."

I try to think of something else to say, and fail completely. I follow Luke back up the steps. Rat-boy is waiting at the top. "Early bath?" he sneers.

"Something like that," Luke says, grabbing the goldfish.

"You won't get a refund, you know that?" Rat-boy's smirking at the prospect of an afternoon off.

"It doesn't matter," Luke says, sounding less patient this time. "Jo, I'll drop you home once you're changed."

I nod, then turn a final time. Frisky is back in his go-kart, and I wait for him to start the engine and give the kart a run for its money. But he doesn't move. I watch him for one ... two minutes and he does nothing.

"But what about him?" I ask Luke. I'm responsible for knocking the stuffing out of Frisky. He's more vulnerable than I'd ever imagined.

Luke smiles. "I guess Frisky's Dunkirk spirit will pull him through."

The journey back home is silent — even the Red Peril's engine sounds subdued — but it's a strangely comforting silence. Luke grips my hand to help me out of the car once we're back in Salzburg Avenue and I have this mad urge to cling on, because it feels like he's transferring some of that strength to me.

"Bye then." I try to pack regret, sadness, a little embarrassment into those two words, because I'm pretty sure I won't see him again. In return, he gives me a final squeeze of the hand, then looks away.

I go straight to bed, exhausted and defeated by the day and my own failure. But I can't sleep. Was it really so hard to go round a circuit a few times, for Frisky's sake? I'm a lost cause. What made me think I could ever change?

I toss and turn for two hours, but my mind's too full for sleep. When I get up, red dye has run all over my pillow. It's time to settle back into my old life, build bridges with the people I rely on, starting with Dennis. I decide to cook his favourite ethically caught tuna steaks as a treat, though I hate tuna.

But as I put on my shoes for the walk to the organic shop, I notice something by the front porch. I open the door, and pick up a small parcel, wrapped in pages from today's *Daily Mail*.

I take it inside, tearing through the pages, until I reach a final layer of tissue paper. It occurs to me that it might not even be for me — could Dennis have a secret admirer? Is this a love token from Councillor Fothergill? — but I'm too curious to stop now.

Inside the tissue paper is a carving of a fish, smaller than my palm and almost weightless. The creature is plump and round, rather than long and thin like a goldfish, and the wood it's made from is palest brown, with the scent of soap. When I shake it, there's a rattle and I notice another tiny fish inside the hollowed-out belly.

A note has been folded up and poked through the gap between the scales. I tease it out and open it. "Not fishing for compliments, but asking for forgiveness," it says, in the curliest of handwriting. "A boor is a bore, however old. Next time, I will listen. And I do sincerely hope there will be a next time. There's a braver Joanna fighting to get out, I know it. Next time I promise I'll help, not hector. Your fishy friend, Frisky."

A warmth passes through me, as if this tiny fish has magic powers.

I am still under Frisky's wing. And however much of a coward I am, the view of the world is so much better from there . . .

CHAPTER
TWENTY-TWO

Syngenesophobia — Fear of Relatives

When you're a head-banger, you lose track of public holidays. So when I woke up this morning and Dennis was still snoring next to me, I jumped to the obvious conclusion.

"Dennis, you've overslept! Get up!"

I say the obvious conclusion, but actually it was troubling. Dennis, I'd bet my life on it, has never overslept in his life. Or been overdrawn or exceeded the speed limit or used milk a moment after midnight if the sell-by date's passed. *Rules are there for a reason, Jo.*

His eyes opened, the pupils shrunken in panic and he snapped up to a sitting position. Then he sank back into the pillow. "Mayday!"

"What? Are you poorly, Dennis?" I asked, my heart sinking. Dennis is the worst patient in the world. Still, he'd cared for me, so perhaps it was my turn as Florence Nightingale. "Shall I call in sick for you?"

Still with his eyes closed, he said, "I didn't mean Mayday as in SOS. I meant May Day as in the bank holiday." He lay there, chuckling gently. "I can't believe you didn't realise."

I couldn't believe it, either. Ten weeks since the accident. Plenty of time to have regained my equilibrium, yet the irrational irritation I felt towards my chuckling bed-mate suggested I had some way to go.

Dennis chuckled through breakfast, then, when he noticed it was winding me up, disappeared in the car. "It might be an idea if you got dressed, Jo," was his parting shot.

So of course I'm still in my nightie. And I've been seized by the urge to do a spot of gardening. It's a little nippy out here, but imagining Dennis's face when he gets back from the shops makes me giggle and warms me up nicely.

First I top up the seed trays I've started leaving out for the squirrels and birds. This is in direct contravention of the rules that Dennis explained to me when I moved in, "I don't agree with feeding wild animals. The only difference between rats and squirrels is the bushy tail, and anyway, leaving out food interferes with natural selection."

At the time, I was too lovestruck to disagree, and my counter-argument — "but they're furry" — wasn't exactly a clincher. But after spotting playful squirrels in Frisky's garden, I think the species deserves a few pumpkin seeds for pure entertainment value.

I haven't turned into a total soft touch: I use all my strength on the weeds, which have the cheek to fight back. Those dandelions in particular don't seem to recognise that I have suffered a head injury and therefore should be given an easy ride — but I have weapons at my disposal. I fetch a hoe from the shed and drive it into the moist earth with my slipper. Slipper! I didn't even own a slipper before February.

All my frustration is suddenly focused on that bloody slipper, the burgundy velour size five embodiment of what's frustrating about my life. Comfy, middle-class, prematurely middle-aged, non-slip.

I push the left slipper off my foot and pull the hoe out of the ground. Then I bring the hoe down on my slipper, striking it on the fluffy upper and grinding at the fabric.

"This isn't what I want," I hiss at the slipper, swinging the hoe back up in the air and down again. The slipper is now coated in mud, but the man-made fibres are holding up well. Too well. I try to slice through the fabric, holding it in place with my right foot. Eventually, it tears slightly and, though it's only a minor victory, I remove the other slipper and prepare to take my revenge on this one too.

"Err . . . Jo?"

I turn, the hoe poised high in the air, like a golf club. It's my mother . . . and my father . . . and Dennis . . . and Lorraine. Their mouths hang open, each expression subtly different, like a set of masks. My mother's is Horror, my father's is Shock, Dennis's is definitely Disgust, and Lorraine's is hovering somewhere between Comedy, Tragedy and Hilarity.

"Hi," I say, waving with the hand that isn't clutching the hoe.

"Aren't you *cold*, Jo?" Dennis asks icily.

"Not 'specially," I reply. I'm not totally sure what to do at this point. A gust of wind propels my nightdress into the air, revealing my pale legs and grey knickers. Dad looks away. "But I might nip in and get . . . changed, now you're here. Wasn't expecting visitors."

"I think we gathered that much," Lorraine says as I scuttle past.

I give Dennis a *look* and he frowns. "It was meant to be a surprise, to celebrate your fantastic recovery. Oh, and another landmark date . . ."

"What?" I rack my brain. I'm sure it's no one's birthday.

He tuts. "It's exactly two years since we became cohabitees. Happy anniversary, Jo!"

I disappear to our bedroom to find something more suitable to wear. Admittedly, a full Pierrot outfit would be more suitable than my current one. I rummage through my quarter of the built-in wardrobe, feeling increasingly irritated. Dennis has a system for clothes, which are always arranged in strict rainbow order, red, orange, yellow, green, blue, indigo, violet. It was a good job he explained it when I moved in, because it wasn't immediately apparent from his section, which ran the full gamut of colours from charcoal grey to slate. It's taken perseverance to get him to experiment with pastel shirts.

I pick a purple cord skirt and a clashing orange top, a protest against the "surprise". I find them all in the kitchen, huddled together. They spring apart as soon as they sense my presence and I realise there's some kind of family conference going on.

"So are the men in white coats stuck in traffic?" I ask.

They manage tight, awkward smiles and I look past them to the breakfast bar. My two ex-slippers are lying there, muddied and mortally wounded. *Je ne regrette rien.*

After a long pause, Dennis claps his hands together. "Right. Is everyone hungry? I have all the ingredients for a top-notch surprise barbecue brunch going begging."

"A barbecue?" This doesn't sound like *my* Dennis. "But what about the health risks posed by undercooked meat? As I'm sure you remember from last summer's safety bulletin, there are 4000 extra food poisoning cases for every degree Celsius rise in temperature. And 1400 people are injured by barbecue equipment."

He raises his eyebrows. "Well, when I said barbecue, I wasn't actually suggesting direct contact with unhygienic hydrocarbons."

"Nor, I'm sure, exposure to the potential carcinogens produced by burning food," I say, feeling strangely giggly.

He looks at me suspiciously. "Yes. Quite right. So who fancies giving me a hand?" He reaches into a large carrier bag and pulls out steak and chicken.

"I will," Mum says, eager to help.

Dad is eyeing up the carrier bags. "Got any wine?"

"We don't really keep it in the house any more, not since, well, you know . . ." Dennis says. "But if you really feel the need . . ."

"I definitely feel the need. I'll go and fetch some," Dad says, disappearing out of the door.

Lorraine nudges me. "Shall we go and lay the table on the patio?"

I follow her out, not bothering to pick up placemats or cutlery. We settle ourselves round the side of the garage, out of sight. Lorraine's the only nice bit of my surprise, and the fact Dennis thinks it's now safe to let me see her must mean I'm on the mend.

She looks knackered, black shadows under those big green eyes and an inch of dark regrowth next to her honey-blonde highlights. But tiredness has always looked sexy on Lorraine, which is a good job as she works insane hours as a midwife, plus having a social life twice as active as the average undergraduate.

"Like the hair," she says eventually. "Very Sarah Ferguson."

I flinch: I'm sure the colour's more chestnut than ginger.

"Thanks. I think. Dennis thinks it makes me look fiery."

She lights a cigarette. "So. Are you really mad, or are you only pretending?"

"What kind of a question is that?"

"A perfectly reasonable one. Don't I have a right to know whether my mate has turned into a loon?"

"S'pose so." I think it over. "I'm not sure I'm any more or less of a loon than I was before. But I might be a loon in a different way, now?"

"Yeah. I mean, you always were weird. I still remember the time you thought the fire drill was

Armageddon." She takes one deep drag from the cigarette, then grinds it out under her kitten heel. In her mind, the one-drag policy qualifies her as a non-smoker.

"I feel like I'm changing, though, Lorrie." I'm thinking aloud now. "I've always been too afraid to do anything out of the ordinary."

"And now? I haven't exactly seen you heading for Everest."

Her casual contempt irritates me. "Um, well, you haven't exactly seen me at all, have you? Not so much as a bunch of sodding flowers."

She shrugs. "I was told not to over-excite you."

"And since when did you obey rules?"

"Yeah. Fair enough. I guess, if I am totally honest, I was worried what I'd find. And your behaviour today hasn't exactly put my mind at rest. Gardening in your knickers isn't normal behaviour. Nor is murdering slippers."

"They bloody deserved it." I giggle.

"Yeah. Too right," she agrees.

"It's not just the slippers, Lorrie. I'm not very good at censoring myself any more. So it doesn't really matter whether it's an inanimate object or a person that's getting on my nerves. I don't hold back. Doesn't matter who it is. Dad. Mum. Dennis."

"Well, you can be as rude as you like to your parents, but try not to alienate Dennis. Most blokes are rubbish with sick women. You're lucky he's not spent the last few months drowning his sorrows in the pub."

I nod. I certainly can't think of a single one of Lorraine's exes who'd have looked after *her*, even though most of them are doctors. Indiscriminate flirting hasn't attracted the kind of man who sticks around. "Yes, I know he's a good one. But he's so over-protective. He watches me like he's my bodyguard and . . ." I hesitate, "well, I almost wonder if he doesn't quite like having a sickly girlfriend at home."

She stares at me. "And why on earth would he like that?"

"I don't know." It does sound rather silly, now I've said it out loud. "Because I won't run away, maybe? I mean, you know how his mother behaved, doing a runner to Spain before he even left school . . ."

Lorraine tuts now. I'm sure it's the same tut she uses when women scream too much in labour, or make unreasonable demands for epidurals or aromatherapy oils. "That's ridiculous. Dennis isn't the type to get hung up about his childhood, and you're getting your knickers in a twist for no reason at all. Sounds to me like you need to pull yourself together, Joey, or people will run out of patience."

Now it's my turn to stare. After all the pussyfooting around from everyone else, it's a shock to hear someone tell me what they really think. "Right. So now I know."

Her expression softens. "I don't want to upset you, but Dennis isn't a saint. All men need attention or they'll look for it elsewhere."

I think about her constant advice when I first got together with Dennis. It feels like someone else's life. "I

260

suppose I should be back in the basque and stilettos as well?"

"Or whatever else turns him on."

"Well, that'll be precisely nothing at the moment."

She looks up, suddenly a bit *too* interested. I wish I could take it back, but it's too late. "Things not good on the bedroom front, then?"

"I'm sure it's a temporary thing," I say, though I'm not sure at all.

She lights another cigarette, leans back against the pebbledash, coming over all Rizzo from *Grease*. "Temporary things in sex can soon become permanent if you don't put in the effort."

"Mmmm."

She looks at the red burning tip of the cigarette, trying to choose the optimal moment for her single, precious drag. "Mmmm? So what's going wrong then?"

I consider whether Lorraine might have some pearl of wisdom to impart, some amazing technique tip that will transform my love life. But I can't shake the suspicion that she'll get more out of any confessions than I will. "Like I say, it's temporary. I don't want to talk about it."

She opens her mouth, as if she's going to insist on the details, but instead she takes her drag, then sighs the smoke out slowly. "Time to set the table then, I guess. What a way to spend a bank holiday."

The sky is grey and the food is bland but we're all trying very hard to pretend to enjoy ourselves.

Mum and Dad sit at opposite ends of the melamine-topped table, ignoring each other. Dennis is next to me (when he isn't fetching second and third helpings of more GM-free, taste-free food) and we ignore each other. Lorraine sits on the patio steps and checks her watch every couple of minutes, wondering how soon she can escape.

At least she can.

The kitchen timer beeps through the open window, and Dennis jumps up to attend to whatever now needs basting or flipping or disrobing from its tinfoil flak jacket.

There is a smoky smell of barbecuing in the air, drifting from someone else's garden, one where the occupants aren't too fussy about salmonella or campylobacter. In contrast, the dishes in front of us contain ghostly chicken with faint marks from the griddle, and a coleslaw of shredded cabbage and onion that's whiter than Dennis's exposed knees. The cheese slices have melted against the plastic wrapping.

I think of Frisky's scary cheese: gooey and germ-filled and almost unbearably delicious. The salty olives, the pine-scented wine, the chewy bread. Is he sitting in his conservatory, while Luke prowls the neighbourhood in search of cat-nappers?

"God, I wish I was there."

Oops. I said it out loud. Lorraine raises an over-plucked eyebrow and Mum, sensing trouble, inspects a pallid chicken wing.

"Where?" Trust Dad to ask the question.

"Oh, I must have been day-dreaming," I say, buying myself time to think of somewhere suitable.

"About where?" Lorraine says, and I scowl at her, *cheers mate*.

"Um." I ponder acceptable locations. Frisky's conservatory isn't going to cut it. Back at work? No, too insulting to suggest I'd rather be at my desk than with my family. Then I remember the fairground and have a brainwave. "Venice! Yes. That's where I wish I was."

Mum and Dad nod: I've got away with it. Lorraine looks incredulous — she knows I hate travelling any further than Swindon.

"Ah yes," I continue. "The Grand Canal. St Mark's Square. A gondola steered by a gorgeous Italian with a massive pole."

Lorraine sniggers and — ugh — Dad winks in her direction.

Mum sighs with longing. "I've always fancied going to one of those masked balls they have there in the winter. The costumes are beautiful. I saw it on TV, it looked so romantic."

"The masks are nothing but a bloody great excuse for a brief encounter with someone else's other half," Dad says. "'Oh, sorry, sweetheart. Thought you were the wife with that mask on.' Ha ha. Wonder if it'd catch on at the Rotary Christmas dance?"

Mum looks stricken until she exerts the supreme effort needed to pull her pursed lips back into shape. It's not as if Dad has ever needed an *excuse* to cop off with someone else's wife.

Dennis appears, bearing steak. There's no charring, no dangerous pink insides. Our steaks resemble one of Dennis's slippers: evenly browned, overcooked slabs of leather.

"So what's the joke?" he asks.

"Jo fancies going to Venice for a romantic weekend," Lorraine says.

He frowns. "But Venice means flying, silly! I prefer somewhere like . . . Coventry, for example. Birmingham's only a few miles up the road. Did you know, Birmingham has more canals than Venice?"

Lorraine helps herself to a piece of steak. "You reckon the West Midlands beats Venice?"

Dennis blushes. "I was most impressed with Coventry, that's all. Modern cities are not always the prettiest, but there's an energy about them you don't find in places like Courtbridge."

"Really," Lorraine says, sounding dubious. "Are you getting paid by them to do PR or something?"

Dennis laughs a little too heartily. "Now, who else fancies some of this steak? One hundred per cent organically reared, and guaranteed BSE free!"

The afternoon passes slowly. By six, all the food has been thoroughly chewed and sits in glutinous layers in our stomachs. Lorraine is giving my father a "therapeutic" neck rub and his eyelids flutter in ecstasy. She's loosened his shirt so she can manoeuvre her healing hands down his shoulders and he emits the occasional deep orgasmic sigh.

Dennis is preparing the decaff. Mum stands by the ornamental water-free wishing well, staring into space.

"Penny for them?"

"Eh?" She seems startled.

"I just wondered what you were thinking about."

"Did you? Me?" She smiles shyly, astonished that her thoughts should be of any interest. "I was thinking about the cats, actually. I bet they're asleep in a big ball. Smelling like biscuits."

I don't quite know how to respond to that, though I suspect she'd rather not know that cats can carry the plague, and kill 275 million small birds and rodents in UK gardens every year. So, after a suitable pause, I peer down the well and ask, "So what would you wish for, Mum?"

She stares into the depths of the well, all six inches of it. "Oh. Well . . . health, wealth and happiness for you and Timmy. Health mainly, of course."

"Timmy couldn't make it today then?"

"Oh. I rung him but he'd gone to New York. Work. Or was it for a party? Dear me, what a life he leads."

Timmy is safer conversational ground. "Yes. Quite a life . . . Mum. Do you think he is happy?"

That puzzled look again. "Well, I should think so. He can have everything he wants. No ties." Then she smiles. "Not that I'd have a clue what to do with all that freedom."

"I think freedom's overrated, Mum," I say. Lorraine is the "freest" person I know, from free love with married men, to free time spent exactly as she chooses, accountable to no one. Yet she's never seemed happy to me.

Mum opens her eyes wide. They were always bloodshot when I was little, from the crying and the pills. Now I notice they're the same ice blue as Timmy's. "Yes, that's right, Jo. People today make themselves so unhappy expecting everything to be wonderful, all the time," she says. Then her head shakes slightly, as if she's disagreeing with herself. "I might be wrong about that, though," she adds.

"No, you might be right." I suddenly feel desperate to understand my mother better. "I mean, we expect to get it 100 per cent right in our jobs, our homes, our social lives, our relationships." I look back at the bungalow. "Especially about relationships."

The words linger between us. She turns her head slightly, towards my father. He is telling a joke: we can't hear his words, but his posture is unmistakable, the way he's leaning over Lorraine and — oh God, now he's going for the punch-line — and as she laughs dutifully, he reaches out a hairy hand to squeeze her thigh.

"I always knew what he was like, you know, Jo." Her voice is a whisper. "Before."

"Before what?" I match her low tone, like an animal trainer trying not to frighten off a nervous stray.

"Before I married him . . . he had quite a reputation in Newbury, you know." And her face is wistful. "The *Alfie* of West Berkshire, a different woman in every pub. But not many people realised that was only part of him. He wanted to settle down, too. He was a bank manager,

266

after all. You know where you are with a bank manager."

Dad has sensed that he's being talked about, and removes his hand from Lorraine's leg. "But . . . you must have loved him, Mum?"

"Yes," she says vaguely. "He had all the lines, you know, Jo. No one had ever told me I was their perfect woman before. And he did want to be a good husband, but I knew all along that marriage wouldn't make him a new person, though maybe I didn't realise quite how hard it would be at times . . ." She hesitates, and her wary expression convinces me she's talking about her zombie phase. "Anyway, it's all in the past. But just remember, Jo. People don't change. Can't change. Refusing to accept that is responsible for so much misery in the world."

Dad's eyes meet mine across the garden and he grins. I've always thought of Mum as the victim — she plays the part so well — but her words make me wonder. All he did was live down to her expectations. She makes it sound more like an arranged marriage than a love match. Maybe she never loved him at all, but he was a safe bet. And maybe he knew that all along . . .

"And he did his best, as a father," she adds. "He was a good provider."

Before the accident, I'd have disagreed: my stock memories of my childhood almost all involve Dad letting me down. But in my flashbacks, he's no cartoon villain, he's just a man who loves to be centre-stage, but isn't equipped for the supporting role of fatherhood. I'd almost feel sorry for him if it wasn't for that final betrayal.

Dennis appears, bearing a tray laden with his decaff brew and his stoneware unbleached mugs and no-sugar sweetener. Is Dennis my safe bet? Am I his? I have a vision of us in this same garden in twenty-five years, clutching the same unbreakable mud-brown mugs. ("Why would we need new ones, Jo? These have years left in them. Made to last.") And all the time wondering whether life might have been different if I'd been allowed to drink from bone china.

"There's another thing," Mum says, an unfamiliar urgency in her voice.

"Yes?"

Dennis is bearing down on us, so I turn my back on him, desperate to hear my mother's wisdom.

"Humans pretend to be unselfish, but in the end, it's every man for himself. You know, like that song in *The Italian Job*. Self-preservation is what it's all about. Whereas cats don't bother to pretend. That's why I prefer them. You know where you are with a cat."

I stare at her for several seconds before I notice that her pinched mouth has softened and curled up at the edges. Then I realise. My mother has actually made a joke.

There's a first time for everything.

CHAPTER
TWENTY-THREE

Melophobia — Fear of Music

Dr Williams is not all that interested in my fascinating conversation with my mother, or in Dennis's safe barbecuing techniques. He's more concerned about my extra-curricular activities.

"You went go-karting? As in, racing round a track in an open-sided, high-risk motor vehicle? Whose bloody bright idea was that?"

"Mine?" I try to lie, but my intonation gives me away. "OK. OK, it was Frisky's idea. But actually I chickened out on the first lap, I'm such a scaredy-cat." In one short minute, I've revealed myself to be an idiot, a wimp and a tell-tale tit.

"Frisky. I should have known. Go-karting and funfairs don't exactly sound up your street." He taps his fingers on the desk, like a headmaster trying to think up a punishment.

"He was only trying to help."

"Oh he was, was he? You know, at medical school we were warned that a little knowledge is a dangerous thing." Mild-mannered Nathan is nowhere to be seen:

269

he's definitely in consultant mode now, bordering on arrogant.

"Frisky doesn't mean any harm. I'm sort of . . . his *project*."

"Well, I don't want a tug of war, but you're *my* patient. I can't have amateurs messing about with your head."

I'm desperate to redeem Frisky. "But he's got a brilliant theory about the flashbacks."

"What does Professor Freeman Van Belle have to say, with his extensive background in neurology?"

But when I tell him Frisky's theory, the cynicism vanishes.

"Proust." He grabs a notebook and began to scribble.

"Eh?"

"Proust wrote about it. In *À la recherche du temps perdu*. The smell of a Madeleine cake dipped in tea transported him back to his childhood. Lots of us have experienced that on a small scale, of course, but Proust expressed it better than most."

"But why smells?"

He draws me a diagram on his pad, like a child's drawing of a fluffy sheep. "OK. Each part of the brain has a different name and a different function. So this bit . . ." he points at his diagram, "is the limbic area, which processes smell *and* deals with emotions and memories. And when the chemical molecules make their way up your nose, they send messages which bounce around different parts — hippocampus, hypothalamus, olfactory cortex and the amygdala —

270

and seem to make those memories triggered by smell much stronger and more *convincing*, somehow, than ones triggered by a name or a photograph. That's why big money is so interested, everyone from perfume companies to supermarkets."

"But there's a big difference between what's happening to me and, I don't know, shops using the smell of bread to make you hang around and buy more stuff."

"Yes, there is, but your visions could be crucial in helping us understand the process. Just think, Jo, you could improve our understanding of the limbic area." His eyes are glossy with excitement.

"What, by donating my brain to medical science?"

"No, you can do it while you're alive. I was thinking of a little piece in the *Lancet*, say? You could be at the vanguard of a new sensory world."

I feel an itch of irritation: I didn't really take Frisky's daft comments about Nathan fancying me seriously, but all the same it's a shock to realise that I'm simply Exhibit A in his marvellous career. "Hmm. I know this sounds selfish, but I don't know if I have the energy for anything that isn't going to help me directly, to solve my problem."

"From my professional point of view, Jo, there's only one person in the world who can stop it happening."

I sigh. "And I suppose he's some top neurologist over in California, with a waiting list as long as the Golden Gate Bridge."

He puts his pen down. "Actually, the expert I have in mind is rather closer to home. In this room, in fact."

I lose my patience. "Yeah, because you've really got the answers."

Nathan flinches. "Not me . . ." he says, in the extra slow voice he must reserve for his worst head-bangers. "You."

"Oh. Well, I'm not exactly making much progress so far."

"Then stop trying too hard. In my experience, the answers tend to have a way of making themselves known. Like women and a good wine, you can't hurry them along." He smiles like a cheeky schoolboy, and I remember why all the nurses rave about him. "Please think about the research, though. Maybe we could name a syndrome after you."

"What, go down in history, like Mr Alzheimer and Mr Tourette? No thanks."

"What about Scaredy-cat Syndrome?" Nathan lifts up his notebook. Next to the brain, he's drawn a cartoon cat, its tail and fur standing on end and its eyes wide open.

He tears off the page and I take it. Every detail is rendered carefully in blue biro, from the whiskers to the two sharp teeth pointing out of the cat's jaw. And when I look more closely, I understand: "That actually *is* me, isn't it?"

"Yup. Cute, isn't she?"

I blush. "I reckon I've lost eight of my nine lives this year. Can I keep this?"

"Sure." He tidies away his Biro in an ancient Power Rangers pencil case, then calls after me as I get to the door. "Oh, and Jo?"

272

"Yes?"

"Go easy on the go-karting. You want to hang on to that ninth life, if you can."

What I neglected to mention to Nathan was that Frisky has already set up our next "date" — for tonight. And by the time I get home, Frisky's on the phone. He's had to promise that he won't make me do anything involving alcohol, aviation, animals, anti-social behaviour, aquatic sports or air-sea rescue. "And that was just the 'A's, Joanna. Honestly. Gave me an entire alphabetical list. Luckily tonight's event is entirely risk-free, but our young doctor doesn't want to lose a hair from your head," Frisky tells me. "It's definitely more than a professional interest. He's not for you, though. Too grey. You want someone darker. Someone at home with nature . . ."

If it wasn't so ridiculous, I'd swear that Frisky's trying to fix me up with dark, nature-friendly Luke. But maybe Frisky *is* right about the good doctor. That cartoon has freaked me out, and his comments do sometimes border on the inappropriate. I guess the only other people he meets are patients, and the ones at Fright Club were mainly hairy blokes.

The trouble is, even if I wasn't attached, I can't imagine being with Nathan. He's a bright boy, but he's seen me at my worst. He needs someone sharper, sassier.

"Where is it?" Lorraine asks. She's reluctantly giving me a lift to Frisky's house for tonight's mystery activity. In return for the lift — and an alibi, as Dennis would never shut up if he knew where I was going — I get a lecture about living dangerously, which is a bit rich. I've been her alibi often enough, but she's gone all pouty because she doesn't like the tables being turned. She's the one who has adventures and I'm the delighted audience, clapping my hands in excitement as she takes her bow, after blow-by-blow accounts of oral, alfresco or adulterous sex.

Lorraine! Of course. *Doctors and nurses*. "Not far now. Listen, Lorraine?"

"Yep?" She's monosyllabic, punishing me for the misdemeanours I'm about to commit.

"If I said I had the perfect man for you, what would you say?"

"Um, let me think. What about, don't talk shit? Is it down here?" She indicates towards Frisky's neighbourhood, the poshest part of Courtbridge.

"Yes, it is. Right and right again, then over on the left by the lamppost. But I really think this one could be for you. Bright. Witty. Sexy Welsh accent."

She frowns. "You haven't mentioned what he looks like yet, so he must be minging."

"No, he's . . ." I try to think of his selling points. How would my brother advertise Nathan to this most discerning of customers? Then I remember the shoes on the desk. "He's got terribly big feet."

"Huh, as if that means anything. It's a myth about feet and dicks, I've done the hands-on research, remember."

"He's tall as well. You told me that's a more reliable indicator. And he has gorgeous brown eyes."

274

She turns down Frisky's road. "Trouble is, Jo, the only men you've been meeting lately are either patients or doctors, so this bloke must fall into one of those categories."

I sigh. "It's down here. The tatty house."

"I'm right, aren't I? So which is it?"

"Doctor. But not all doctors are the same."

"All the ones I've met are."

I've heard her rant about male medics a million times before. Doctors, apparently, are never motivated by generosity of spirit and a desire to help people: instead it's greed, power and a desire to fondle women with impunity. "Ah, but Lorraine, you've never been out with a brain specialist."

"What, the kind of bloke who was good at woodwork at school and now wants to take his junior hacksaw to your skull?"

I've never thought of Nathan drilling holes in people's heads before, but I suppose it's all in a day's work. The scene from *Indiana Jones* where they're forced to eat monkey brains enters my mind and won't go away. "He's very nice," I say, knowing how weak that sounds.

"And since when have I ever fancied nice? Thanks but no thanks." Lorraine pulls up outside the house. "Right. So you'll call me when your outing is over."

"If that's OK? I do appreciate this, Lorrie." I try to win her over with the nickname I used back in the days when we used to prowl fairgrounds together.

"As long as you know what you're doing. And what you've got to lose."

"But . . ." I want to challenge her, ask her why she's so keen I stay with Dennis, when for the last three years she's been slagging him off as a bloody boring bastard. What's changed? Then it occurs to me. *Now I'm a head-banger, she thinks he's the best I can do.*

"What?" she says.

"Nothing. I'll call you later, so long as I'm still in one piece."

Frisky greets me in a burgundy quilted dressing gown, Courtbridge's answer to Oscar Wilde.

"I'm not early, am I?" It's past six, and Frisky's body-clock usually runs to Greenwich Mean Time, so his state of undress surprises me.

"Oh no, just need to finish my ablutions, my dear. Why don't you join Luke in the garden?" And he disappears without another word.

The house is still a work-in-progress, though in fact I struggle to see any progress at all. I walk through the conservatory into the garden, which is dazzlingly green. The bluebells have died back, the oaks are covered in wiggly leaves and the last pink blossom clings stubbornly to a row of fruit trees next to the caravan.

Finally I spot Luke. He has his back to me, and his frayed grey T-shirt is damp with sweat that clings to his shoulder-blades, so they look like sprouting wings. I say nothing for a moment, watching his jerky movements.

He stops, then turns warily. I think I catch a hint of a smile when he realises it's me, but maybe he's grimacing against the light. "I didn't think you'd be back, after what happened with the go-karts."

276

"But it must have been you who delivered the little fish, surely?" Frisky's wooden fish is hidden in my underwear drawer; every time I take out fresh knickers, I get a whiff of spice. It's taken me a whole week to work out why it seemed so familiar, then I remembered: it's sandalwood, like my father's favourite aftershave. But so far, so good. No flashbacks.

"Oh, *that's* what it was. He was very mysterious about that package."

"Well, I thought I ought to give him a second chance."

"Really?" Luke scowls like James Dean.

There's a pause and I try to think of something to say, to break the silence. I look down at his hands, holding secateurs. I spot the pink scar on his palm. "Pruning? Is this the right time of year?"

He shrugs. "I don't know. The gardening season's different here. Back home, I could plant any time of year and it'd grow, no matter . . ." He cuts the sentence short, as if he's annoyed at himself for giving anything away.

"Back home?" I repeat, casually.

"San Francisco," he mumbles. "Guess this is home now, though." He peers around him and his face turns mellow.

"You don't like England?" I say, then feel stupid. How could the miniaturised Court Bridge compete with the Golden Gate? "Not so many earthquakes, at least."

"No, no earthquakes at all." He flicks the clip on the secateurs, snapping the blades back together. "I better put this away. You'll need a chauffeur." I hear America in the elongated "firrr" of the last word and I wonder why he's here and if he'll ever go back.

He walks towards the caravan and I sense Frisky behind me, in the open doorway of the conservatory. He's changed into smart black trousers, a lilac shirt and a darker purple cravat. "Impossibly shy, that boy, but he'd be devastated if he knew it makes him seem rude and surly. Such a shame no one will persevere."

"Maybe he doesn't want anyone to persevere."

Frisky laughs. "Everybody needs somebody, as the Blues Brothers had it."

I stand back and look at the huge villa, four storeys of it, and wonder who Frisky's somebody is — or was. I think of these two men, rattling about, avoiding each other, with that inexplicable gulf keeping them apart. "Yes," I say, softly. "Now, about where we're going tonight. Can I have a clue?"

Frisky taps the side of his nose. "Not yet, Joanna. But don't fret, you'll find out soon enough."

Frisky insists we sit together in the back seat of the Red Peril again, and now Luke won't look at me at all.

We leave Courtbridge and as we take the ring road, Frisky begins to hum tunelessly, which seems to be driving Luke mad. Every now and then I see him reflected in the rear-view mirror, glaring at his grandfather. Of course, when Frisky realises, he ups the volume, winking at me.

"Will you can it, please?" Luke snarls.

278

"Temper, temper," Frisky says. "I'm only doing it to disguise the rattle of that bloody engine. Can't you drive less noisily?" And he winks at me, trying to recruit me to his side of the argument.

I turn away and watch Courtbridge whiz by. This is my favourite time of year: just after nature has woken up, but before Wimbledon and the hay fever season. We pass row after row of red-bricked semis, sporting hanging baskets with yellow and blue primroses, the last line of defence against the grey tarmac of the dual carriageway.

I wonder what Luke makes of summer here? Don't all the girls in San Francisco wear flowers in their hair? My blurry mental image includes women like the ones in the old Timotei adverts, wearing linen smocks and hempseed kaftans. They're hanging out in the street, jazz and blues notes spilling out from cafés. Though, isn't that New Orleans? In San Francisco, flamboyant gay men lean out of open-topped trams, flirting with the conductors as they head up and down the steep streets. Staring death by earthquake in the face, living for the moment.

Anyway, whatever it's like in San Francisco, even the prettiest Wiltshire spring must be a let-down. So what *is* he doing here? Why move halfway round the world to a place you don't like, living with a relative you clearly loathe?

Luke stops the car outside a row of shops in a seventies' breezeblock arcade; there's a tanning centre, a modern blond-wood and chrome caring-sharing pawnbroker, a Chinese herbalist offering help with insomnia and impotence (I wonder how Dennis would react if I bought him ginseng teabags to keep his pecker up) and an off-licence. The place is deserted, except for a small cluster of kids kicking an empty Coke can around.

"That's what I like to see," Frisky says as he scrambles out of the car, "young people involved in traditional country pursuits, rather than surfing the infernal internet."

He leads the way towards a shop I hadn't noticed before. It's not really a shop at all. A third of the width of the other frontages, with indecipherable writing above the door. Japanese? Chinese?

Frisky pushes open the reinforced metal door — we're not in Kansas any more, Toto — and walks down a narrow corridor. Everything's scuffed: the rubber floor, the beige walls, all the way up to the pine-clad ceiling. There's a smell of damp and it feels as if we're going underground.

"Mr Clint!" Frisky spots a thin boy in the distance, at the end of this never-ending corridor.

The boy turns and he isn't a boy at all. His body *is* boyish, slim arms poking from a grey short-sleeved shirt that hangs off a narrow chest. But his face is much older, with ground-in lines on his forehead. "Sir Roger," he says, bowing his head briefly.

Frisky raises his eyebrows at me, whispers from the corner of his mouth. "He got the wrong end of the stick when we first met and now it's too embarrassing to explain. But it does mean I get a discount on the sake," he whispers, then turns to the man. "This is Joanna, a friend of mine."

Grey-shirt man nods. "Friend. A very beautiful *friend*, Sir Roger."

Oh God. He thinks I'm Frisky's girlfriend.

"And this is my grandson."

Luke greets the man in what sounds suspiciously like Japanese. Curiouser and curiouser.

Mr Clint looks at Luke, then me. "Ah, grandson and grandson's friend." He seems relieved.

"No, not his friend, *my* friend," Frisky begins, then shakes his head. "Oh, it doesn't matter. I'm sure it's less embarrassing for you, Joanna, if he thinks you're Luke's girlfriend."

I consider this as Mr Clint leads us off to the left, down another corridor. I imagine Luke taking me on a city tour of San Francisco, introducing me to his cool friends in their cool apartments, telling them all about me and . . . and this is where I blush like I used to whenever Lorraine sussed out my latest crush on some impossibly with-it boy at school. Because what could Luke, with his motorbike and his studied surliness and his mysterious past, possibly tell his mates about me? "Here's Jo, she works in local government and has given up her glamorous life in a Wiltshire bungalow to be with me." Or, "Meet Jo, she survived a life-threatening encounter with a push-bike and now divides her time between hiding from the mad woman who runs the mobile library, and feeding the ducks with her mother."

Fortunately the room we're shown into is dark, so no one can see my flushed cheeks. It's a tiny space, not much bigger than an average bathroom, with no windows. As my eyes adjust I see plastic chairs dotted around the walls, a smoked-glass coffee table in the centre of the floor, and a TV monitor with an electronic box beneath it. Mr Clint fiddles with a remote control, cursing in his own language, before the screen pings into life, revealing a group of happy-looking Japanese teenagers holding . . . oh God. Holding *microphones*.

"Frisky?"

In the blue glow from the screen, his skin resembles a dinosaur's. "I racked my brains, Joanna. Something edgy, but not risky. Something fun but challenging. Not involving wildlife or speed or combustible materials."

"But . . ."

He rests his hand on my arm. "Hear me out, Joanna. There is method in my madness. OK, I know you're scared of bombs and armed robberies and implausible diseases but there's more than that. It's my contention that the thing that scares you most is *speaking up*."

I'm about to reply that actually I'm more bolshie than I ever was before my accident, but then Mr Clint adjusts the volume on the huge speakers that cling to the walls. Plinkety-plonk electronic music fills the room. He nods, satisfied, then backs politely out of the room, without turning his back on us.

"So what's the cure for a girl who doesn't like to be heard?" Frisky continues. "I couldn't think of one, until I remembered Mr Clint. Big hit in these parts, especially since the Honda factory moved in. Because there's nothing a Japanese car executive thousands of miles from home likes more than a top notch night of karaoke . . ."

"But I can't sing, Frisky." I feel a wave of nostalgia for the go-kart track.

"Doesn't matter one jot, Joanna. The secret of karaoke isn't the voice of an angel, but the soul of a rock star. It's about letting it all hang out."

"I've never let it hang out in my life, Frisky. I wouldn't know where to begin."

"About time you learned, then, my dear. And . . ." he smiles as Mr Clint reappears, holding a small tray with a porcelain flask and three cups, "to help you find your voice, there's always sake."

I turn to see Luke cowering in the corner. "Not a fan of karaoke?"

"I just don't like sake."

Frisky tuts. "How rude, Luke. A sip of sake wouldn't exactly kill you, would it? No bloody cultural awareness, Joanna. Anyone would think he's still hung up about Pearl Harbor."

Luke seems to shrink several inches and I want to stick up for him, ask him whether he really did speak Japanese back there. And if so, where he learned it.

"Bloody Americans," Frisky adds, for good measure. "Now, what should we choose as our opening number?"

There is no escape. I reach out to pick up one of three beakers on the tray, and fill it with liquid from the flask. When I hold it to my nose, it smells of nothing but alcohol, and I down it in one, like medicine. My throat burns, but in a good way.

"That's the spirit, Joanna. We'll have you belting out songs like Shirley Bassey before you can say, 'Diamonds Are Forever'."

Frisky's confidence in my diva tendencies is ill-founded. In the time it's taken me to finish most of the flask — this sake is surprisingly moreish — I haven't sung a note, but he's spanned a wide musical repertoire, from Cole Porter and ABBA to The Prodigy. Frisky's "Smack My Bitch Up" lacks a certain street-level conviction, but you can't fault him for effort.

"Where do you know the modern songs from, Frisky?" I ask him as he sits down for a rest after an energetic rendition of "The Real Slim Shady".

"Oh, I like to keep up with the latest grooves. One Extra on my digital radio is rather good for hip hop. Whereas young Luke is an old fart, doesn't listen to anything recorded after the millennium, do you?"

Luke glares back but doesn't say a word. I wonder if they're like this at home.

"I'm feeling quite hoarse now, Joanna, don't you think it's time you took the baton? Or rather, the microphone? After all, this session is meant to be for your benefit."

"In a minute. I'd rather listen to you."

"Now that I don't believe for a single moment." He leans over to pour some sake and a few tiny drops fall from the flask. "Ah. Terribly quaffable, isn't it? So, what's stopping you, my dear?"

I sigh. More pop psychology. "I'm not much of a singer."

"Ha! Hasn't stopped me, has it? Let's think about this. You're among friends." He glances at Luke. "Not that *he's* helping. But no one's going to laugh."

"It's not that, Frisky. It's just that . . ." and then I hesitate. Why *is* this such a big deal for me? My objections to go-karting were reasonable enough, but no one ever died singing karaoke. Yet somehow I can't bring myself to do it. "The thing is, I'm actually more than capable of speaking up these days. In fact my family have a job shutting me up. So I can't see why belting out a chorus of . . . I dunno, 'Rescue Me', is going to turn me into a new woman. No offence."

Frisky grins. "None taken. But don't you ever stop analysing, Joanna? Because my other reason for bringing you here is to get you to be more spontaneous. Maybe even have fun. Let that foxy red hair down."

I take a sip from my tiny beaker. "I suppose you're right. I do want to, but . . . I can't explain it. It's like I'm looking at the world from the outside. Like that story, the little match girl, who peers into all these cosy sitting-rooms, but is never allowed inside."

"And what happened to her?"

I smile ruefully. "She froze to death."

"Right. Not exactly a role-model, then, is she?"

"No. But that's how it feels. I want to come in from the cold. But it's frightening. Unsettling. I don't know where to start."

"Hate to sound like a do-gooder, but with a single step? Or a single note?"

I want to say yes. I really do. "I don't know what makes me so *pathetic*."

"Oh bugger. What is it with girls, putting themselves down? Trust me to get it wrong, as usual!"

"It's not your fault that I'm stuck in a rut that's lasted decades, Frisky. It's bound to be tricky to climb out of it." I drain the last of the sake. "Mind you, this is helping. I know it shouldn't, but it's warming me up a treat."

"Right," he says, springing up from the chair. "Let me go and fetch *more*. Luke? Keep our guest entertained, will you?"

Frisky bounces off down the corridor to see Mr Clint. Luke and I look at each other. "You're not much of a singer either then?" I ask, eventually.

"I kinda liked it at school," he says. "Sang in a band. Rock, you know. That's why he said that about liking *old* music. Just because I hate the dumb rap stuff he *pretends* to like."

"You were a singer?" It's the last thing I would have expected of grumpy Luke.

"Only in high school, like I said. Isn't every guy in a band?"

I try to imagine Dennis in a band. Pouting at teenage girls. Going without socks. Bumping and grinding with an electric guitar. It makes me giggle. Or maybe that's the sake taking effect. "No, not every guy. So didn't you want to take it further? Play one of those huge stadiums?"

He shrugs. "Maybe I day-dreamed a little. The girls, you know."

"Popular, were you?" It's easier to ask questions when I can barely see him.

"I was the only one whose voice had broken. And the guitar distracted them from my zits."

The sound of Frisky's laughter drifts from the corridor. He sounds as though he's going to be a while. "So did you have a good voice?"

"I dunno. OK, I guess. But then I used to listen to the bands I loved — Guns 'n' Roses, Van Halen, you know — and decided as I'd never be that good, there was no point being average."

I can't reconcile what he's saying, with the way he lives now. Once, he had ambition. Once, he wouldn't settle for anything less than wonderful. Now he lives in a caravan. "And did you find something you could be the best at?"

He looks away. "Ah, you wouldn't believe me if I told you."

"Try me," I say, emboldened by the dark.

"Geology."

"Rocks?"

I catch a glimpse of a smile as he says, "Not any old rocks. Tectonic plates?"

My fuddled brain takes a while to remember what they are. "Uhhh . . . earthquakes?"

"Yup! Seismology. If you're a boy growing up in California, chances are you're either gonna get into surfing or quakes. And I never did like getting saltwater in my eyes."

I think back to my silly remark in the garden about Wiltshire having no earthquakes. "So is that what you did, then? Became a seis-molo-gist?" The word sounds strange, like a snake hissing.

He nods. "Yeah. Not as exciting as it sounds." He sounds bored now, like he wants to shut me up.

I strain to hear whether Frisky's on his way with more sake. Nope. It's gone suspiciously quiet in the corridor. Luke is fiddling with his watch: in the gloom, the fluorescent Roman numerals stand out, and the tin dot of radioactivity on the second hand seems to slow down before my eyes.

A jingle-jangle electronic tune leaks from the speakers, like toxic waste. "Do you know how we turn this off?" I ask.

Luke looks up. "Don't think you can. It's a force bigger than both of us." And then I think . . . maybe I'm wrong, it could be a trick of the light . . . he *winks*.

"In that case," I must be more pissed than I thought because I can't quite believe I'm going to ask this until the words are out of my mouth, "maybe you'd join me in a song? Just to get Frisky off my back? He's not going to let me off until I've done one." There! I *did* say it. Bloody hell.

He turns his head slightly, so I can't see how he's reacting. Oh God, maybe I've gone and done it now. Old Brooding-pants wouldn't lower himself to doing something that might be even remotely embarrassing. And I don't think that was a wink at all. It was a twitch of irritation . . .

He mumbles something which sounds like "shit". Well, that's charming. I'm about to say something I'll regret when he walks across to the ring-binder that Frisky's left on the coffee table, and picks it up. His face is silhouetted against the TV screen. "So which one?"

"Eh?"

"Which number are we going to murder together?"

"But . . ." I hesitate. "But you said it was *shit*. Which was unnecessarily offensive, really, when you think about it."

He says patiently. "No, Jo. I said *sure*. Now help me choose a song before I change my mind."

Frisky nearly drops his tray when he comes back into the karaoke room. Luke and I are side by side on plastic chairs, hunched together over the songbook, reading through the list. Actually, we've only got to the "B"s — every teen title brings back a rush of memories.

"I used to love Adam Ant," I say, as I try to work out whether I have the vocal range to carry off "Stand and Deliver". Actually, I don't have the vocal range to carry off "Humpty Dumpty Sat on a Wall" . . .

"He was a *pussy*," Luke says. "Aerosmith on the other hand . . ."

"Not for me. They must have been bigger in the States than here. It must be weird for you, living here. What is it they say? Two countries divided by a common language. But we're divided by music, and TV and books, too, aren't we?"

289

"Ah, it's no big deal. And you had *Sesame Street*, didn't you?"

"Yes, but we also had *Blue Pe* . . . oh, hello, Frisky."

Luke moves away from me so quickly that his chair nearly topples over.

"My, my. I turn my back for a second, and *look* what happens. A love-in."

Luke and I pull faces at each other, but there's something else there: it feels like an alliance against Frisky's merciless bossiness. Or maybe it's my imagination. Even so, I realise I've finally relaxed. "Hardly a love-in. Luke and I were just trying to pick a good song for my karaoke debut. And he's agreed to do the backing vocals." There! Backing vocals. That sounds so much less intimate than "duet".

Frisky frowns. "Oh. Right." He puts the tray down with a bang. "Well, I'm glad you've changed your mind," he says, sounding the opposite. I think he must be feeling left out. "So what's it going to be?"

I flick through the book. Already my courage is fading: the microphone seems to glow with menace, though logically I know it's only the LED power indicator showing it's switched on, ready for me to mangle a musical classic.

The most popular titles are in bold. "Stairway to Heaven"? Too slow. "Bat Out of Hell"? I reckon Luke might love that one but Nathan would never forgive me for head-banging. "The Greatest Love of All" is surely kamikaze karaoke — only Whitney and Dolly have the voices to carry that off.

"So much choice," I say, feebly, flicking backwards and forwards with increasing impatience. "Like a Virgin"? The thought of doing *sexy* in front of Luke makes me cringe. I plough on. "Hotel California"? No. "Billie Jean". No. "American Pie". God forbid. "Crazy" is way too close to the mark, and "Love Shack" is worse than "Like a Virgin" in the inappropriately sexual stakes. "I Got You Babe" is wrong without a beehive and a facelift, and even a karaoke *ingénue* like me knows that "Summer Nights" is so over-exposed.

"For Pete's sake, Joanna. You know we pay by the hour in here. It's not life or death." Frisky takes the book from me. "Let me choose."

Before I've finished refilling my beaker with sake, Frisky's on his way to the computer monitor to key in the song he's picked. "So what is it?"

"Wait and see." He hands the microphone to me, then finds the second behind the TV and gives it to Luke.

Luke and I face the screen. I hold my breath as the computer locates the tune.

"Get ready!" flashes in front of us, followed by a countdown. "FIVE, FOUR, THREE, TWO . . ."

It starts with piano scales as practised by beginners, up and down the keyboard. But these are different. These are scales that *millions* of people worldwide would recognise in an instant. "Frisky! I can't believe you chose *this*."

But he holds out his hands, as if it was beyond his control. "It's the law. All karaoke sessions must include this record."

I turn to Luke and he winks. It's definite this time, no trick of the light. I gulp, but that's more about the song than my singing partner.

Honest.

We miss our cue — somehow it doesn't seem right to hear the music stripped of Freddie Mercury's voice — and exchange expressions of embarrassed camaraderie before launching ourselves into the most murderous rendition ever attempted of "Bohemian Rhapsody".

Actually, it wasn't that murderous: not even manslaughter. Luke hasn't lost the voice that won him pre-pubescent admirers in high school, and I managed to satisfy Frisky with my enthusiastic backing vocals. Right at the end, Luke stopped singing and spoke those final lines like a poem, as if he meant them. "Nothing really matters . . ."

When the number finished, there was a moment of silence that seemed to last a very long time. Luke looked like he was about to put his arm around me, to say *we did it, kid*, or something similar, but then stopped, his hand caught in mid-air and his lilac-grey eyes widening in panic. Then the plinky-plonky music began again and we pretended it had never happened. It would be so much easier if we were both men; the achievement, minor as it was, definitely called for mutual backslapping or a chummy high five.

Frisky talked me into a few more songs, "now you're all warmed up", and it got easier and easier, thanks in part to the sake, I am sure. It felt liberating and I began to understand that the point of karaoke isn't how you sound, but how loud you are.

But while I was yowling my way through glam rock and ballads with Frisky, Luke had returned to his seat by the wall. He didn't look at me and after a while, I began to wonder whether I'd imagined that moment of solidarity.

Mid-"My Way", there was a knock at the door and we were booted out of our room by the next group, a bunch of raucous women celebrating "Mental" Madge's fiftieth birthday. Frisky gave her a big kiss and tried to persuade them to let us stay, until Mr Clint distracted us with fishy-smelling green tea.

And now I'm in the back seat again with Frisky, heading for Courtbridge.

"Now, that was fun, wasn't it? Go on, Joanna, admit it!"

"Yes. I'm hoarse, but happy." My voice is husky from sake and singing.

"Ah, I know the very thing for that. Luke, stop at that garage! LUKE!"

Luke slams on the brakes and steers sharp left, brave manoeuvres given that the Red Peril is held together with filler and could disintegrate at any moment. He stops in the middle of the forecourt, pulling on the handbrake with an ugly screech. Frisky tuts, then disappears into the little shop.

He emerges holding a bag, the silhouette of a half-bottle showing through the brown paper. Surely not more booze?

"This'll sort you out," he says as he climbs back in beside me.

"Frisky, I appreciate the thought, but I feel rather drunk already so I think I'll pass."

He frowns at me, then smiles that Austrian-blind smile, his face rippling upward in amusement. "Oh, the Scotch is for me. *These* are for you." He reaches into the bag. "Close your eyes."

I want to protest, but it seems churlish after all the trouble he's taken tonight. The sake bill alone must have been a week's pension. "OK, then."

"Now open your mouth," he says. I hear the ripping of plastic and then rustling. "Here we go. This'll sort you out."

He places a hard pellet on my tongue. My tastebuds begin tingling instantly, and the heat spreads to my throat and before long, there's an icy blast of menthol and . . . what is that? . . . eucalyptus, yes, that's it, feeling like it's freezing the hairs inside my nose and . . . oh no. Not here. Not again . . .

CHAPTER
TWENTY-FOUR

Theatrophobia — Fear of Theatres

"Aa-ah-ah-uh-ah-ah-aaah . . ."

Earth, *please* swallow me up. If there's ever a good time for the four-minute warning to sound, it's now.

"Aa-ah-ah-uh-ah-ah-aaah . . . oh, lovely. A Fisherman's Friend always clears out the passages, eh, Jo?" My father stands dressed only in his Y-fronts, practising his scales. The waves of menthol that waft from his wide open mouth help to mask the sweaty feet smell of the men's changing room.

Actually, Newbury Amateur Operatic Society only has one changing room, but a curtain made from old bedsheets hangs from the ceiling to preserve the modesty of both sexes. The men dress on the window side of the curtain, because no Peeping Tom would want to eye up the male members. Behind Dad, there are two pigeon-chested teenagers who joined because their mums are in the chorus and bullied them into it. Huddled by the radiator are a couple of middle-aged men who only come because they're worried their wives might fall under my father's spell (he has *that* kind of reputation). And the rest of the blokes are Life Honorary Members, all retired, who'll be in the cast until they die. Literally. One had a heart attack in the wings just before curtain-up on the opening night of *Brigadoon*, perhaps because he was so excited about the two lines he'd been allocated. Luckily someone else knew the words; the show must go on.

My father begins to dress. First, he covers those skinny legs with a pair of scratchy-looking brown trousers that are too big for him. Joyce the wardrobe mistress hates male costumes. She prefers creating vast polyester frocks in clashing colours, and never lets fact or historical detail get in the way of her designs: for *South Pacific*, her exotic islanders wore pink and violet "grass" skirts made from recycled nymph costumes, previously used in *A Midsummer Night's Musical*.

So Joyce always leaves the men's costumes till last, buying them from nasty charity shops in Reading. Dad draws the line at wearing dead men's shirts, especially since the legendary *Oklahoma!* lice outbreak, so he's brought in one of his own from home. He takes a brand-new shirt out of a Burton carrier. "You get bags more buzz at Burton, eh, Bean?"

Buying a new shirt is the only way to get an uncrumpled one. Nothing in our house has been ironed since The Diagnosis ten weeks ago. I've mastered the washing machine (well, apart from the incident with my green PE knickers and the 60 degree whites cycle). But I won't iron in case I scorch the shirt, or my arms, or forget to switch it off and the house burns down while Mum's at the hospital and I'm in double Geography. I didn't used to worry about stuff like that, but now I know you can't take anything for granted.

"It looks fine, Dad."

Mum's at the hospital tonight. She always packs a picnic on the days when Timmy has his chemo: Cresta orangeade and cherry drops for his sore mouth, crust-free ham sandwiches cut into tiny triangles and a Fry's Turkish Delight, which is soft enough not to make his mouth ulcers sore. It all goes in a hamper, together with toothbrushes and toothpaste, and a bundle of fresh T-shirts and pants, in case Timmy's *poorly* later. Actually, Timmy's clothes are the only things that still get ironed.

After making the sandwiches, Mum nips to the newsagent for a new set of comics: the *Dandy*, the *Beano* and Timmy's violent favourite, *Warlord*. He's very fussy about the characters he likes: Korky the Cat is "spaz!" but Bomber Braddock and Roger the Dodger are "ace". Sometimes Mum also slips in the latest copy of *She* or *Woman's Own*.

"I don't know why you buy those things," Dad said this morning, when she came back from the corner shop, "the stories are always the same."

"I need to escape, Ted," she said.

"By reading about . . ." he picked up an old one, from a pile lying on the telephone table, "'My Bigamist Husband'? Or, hang on, 'My Holiday Romance Hell'?"

"It helps to read about people who've had horrible things happen. Makes me feel better, to know some people are worse off than us."

Dad flinched. "Except they're not, are they? Worse off than us? How much worse does it get than this, Lynda?"

My mother's eyes narrowed and I wasn't sure whether she was going to break down or lash out. After a few seconds, her shoulders dropped further than normal. "I suppose you haven't changed your mind. About coming with us to the hospital?"

It was Dad's turn to look away. "Regional managers' briefing. You know I would if I could."

"Do I? The regional managers, don't they have kids?"

"Yes, of course they do, but it's not done to mix business and family at the bank. You know what they're like."

"And I suppose you're still going to the dress rehearsal, too?"

Dad sighed. "Well, who else is going to play Henry? Cyril, who couldn't hear his cue if it was blasted into his lughole from a megaphone? And if I did come with you, who would look after Jo tonight?"

Mum looked up in surprise, as if she'd forgotten I was there in the kitchen. I pushed my Sugar Smacks around the bowl. Not my Peter Rabbit bowl of course. That was beyond repair after Timmy hurled it across the room. But at least he hasn't told them about the stockpile.

"Using one child to avoid your responsibilities to the other, Ted? I didn't think even you would stoop so low."

She left the room before she could hear Dad's whisper, "I learned all I know about that from you."

So tonight, Mum'll stay over at the hospital, tossing and turning on a put-me-up bed that must have put up hundreds of parents, but never given one a good night's sleep. Even Mum, the world's deepest sleeper, now has insomnia.

"Will you do my make-up for me, Bean?" My father reaches across to a small plastic box, and pulls out a tin of foundation the colour of boot polish. He hands me the tin and a dirty sponge, then moves two wooden chairs so they're facing each other. He wraps a stained peach towel around his neck and pats the chair opposite him. "Come on then."

I grind the sponge into the dried-out make-up, while Dad holds his salt-and-peppered fringe off his forehead. When he closes his eyes, little creases appear, running from the outside edges of his eyes to his hairline, but as he relaxes, they melt away. His skin is brown, though it's still May; he only has to go out in the garden for five minutes to catch the sun. Everything about his face is manly, square and solid: perfectly straight eyebrows, a long symmetrical nose, and plump lips. He's a looker, my father.

In the corner of the changing room, three of the old boys are practising their dance routine, humming "I'm Getting Married in the Morning". Luckily most of them were changed before I got there. If there's anything worse than Dad in his pants, it'd be them in theirs.

I begin on his cheeks, and as I press the sponge down, it emits a sour, flannel smell. Dad's nose

299

wrinkles, but he doesn't complain. He just takes another lozenge and sucks hard.

I step back to examine my handiwork. He's now as orange as Morph, but the colour hasn't disguised the purplish-grey tiredness under his eyes.

"Plaster it on, Jojo. The footlights will make me look like a dead body unless there's at least half an inch of the stuff on there."

Dead body. My hand stops halfway to his face.

Timmy's going to die. I know he is. He's so white now, that if we put him on stage, the footlights would shine through him, proving he's nothing but bones and organs linked by veins carrying poisoned blood. *Toxic Timmy the Leukaemia Lad*.

Dad opens his eyes. "I keep forgetting how hard this is on you," he says.

"I thought I was quite good at putting it on," I say, though I know he's not talking about the make-up.

"I'm not talking about the make-up. I know you and Timmy bicker, but it doesn't mean you don't love him. It's bound to be scary. And all the running backwards and forwards to the hospital, means me and your mum don't have much energy left for you."

And when *did* you have energy for me before? I want to ask, but now I'm twelve, I know that's too babyish a question. "It's OK, Dad," I say, reloading the sponge with make-up. He lets go of his fringe and reaches out to touch my hand.

"You know, we do love you every bit as much as we love Timmy, Bean. He needs us more right now, that's

300

all." He gulps. "Sorry, that sounded like a line from one of those slushy TV movies your mum likes."

I want to believe him. I even think that *he* thinks he means it. But I've got eight years of evidence, eight years of them putting my brother first. And what will happen if Timmy does die? Won't they wish it was me?

"Hey . . ." Dad's hand moves up to my cheek, and his thumb wipes away a tear that's welling in my left eye. "I know you're worried about him. Your mum's wrong when she says you don't seem bothered."

I can't tell him that the tears are for me, he mustn't know what a selfish daughter he has. Instead, I say, "Dad? Is Timmy going to be all right?"

He hesitates. "I think so, Jelly Bean, but I can't promise anything. Nobody knows anything for sure in this life, eh? All we can do is hope for the best and . . ." He looks away.

In my head, I finish his catchphrase, the one he suddenly realised he couldn't say out loud. *And prepare for the worst.* That's what *I'm* good at, and when the bombs are on their way, and I can finally put my plans into action, that's when they'll be proud of me.

"Hello Ted-eeee?" Charmaine's squeaking door-hinge of a voice could penetrate a lead-lined nuclear bunker, so the curtain is no barrier at all. "Are you decent?"

She doesn't wait for an answer: she pokes her head through a gap between two sheets, like a pushy child playing peek-a-boo. Her face is covered in stage make-up, her complexion so bright it looks as if all her freckles have joined up to make a giant rusty blob.

"Charm, I'm sure it's bad luck to see me beforehand," Dad says, all twinkly-eyed.

"No, silly, that's brides and grooms!" She laughs. "Hello, Joanna, sweetie. How are things?"

I ignore her, focusing on Dad's face. I grind more colour into the shadows under his eyes, but it makes no difference.

"Oh, you can't do it like that, Joanna, you'll rub his face off, hang on. Cover yourselves up, boys, I'm coming round!"

There's a wolf-whistle from Derek, the retired accountant who is playing Colonel Pickering, Dad's musical sidekick. I hear the click-clack of her heels on the parquet floor, and in moments, she's behind me. Her tiny hand darts over my shoulder to grab my sponge. I turn on her. "I'm doing *fine* thank you, *Mrs Craig.*"

Her costume is very low cut, with a black bodice, full green skirt, and a seal-grey crocheted shawl that makes her eyes look more steely than usual. Her red curls stand up several inches from her scalp, making her head look enormous and her body even smaller. I suppose if you were a man, you might think she was attractive.

"Doesn't look fine from here," she said. "It's uneven."

"Girls, girls," Dad protests, half-heartedly. "Much as I love being fought over, it's only the dress rehearsal."

Charmaine pouts. "Well, if she's done your foundation, let me finish you off."

Dad's wonderful eyebrows pop up and then down, as if he has no control over them. I will him to say no, to tell the daft tart that I'm doing OK, that she ought to concentrate on trying to look less freaky for curtain up.

"Bean, would that be all right? You've done a great job, love, but Charmaine has a few years more experience in the make-up department."

"Oi, Teddy! Not that many years," Charmaine says, not waiting for my answer and nudging me out of the way.

As she leans in to fluff up his hair, Dad gives me a resigned look and mouths, "sorry". I watch as she takes a lipstick out of her frilly toilet bag. "Pucker up," she says, and then giggles as she applies it to his lips: the brownish colour looks all wrong, as if he's appearing in *It Ain't Half Hot, Mum*. When she's finished, she whispers something in his ear and, before pulling away, brushes her own lips against his cheek.

"Just you wait, Henry Higgins," she says, when she finally tears herself away. Her lipstick is smudged.

My father waves weakly, as she disappears back behind the curtain. "How do I look, Bean?"

"You look the part . . . Wish Mum could see how hunky you are," I say, extra loud, so Charmaine gets the message: hands off my dad!

CHAPTER
TWENTY-FIVE

Dishabiliophobia — Fear of Undressing in Front of Someone

Friends are the new family, according to one of the magazines Mum keeps buying me. This doesn't make me feel any better about my life, as the article also said the average Briton has eighteen friends. I can count mine on the fingers of one hand.

The trouble is, scaredy-cats don't make friends easily. As children, we hide behind our mothers' skirts, frightened that the bolshier kids will decapitate our dolls. Doesn't change much when we reach adulthood.

Despite being my best friend, Lorraine's exactly the kind of girl who would happily dispatch my dolls to toy heaven, then still expect me to plait her hair next day. At parties, she's the one holding court in the corner, while I am putting crisps in bowls and comforting the obligatory weeping guest. I'm not a "must have" friend; I've lost touch with most of my classmates from Reading University. I lived at home then, so never really bonded, and I sometimes wonder if they're meeting up all the time, peering at the old photos and trying desperately to remember my name. "Was it Jane? Or Joan? The nervy one? I wonder what happened to her," they might say, in between trying on wedding dresses and patting each other's baby bumps.

But Lorraine is still here, and we're out to play for the first time since my accident. I'm relieved she didn't force me to go clubbing or pulling. Maybe she thought it wouldn't boost her chances tagging along with "Loon" (her current nickname of choice: since primary school there've been dozens, including Joey Deacon, Virgin, Hermit, Ostrich, Bungalow Bore and Super-Square — the last one sung rather than spoken, to the tune of *Wonder Woman*).

Instead of a wild night out, she's booked us into a day spa. She picked me up, N'Sync blaring and the sunroof open, to drive to a mock Tudor house built on a ley line near Glastonbury. The sign outside reads "Earth Customs" with "We Make Your Baggage Disappear" in smaller letters underneath. We've checked in, completing a hippie-dippy health question-naire that helps the staff decide whether we should go through the Green Channel ("nothing to declare") or the Red Channel ("where our customs will help you offload your stress, insomnia, irritable bowl, jittery skin and restless legs").

"Have you noticed," I ask, as we carry our hempseed slippers and unbleached cotton robes to the changing rooms, "that everyone else here is *pregnant*?"

"Oh terrific! I spend my entire working life with breeders, and I can't get away from them in my time off."

A woman with a tiny neat bump, as if she's eaten one holistic muffin too many, glares at her.

"Don't they have anything better to do than loaf around looking obscene?" Lorraine continues, as she strips off completely, revealing her perfectly trimmed runway of pubic hair, flat stomach and enhanced breasts. They're quite something, those boobs. I've seen them before, post-op when they were newly stuffed, but now the scars have healed completely and the twins bounce lightly as she moves around. They make me think of that song, "Like a Puppet on a String".

"Well, I suppose they don't, really," I reply, feeling quite shy at showing my pasty body. "They probably need distractions from the forthcoming bodily Armageddon."

"They're bloody everywhere," she says. "Not just here but on the street, in the supermarket. In the old days, pregnant women used to stay at home and wait."

Now, Lorraine has never been what you'd call the epitome of compassion. When she announced her decision to become a midwife, I didn't understand it at all, until she explained that she couldn't stand offices, needed endless excitement but was too thick to be a doctor, too weak to be a fireman and too short to be a policewoman (they've changed the rules now, of course, and I can't help thinking she'd be quite a hit with a truncheon). And she also hated old people and cheeky kids, so training as a general nurse wasn't an option.

Which left midwifery, "Healthy people, lots of drama, plus the kind of view that'll remind me why I'd rather die than hear the patter of tiny feet."

But this level of vitriol is new. "Seems a bit harsh," I say, and she shrugs, sending the boobs up and down, a movement that now reminds me of raised eyebrows.

We immerse ourselves in the overgrown wooden barrel that someone with a very vivid imagination has labelled "natural swimming pool", and after a few minutes' chit-chat about soap stars, she points at two more pregnant women. One is strapped into a navy blue school-style swimsuit that looks more like a punishment than swimwear; the other is confident enough to wear a bikini, her distended stomach forming a curved ledge for her breasts.

"Twenty-two hours, epidural, no stitches," she says, nodding towards the woman in the swimsuit. "And the other one is going to assume she'll sail through it, maybe with a bit of Indian head massage from some right-on *partner*. No chance. Caesarean."

I stared at her. "What?"

"Whenever I see a pregnant woman, I can't help predicting her labour."

"Ri-ight."

"Oh, don't look at me like that, Jo. It's hardly a major crime. I have a stressful job and if a little harmless speculation stops me taking out my frustration on my delightful patients, then that's a good thing, isn't it?"

"Well . . . I suppose so. But you never used to be like this."

"Like what?"

I examine my water-wrinkled fingers in close detail, as I try to work out how far I can afford to go without damaging our friendship. "I suppose you seem a bit . . . angry." I wait for her to lash out but she doesn't so I plough on. "And, kind of, *bitter*."

"Bitter?" The echoey room removes any expression from her voice. "Yeah. I suppose that's pretty fair."

"But why, Lorrie?" Even with her hair damp and her eye-shadow smudged by the steam, Lorraine looks better than anyone else in the whole spa. So she's gorgeous. She has a cool car. A small but immaculate flat with a Juliet balcony and a power shower. Endless men at her beck and call. OK, she has a love-hate relationship with her job, but at least as long as babies are being born, she'll never be unemployed. And in the event of worsening international relations, her place in a nuclear fall-out shelter is guaranteed.

She sighs. "I can't believe it myself but I've realised I want one."

"One what?"

"A bloody baby." She looks distraught. "And not just a baby, but a bloody husband too. Can you believe it? Me?"

I don't know what to say. For as long as I've known her, she's insisted a baby would be "about as welcome as a sexually transmitted disease, thank you very much. Which, when you think about it, is not a bad definition of pregnancy."

"So what's changed your mind?"

She shakes her head. "Not a clue. It's definitely not being a witness to the miracle of birth day after day."

"No. I bet it's not. So . . . what are you going to do about it?"

"Find myself a man, I suppose."

I laugh so loud that Bikini Bump woman looks up from her copy of *Baby Makes Glee: Preparing for your Precious Bundle*. "Well, Lorrie, that's hardly going to be a big challenge for you, is it?"

She frowns. "It's one thing pulling a man for gratuitous sex. Quite another finding a keeper. I've never shown any talent in that direction." Unlike her four elder sisters, all married off, with a clutch of little ones. I always wondered whether the reason Lorraine was so loud at school was because no one ever listened to her at home.

"Only because you didn't want security till now. You need to refine your targets."

"How do you know I haven't been doing that?" she says. "I might have been out hubby-hunting already for all you know."

"Have you?"

Lorraine sighs again. "Let's just say, I wouldn't bother buying your bridesmaid's dress yet."

"Oh, but Lorrie, you're probably looking in the wrong place. A nightclub isn't exactly ideal territory for keepers." It's a novelty to be the one offering advice.

"Right. And where is, then? Work, I suppose, like you and Dennis? The only men I meet are fathers-to-be, married hospital porters and married consultant obstetricians. Not prime candidates for Mr Right." This time there's no mistaking the sourness in her voice.

"But don't you think you'd be bored with a steady bloke? I mean, look at Dennis. As steady as they come. And he'd drive you crazy, wouldn't he?" I try to lighten the rapidly darkening mood.

But she doesn't laugh. Instead she slaps the water, and the way she does it, I have a strong suspicion it's me she really wants to slap. "I said to you before, you're not being fair to Dennis. He's a perfectly good boyfriend."

"Perfectly good. Yeah. Perfectly good for a loon, that's what you mean, isn't it?"

"Oh, pur-lease. Turning it round to yourself, again. Because none of us can compete with a coma, can we? You need to get over it, Jo. I dunno, get back to work, do something to distract yourself from being self-obsessed." She gives me a false smile. "Or maybe you and Dennis should have a *baby*."

And she pushes herself out of the pool and slops towards the changing rooms, her swimming costume leaking water and her footsteps leaking irritation. I sit in the pool on my own (it's not big enough for me *plus* a pregnant woman) and try to make sense of it all. A baby? Me? Poor thing would grow up frightened of its own shadow.

But I suppose she has got a point about the self-obsession. Before the flashbacks, I'd have protested like crazy at the idea that I was a spoiled brat, but now I can see that the "tragedy" of my childhood wasn't parents who ignored me, but my own fixations and inability to relate to the real world. Unless . . .

Unless my crazes were my only way of blocking out reality: Timmy's illness, Dad's constant stream of women, Lorraine's relentless teasing, none of which I had a hope of controlling. In the midst of all that chaos, the twelve-year-old Joanna Morgan only ever seems ahead of the game when she's planning for the nuclear holocaust. It gave me a sense of purpose, however warped.

I shake my head and wet hair slaps my neck. That's crazy. I was just suggestible. Mr Blake has a lot to answer for.

Lorraine and I meet again at lunchtime. We chomp our way through organic bean salads and moon-harvested vegetables without mentioning our spat. We sip tea that promises to restore our equilibrium and chat about our forthcoming treatments. But I know neither of us have forgotten it.

That article of Mum's said that four-fifths of female friendships end due to rivalry or jealousy, and while I'm being inexpertly manicured by a teenage beautician, I wonder if that's what'll happen with Lorrie and me. Friendship depends on the preservation of the status quo. Which isn't a problem, normally, because how many of us really change once we've reached adulthood?

But just occasionally something happens that can't help but upset the status quo, change you for good.

That's when you really know who your friends are.

CHAPTER
TWENTY-SIX

Illyngophobia — Fear of Vertigo

I'm in trouble again. First of all, Dennis discovered my squirrel feeding. Then the new edition of *Civil Protection Chronicle* arrived this morning, with a fascinating snippet on the diary page:

Courtbridge Council Deputy DPPCD Dennis Diffley seems set to attract the wrath of the nation's bakers with his new campaign, if an email sent to the Diary is to be believed. Diffley, 40, is apparently deeply concerned about the hazard represented by cakes and scones, responsible for 493 injuries a year. The email suggests "it's only a matter of time before Dennis launches 'Courtbridge Against Cakes', the nation's first campaign against baked-goods-related accidents". And though it's possible that it's a joke, the fact that the email's author is none other than Diffley's live-in partner suggests there could be more than an element of truth there. Standby for the backlash campaign. May we suggest "Save Our Scones" as a slogan?

★ ★ ★

Bloody Mikey must have forwarded the email to the magazine. Dennis, predictably, fails to see the funny side.

"Oh, well done, Jo. Now I'm a nationwide laughing stock."

My chest hurts from suppressing my giggles but I know I daren't let them out. "But anyone who knows you will know it's a joke. And isn't all publicity good publicity?"

"No, it isn't. And supreme timing, as well, what with —" and then he stops, mid-sentence.

"With what?" I ask, hoping he'll leave soon so I can go into the bathroom to laugh myself silly.

"Oh, nothing," he snaps. "I'd better go to work and get the worst over with. I'll be late tonight. Meeting in the Midlands. Safety thing. You know."

After a truly satisfying fit of the giggles, I pick up the phone to share the joke with Lorraine, but then realise that it'll probably only result in another lecture about Dennis being a paragon. And calling Mikey at work is too risky. Not to mention rather disloyal.

I potter about a bit before deciding I need to do something. Mum's busy sussing out possible studs she's found on the internet for Beatrice, her youngest Maine Coon cat (even though Timmy thinks it smacks of eugenics), and the prospect of a day with only squirrels for company makes me edgy. Actually, I feel edgy all the time at the moment, a kind of restlessness that reminds me of the time before I took my finals, or moved in with Dennis. Except I have nothing to be

313

nervous or excited about. And no idea how to spend my day.

Frisky! I bet he'd appreciate some company, and perhaps I could offer to run an errand or two. The perfect way to make myself useful. Ha! Now who's self-obsessed, eh, Lorrie?

I leave the house before I have time for second thoughts, strolling along Salzburg Avenue, making more of an effort to notice my surroundings. It's the last day of May and the skeletal trees that greeted me when I arrived home from hospital have filled out nicely with plump leaves. In the distance, I see the mega-fit pensioner who lives opposite jogging ahead of me, with her fatter sister. They're both clad in yellow Lycra, like resting actors hired by a supermarket to promote the health benefits of bananas, and they slow down as I approach. Usually I'd ignore them, but the new self-improving Jo greets them with an open smile.

"Hello dear," the fitter one says. "Out for a constitutional?"

"Something like that," I say, nodding manically. "And you two?"

"I've been persuaded to take up running," the fatter one says, sweating and out of breath. "She says my love handles have turned into love mountains." She giggles between puffs.

"Right," I say, trying to avoid looking at the rippling flesh under her bodysuit.

"And how are you *feeling*?" asks Fitter, in a voice which instantly tells me that she *knows*, although we've never spoken before.

314

"Better, thank you." Now doesn't seem the right time to confide my recent realisation that my entire life is a void and I'm in desperate need of something to fill it.

"We came round the day after you came back from hospital, to ask if there was anything we could do, but your partner said everything was taken care of."

"Right," I say. Dennis never mentioned that. But then he has a pathological hatred of prying neighbours, after social services kept turning up on his mum's doorstep in response to anonymous tip-offs of neglect. "He likes to keep himself to himself."

"Oh, don't worry. Nothing worse than curtain-twitchers. We know what *that's* like," Fatter adds, nudging her sister. "When we first moved in, oh, we couldn't leave the house without some nosy parker coming over to offer cups of sugar, when they clearly only had one thing they really wanted to know."

Fitter laughs, a meatier sound than Fatter's girly giggle. "Yes, we wouldn't have minded if they'd asked us outright, 'are you a pair of dykes'?"

I look from Fitter to Fatter and back again. Come to think of it, they look nothing like sisters. "Are you, then?"

"Oh, *bless* her," Fatter says. "You hadn't realised, had you?"

"I suppose I didn't expect anything . . . um . . . *unorthodox* on Salzburg Avenue."

Fitter grins at me. "So I suppose you didn't know that your next-door neighbour has a sideline as an escort?"

315

"What? Mrs Cronin with the flowery washing-up gloves?"

"Uh-huh." She nods. "With a specialism in rubber. And then you know Mr Davies at number six has been in the local paper with his prize-winning marrows?"

"Not quite as shocking," I say.

"No, but not all the contents of his greenhouse are what you'd exhibit at the Courtbridge Horticultural Show."

Fatter giggles again. "Yes. Though his other *produce* should win prizes. I'm sure he'd be happy to offer you a sample if you need help relaxing."

"Camomile?"

She shakes her head. "No. Cannabis."

I try to imagine what Dennis would say if he came home to find me halfway through a joint. And God only knows what effect the stuff would have on my flashbacks. "I think I'll stick to coffee, thanks."

"Fair enough," Fitter says, "but do remember, if you ever want some company — and either coffee or something stronger, you know where we are." She punches Fatter lightly on the arm. "Now no more gossip for you, madam. You're not going to get a beach body standing at the street corner yacking, are you?"

They trot off, waving as they go. I look back at the cul-de-sac: Salzburg Avenue seems a very different place now. How stupid of me to judge it on appearances. I could have made an effort, talked to Mrs Cronin across the fence, asked Mr Davies for gardening tips, gone jogging with Fitter and Fatter. Instead I battened down the hatches and let my suspicions about the rest of the world grow . . .

Still, maybe it's not too late to learn to look outside instead of in.

By the time I get to Frisky's, my face is the colour of chewed cherry Hubba-Bubba. My hair is damp with sweat. My breath smells like feet because I forgot to brush my teeth before leaving. And I am ravenously hungry.

If it hadn't taken me over an hour to get here, I'd turn around now. I started the journey hoping that perhaps Luke would be at home. With my new-found curiosity about other people, I was determined to discover more about him.

But now I really don't want Luke to see me like this. It's bad enough that I "fainted" in the back of the car after the Fisherman's Friend incident, without greeting him on his own doorstep looking like a bag lady.

I ring the doorbell. After a few seconds, there's movement behind the frosted glass panel in the door. The figure seems too sprightly to be the lugubrious Luke and, sure enough, it's Frisky who opens the door. He beams when he sees it's me, but then his face changes.

"Good God, Joanna. What the blazes happened to you?" He ushers me inside.

"I . . ." I'm about to tell him my new plan, but then I stop. It does seem rather patronising, offering to run errands for a man with more va-va-voom in his little toe than I have in my entire body. "I'm absolutely fine, just thought it would be a nice day for a walk."

He frowns. "Really? I mean, it's lovely to see you, but you look a little . . . how should I put this . . . dishabille?"

"A mess, you mean?"

"That's another way of putting it. No matter. Why don't you *freshen up*?" He leads me up the stairs, with bare treads and stripped ornate balustrade. I wonder what state the bathroom's in: two men together won't have made cleaning their top priority.

He pushes open the rough pine door. "Use whatever you like, Joanna. Fresh towels in the airing cupboard. And shall I toast you some nice teacakes? I always find they're just what the doctor ordered when I . . . ahem . . . am feeling absolutely fine."

My mouth waters. "Yes, please, Frisky."

The bathroom is not what I expected at all. The suite is old, but it's *properly* old, chunky and manly. The toilet has a heavy chain and porcelain pull, the bath taps have spouts as wide as my wrist, and every surface shines. Including the speckled mirror.

Shit. I look worse than I thought. Circles under my eyes so dark you'd think my mascara had run, and sweaty hair drying in uneven clumps. Not so much dragged through a hedge backwards, as dragged upside down, backwards and forwards, from Greenham Common to Savernake Forest. On a more than averagely drizzly day.

Oh, and look at my fuzzy patch. It's now two-tone, red on the top, with pure white growing through, like Santa's fur-lined cloak.

Inside the cupboard, a dozen navy towels are stacked neatly next to a hot water cylinder that's taller than I am. I take one, then inspect the contents of the oak cabinet above the basin.

The top shelf is straight from a 1950s' chemist: royal blue glass jars full of obscure tinctures, a pot of Vaseline, a big bottle of Original Listerine, six creamy squares of Imperial Leather soap, a large natural sponge and a pumice stone.

The bottom shelf tells a different story: expensively packaged vitamins promising better immunity (and possibly eternal life), hair gel, individually packaged eye drops and male moisturiser. At the back there's a black metallic bottle of aftershave so trendy that it doesn't have a name. I take the top off and spray some into the air, then sniff.

A longing so powerful it makes my legs feel wobbly, takes my body hostage. Then, almost as quickly, the scent evaporates.

I think that aftershave might belong to Luke . . .

When I look into the mirror again, my reflection is slightly less scary: colour has appeared in my cheeks to counter-balance the black circles under my eyes. I dig my fingers into the male moisturiser, which seems a lot like female moisturiser but with macho blue colouring, and it sinks into my thirsty skin. The hair gel makes my fringe look quirky rather than greasy, and the eye drops restore a little sparkle. I round it off by gargling with Listerine. I don't look glamorous, but more importantly, I no longer look scary.

The spicy smell of teacakes wafts towards me as I walk downstairs. I find Frisky in the kitchen. He wasn't expecting company, but he's perfectly turned out: starched blue shirt, belt with polished buckle, tweedy trousers that emphasise how slight he is. His presence is so imposing that I always imagine him as a giant, but as he moves, the bottoms of his trousers ride up, revealing old men's ankles, gnarled from sun and walking.

"Now that's a transformation, Joanna," he says, kissing me on the cheek. "I don't know how you women do it, but golly, it's nice when you do! Come on through."

The table in the conservatory is beautifully laid: tablecloth, huge hotel plates and the kind of posh silver cutlery that always feels too big for my hands. There are toasted teacakes, plus thick toast in a wire rack, bright yellow butter in a pottery dish, and jars of Marmite, Tiptree Little Scarlet strawberry jam, Seville marmalade, and clover honey, with the comb submerged like a sticky shipwreck. Plus a pot of coffee and a crystal jug of orange juice.

"Juice from a carton, I'm afraid," he says. "If I'd known you were coming . . ."

"It's fine. No, it's five star, Frisky. I can't believe you'd go to this much trouble." My stomach gurgles in anticipation. "Unless you're expecting Luke for breakfast too?"

He gives me a curious look. "Ah, no. The grandson is otherwise occupied. Why? Hoping to see him, were we?"

320

I shake my head a little too eagerly. "Oh, no, I'm enjoying spending time with you, keeping my fingers crossed he wouldn't turn up. He can be . . . temperamental," I add, hoping Frisky will fill in some of the gaps.

"Well, I dare say I'm not the easiest person to live with either," Frisky admits. "But he's a good boy, really, considering . . ." And he leaves the sentence unfinished, so that Luke seems more mysterious than before. Eventually, he pours the coffee. "So this is all ours, Joanna. Sometimes we all need a little TLC. Toast, love and coffee. Now don't let it go cold."

I take a first, satisfying bite. Fantastic. Frisky peers contemplatively into his cup of coffee as I demolish the bread and teacakes, munching noisily, with the occasional *mmmm* for good measure. Finally I push the plate away from me, proud to have left one last quarter of toast in the rack.

"Better?" Frisky asks.

"Much." Though the pleasure fades as I remember I was meant to be looking after Frisky, rather than the other way around.

"You don't have to tell me, Joanna. Whatever it is." He tops up my coffee for me. "I'm very happy to keep secrets, of course, but I'm equally happy to accept this as a nice, spontaneous visit from a friend."

A *friend* . . . I feel warmer, suddenly. It's all so simple. "Let's just say I am feeling a bit inconsequential."

"Oh dear. The old, 'What am I doing here? What's the point?' state of mind, eh?"

"Yeah, that's the one. It's not the fact that life's been passing me by. It's the fact that for so long, I didn't notice."

"You've noticed now. That's the main thing. So, what are we going to do to help you kick the 'woe is me' feeling?"

I sigh. "Thanks, but I think it's down to *me* on my own, isn't it? I've spent enough time navel-gazing and not nearly enough time *doing*. Isn't there something I could do for you for a change, maybe something round the house?"

He takes the final piece of toast and spreads it with the thinnest scraping of butter. "I'd *never* ask a guest to do chores . . . but let me think. Ah! How's your decorating?"

I shrug. "Never done it."

"Perfect. A challenge for you — and a freshly painted room for me. Prepare yourself for a brush with interior design, Joanna. That'll sort you out. Nothing like decorating when you feel a bit so what-ish. Just what you need."

I smile as graciously as I can. I did ask, after all, but why is it that everyone — from Lorraine to Mum to Dennis to Frisky — knows what I need? Can't I be allowed to work it out myself? The difference today is that I believe only Frisky has my best interests at heart.

We buy paint at the DIY store near the hospital. I've never been to a DIY store before: always had a dad to buy nails, a landlord to fix blocked U-bends, or Dennis to stock up on lawn food. It's Pensioner Discount Day

322

today, so I'm surrounded by wrinkly couples, and balding builders. The skyscraper aisles make me light-headed but everyone else is unfazed.

When Frisky asks me to choose the paint, the selection is mind-boggling: rows of pure brilliant white fill two aisles, and there's an entire section devoted to "hints of" blueberry and lime blossom and toffee. Probably beetroot and spring onion and Heinz ketchup too, for all I know.

Silenced by choice, I point at an inoffensive cream.

"Oh, Joanna! Magnolia?" Frisky's voice is teasing. "All the colours of the rainbow, and this is what you choose?" But he takes out a calculator and does some sums before loading four vats of magnolia into our trolley. In the long queue, I don't recognise most of the things in people's baskets: lengths of plastic *stuff*, tubes of specialist solvent, and boxes of fish, blood and bone, which my mother would probably make into a nutritious milkshake to "build up my strength".

Back at the house, he finds me an old pyjama top which would look charming on Gwyneth Paltrow, but makes me look like an inmate of a secure hospital. An elastic band holds my hair out of my eyes, while Frisky looks ready for action in pristine blue overalls. "Ready to see the Herculean nature of our task?" He leads me into the front room. "I'll fetch dust-sheets."

At first, I only see the room's scale — newly plastered walls double my height, and the floor-to-ceiling bay window that looks even bigger from the inside than it does from the street. Then I begin to notice details. The ceiling rose, the coving, the picture rails and . . . oh, that fireplace. A masterpiece in grey-veined marble, dominating the space.

Was this a room designed to impress visitors? I imagine a Victorian patriarch pacing the floor (a rather sorry-looking set of bare boards now, but in its heyday, perhaps adorned with exotic rugs shipped from the "colonies"), waiting for vital news in a new-fangled telegram. Or, later, perhaps a group of chic flappers downing absinthe from sugar-heaped teaspoons and sighing over the futility of love.

Frisky comes in, a pile of old sheets in his arms. "What do you think?"

"It's a wonderful room. But, Frisky, I might mess it up. The last time I painted anything was a bunch of flowers at primary school. And no one could tell what they were."

"Luckily, painting a room requires no artistic ability whatsoever. There's an old expression, 'if you can piss, you can paint'. Excuse the vulgarity." He lays out the dust-sheets, stained with splats of old paint. "Anyway I need your help because I am *banned* from stepladders on account of the old vertigo."

Frisky admitting to weakness — whatever next? It does the trick, though, because I feel useful for the first time in months. He leaves the room again and returns with brushes, rollers and a plastic tray. He shows me how to load the roller — "better too little than too much, but you'll find that out soon enough" — and explains when to use the brush — "for the fiddly bits, the skirting-boards and so on".

I take my roller and sink its woolly coating into the paint tray. When I lift it again, it's twice as heavy. I stalk my patch of wall, raising my roller arm tentatively, but before it makes contact, a cold slick of paint drips down my wrist, past the sleeve of my pyjamas.

"Euch." I swat at it, feeling the paint soaking into the fabric.

"Ah. I forgot that bit," Frisky confesses. "The bit about speed being of the essence if you don't want to end up painting yourself."

"Now you tell me." I try again, this time moving the roller so fast it sends a splatter of cream spots across the bare wall. "Shit."

"The beauty of painting is you can cover up your mistakes," Frisky says.

Finally I make contact, drawing the roller across the smooth beige plaster. I keep walking, pulling the paint along the wall in fascination, like an Andrex puppy dragging a loo roll through the house. By the time the paint's wearing thin, the stripe stretches halfway to the window. "Ooh. I've done it."

"Great! But you will need to go over it a few times more. Build up a rhythm!" He disappears back into the hall, reappearing with a stepladder and a radio. A thunderous beat comes from the speakers.

"Not rap again, Frisky."

"Spoilsport." He retunes to a rock station, playing a track I don't recognise but I'm sure Luke would love, by Bon Jovi. "This'll work for painting. Follow the beat . . . one . . . and a-two . . . and a-three . . ."

★ ★ ★

"Time for a breather." Frisky is right behind me.

I'd forgotten anyone else was here. I've been up the ladder (trying not to dwell on the fact that fifty Britons die every year from falling off ladders, and another 200,000 accidents are caused by DIY), while Frisky works on everything below the picture rail. I felt faint at first, but then I became so absorbed that after a while I couldn't hear the music: all that mattered was avoiding streaks and lumpy bits, making the paint as even as possible, focusing on the area nearest me.

"Now shut your eyes," Frisky says, "I'll keep hold of the steps. There's nothing like an aerial view."

I do as I'm told. "It's like one of those TV makeover shows, except they usually wait till everything's finished."

"Go on then. Open 'em."

I hesitate, then go for it. "Oh. OH! It *is* finished. I hadn't realised."

One coat of magnolia and it's a different room. There's hardly any sunlight now, yet everything looks brighter, fresher. *My* walls seem flawless, though my first attempts were all over the place.

"Wait there," Frisky tells me. Standing still, I notice how achy my arms and legs feel, how my shoulder feels sore. But the euphoria is much stronger: today I've actually *achieved* something, made a difference.

"Ta-da . . ." Frisky comes back with two glasses of amber-coloured wine, and a biscuit barrel. "Time to celebrate."

"Bit early for me."

"It's ten past six, Joanna. Sun's definitely over the yard-arm and besides, we've been working for five hours. You deserve it."

"Five *hours*?" I reach out for my glass, trying to ignore my conscience. Poor Dennis must be worried.

"Ah, hold your horses, Joanna. A finishing touch is called for." He reaches into a pocket of his overalls, and pulls out a thin brush and tiny tin of model paint. "I know it's silly, but I always like to sign a room when I've finished." He helps me down from the ladder, holding my hand. He flips the lid off the tin, revealing shimmering gold paint. "On the far side of the chimney breast should be safe, Luke wouldn't approve."

"He's bound to see it in the end, though, surely?"

"I usually cover it with a second coat. But I know it's there, and I like to think of people in years to come, stripping back the paint and wondering who I was." He bends down and paints "Frisky" in curly gold letters. "Your turn."

I reach out and write "Joanna" half an inch above the skirting-board.

"One last thing," he says, taking the brush back and painting a tiny golden fish below our names. "This is for luck."

"Where is Lucky the goldfish by the way?" I ask, as we sit down on a dust-sheet and toast our achievement with wine and chocolate chip cookies.

"Ah, Luke keeps him in the caravan, in case of break-ins."

"Right. How . . . unusual. Frisky, what do you think Luke will think? He won't be annoyed we've gone ahead while he's away?"

"He's got bigger things to worry about than the colour of the parlour walls, Joanna."

I stare at him, not wanting to sound too eager to know what the "bigger things" might be. "It's none of my business, of course."

Frisky seems to be thinking it over. "He's a terribly private sort, but I think as you're spending time with us, you ought to know the facts. It's his parents. My daughter, and her American husband. They died, you see, five years ago. Very suddenly."

"Oh. I see." I feel sick. And ashamed of myself for being nosy. "You must have been devastated, too. I'm so sorry."

He gazes into the distance. It's almost as if he's trying to remove himself from here, from pain. "Thank you, Joanna. It was very shocking, but then being an old man brings a certain familiarity with death. Whereas Luke . . . well, as an only child, I think he's struggling with being alone in the world."

I wonder where Luke is. How do you get over losing both parents? That must be why he left America, but spending time with his grandfather doesn't seem to be any comfort. They should be united in grief, but all they do is bicker. "I . . . I suppose it ought to help the two of you, being together," I say eventually.

"Yes," he says, "it ought to." And there's so much pain in his voice now that it seems to expand to fill the room. "Golly, I can't believe I'm burdening you with

328

this, Joanna. One has to try to move on. Let's drink to more cheerful times, my dear. To progress." We clink glasses.

"Progress. And paint!"

He smiles. "Ah yes. Now, about paint. Lovely job you've done, but before you get going, you *might* like to take a little peep in the bathroom mirror."

"OH MY GOD!"

"It's not *that* bad," Frisky soothes. "Although admittedly, it is something of a mystery that we had enough to finish the walls, when you got quite so much on yourself."

There is paint *everywhere*. Streaked across my fringe like the highlighting efforts of an unsupervised salon junior, splodged across my forehead, cheeks and chin like a drunken clown, across my hands and under my fingernails like a French manicure gone awry. On the plus side, my white fuzzy patch is very effectively camouflaged.

"How do I get it off?"

"Ah . . . well, the thing is that paint seems to stick to skin more effectively than it sticks to walls. Mind you, at least this is only emulsion. Gloss is practically indelible."

"So?"

"After years of experimentation, I've concluded that the only way to remove paint from hair and skin is with a nailbrush, soap and a heck of a lot of elbow grease." He reaches into the bathroom cabinet. "Here are the

first two. The last one you'll need to supply yourself."
And he leaves me to it.

I unwrap the soap from its cardboard casing: a
brand-new cake from Frisky's stock of Imperial
Leather. I run the hot tap, and the ancient boiler
supplies steaming water. I start with my hands and
wrists, scrubbing with the nailbrush until the skin is
pink but the paint itself holding firm.

I decide to change tactics. I fill the basin with water
as hot as I can bear, then rub the soap between my
hands, until the water turns opaque like Pernod. I duck
down, to splash my face with water, in preparation for
the Great Scrub. I'd forgotten how well this soap
lathers up. My father used it for shaving and Timmy
and I would stand in the bathroom, watching him
turning himself into Father Christmas with his foamy
beard, then slicing through the froth, turning back into
Daddy again. One of the few unambiguously happy
memories of my childhood.

But if it's so happy, why does that clean smell,
tickling up my nose, make me feel lost? Why am I
feeling dizzy, even though I'm gripping the basin?

Oh bloody hell. This is the last thing I . . .

CHAPTER
TWENTY-SEVEN

Xyrophobia — Fear of Razors

"But why doesn't it make your skin bleed?"

I tut at my brother's stupid question, although it's something I've often wondered myself. If a razor-blade is sharp enough to slice through Dad's spiky stubble and reduce it to iron filings in the basin, why doesn't it cut his skin to ribbons?

My father turns round to look at us, his chin striped foam-white and tan, like the lawn when he's halfway through mowing it.

"That, young Master Morgan, is a very good question," he says, dipping his blade in the soapy water, "but one, sadly, I cannot answer." Dad's been speaking like Lady Marjorie from *Upstairs, Downstairs* ever since he brought the house down with his performance as Professor Henry Higgins.

The *Newbury Weekly News*, as he keeps reminding us, pronounced that "Ted Morgan could give Rex Harrison a run for his money." He doesn't repeat the next bit though, the part where the reviewer said Charmaine's cockney accent was inconsistent, but her performance was saved by the obvious *chemistry* between the two central characters. When Timmy asked how you could tell if people had chemistry, I thought Dad might snap at him, but no. My brother can officially get away with anything these days.

"But Timmy's wrong, because the razor does cut you sometimes, Dad, doesn't it?" I chip in. "And you have to use pieces of toilet paper so you don't bleed."

"Another good observation, Bean. The risk of skin damage is considerably reduced by the application of a generous lather. But quite why that is I have no —"

"Where ARE they? Where the bloody hell ARE they?"

My mother enters the bathroom shrieking, and pushes my father out of the way. She flings open the medicine cabinet, attacking the shelves and sending brown bottles and packets of Elastoplast plopping into Dad's shaving water.

"Lynda. Will you calm down? What are you looking for?"

She moves away from the cabinet and the soapy soup of medicines: it looks like the sea after a shipwreck. "My pills. I can't find my pills." Her eyes are glazed, she doesn't seem to recognise us.

"And they're not in the bedside drawer?"

She shakes her head and begins to cry. I'm used to Mum crying, but the tears are falling faster and faster, like she's lost control of her eye muscles. Dad looks at Timmy and me. "Jo, take your brother to play downstairs will you, while I look for Mum's tablets?"

332

Dad pleads with his eyes. His face is still half-covered in foam. "Come on then, Timmy." My brother is staring at our mother, and resists my attempts to pull him away. If I hold on too tight, within minutes the shape of my hand will appear as a bruise on his skin.

"Go on, mate," Dad says, snapping out of Henry Higgins mode and doing his best to sound reassuring. "Nothing to worry about. Mummy's just . . ."

And he stops and I wait for the familiar excuses. "Mummy's just tired . . . Mummy's just not feeling well . . . Mummy's just a bit dizzy and needs to lie down."

But he doesn't say anything at all and now his eyes look weirder than Mum's. Eventually he says, "Do as you're told, please, Timmy."

Without any more persuasion, my brother leaves the bathroom and I follow him. Mummy isn't tired or dizzy or poorly. She's crazy. I want to live with Lorraine and her sisters. Never mind the chaos and the mess and Lorraine's mum's varicose veins and gristly casseroles and hand-knitted beige cardigans that make you itch just to look at them. Her house smells the way a home ought to — of garlic and Tweed by Lentheric.

I switch the TV on and promise Timmy a Nesquik if he sits quietly and does a jigsaw. He doesn't protest. The illness means he's sleepy most of the time. At first I preferred him sleepy, but it seems all wrong. I almost miss the old Timmy.

I can hear thumping and crashing and raised voices from upstairs, as they hunt for the tablets. I asked Dad about them once and he said they keep Mum happy but I said I didn't think she seemed all that happy and he smiled the way Arthur Daley does in *Minder* when Terry's caught him up to no good. Then Dad said, "You don't remember how she was before."

I mix up the Nesquik — a scoop of banana from one carton, and a scoop of chocolate from the other — and stir in the milk splosh by splosh, like Dad does. I open the serving hatch and Timmy's watching *Tiswas*, which Mum hates because it's so noisy (and Dad loves because of that girl Sally with the dark hair).

I close the hatch. Maybe now could be a good time to add to my stockpile.

The more my parents worry about Timmy, the more I can save. I could have a battalion of Russian spies hiding in my bedroom and no one would notice. On the downside, no one gets time to go to Sainsbury's, so the cupboards are nearly empty and there's not much choice.

So far, the space under my bed contains:

A copy of my "bible", *Protect and Survive*, which I bought for 50p from the council offices during a school trip. If there is an impending threat of war, the booklet will be given away for free, but then I read somewhere else that it'd take four weeks to print enough copies, and I don't hold out much hope of getting hold of supplies once everyone's in a state of panic. Lucky for Mum, Dad and Timmy (and Misty) that I'm prepared.

Cutlery: a knife, fork and spoon. The booklet says "cutlery, crockery, tin-opener, bottle-opener" and doesn't specify whether every member of the family needs their own, but I guess we can take it in turns and

I daren't take more than one set. I also don't really understand the bottle-opener thing as we are going to be short of space, but maybe the government thinks grown-ups need beer or wine to cheer them up. It *will* get pretty boring sitting in the inner refuge for fourteen days, until the fall-out subsides. Kids are allowed magazines and favourite toys, so maybe wine is the adult equivalent.

A torch (nicked from the garage), candles, matches and a radio with spare set of batteries. My old wind-up Sindy alarm clock and a calendar. I think the idea behind the calendar is that if the radio breaks, you can tick off the days. I look at the calendar. July already. I wonder if we'll make it to the end of 1982 without war starting.

Sometimes it doesn't seem very likely.

I've also hidden tissues, loads of carrier-bags, two stolen toilet rolls, and a notebook and pen "for messages" (are we meant to get Rover to deliver them to the outside world?). I'm collecting plasters and aspirin from the bathroom cabinet, though Mum's raid this morning is a set-back.

There are lots of things I can't hide under the bed, even if Mum and Dad never go in there, e.g. two bins (one for our *toilet* waste — yuk — and one for rubbish), sleeping bags, thick clothes, wellies so you don't get fall-out on your socks, a spade (as if we're going to do some gardening to take our mind off Armageddon), a lavatory improvised from an old dining chair and a bucket, and containers for the two pints of water we each need to drink every day.

So for now I'm focusing on food. The government says every person aged over five needs six pounds of biscuits or cereals, four and a half pounds of canned meat or fish (e.g. pilchards, I've got some under my bed but I can't imagine eating them if they were the last food on earth so I've been buying Spam with my pocket money), four pounds of canned vegetables, a pound of butter or peanut butter, a pound of jam or honey, six cans of soup, tea and coffee, a pound of sweets, a pound and a half of sugar, and *fourteen* cans of evaporated milk.

This is meant to cost £15 per person, i.e. thirty weeks' worth of pocket money times four, which means either I need to get a paper round, hope that the bombs don't drop before I am fourteen (might have kissed a boy by then, too), or improvise. The canned veg has been a doddle: having tasted cold carrots, cold peas and cold baked beans, it's got to be Heinz every time. Dad's going to fart whatever we eat, after all.

I've been eating everything cold, not that anyone's noticed. The Pot Noodles were a mistake. I tried them on their own, and the noodles were like chewing fingernails, and the powder caught in my throat and made me choke. I added cold water — there won't be any hot in the inner refuge — and it was no better. The water went a rusty colour, but the flavouring sat on the surface, crusting like a spot. I flushed the liquid down the loo, and buried the carton and the still-rigid noodles at the bottom of the kitchen bin.

The Nesquik would be good in the shelter, so I transfer enough of the banana powder into the chocolate carton. *That'll cheer Timmy up*. But then I stop: cheer him up, when we're crammed into a space no bigger than a tent, waiting for the all-clear? Cheer him up when we get ill and we can't tell whether it's the awful food or radiation sickness? Cheer him up if one of us doesn't get home in time when the four-minute warning goes? Or if poor Misty panics and makes a run for it, out into ruined Greenham Lane?

I feel tears stinging in my eyes. I can't think like that. Because what else can I do but try to save our lives? The alternative is to bury my head in the sand like Mum and Dad and every other adult I've ever met except Mr Blake. But even Mr Blake's moved on from war . . . we're doing the New Ice Age at the moment, with Test Tube Babies to follow.

I take a carrier-bag from under the sink, and fill it with the Nesquik container, a couple of dusty tins of beans from the back of the larder, a small bottle of disinfectant, and a tea towel. Before I sneak it upstairs I take my brother's drink into the living-room.

"Here's your favourite, Timmy . . . *Timmy?*"

The TV's still on — a child dressed in full school uniform is about to get covered in pink gunk by Suggs from Madness — but there's only a Timmy-shaped dent in the sofa cushion where my brother should be. "Timmy?" I raise my voice, but not enough that they'll hear me upstairs. Misty bounds in, ears pricked and hoping I actually said, "walkies".

I peer through the French doors into the garden, but there's no sign. He's probably gone upstairs. That's it. Gone to look for Mummy.

But when I go into the hall to follow him upstairs, I see something frightening. The front door is open: not wide, but as if whoever left went quietly, without shutting the door, in case someone heard it slam.

"Dad . . ." I call out but my voice is small. I run up the stairs, two at a time, and find my parents in their bedroom. There's a pile of pill bottles on the duvet and Mum is still crying, mewing like a kitten. They look up at me, as if they'd forgotten they had a daughter.

"I can't find . . . The front door. I mean, Timmy's gone. Open. Disappeared. TV's on but . . ." The words come out in all the wrong order.

"Calm down, Jo," my father says and I hear the careful, reassuring tone he uses on my mother. Except even as he speaks, he's crabbing towards the door.

"I left him to make him a Nesquik. He was watching TV. But he's not now. And someone's left the front door open."

Dad's coolness is gone. So is he: he thumps down to the hallway and shouts, "Timmy? TIMMY! Stop playing games."

Mum gets up and walks into Timmy's bedroom. For a moment, I'm convinced he must be there, and I wait for the inevitable telling-off for scaring everyone. But over her shoulder, I see what she sees: stillness. When my brother's in his room, it's never still. He throws jigsaws and games across the floor, *literally* throws them and plays with them where they land for a few minutes, before finding something else to throw. When he's asleep, his limbs thrash about as if he's drowning and the toys on his bed are tossed into the air like ship's passengers.

The stillness is eerie. Before I can stop myself I think, this is what it would be like if Timmy doesn't make it. *This* is what my brother would leave behind . . .

When my mother turns, her face is warped like a melted candle and I'm convinced she's thinking the same thing. "Timmy. My Timmy." I'm invisible as she races down to where my father is crashing about, hunting not a lost packet of pills, but a lost son.

"How long did you leave him for?" Dad asks when I walk into the kitchen.

"I don't know . . . a few minutes?"

He faces my mother, grabbing her upper arms. "Lynda. We need to look for Timmy, you understand that, don't you? We need to look now. He won't have gone far."

"But where *could* he have gone, Ted? He's eight years old." She sounds confused.

"Oh, bloody hell. Lynda, if I knew that . . ." Dad pushes past her into the hall, grabs two sets of door keys from the *Country Diary of an Edwardian Lady* rack above the telephone table, and beckons to me. "I need both my girls to be very sensible now. Timmy will be somewhere nearby, we know that. I need both of you to search together — and you must *stick* together." He turns to me. "Jo, you keep hold of the keys. I'll go towards town and you two head towards the common and the base."

339

"But what if . . ." I know I shouldn't say this, but I have to. "What if we don't find him?"

"Then it means I've probably found him already. But whatever happens, we'll meet back here in an hour. Hang on, let me get some food, he's bound to be hungry by now." He goes back into the kitchen, and returns with a bag. *My* bag, for the stockpile. "What's this, Jo?"

"It's . . ." I hesitate. "I was packing for a picnic."

He stares at me, obviously not believing I'd take beans and Nesquik on a picnic. But he shakes his head. "It doesn't matter. Don't let Mum out of your sight, Jo. And keep your eyes peeled for Timmy. He can't have gone far."

"You said that already, Dad."

He smiles, but his eyes don't and it makes me more afraid. "Yes. I suppose I did." He kisses me on the forehead. "If I say it often enough, it has to be true."

He pulls my mother's shoes out of the understairs cupboard. It smells of leather and damp. Mum lifts her legs as he pushes the shoes on to her feet. He kisses her on the cheek then pats her bottom. "Off you go. One hour. That'll be all it takes."

It's hot and sunny outside, and Mum and I blink as we walk up the hill, peering up the drives of dozens of houses like ours. Or not quite like ours: outside each one I mentally calculate the chances of each building surviving a one-megaton blast. As we move towards the common, there's a mix of flimsy new semis which will be blown apart like matchstick models, and sturdier Victorian houses. Though, of course, the closer we get

340

to the common, the closer we are to ground zero. And nothing but a lead box buried a mile below the earth will save you there.

Mum is going through the motions of looking for Timmy, but her eyes are glazed. I'm not sure whether she took too many pills when she found them, or whether this is shock at my brother's disappearance.

"He's probably playing hide-and-seek," I say. Then, as a test, I try, "You know how naughty he is." If she's even half with it, she'll tell me off for that.

She doesn't. Instead she calls out, "Timmy. Where are you, Timmy?"

The houses are more scattered as we walk towards the airbase perimeter, with privet and gorse hedges shielding the well-heeled occupants from the chaos. A big sign reads "Women's Peace Camp" in green, white and violet letters, and it's spawned lots of smaller boards picturing doves and that female sign, the one that looks like an O with a + sign attached. We've driven past often enough, but I've never been here before: it seems like a waste of energy to protest against a few more bombs, when there are already enough in the world to kill all of us twenty times over. Better to protect yourself.

I can see their tents in the distance; the different colours and shapes make it look untidy, like a hurricane at a rubbish tip. No wonder Dad's mates at the Rotary hate this place. They're the sort who think women should be seen, not heard, and *always* tidy.

But as we get closer, order emerges from the chaos. As well as tents, there are caravans painted with flowers and fruit, toilet cubicles, and a huge central structure made of canvas and polythene.

Mum and I approach nervously. I couldn't look much less like a peace woman, in my pink stripy pedal-pushers and T-shirt with a glittery gold lion on it. My mother is more of a hippie, in her long, floral skirt (like the one Lady Diana Spencer wore in that photo where you could see her legs) and a creased lemon-yellow blouse. She forgot to put on a bra this morning, so her boobs jiggle as she walks and — yuk — her nipples are sticking out. Her legs are unshaven, covered in little crescents of hair, but she's still too clean to be one of *them*. They're probably going to shout at us for gawping, throw a bucket of dirty water to make us go away.

But what choice do we have? My little brother loves drama, and this is the most dramatic place on our doorstep right now.

"Shall I go?" I ask Mum, and she nods. I walk up to the first tent. It's like a Red Indian wigwam, decorated with ribbons and symbols. The camp is smaller than it looks on TV: next to the high fence, it seems no scarier than the Cub Scout weekend Timmy went on last summer (Dad had to go and get him after one day because he was missing his mummy).

"Hello?" I hover at the entrance to the tent, not knowing what to say. "Anyone in there?" I wait but I can't hear anyone inside. "Hello?"

"Looking for someone, my love?" I turn round to see a very pretty woman, a bit older than Mum, behind me. She has a Welsh accent like Ruth Madoc in *Hi-Di-Hi*, bobbed mousy hair with a grey streak in the fringe, and pointy features that make her face look wide awake. No BO or piercings, but she does wear a purple peasant waistcoat with muddy frayed jeans.

"Actually. Yes, we are." I wave at Mum, who doesn't notice. "My brother."

She laughs. "We don't tend to get too many men round here. Unless they've come to make trouble."

"No, he's my *little* brother. He's eight and about this tall —" I hold my hand up to my shoulder, "— with light brown hair. Well, he doesn't have much hair at the moment. Just tufts, like a new baby. Blue eyes. *Very* pale." I feel queasy as I picture him. "He's not well."

Waistcoat Lady looks concerned. "I haven't seen a little boy. But don't worry, if he's here, we'll find him. Maybe he's hiding in one of the benders. Come on." She calls across to Mum, "You too, dear. We don't bite, whatever it says in the *Evening Post*."

Mum approaches reluctantly, and we follow Waistcoat Lady, zig-zagging between tents and washing lines. I wonder how they dry their clothes when it rains. Or dry themselves. Some of the tents look as though they'd float away in the lightest shower. A couple of tents further in, we reach the campfire area, where women sit on deckchairs and orange boxes drinking tea; they stare at us, but they don't seem hostile, simply curious. At their feet, two tiny little girls dressed only in flowery pants are playing marbles.

"Wait here," Waistcoat Lady says. "Biscuits and tea are on that table. I think your mum could do with some."

I approach the trestle and take a few digestives for Mum while I scan the area for mugs and a kettle. I can't help glancing over at the women. They're mostly quite young, teens and twenties, and they could be art students from Newbury College, except they're not wearing lipstick and their hair is either cropped or tangled-looking. The boys on the pull at the Wagon and Horses wouldn't like that.

I know what Dad thinks of them. He's said so often enough. "*Bloody scroungers*. Russia is a big fat bully and will invade us if we can't protect ourselves."

I've seen how bullies operate so maybe he's right about needing our own bombs. I don't think I'm going to say that out loud, though. Instead, I spot a cauldron of water hanging over a fire. It must be what they use to make tea.

"Timmy!"

Mum cries out and I look up and there is my brother, walking towards us from the far end of the camp, one hand held by Waistcoat Lady, and the other by a younger woman with blue-black hair. He looks like a little prince with his devoted courtiers. My mother races forward, snapped out of her trance, and takes him in her arms.

However much he annoys me, my heart feels like it's growing too big for my ribcage. It must be relief.

Waistcoat Lady beams at Timmy. "What a charmer your brother is. He's been learning how to play the drums with Mags."

Mags with the blue hair shrugs. "I thought he was one of the weekenders' kids. We get people coming on

Saturdays, you know. Day-trippers." She spits out the words in angry cockney.

"Ah, Mags. Don't be such a hard-liner." Waistcoat Lady ruffles what's left of Timmy's hair; people can't help doing that kind of thing. No stranger ever touches mine, unless you count the nit-nurse.

I see it happening before they do: with Timmy still in her arms, my mother's hairy legs begin to buckle. I race forward and Waistcoat Lady notices too because she catches my brother as Mum crumples, rather elegantly, to the ground.

"Don't grip him too hard!" I scream. "He's got leukaemia!"

All the women look at me now, and Mags gives me one of those grown-up *meaningful* looks. Waistcoat Lady eases Timmy to the floor and he crawls towards my mother, who is awake but has dreamy eyes, her skirt splayed out and her doll-legs straight ahead of her.

"Leukaemia." Mags gives me a second serious look. "Did you hear that, Gillian?"

Waistcoat Lady nods.

Mags touches my hand. "This is important. You live round here, right?"

"Yes. All my life."

Mags sighs. "I knew it. Gillian, we need to —"

My mother moans and I think she's going to faint again. Waistcoat Gillian places her hands on Mum's shoulders and whispers, "You're all right now, my love. Everything's fine."

"But, Gillian, we have to let her know what this is —"

"Later, for pity's sake, Mags. Sometimes a protest march isn't the first thing to organise. Sometimes," she says pointedly, "a cup of very sweet tea is more of a priority."

Mags pouts but scuttles off to fetch one. Gillian crouches down next to Mum now. "So what's your name then?" Mum doesn't seem to hear her.

"She's Lynda. Lynda Morgan. I'm Joanna."

"And this little ruffian?" She strokes his hair again. I wish she wouldn't do that, it only encourages him.

"Timmy."

Timmy beams at her, cute as a flipping button, and Gillian beams back. "And would Timmy like some chocolate?" She frowns. "If he's allowed, of course. With his *illness*."

"He doesn't have much of an appetite," I say, "but funnily enough he always seems to have room for chocolate."

"I've got some in my teepee," she says. "Come with me if you like."

I follow her back towards the edge of the camp. "Have you been here since the start?"

"No. I saw it on the news last summer when the marchers first left Wales and I thought the women were so brave. Never thought I'd have the guts to do it too, but I came for a visit back in January, brought some food and then . . . I can't explain it. It felt like the right thing. The only thing to do." She pushes through the flap in the teepee. "And it's so much easier now the weather's drier. The mud! You wouldn't believe what it's like. Right. Chocolate."

I peer through the flap. There's not much room, but Gillian's made it cosy, with photographs of mountains pinned to the fabric, and a leather pouffe with ethnic embroidery next to the red sleeping roll. Hanging up there's a toilet bag like my granny's. A big black umbrella is propped up against the wall of the tent, and there's a pile of books next to it, with titles like *Woman-Hating* and *Gyn/Ecology: the Metaethics of Radical Feminism*. Right at the bottom, there's a battered copy of *Jane Eyre*.

She rummages through numerous carrier bags. "Everything gets soaked when it rains, even with all these bags. Right, what about a Mars bar? Helps us work, rest and preserve world peace."

I giggle. "You're different from what I thought."

"What, because I look like I might wash occasionally?"

I blush. "Yes."

"You seem a sensible girl, Joanna. So here's a good lesson for you. Don't believe the papers. They have just as much of an agenda as we do. Except ours is about saving lives. You can work out for yourself what theirs might be."

I nod, though I don't really understand. "Gillian?"

"Uh-huh," she says, pulling out a crushed Kit-Kat and giving it to me.

"You know what the other lady, Mags, with the blue hair . . . what she said about Timmy's illness? About something we needed to know?"

"I don't think . . ." Gillian hesitates. "No, you're old enough to hear it. We're not scientists, Joanna, so this

347

isn't definite or anything, but we read all the research. You know that Greenham isn't the only military establishment round here? There's also Burghfield and Aldermaston. That's where they invent the weapons and test them."

"I know about Aldermaston." It was on the map in the book I borrowed from the library, of sites the Russians would bomb first.

"Good girl. Well, there's anecdotal — that means, unofficial, unverified — evidence that more children living around there might be getting cancer than usual. Cancers like leukaemia."

"And you think . . ." I can't say it.

"It's *possible*, no more than that, but possible that your brother's illness could be part of that, what shall we call it, that *trend*. That something the plants are putting out into the atmosphere could be making people ill. Especially children."

I nod. I don't even feel surprised. As usual, most grown-ups ignore the damage they're doing to the planet. "But what can we do?"

Gillian touches my arm as she emerges from the teepee. "*Here* is what we do, my love. The camp's not only about bombs. It's about the planet. About you. The next generation. People can laugh as much as they like but I look at your brother and I know we're right. Things have to change."

"But nothing ever changes, does it? The Russians are bullies. They won't respect us unless we can fight back."

She raises an eyebrow. "Is that what *you* think, Joanna? Or what someone else thinks? We ought to talk it through properly. But for now, I think chocolate is the priority, eh? Can't have you fading away."

CHAPTER
TWENTY-EIGHT

Dromophobia — Fear of Crossing Streets

At last I have a theory about where the flashbacks are leading me.

Right now, they're leading me to London, Dick Whittington style, as I try to follow the trail. I wouldn't normally go out of my way to visit my brother. Even crossing the road would feel like too much effort. But I can't get the latest flashback of the camp out of my head and I know that Timmy must be part of the answer.

When I rang his mobile, he tried to use his "*horrible diary*" as an obstacle to meeting much before the 2012 Olympics ("you could come as my guest, bound to be hundreds of champagne receptions and I'm brilliant at blagging"). But I played the head-banger card, told him my own diary was horribly empty, and offered to be on standby 24/7 for a free slot. He then fired below the belt.

"But you hate London. It scares you silly."

"I must face my fears," I said solemnly. He relented with a sigh.

He's right about London, of course, and I consume a whole bottle of Rescue Remedy before I board the train. At Paddington, I'm unsteady on my feet, but wobble through the crowds to the taxi rank. The cab to Timmy's offices costs me twelve pounds though it can only be a mile away and most of the journey we're in stationary traffic.

The ad agency is based in an old varnish factory, now known as the Shiny Happy Place. It's a tall, narrow building in city-browned brick, and probably once had a quiet dignity. Not any more.

Through the high lead-framed windows, I can see malnourished blonde receptionists perching on bar stools, alongside an espresso machine the size of a family saloon. After fiddling for several minutes with the entryphone (this area of town is what Timmy calls "high energy" and what the cabbie called "well-fucking dodgy"), I finally catch the eye of one of the girls. She manoeuvres herself slowly off her bar stool, so her skinny jeans don't split, and opens the door two inches.

"Are you lost? The Tube's back up that way," she says, peering through the gap.

"No, I think I'm in the right place. I've come to see Timmy. My brother."

She stares at me. "Timmy?"

"Timothy Morgan. Your boss?"

Her eyes flicker in recognition. "Oh, the Morg. And you're his . . . sister? You know, I'd *never* have guessed that." She opens the door fully. "He's in the penthouse."

The smell hits me first: varnish. But I bet it's fake, created especially for the factory by a Parisian "nose" to hint at the place's history without giving everyone solvent headaches. Then I look up: this handsome industrial building seems to be midway through conversion to a children's play centre, all primary colours and climbing frames. The receptionist points to a tiny glass bubble lift, but I feel dizzy looking at it, so take the spiral staircase instead. On my way up, I pass more tight-jeaned young women, and several forty-something men trying to compensate for receding hairlines with ponytails and George Michael beards. I can't quite believe my little brother is their boss.

The stairs go on and on and I'm nauseous by the time I reach the "penthouse" — more like a balcony placed strategically and, knowing Timmy's inflated ego, symbolically above everyone else. There's a huge bed, a suspended plasma screen the size of a pool table, an actual pool table, plus a metal desk hanging from the ceiling on thick dungeon chains. Behind it sits a woman who . . .

Bloody hell! A woman who is the spitting image of my mother. Well, my mother twenty years ago, if she'd had the benefit of £300 highlights and a wafty-fabric wardrobe from Ghost.

"Aha! Jo, isn't it? You do look a bit like the Morg . . . I mean, Tim." She gets up from her ergonomic chair and shakes my hand. Then she leans into a microphone on her desk. "Will the Morg return to base immediately?" Her voice echoes round the building.

352

She makes me a camomile tea and I wait. *Come on, Jo.* You can stand up to your brother. You've seen him naked. You know his secrets.

Out of the blue, I think of Luke. What was it Frisky called him, an only child who's struggling with being alone in the world? I remind myself that I should be grateful to have a brother.

After several minutes, the lift slides up to our level and Timmy steps out, with all the humility of a rock god. He wears tweed breeches with a neon green thread, and a matching T-shirt. "Yo, sis!" he says, air-kissing me from three feet away. He turns to our Mum-a-like, "So, who got the good looks in the Morgan family, Karine?"

She tuts at him, then reaches forward and *ruffles his hair*. And he makes a noise I can only describe as a purr. I have to look away.

"Join me on the bed, sis," he says and beckons me over. I balance on the edge of the silk Playboy duvet cover, and sip my tea. "So, what on earth's so important that you've ventured into our dangerous capital?"

"Well . . ." I'm not prepared for such a direct question, so soon. "I wanted to see you. The last time I was only semi-conscious, after all."

"The only way to survive Courtbridge, if you want my opinion," he says. Then he lights a cigarette. "Is that what you want? My opinion?"

"What do you mean?"

"Let me guess what's going on, sis. Some kind of road to Damascus, seen the light, the future's bright,

353

the future's Orange, near-death experience moment that's made you want to bond with me. Lovely. But can I be brutally honest?"

"Can I stop you being?"

"What have we got in common? Apart from *les parents*. And if we've nothing in common, well . . . is there a point?" He lies back on the bed, eyes closed.

In a few blunt words, my perfectly honed speech about letting bygones be bygones, my questions about happiness and childhood memories, has been rendered redundant and naïve. "Just a minute, Timothy. EDWARD HORATIO Morgan." I always hated the fact he had three names when I was plain Joanna. "You got away with it when you were eight, but you're not going to bully me now. And when did you become a bloody mind-reader?"

He opens one eyelid — God how I hated it when he used to do that — and smiles lazily. "Now don't get those knickers in a twist, sis. You might dribble on the duvet. Silk stains terribly."

I stand up: it's difficult to be assertive on the bed. "Stop it! Yes, I would like us to be closer, but I'm fully aware that having the world's most arrogant *twat* as a brother makes that impossible."

Timmy waves his hand in the air. "Hold on a sec. Karine, would you mind taking an early lunch? And telling Liam at Saatchi's that I can't make it for the one fifteen appointment? Looks like this might take a while . . ."

I look at the time, projected on to the warehouse wall in pink letters. Three minutes past one. "So you had

354

generously allocated *fifteen minutes* to this? Well, lucky old me."

Karine backs away, muttering about working from a hot desk downstairs. As she leaves, Timmy presses a switch, and a metal blind descends from the ceiling to the floor, so no one below can see us.

"All right, Jo. What is this *really* about? Do you need some money? I'm more than happy to write you a cheque if I can take a raincheck from the family therapy."

"Money? God, you've got no idea, have you? No. I want to make sense of the past."

"I *knew* it!" He punches the air like a footballer. "I knew it had to do with the Meaning of Life."

"Can't you ditch the sarcasm and actually listen to what I've got to say for once, Timmy?"

He shrugs, but his face is softer. "I suppose I could try."

I take a big breath. "I'm not mistaking you for the Dalai Lama. I don't want your views on the afterlife, or my progression up the career ladder, or my image."

"Ah, now that's probably the only thing I'd be any use at. Those pastel colours, Jo, they're so draining. I've got a mobile number for the best personal shopper in London." He withers under my glare. "No? Sorry. Carry on."

"I don't envy your stupid job or your gaudy clothes. But I'd like to claim back my share of confidence that somehow got allocated to you. And that certainty you've always had about what you want out of life."

For the first time, he looks interested. "They're not *that* gaudy, are they? My clothes? Gaultier is the only designer that always works for me. As for the confidence thing, well, I've never really thought about it."

"Could you try now? Just for me?"

He stubs out his cigarette between the breasts of a nymph-shaped onyx ashtray, and picks up a Rubik's Cube. "Helps me think," he says and begins to click and twist the rows. "Um . . . knowing what I want. Let's see. Nearly dying as a kid probably helped." He peers up from the cube, to see whether this is enough.

"No, I don't buy it Timmy. I've nearly died and it's made me *more* confused. And anyway you were rocky from birth."

"Fair point. Maybe it's down to Mum."

"So you'll admit you were her favourite?" I snap.

His eyes open wide. "What, and you weren't *Dad's* favourite?"

"No way. You were the apple of *everyone*'s eye."

"Bollocks, sis. Always the same in families. Mummy's boys and Daddy's girls. Way of the world. But that's not my point. My point is we both had a parent on our side."

I'm too intrigued to argue the toss. "Go on."

"So in theory we should *both* have grown up with high self-esteem." He's frantically twisting the cube now, thinking aloud. "But maybe . . . OK. How about this? Mum was the underdog in our family, wasn't she? Had to support Dad, all she got a say on was what was for dinner, or what brand of washing powder to use."

"I suppose so." I decide not to tell him about what I learned at the barbecue: that Mum had made that choice consciously, aware of what it might cost her.

"And all the time, he was knocking off endless girls at the bank or the operatic society."

I flinch. No one's ever said it out loud before, and the bluntness makes me realise that however pragmatic my mother was, she couldn't have predicted quite how bad it would be. "But you didn't know that till you were older."

"Well, no, but I did sense that she was unhappy and put upon. What if she spoiled me precisely because she wanted me to live the life she couldn't? Make me believe anything's possible? Wouldn't be the first mother to live vicariously through her kids." He stops fiddling with the cube and holds it up, each side the same fluorescent colour.

It does make a strange sort of sense. Except . . . "How come I didn't grow up feeling the same? Like I could have anything I wanted?"

He folds his hands behind his head and lies back against the pillow. "Well, it was only a theory. Maybe I was born with the selfish gene. Like you said, I always was a brat. But Mum's lessons worked. I do have everything I want." He waves at his surroundings.

"Really? No deep longings? No horrible inadequacies below the surface?"

"No. Sorry, sis. Just a bad boy who never intends to grow up." He grins and for once, I allow myself to fall for the charm.

"Great if you can get away with it," I say. And why shouldn't he? I've focused on Timmy for so long, blaming him for my insecurities, and all he's done is pursued what he wanted.

"The thing you need to remember, Jo, is that sometimes selfish is *good for everyone*. Sometimes selfish is the *right thing*. Look at this place," he stands up, peering down at his domain through the blind, "being selfish has got me here, sure, but it's also given jobs to twenty people. And created some of the best ad campaigns the British public could hope for."

"So I should look after *numero uno*, for the sake of everyone else?"

"Yup. You know, people *like* being manipulated, if it's done with panache."

"Ri-ight." And I wonder whether that's what he's doing to me.

"And don't forget, some would say shyness is only another form of selfishness. The passive-aggressive sort. The trick is not to think *too* much. Go with your gut." He presses a button and the privacy blind begins to retract. "Speaking of guts, now we've cracked the code, why don't you join me for sushi? Might as well use the booking Karine made. Think of it as an open apology for making your entire childhood a misery."

By the time we've got a cab to the sushi bar, Timmy's all smiles. He greets the waitresses like he lunches there every day — for all I know, he does — with treble air-kisses and an enquiry about the availability of *anago*.

358

"What's that?" I ask, as we take our seat in front of a conveyor belt.

"Conger eel," he says. "Only in season for a while but when it is . . ." He smacks his lips. "So. Just pick off the dishes you like and stack up the plates, that's how they work out the bill. Beats the conveyor belt in *The Generation Game*, eh?"

I hesitate. If I really want to turn my back on my fearful days, I should be diving in, stuffing myself with raw fish and eels so fresh they probably twitch on your tongue, but the thought makes me want to retch. And then I think of Timmy every Christmas, demanding circumcised sausage rolls: if I'm really turning into a woman who knows her own mind, then surely I can eat exactly what I like. Go with my gut. Even if my brother mocks me for it, as he undoubtedly will.

Timmy looks at me. "You know, if you don't fancy raw fish, the omelette *nigiri* is *really* good, here." And he picks up a saucer with three blocks of rice with bright yellow toppings.

It's probably the most considerate thing my brother's ever done for me. "Thanks," I say. To stop them, I pick up the *nigiri* with my fingers and chew carefully. I wouldn't say it's the best thing I've ever tasted, but it doesn't make me puke.

I follow it with some more veggie stuff — a salad, some of the same chewy rice topped with avocado and peppers. Timmy tries hard, making enquiries about Dennis and Lorraine, and it's only because I recognise that too rapt expression from years ago, that I know he's not really listening. But I can't expect miracles.

My brother pushes a single wodge of tuna around his plate before eating half of it.

"That all you're having?"

He pats his chest. "This six-pack takes a lot of sacrifices, sis."

No, I definitely wouldn't want to make those kind of sacrifices.

On the train back to Courtbridge, I feel slightly resentful that Timmy didn't have an instant solution, but then again maybe he's right. Maybe shyness *is* plain old egocentricity and everyone would be happier if I swapped my self-obsession for good old-fashioned selfishness.

I decide to start by ordering myself a double vodka and orange from the buffet bar. The fact that Dennis would disapprove makes it taste ever sweeter.

CHAPTER
TWENTY-NINE

Taphephobia — Fear of Being Buried Alive

Selfishness is harder than it looks. I've been busy telling Mum I don't like quinoa casserole (and having to admit that all the other casseroles she's supplied since the accident have ended up in the bin). Telling Dennis that I *like* squirrels and will go on feeding them, whatever he says. And telling Lorraine that I'm going to keep seeing Frisky whatever happens.

Maybe when you've done what you want for as long as Timmy, you get used to the way people look at you. Like you've kicked their puppy or criticised their children.

Frisky, meanwhile, feels so responsible for the two "funny turns" I've had while he's been around, that he's on best behaviour.

"I've taken very special care with your latest . . . what shall I call it? . . . date with danger. This one took some string-pulling, my dear, but it's worth it. You'll love it. Oh, and make sure you wear sensible shoes."

So now I'm back in the Red Peril, wondering how I got myself into a situation where I'm at the mercy of a madman's whims, while Frisky hints at his other plans for summer outings.

"We're definitely going to have to find a way to get you airborne, Joanna. In a strictly non-acrobatic sense, so as not to aggravate the good doctor. But there's nothing like seeing the English countryside from above for making the pulse race a little faster."

"I did fly once, when I was nine. To Spain." I don't add that I was too busy screaming to appreciate the countryside, and that the stewardess threatened to lock me in a lavatory ("She'll provoke hysteria in the other passengers!"). After that, all our holidays were in draughty four-star Norfolk hotels full of clothes moths and old people.

"Oh, I'm not talking about a *charter* flight," Frisky says ominously. "Then there's water. Messing about on rivers, like *Wind in the Willows*. I'll be Toad, you can be Mole. And I'm afraid Luke is *definitely* ratty."

Luke catches my eye in the driver's mirror and looks heavenwards. I caught a trace of *that* aftershave when I climbed into the car, and it made me blush all over again. I try to work out his mood, how his loss is affecting him, but his face gives nothing away. I was granted a flash of his all-American teeth when he smiled earlier, made more dazzling by his tan. He looks out of place in boring old Courtbridge, like a stretch limo at a car-boot sale.

"So that's air and water. We've done speed and thrills . . ."

"Don't forget public humiliation by making me sing karaoke. Oh, and advanced DIY. I can honestly say you've changed my life, Frisky." It comes out flippant, so I try again. "I know it might not seem that obvious yet, but you have. Both of you," I add, including Luke in my thank you. "You're my favourite men."

Frisky chuckles. "I wonder what your *partner* would have to say about that," he says, and guilt nibbles at my contentment, until my brother's voice kicks in. *Sometimes selfish is good for everyone.*

The drive goes on and on, with Luke consulting a series of maps, enclosed in protective plastic covers, as though we're on an army expedition. Once we get off the main roads and into proper countryside, his face relaxes and he manoeuvres the Peril with confidence *and* delicacy, so that the car seems to transcend its mechanical limitations and float along the hedgerows. It's a glorious June day, and the view is straight from the pages of a "Visit England" brochure.

Finally he pulls up and turns round: his cheeks are pink and his eyes wide. "I think we're here."

Here is the corner of a meadow, somewhere an hour to the west of Courtbridge. Unless those sleepy-looking cows turn into raging bulls on demand, I can't see anything that's going to test my courage.

Perhaps it's a nice, straightforward picnic. How lovely. Then it occurs to me: it could be a test of self-sufficiency, where we'll be expected to catch *and* kill our lunch.

Frisky's out of the car, peering all around. To our right there's a small woodland glade, and a wall with a derelict, pebble-dashed bungalow behind it. He whistles, but it's not a casual whistle. In fact, I'm sure it's the tune the aliens used in *Close Encounters*.

"You haven't brought me to meet little green men, have you?" It's not that ridiculous. Wiltshire has so many crop circles in summer that they barely get a mention on the local news any more. Space invaders clearly have a soft spot for this area as a holiday destination.

"Ha ha, not quite," he says, as an unmistakable whistled reply drifts towards us from the area by the bungalow. "This is *such* fun. I always wanted to be in the S.O.E."

He repeats the whistle again as he moves towards the densest patch of trees. Out of the corner of my eye, I glimpse a camouflaged shape. The shape emerges from behind the branches: it's not an alien, but a bald middle-aged man in combat jacket, waterproof trousers and a khaki baseball cap pulled down so far you can only see his lips and chin.

"Wing Commander Freeman Van Belle?" he hisses.

"That's me," says Frisky, holding out his hand. I wonder if Frisky really was that high up, or whether it's a little white lie. Combat Man's wearing fingerless gloves, although the temperature's in the mid-twenties. "And you must be Lionel?"

The man nods. He's slightly overweight and his teeth are veined with nicotine stains. "No one followed you?"

Frisky seems to be fighting the urge to giggle. "Nope. There are only three of us. This is Joanna, a friend of mine, who shares our fascination. And then this is my grandson, Luke."

Lionel acknowledges Luke but ignores me. Whatever his fascination is (Paint-balling? Radical far right survivalism? Taxidermy?), I very much doubt we share it. But I *am* intrigued . . .

"It's not covered by Official Secrets no more, but we still like to keep it *need to know*, yeah?"

"Mum's the word, old chap," Frisky assures him.

Lionel finally looks at me, but only from the knees down. "You told her to wear sensible shoes. Good girl. Birds usually turn up in heels. You wouldn't believe it."

"Oh, Joanna always dresses appropriately," Frisky says, then winks at me. "Shall we make a start then?"

We follow our prickly guide towards the derelict bungalow. He pulls out a huge bunch of keys to unlock the heavily padlocked gate, then leads us up the path and opens the front door. Maybe he has some kind of uniform in there for us? But as we step inside, there's no paramilitary kit room or secret stash of Kalashnikovs. Instead, we're in a white-washed tunnel that stretches way beyond the length of the bungalow. It's completely disorientating, until I smell the distinctive smell of municipal grade disinfectant, and suddenly know where we are.

I turn to Frisky. "It's a bunker, isn't it? A regional command centre?"

He claps his hands together. "Well spotted, my dear. Our friend Lionel here is a local enthusiast — took me a while to convince him, but he's agreed to give us a little tour. Isn't it fun?"

I stare down the tunnel. *Fun?* No, but oddly thrilling. I dreamed of places like this when I was twelve, of being one of the Chosen Few. Now I'm here, twenty years too late. "Thank you, Lionel. I'm sure it'll be very interesting."

He nods solemnly. "Best untouched example in the south of England, this one. You wouldn't believe what some bastards have done with shelters. Mushroom farms. Conference centres. Party venues. I mean. Parties? No bloody decorum."

Lionel doesn't look like much of a party animal. We walk in silence along the corridor, which slopes downwards. A set of stretcher-like beds projects from the wall, shelves for people. I wonder who'd have slept here, outside the shelter; the lower ranks, perhaps, dispensable enough to be endangered by a light scattering of fall-out. Or maybe these were for sentries, tasked with shooting desperate civilians whose only hope of survival lay underground.

Lionel stops and I look up at the enormous metal doors that shield those inside from blast and intruders. They must be twice my height at least. He takes yet more keys from his gaoler's bundle, before winding back the metal wheels that control the door levers. Finally the doors begin to slide open.

"This would have been what they called a Regional Government HQ — which evolved from the more basic War Rooms built after the Second World War. These were the Rolls-Royces. The next level up, the top of the range Aston Martin, was unique. Codenamed 'Turnstile', meant to be top secret, but everyone knows it's twenty miles up the road, in a quarry near Corsham. A complete underground city, with roads and a pub."

"Ah, that's the spirit," says Frisky, "raising a pint glass to the end of the world."

Lionel looks at him. "Well, you can bet the Russians would have stockpiled the vodka too. Anyway, that's where you'd stand the best chance of making it, but this would have been the next best thing."

The door slams shut behind us. Slam is too small a word, somehow. When this door closes, it feels like the metal separates us from all that's good about the world: no more trees or flowers or animals or art — the smell of damp overpowers the smell of disinfectant, and the only colour is accidental, rust-red watermarks bleeding through grey concrete floors and cream-painted walls.

The corridor continues more steeply downhill now, towards another barrier: an even bigger pair of doors, like the opening to a bank vault. "The second blast doors," Lionel explains as he manoeuvres one of them open, "always open into a dog-leg corridor, to absorb the shockwave. These buggers literally weigh a tonne. But engineered so you can still open them if you're the one human left alive."

He flicks a switch and illuminates a dead-end. "We're on mains, but there are diesel generators outside, on the left-hand side of the bungalow. National Grid would be a goner if 200 atom bombs landed on the UK. And the air purification system here uses the same filters as your average Dyson." He looks at me, because as a woman, presumably vacuum cleaners are all I understand. If only he knew.

We turn sharply down another corridor. The first door is marked "Decontamination". I peer inside.

There's a shower without a curtain, and a large bin marked "Contaminated Clothing". "It's like that film with Meryl Streep, where they almost scrubbed her eyes out."

"Fat lot of good that'd do. They didn't keep spare clothes here, so if you did make it back in the bunker after a recce outside, you were presumably supposed to wander about starkers. Or maybe just go back to your dorm to die," Lionel says and ushers us back into the corridor. Luke frowns, surveying the space from floor to ceiling, as if he's planning to build his own bunker.

"How long would they be underground?" Frisky asks.

"Councils were meant to have rations for thirty days, for 200 staff. Trouble is, most councils didn't plan to buy stores till the preparation phase, which meant they'd be joining the queues of terrified civilians at Tesco's. Only grub here is a few tins of salmon from panic buying during the Cuban Missile Crisis."

He leads us to another door. "This was the telephone exchange, linked to every other bunker in the country. No bugger wanted to admit you might never hear a dicky bird from the outside world. No way of knowing if you were on your own down here."

The exchange seems to date back to the 1950s, with row upon row of wires and sockets. I imagine women down here, waiting for the call. Were they chosen for telephony skills, or their potential as the brood mares of the post-nuclear generation? "How did they pick the staff?"

Lionel smiles: now he's in his stride, he seems to have forgotten that I'm a pathetic *girl*. "The controllers — basically, the new prime ministers for each area — knew they had a place, and so did senior staff. Then they could pick who they liked. No one with faddy diets or claustrophobia. First you'd know would be a letter when the authorities thought war was coming, telling you to report to HQ with clothes, a toothbrush and maybe a few magazines to read."

"And their families?"

Lionel shrugs. "No room at the inn. But the authorities did promise to pay your salary into the missus's bank account though."

"As if there'd be any banks left standing." It's the first thing Luke's said since we got in the bunker.

"Bang on," says Lionel. "Then this is the sick bay." It's a tiny room with a couple of bunks and a small first-aid cabinet. "Not exactly geared up for major operations. The canteen had better kit, which tells you all you need to know about the plans for anyone who got sick." He draws a heavily bitten finger across his throat in a slicing motion.

The canteen is the most normal place we've seen. It could be a school or hospital dining-room, with an adjoining kitchen that Gordon Ramsay wouldn't turn his nose up at. Huge ovens, freezers and a hostess trolley arrangement. I wonder what they'd make from the tinned supplies: apple crumbles and custard, to remind the occupants of homes that no longer existed?

"Time to go deeper." Lionel leads us down some steps. "Where the real action is."

This is more like what I expected. There's a control room, with Perspex curved windows at waist level on two walls, a cross between a submarine and the Starship Enterprise. Plastic covers protect maps of our bit of England, each one divided into smaller zones. I spot Swindon and Newbury and Courtbridge too.

"Ah, bit more sophisticated than the old RAF control rooms," Frisky says.

"Same principle, though. They'd write casualty estimates on the plastic sheets with chinagraph pencil, so they could change them easily. And then here's the boss's office."

It's like the set of a '70s cop show, with wrinkled tobacco-brown carpet, padded swivel chairs, and a melamine bookcase that, above ground, would display darts trophies and photographs of ballet-dancing daughters.

"This is where the controller would make the life or death decisions. Shooting looters on sight, abandoning the walking dead, who'd already taken a fatal hit of radiation. Civil servants would become gods." He pushes open the door to an ante-room. "And this is where the Voice of God was broadcast from. Every bunker had a radio studio, though the chances of hearing the news depended on finding a radio under the rubble that was once your house."

I think of hiding in the science prep room, of my painstaking plans for the "inner refuge" at Greenham Lane: the stockpile of food, the improvised toilet, the radio that I later found out would probably have been knocked out by the shockwaves within seconds of the blast. It seems at once very sad and hilariously funny. Was I the only person in Britain daft enough to take that advice seriously?

"Do you mind if I take another look?" I gesture back towards the control room.

"Take your time," Lionel says.

I walk up to the largest map, with Oxford at the top edge, and the Isle of Wight at the bottom. USAF Greenham Common is marked and I find Aldermaston and Burghfield, picturesque Berkshire villages that should be famous for pub cricket teams or local ale, but instead became notorious worldwide for marches and bases. Strange, strange times.

"So when your children ask you what you did in the Cold War, what will you say?" Luke is standing behind me.

"You wouldn't believe me if I told you."

He smiles. "In America, we were told to duck and cover."

I smile back. "We were meant to protect and survive. I was so frightened. And so jealous of Americans — I used to watch all your TV shows and in every one there was a yellow sign in the background, pointing to the fall-out shelter in the basement."

He shakes his head. "You know, I was more worried about the San Andreas fault. Russia seemed one hell of a long way away."

"Were you ever in an earthquake?"

"Nothing big. As kids, we got used to waking up to tremors. But we all knew about 1906. Hundreds, maybe thousands, died in the Bay Area. I was kinda fascinated as well as scared. Like being a soldier, maybe. You don't want bad stuff to happen — but if it never does, what was the point of all the drills?" He laughs at himself. "Final twist was, when the last one hit in 1989, I was on a study tour to Japan."

"Was it the fear that made you choose your career?"

He nods. "Kinda fear, kinda fascination. But also, I love my city. Wanted to help beat nature. Save us all, you know, like a seismic Superman. But sometimes danger comes when you least expect it." He stares at the floor. "But I guess you know that already, from what happened to you."

Luke looks so unhappy that I want to reach out and hug him, but I don't think he'd appreciate it. I wonder whether Frisky's told him that I know about his parents. Eventually I say, "I only chose my job with the council to try to get a place in a bunker like this. So my whole career was based on fear." I shake my head. "I didn't want to save the world. I wanted to save myself. Now I've seen this, I think I'd have preferred to go up in smoke like everyone else."

"Funny, most kids think they're gonna live for ever," he says. "Not us, huh?" He smiles at me and there's such warmth, such understanding in his face that for the first time, I feel good about being different.

Frisky emerges from the controller's office. "Joanna, my dear, have you seen all you want to see? Only Lionel doesn't like to spend too long here, in case he gets into trouble. And he's already done us a huge favour, hasn't he?"

Lionel shuffles on the spot. "I'm only supposed to have the keys to show round prospective purchasers."

"What? They'd turn this place into a nightclub, like the others?"

"Or a mushroom farm, yes. Ruddy unbelievable."

"Thank you for showing us round, Lionel," I say. "I appreciate it."

"It's good to be with people who *get* it, you know. Most people think I'm nuts."

That makes two of us, Lionel. "Can I ask you one last question?"

"Fire away."

"It's just . . . I mean. I never realised, till now, quite how futile it was. All that effort."

"This ain't the half of it. They even built a shelter at Eton. And there was a masterplan for moving paintings from the National Gallery. But none for moving the population of London."

"Exactly. Doesn't it make you angry?"

"I know it sounds weird," he says, "but it makes me feel better. They wanted to save paintings . . . well, it makes me think they believed — against the odds — that the human race would survive." He shrugs, embarrassed now.

Maybe it's the stale air making me all emotional, but now I feel like hugging Lionel as well as Luke. I settle for saying, "That's *such* a positive way of looking at it."

Lionel narrows his eyes, unsure whether I'm being sarcastic. "Better show you out, before you get too comfortable."

373

When we surface, it feels like we've been underground for days, not minutes. After those government-issue beiges and browns, the million shades of green in the fields make me light-headed. And the sounds — I'd got so used to the hum of the ventilators that the birdsong and even the distant traffic makes me want to sing "All Things Bright and Beautiful" at the top of my voice.

We say goodbye to Lionel, and board the Red Peril. "So?" Frisky asks me.

"It was brilliant. Really. But what was my lesson meant to be?"

"Whatever you choose, my dear. Although . . ." Frisky grants me a mischievous smile, "there was an element of proving that life's about more than preparing for the worst. Oh," and he reaches into his trousers, "I nearly forgot. Your latest fishy souvenir."

He hands me a slightly rusty tin of sardines, complete with tiny metal key. "Um. Thanks."

"Vintage. *Borrowed* it from the bunker canteen. You never know when you might need a long-life snack. And while I remember, date for your diary. Three weeks on Sunday. This one you'll never forget."

Three weeks on . . . shit. "Um, well, Frisky. That's tricky. Family celebration." It's only a little white lie. Actually it's the Emergency Readiness and Resilience Exercise — the first one Dennis has ever commanded. It's all he's talked about for weeks.

I shiver slightly as I imagine what my boyfriend would have been like during the Cold War. Would he have left me to die above ground while he saved the world from below?

Frisky looks put out. "Well, I'm sure you can make an excuse. This one is *important*, Joanna. Find an excuse to skip the celebration. You won't regret it."

I catch sight of Luke in the mirror. He raises his eyebrows as if to remind me, *there is never any point arguing with Frisky*.

CHAPTER
THIRTY

Arachibutyrophobia — Fear of Peanut Butter Sticking to the Roof of the Mouth

"This is probably the least ethical thing I have ever done", says Dr Williams.

I am lying on Dr Nathan Williams' examination couch, my eyes shut, my nostrils flared and my arm attached to a meter that's monitoring my pulse, as he prepares for what I hope will be the last phase of my treatment.

"I could sign a consent form, if it helps."

"What, that you consent to have the smelliest things I could find in the supermarket waved under your nose, like a reality TV contestant? I'd be laughed out of the hospital."

"If this is reality TV, does that make you Big Brother?" I open my eyes as he rummages in the carrier-bags. "Seriously, Nathan, I appreciate this."

The idea came during the last appointment we had, when I told him I felt frustrated because I knew the flashbacks were trying to tell me something. "But they're not coming fast enough."

After lots of prevarication, he finally suggested attempting to trigger a flashback by exposing me to a range of smells, under medical supervision. It does seem a bit barmy, but no more so than the last few months of my life.

"Have you had any more since the one where your brother went missing?" he asks, his back to me as he spoons out the stuff he's bought into Petri dishes. Maybe it's his way of reassuring himself that this is medicine and not domestic science.

"No. Haven't had one for three weeks."

"But the ones you've had are still in chronological sequence?"

"Yep."

"That's the strangest thing. I'd expect the flashbacks to bounce around time, like the ball in a pinball machine. This is more linear, which suggests there may be an end point." He turns around, a solemn expression on that kind, lined face. He's wearing a lab coat today, the first time I've seen him in "uniform" since I was an in-patient, and his long fingers are encased in rubber gloves.

"Unless the flashbacks are going to continue until the present day." The thought makes me queasy. "All my worst moments since the age of twelve. If only my memory would throw up a *nice* flashback: the day I learned to swim, say, or passed my A-levels."

"Do you know what's going to happen, when you're having a flashback?"

I think it over. "No, not really. But when I come to, God! It's so frustrating because I want to put right all our mistakes. Especially mine."

"Like what?"

"Well . . . you know what I said about being a scaredy-cat? The thing I've understood is that I got so much worse after my brother got ill. I mean I was always worried about nuclear war and the bogeyman and the dark before that, but it didn't stop me having fun."

"And afterwards?"

"Afterwards, I was full-on weird. The hoarding of baked beans began the same weekend that Timmy was diagnosed."

Nathan shakes his head. "Yes, but they were scary times. Midge Ure dancing with tears in his eyes. That German girl with the hairy armpits singing about ninety-nine red balloons. And it's all part of puberty. The obsessions, that is, not the armpits."

"I know. But most people grow out of it." I pause, trying to decide whether to confess how pathetic I really am. I take a deep breath: if I can't confide in my doctor, who else can I talk to? "I didn't grow out of it, you see, Nathan. I've spent my entire life blaming other people. *Oh poor little me, no wonder I am frightened of heights or whatever, it's because my brother was spoiled, because my mum was out of her tree, because Dad had affairs and let me down.*"

378

"So now you're blaming yourself for everything, including world poverty and the price of potatoes. There is a happy medium, Jo. And don't forget that having a brother with cancer is a big thing for a twelve-year-old to deal with. It sounds to me as though your hoarding was a coping mechanism for a situation that was out of anyone's control."

I stare at him. "Go on."

Nathan thinks it over. "Well, your family was facing a disaster that you couldn't understand. So instead of looking into that abyss, you focused on trying to prevent another disaster and I suppose, living where you did, it was the obvious thing to capture your imagination. Protecting *to* survive?"

His words startle me. Didn't I reject that theory as bonkers a few weeks ago? But the way he explains it, I don't feel like such a freak any more, just a child trying to deal with scary grown-up things. "You're right. You're bloody right, doctor." He looks hurt. "Sorry, it's the white coat. You're a star, Nathan."

"Yeah, well," he says. "So long as you let me write it all up in the *Lancet*."

I nod vaguely. All those years fearing the worst, but missing the obvious point: Timmy survived. *I* survived. And the flashbacks are like a big fat alarm clock going off in my head, saying, *wake up, Jo, there's still time to get things right*. An image of Luke, pruning the hedge in Frisky's garden, pops into my head. I chase it away. "Mind you, Nathan, it's one thing knowing my problem. Quite another doing something about it."

Though maybe I'm already changing, whether I want to or not.

"All in good time, Jo. Remember what you've been through since the accident. You're doing brilliantly so far. Your physical recovery is astounding," he breaks off, looking at me so intensely that I feel almost like squirming, "so cut yourself some slack, eh?" He seems impatient now, pulling at the end of his rubber glove. "Right, are you ready for the first smell? We can stop at any time, remember that. Now close your eyes . . ."

I let my lids droop, and take a deep breath. When I first came round from my coma, I used to lie in bed with my eyes closed, and my other senses became more responsive to compensate. That's what it's like now: my skin tingles, my tongue moistens, as if to taste the air. The tiny hairs in my ears strain to interrogate my surroundings, although Nathan has closed the curtains to block out noise and light.

But it's my sense of smell that's on highest alert.

"Ready, Jo? Number one, coming up."

I hear the surprisingly light foot steps I heard when I was first emerging from my coma. There's a draught across my face before the smell hits me.

"That's easy," I said. "It's coffee. Fresh ground."

He sighs. "This isn't a guessing game, Jo. Your flashbacks are about the chemistry in the smell reacting with your brain. So work harder to *really* smell it. Don't tell me what the thing *is*. Tell me what it's *like*."

"Umm. OK. Well, it's bitter. Burned. With . . . a tobacco-like smell behind it. Not cigarettes, but the dried leaves old men buy in boxes."

380

"Very good. And are you feeling anything yet? Any pull back to 1982?"

"No. Sorry. We weren't the kind of household to brew fresh coffee."

"Never mind. Plenty more smells to play with."

I hear a knife slicing through something crunchy and before Nathan gets near me I know what it is. "Apple."

"Go on, describe it," he says, holding it so close to my nose that I'm sure I can feel the juice, spitting like bubbles from a glass of freshly poured champagne.

"Right, it smells of . . . I know it's apple, but when I concentrate it smells more like a lemon. Acidic. Or maybe I can taste that."

"Does it have any associations?"

I squeeze my eyes together even more tightly. I want to produce a real, live flashback for Nathan, after all he's done for me. But all I can summon up are images straight from a women's magazine: happy families round a dinner table eating apple pie, children in playgrounds munching core, pips and all.

"Nothing yet."

He takes the fruit away. The next smell is earth and malt vinegar. "Beetroot. Yuck! Take it away."

"Might trigger something, if you hate it that much."

"It might trigger a wave of vomit, if you keep it there any longer."

He replaces it with a smell that's simultaneously sweet and savoury, cloying and nutty. I get a weird sensation in the roof of my mouth, dry and uncomfortable. "It's peanut butter, isn't it? Evil stuff."

381

And so it goes on, a production line of aromas: fresh orange juice ("citrus and sulphur ... no, really. It smells of fart!"), Marmite ("it's tickling my nose ... molasses and toffee and beer"), and honey ("that smells of summer, but not specifically the summer of 1982, sorry").

By now, Nathan's voice is flat with disappointment. I try to figure out why it's not working. "I think perhaps it's because the things you bought, well, they're all a bit *wholesome*. We didn't eat anything without E numbers in it when we were kids."

"Ah. Well, the next one doesn't have E numbers, but it is a bit more *fast food*."

He wafts the dish under my nose. "I'm getting vinegar again. But fruit, as well, mature fruit. Garlic. Something spicy. I know! It's HP sauce, isn't it?"

"Yes. Dead right. But remember, it's not 'name that sniff'. Concentrate, Jo."

I'm getting bored, and feeling a complete failure, but I try again to show willing, inhaling furiously.

Finally ... an image that's all mine. A plate of steaming chip-shop chips, covered in stripes of brown sauce, on the kitchen table. Sitting opposite me, my father, scowling, not at me but at life. No, he's scowling about my mother, who isn't here. "She'll make me a laughing stock, hanging round those women. Tell her to stop, Jo, she takes no bloody notice of me because I'm part of the male conspiracy."

"You're having one, aren't you? Your pulse has shot up."

382

Nathan's voice cuts across my father's, and the image evaporates faster than the steam from the fish supper.

I open my eyes. "I *was* having one."

"Ah. Shouldn't have said anything, should I?"

I feel very tired and very hot. The atmosphere is overwhelmingly intense, because all my senses are so heightened. "I'm not sure I can face having another go, Nathan."

"Oh, please. For me. I've only got one smell left. I promise I won't talk." He looks strange in the semi-darkness. Concentration makes the lines on his face more defined.

"All right then. The last one." I close my eyes again and wait. "Syrup . . . sugar syrup. It smells artificial, like perfume . . . it's a strawberry, isn't it?"

He doesn't say anything, which seems odd until I remember he's promised not to. "Strawberries. I love strawberries." I feel the coolness of the fruit as he holds it closer to my nose and it brushes against my lips, tiny hairs catching on my skin. An impulse makes me open my mouth and bite into the strawberry.

It's perfect. Intensely sweet and yet tart enough to save it from being sickly. A drop of strawberry juice leaks out where my teeth have sliced the berry, and slides down my chin. I lean forward slightly to taste the other half and . . .

My lips meet someone else's lips. Images flood my brain, not of childhood but of *now*, of a man's face, close to mine, of black pupils enclosed in pale lilac-grey irises, not Dennis's eyes but . . .

My own eyes snap open just as Nathan springs back. For moments, no, it must be several seconds, we stare at each other: Nathan's eyes seem to be begging me to speak first, but I can't. Finally, resignedly, he says, "Jo, I am *so* sorry. I can't . . . I have *never* done anything like that before. With a patient, I mean. It's utterly the last thing I would ever do."

I shake my head slightly, not quite trusting my eyes and my ears and my lips. "Um. It's fine. Really. I mean. Extraordinary situation, quite clearly. Not typical in any way." I sit up a little too quickly and tiny sparks of light appear at the edge of my vision. "Forget about it."

Nathan pulls back the curtains and lets light back into the office. "Are you sure?"

"I know it wasn't serious. It really doesn't matter."

He nods, but looks terribly glum. "I don't know what came over me. It must be the situation. Serves me right for meddling in things I don't understand."

I sigh. "But that pretty much rules out the entire brain, doesn't it?"

He seems bashful now. "No. Just women."

There's another pause as I try to decode what he's said. Does he mean this wasn't an accident after all? That the resemblance between this experiment and 9½ *Weeks* was part of some grand plan? That he thinks I was leading him on? "Right."

"I think it might be better, Jo, if I transfer your case to one of my colleagues."

"OK." I'm still confused. I have never, ever, inspired recklessness in a man before, still less provoked them to an act that could lose them their job. After all, I am

Joanna Morgan, the less attractive half of the Lorrie-Joey double act, the wallflower to Lorraine's *femme fatale*. Unless . . . maybe I got that wrong too. Maybe Dennis isn't the only man who fancies me. The thought makes me even more light-headed.

He seems relieved. "But one thing, Jo. I think that whatever happens, you're nearly there. Your brain will tell you when everything's sorted." And he taps his forehead.

"I'll take your word for it," I say, wondering if he's right. And whether my good old brain also holds the key to another mystery.

Because the eyes I wanted to see, the lips I wanted to be the ones touching mine didn't belong to Dennis. Or even Nathan.

They belonged to Luke.

In an ideal world, after an excruciating moment with a strawberry and a consultant, it's best to go your separate ways with the minimum of delay. Especially when your head's so full of new ideas and possibilities: that you might not have been a crazy child, that you might just be attractive, that your future is potentially more exciting than you'd ever imagined.

However, there's a hitch. When you've spent days planning a blind date between the aforementioned consultant and your best friend, and when that date happens to be scheduled for precisely forty-five minutes after the embarrassing moment . . . well, it's tricky, to say the least.

We drive to the centre of town in Nathan's car, a sporty black VW. He keeps his eyes straight ahead and his hands welded to the leather steering wheel. When he absolutely has to change gear, he does it *very* quickly, his arm shooting out on to the lever and back to the wheel in a blur. Because the gear stick is only inches from my knee.

Lorraine is waiting for us in Matches, sitting at the long purple glass bar, chatting to — or rather, chatting *up* — one of the owners. Nathan trails behind me and when I step aside, so she can see him properly, I know instantly it's not going to work. She appraises him as if he were a dog at Crufts, and from the curling of her lip, I know she won't be declaring him "Best in Show".

"Nathan, this is Lorraine, my oldest school friend. Lorraine, this is my specialist." They swap fleeting, going-through-the-motions smiles, and it's all I can do not to groan. Can't we all admit there's no point being here, and go home now? Then I can start planning my new life.

"I need a drink," I say, with feeling.

"Seconded," Nathan says. "Lorraine, you look like a girl who knows her way round a cocktail menu. What would you recommend?" Oh God, he's actually *trying*. Hasn't he worked out that she'd eat him alive? If she could be bothered . . .

Lorraine reaches over for the menu and flicks it open, with a hint of a sneer I hope Nathan doesn't see. "Whatever floats your boat, doc. I know what Jo will want though." She winks at the barman. "Give us one of those," she says, pointing at the menu.

386

He does his bit behind the bar, throwing bottles about and showing off, before placing a glass of dark purple liquid in front of me. "Go on," Lorraine says, "it's Charlotte Church's favourite tipple apparently."

I raise the glass to my lips. It smells familiar, but then after my afternoon's sniff-a-thon, I'm probably imagining things. I take a tiny sip. "It tastes of fruit. Blackcurrant maybe, a bit like . . ."

Lorraine is impatient. "It's a Cheeky Vimto, a grown-up version of your favourite drink when we were kids."

But I work it out for myself, as the glass begins to go out of focus. And as I realise that Nathan is going to witness one of my funny turns after all . . .

CHAPTER
THIRTY-ONE

Enochlophobia — Fear of Crowds

I suck hard on my straw to savour the last drops of pop and there's a loud gurgle as the liquid travels towards my mouth.

"Ugh."

Warm Vimto tastes like jam, hot and sticky on my tongue. I finish the can, even though it could be a while before Mum remembers to get me another drink. After all, today she is Saving the World.

I should be grateful, because she's saving it not for herself, but for the Next Generation, meaning Timmy and me. Six weeks ago she barely had the energy to get out of bed. Oh yes, there's been a change in my mother.

Her pills have been replaced by a small brown bottle of flower essence, and her flowery dresses exchanged for baggy tops and bottoms in greying unbleached cotton. But the real change is in how she behaves, and it's not an improvement. Instead of whining, she snaps. Not just at me and Dad but, unbelievably, at Timmy too.

And he can pout all he likes but the fact is, this is all his fault.

If he hadn't run away that day, we'd never have ended up at Greenham. We'd never have met Gillian and Mags and the other women. And Mum would never have been *activated*.

"How are you getting on?" Gillian peers into my carrier-bag.

"It's getting harder," I admit. "I can't find any of the big ones any more."

"I know. I don't think any of us quite grasped how tricky it would be to get our hands on 100,000 stones."

"If we were allowed to count gravel, then we'd have it done in no time. Couldn't we say the tiny ones represent the little children in Hiroshima?"

"Hmmm." She looks dubious. "Nice idea, Jo, but I don't think that's quite the dignified effect we were hoping for."

I was suspicious when Mum announced we were off to the camp for a "treasure hunt". It sounded a bit conventional, and anyway what would the treasure have been? Carob brownies? Instead, I was told to look for stones. The idea is to collect one beautiful stone for each person who died thirty-seven years ago today, when the Bomb dropped on Hiroshima.

One of the women had read that 100,000 people were wiped out in seconds on 6 August 1945. The images from Mr Blake's film still appear whenever I close my eyes. There were bodies on the newsreel, but hundreds, not hundreds of thousands. People must have been turned into fall-out, then returned to earth as radioactive rain.

I want to make a good job of the collection, but the area nearest to the camp has been stripped of stones, so Gillian, Mum and I have followed the perimeter fence for a mile or so, towards the Forgotten Gate, where the ground hasn't yet been harvested. Timmy has been excused, of course, he's in one of the teepees, being presented with bagfuls of sweets to tempt his temperamental appetite. He's on a break between treatments, but you can still tell he's ill. Last summer his skin turned light gold in the sunshine, but this year he's stayed the colour of typing paper.

I crouch down, rub away at the hot earth with my hands. My nails are black and my fingertips sore, but I keep telling myself *this is nothing* compared to what the people suffered in Hiroshima.

My excavations reveal two smooth stones, one as big as a crab-apple, the other slightly smaller and flatter. I hold the smaller one in my hand and wonder who this might represent: the woman with her skin burned in the pattern of her kimono? No, she survived at least long enough to be filmed. Perhaps it's her sister or her husband or her son.

"This is really important to you, isn't it?" Gillian says. "After that film you saw?"

Gillian's easy to talk to. Dad thinks that the women at Greenham spend their time plotting to overthrow the government, "and at the bloody taxpayer's expense", but actually, they talk about everything. Cruise missiles, yes, and Aldermaston, and die-ins. But also Northern

390

Ireland and favourite foods and Nicaragua and *ET* and Russia and the big fire on *Crossroads* and how to be happy. They plan mischief and non-violent protests, paint banners and answer letters from all over the world. They open bottles of wine and drink it from plastic picnic mugs, and someone will get out a guitar or a clarinet, and I wonder whether the baby-faced American soldiers ever hear the music through their dormitory windows.

It was the talking that made Mum flush her pills down the toilet, and take up the flower remedies instead. Mags told her that her drugs were "a chemical cosh, prescribed by male doctors as part of the plot to keep women enslaved". Gillian said that was all very well, but any drug was difficult to withdraw from ("and you should know, Mags, I'd like to see you lay off pot") and so Mum should tail off gently, but Mum ignored her and apparently that's why she's been having nightmares and headaches, and a million other symptoms. But "that proves what the Valium's been doing to your system" (no prizes for guessing that's Mags again).

"I want to do it right," I tell Gillian. "For the people who woke up in Hiroshima that morning pleased it was a sunny day."

"I think it's time to go back." Mum appears, shielding her eyes from the bright sun with her hand. I lean on her as we walk back the way we came. The unfamiliar sensation of her hand gripping mine makes me feel fizzier than the Vimto.

It's only since we've been coming to the camp that I've realised how beautiful she is. Camp dress code doesn't suit most women but with no make-up and those horrible loose clothes, she *shines*. I can almost see why Dad fell in love with her.

And I wonder when he fell *out* of love with her.

Even though she's more beautiful than ever, he's furious with Mum, for "messing around with things she doesn't understand". Actually, I think he's more worried that some bloke from the Rotary could come down to the camp after a night at the pub to hurl abuse and might spot Mum. Dad's convinced this would be the end of his career.

The camp is ahead of us now, busier than usual because of the final preparations for the demo. I can see a TV crew: a cameraman, a guy with headphones, and a young male reporter sweating in his navy suit. As we approach, one of the women points at Mum, and I spot that Timmy is being filmed.

"Are you Mrs Morgan?" The reporter has a posh accent, and looks like Sebastian from *Brideshead Revisited*. "I'm James Donaldson, from *Thames Valley Today*. And I've been chatting to young Timothy here. What a *brave* little chap he is."

Mum frowns at the journalist. "What have you been talking to him about, exactly?" Her voice is steely, no longer softened by pills.

"Give us a minute." Mags takes Mum to one side. "I told him about Timmy's illness and —"

"What the hell did you do that for? Mags, I can't believe you'd do that."

392

"Look, I know he's a scumbag reporter and we can't trust him any further than we can throw him, but he's here and he's keen and there *is* more at stake here than just Timmy. You know that, don't you? And telling the world about Timmy is our only chance when the newspapers are full of stories about whether Ling-Ling the bloody panda is pregnant."

"But I don't want my family's business broadcast on the news." Mum sounds less angry now, and I can already tell who's going to win this argument: Mags is as determined as her namesake at Number Ten.

"Family is political, too, Lynda. You know that, don't you? Timmy's illness is *evidence*. He bears witness to what the authorities are doing to all our kids."

I don't think now is the time to remind Mags she hasn't got any kids, and regards motherhood as a further form of enslavement. Oh, and has even said if she ever did become pregnant and gave birth to a boy child, she'd have it adopted.

Mum sighs so deeply that for a moment it reminds me of pre-peace camp days, then she trudges back to the reporter. "So what do you want to know?"

The reporter gives the thumbs-up to his crew. He ushers Mum towards Main Gate, and positions her so the camp is behind her while the cameraman sets up his tripod.

Gillian stands next to me, watching. We're too far away from Mum to hear what she's saying. "Your dad's not going to like this much, is he?"

I shake my head. "Maybe we have to do this, like the children in the Hiroshima film. Maybe it's the only way

393

people will take notice. But do you believe it, Gillian? About the bombs and the experiments causing Timmy's leukaemia?" She's the only adult — apart from Mr Blake — I trust to be honest with me.

"Jo, I don't know. I wish I did. I do believe we're doing pretty terrible damage to the world, and that humans are suffering as a result. But whether that's directly to blame for what's the matter with your brother? I can't see how any of us could ever know for sure."

The reporter beckons Timmy to stand next to Mum, and the cameraman crouches down to film his face close up.

A fleet of cars pulls up alongside the camp: old bangers, Volvo estates, a shiny metallic green Cavalier. "That'll be the cavalry then," Gillian says, then slaps her own wrist, laughing. "*Naughty* Gillian. This is strictly a military-language-free zone."

Women spill out of the cars, embracing the camp dwellers. Boots are opened, and bags of stones stacked inside, the suspensions dipping slightly with every new load.

Gillian and I walk towards the cars and a woman who's driven from Bath specially for the occasion offers to give us a lift into Newbury. A dozen women have gone ahead, with still more stones. I sit in the front of the car, and as we approach the outskirts of town, I see kids doing normal school holiday things. Boys Timmy's age eating blue Slush Puppies and Cornettos outside a newsagent's; girls my age queuing outside the Corn Exchange to try to get in to see *An Officer and a*

Gentleman despite the 15 certificate. For a moment I long to be normal, not to feel the weight of the world on my shoulders.

But if I didn't feel that, I wouldn't be me.

The woman keeps getting lost in the one-way system, taking the ring road off in completely the wrong direction, and then getting stuck in traffic. I begin to panic: what if we're late? What if Mum hates me for letting us down?

Finally, Gillian manages to navigate us to where we need to be. We stop a couple of streets away from the war memorial, and take a bag of stones each; mine is only a small carrier, but it still digs into my palm. I open my mouth to complain but then remember why we're doing it, and close it again.

There's a crowd around the memorial now, and as we approach, I realise not everyone's there to congratulate us. In fact, there's a lot of shouting going on.

I look around for Timmy and my mother, but I can't spot them among the angry faces. A woman of Mum's age is jabbing her finger in the face of one of the camp women, screaming, "My father died in the war under the Japanese, how dare you do this? How bloody dare you."

Other people in the crowd murmur in agreement, and I feel torn. Are we being disrespectful? I think it's right to take a stand, but I still don't know whether Mutually Assured Destruction will save us or destroy us. That's why you have to act personally as well as politically: my stockpile is the Morgan safety net. Not that I'm making much progress with it. Mum's more or less stopped shopping because she spends all her time at Greenham — and when she ever is at home, she'll be sneaking in some of the women for a soak in a Badedas bath (sometimes they run out and have to use Timmy's Matey), or making cabbagey stews to take back to the camp.

Where *are* Mum and Timmy?

A man in his late teens breaks ranks and takes one of the larger stones from a bag that's been left open on the ground. For a few seconds, I think he's going to throw it at the protesting women, but instead he moves forward. I peer through a gap in the crowd: the concrete steps of the memorial are piled high with stacks of stones, like the Cornish dry-stone walls we studied in geography.

Finally I see Timmy and my mum, at the front of the group of protestors, next to Mags. I bet Mags pushed them forward, knowing it would make a good photo. She hates the media but doesn't seem to mind playing them at their own game.

The man takes his stone and places it carefully on top of others, on the lowest step. "You're doing the right thing," he tells the woman who was being hectored. "If we fought for nothing else, it was the freedom to speak our minds."

I look around me, to see what the reaction is, and on the other side of the street, I recognise a figure in a navy suit who's stopped to watch.

"Dad," I whisper, hoping he hasn't seen me, but knowing from his expression that he has. He looks smart, his hair is perfectly styled. Of course. Savannah's salon is round the corner. While Mum has been saving the world, Dad's sneaked away from the bank for a cut and blow dry.

"You bloody idiot!"

It's the woman with the jabbing finger, turning on the young man who placed the stone. There's a horrible pause, and then she turns round and thumps the man in the arm, a proper *thwack* that reverberates around the crowd and I swear I can physically *feel* the change in mood, as people turn on each other, shouting and jostling and pushing.

"Come on, Jo," Gillian says, trying to guide me out of the way, but the crowd is closing in on itself. I can see Mum and Timmy being shoved, right at the centre of the protest, and both their mouths contort into "O"s of panic.

"My little brother," I shout, pummelling at a man's blue T-shirted back with my fists. My nails are lined with earth, from digging away at the soil, and our bagfuls of stone-souls are trampled as people push and push . . .

"TIMMY! LYNDA!"

It's my father's voice. "Get out of the bloody way! That's my son in there, he's very poorly, he'll be hurt, let me through."

Sweat drips down my forehead. I try to call my father's name, so he knows where to find me, but my body's squashed and my lungs don't seem to be working and neither is my voice. *But he saw me just now*, I tell myself, *he'll be coming for me too.*

My sleeve is damp and I turn my head as much as I can to see that Gillian is crying. "Jo," her breath is short. "This isn't . . . how it was meant to be. Not at all . . . the way it was meant to be. But we'll be out soon. I promise."

The man with the blue T-shirt moves, and through the space below his armpit, I see — thank goodness — that Dad has reached my brother and Mum and is elbowing the protestors and the angry women out of the way. "Shift, go on, bloody MOVE IT, my son has leukaemia."

Finally that section of the crowd seems to hear my father and the people disperse like ripples in a pond, leaving my family huddled together, like the silhouettes in the circle on the cover of the *Protect and Survive* booklet. Except there's one person missing.

Now my father will come for me.

But as blue T-shirt man moves again, I get a last glimpse of my father ushering Mum and Timmy away, even as I feel the crowd crushing me.

He's abandoned me.

Someone shouts that the police are on their way, but that only inflames the people around me, and Gillian is praying now, mumbling under her breath, and although she's right next to me, I have never ever in my life felt more alone than I do now . . .

"Jo! JOOOOOO . . ."

CHAPTER
THIRTY-TWO

Optophobia — Fear of Opening One's Eyes

"At zero eight zero four hours this morning, reports were received of a large explosion in the Courtbridge industrial zone. At zero eight twelve hours, the first local residents began calling to report breathing difficulties and eye irritation."

Dennis looks up from his notes, fixing his audience with a steely stare. "Let us synchronise watches. It is now zero eight thirty-seven hours and the District Emergency Plan is officially in action. Good luck."

My soul mate pauses at his podium, as if he's expecting a round of applause. Luckily his colleagues realise that, even though this is only a readiness and resilience exercise, applause would be unseemly. That can come later, in the pub.

The different teams scatter to corners of the school hall, which is the nerve centre of today's activities. Each area has a sign, crafted by yours truly last night, using Clip Art and a colour printer. At the back, by the netball hoops, there's Command Control, which I typed in a bright red Courier font, set off nicely by an image of two manly hands shaking. Shaking each other, that is, rather than shaking in fear at the prospect of having to command or control anything.

Command Control is staffed by Dennis, plus the Police Sub-divisional Superintendent, the Regional Chief Ambulance Officer, the Divisional Head of the Fire and Rescue Service, and, of course, good old Mrs Fothergill. I wonder which of the three she's currently screwing; perhaps there'll be a performance-related bonus to the one who makes the best impression today. She's steered clear of her usual outlandish colours and is wearing black, presumably as a mark of respect to the "un-dead" — our volunteer victims who will be arriving over the next few hours. Though whether the plunging neckline and soaring split in her skirt can actually be regarded as respectful is open to debate.

By the gym monkey bars is Communications, which I put in a nice clear navy Arial Narrow, accompanied by a picture of a microphone. Our public relations officers, used to issuing press releases about Trading Standards unsafe toy campaigns and Christmas tree recycling services, are looking positively ravenous about disaster management.

The Casualty Bureau (a user-friendly buttercup yellow Nimbus Script with a picture of a syringe) could be mistaken for the telethon team after a gruelling night of *Children in Need*, while the Scientific Advisory Panel (green Verdana, microscope) are colonising their tables with maps and books, and a very nifty laptop which models weather fronts and cloud formations. Though I think the fact that Dennis prewarned them they "might be advised to have wind patterns and the industrial chemicals database fully updated" is borderline cheating.

He is *determined* nothing should go wrong.

Triage don't have a table or a sign (shame, really, I have a lovely purple Times New Roman left over) as they are going straight outside as soon as the first casualties get here. The playground currently resembles a camping and outdoor pursuits trade show, with an impressive line-up of decontamination tents, toilet tents, treatment tents and rest tents. Unlike in a proper disaster, the tents were requisitioned from central stores seven days ago and they've all been put up overnight, but Dennis will be insisting the medical staff delay using the facilities until what he calls "average erection times" have elapsed, to keep the exercise realistic.

I've been happy enough to do little jobs for him this last week. He sees it as a form of rehabilitation, I think: beginning with an unsupervised supermarket shop for teabags and instant coffee (I passed this test, though Dennis felt my choice of luxury chocolate biscuits rather than own-brand was reckless). Then I collated and stapled eighty-five briefing documents (a tick in the box for basic admin skills) before I was let loose on the signs.

But I'm not trying to prove anything. The reason I've been volunteering for mind-numbing tasks is that since my last flashback I've been fighting to keep myself together. I keep replaying my father's betrayal, over and over. I've avoided his phone calls, told Mum I'm busy and decided my scaredy-ness was, in fact, the right

401

approach after all. So much for misjudging Dad all these years, and for Timmy's theory about me being a daddy's girl. One thing my flashback proves is that you can only rely on yourself in this life.

Admittedly, Dennis comes a pretty close second in the reliability stakes, but even he's been sneaking round like a spy, planning today's drama.

"Hey, Joanna," Mikey calls across the room. "Great to see you back in action. You're looking gorgeous."

I let Mikey kiss me on both cheeks. "Yeah, right." Before I can stop myself, my hand darts up to my head, to cover my fuzzy patch.

Mikey and I are without portfolio. Presumably as our non-emergency jobs involve accident prevention, we've already failed in our duties. We're going to work as runners, relaying messages, fetching refreshments and, unofficially, snitching to Dennis on any team that isn't taking the exercise seriously enough.

"Surprised he let you come back for this," Mikey says. "Won't all the excitement endanger your health?"

"Nah. I'm as normal as I'm going to be now. And I wouldn't have missed his day of glory."

"Wanted you to see him being all *masterful*, I bet. There'll be some action in the sack later, no doubt, girl."

"Don't be coarse!" I giggle and hit him on the arm. "It's good to see you, though, Mikey. Listen, I've got a bit of a favour to ask."

"Let me guess . . . you want to borrow my fluorescent tabard for a kinky quickie with our emergency planning superhero."

402

I shudder, and I can tell Mikey's noticed. There's been no sex since Coventry. "I wouldn't want to tear him away, even for a minute."

"Yeah, but it wouldn't take him that long, would it? What, thirty seconds, tops?"

This time I don't giggle. "Not everything in life is about sex, Mikey," I say primly.

He nods over towards Councillor Fothergill, who is leaning unnecessarily low over a map of the area, revealing so much over-cooked cleavage that I catch a glimpse of both nipples. "Mrs F appreciates the importance of a good dollop of sensuality to keep up morale."

"Hmm. They'll be pulling the fire chief and ambulance boss apart within the hour, I think. Hasn't she bonked both —" I stop mid-sentence, remembering that Mikey's not meant to know that. "Anyway, that favour. Basically, I have somewhere else I need to be later on and I wondered if you'd cover for me."

Mikey looks like Christmas has come early. "Ooh. Subterfuge. I love it. But only if you tell me why."

"I have to go and meet someone . . . about my accident." *There.* How innocent does that sound?

"I didn't realise the NHS did routine appointments on a Sunday. And why would you need to keep that secret from the lovely Dennis?"

"It's more of a . . . psychological thing. More *ad hoc*."

"You can't be mysterious with your mate Mikey, you know, Jo. *Especially* when you need me."

403

"OK, OK. I know it might sound weird, but there's this guy called Frisky."

"Ooo-er. And is he?" He actually skips on the spot.

"Frisky is eighty-five years old, Mikey. He's a nice old chap I met at the hospital and he's, well, taken me under his wing. We go on trips together. He wants to show me life beyond public protection." I decide not to mention Luke, but just thinking about him makes me feel wobbly. I haven't seen him for three weeks, but I've decided today will be the last time. I need to stop kidding myself. Dennis is my destiny. He might not be perfect, but neither am I and he will never let me down. All Frisky does is make me believe things could be different, but they can't.

Mikey whistles. "Eighty-five? Now that's what I call an older man. Not that it means he doesn't still fancy his chances, Jo. The male capacity for self-delusion is one of the last faculties to go, you know."

"He's a kind person who wants to help me." Even though I'm about to let him down. "So you'll do it?"

Mikey winks at me. "Course I will. So where's he taking you?"

"Now that is something I'd like to know myself. Frisky has a terrible fondness for surprises."

Three hours on and Courtbridge is in the grip of a major disaster, but Dennis hasn't broken a sweat. Two chemical tankers have exploded (admittedly, in a factory that doesn't actually exist: all our industry is small-scale, making catnip toys or organic chutney) and, though initial indications suggested a terror attack, it's now clear that the blasts probably resulted from a factory supervisor falling asleep on the job.

The playground is full of "casualties", volunteers with cards in their pockets to remind them what symptoms they should be exhibiting. A few have emptied out capsules of fake blood from their own personal am dram collections, though in fact no patient at the Casualty Reception Centre is meant to have been caught in the explosion itself. They're workers at other factories or local residents, all struck down by breathing problems, eye irritation and a rather worrying yellowy-green discharge from the lungs.

I've been allocated the job of relaying patient information to the woman who updates the "facts and figures" electronic display. It's a cross between a cricket scoreboard and the Eurovision totaliser. So far, I have passed on the sad news that three people are known to have died at the factory itself, two have expired here after their lungs filled with gunk, and we have six stretcher cases and twenty-three walking wounded. The latter are being forced to endure decontamination showers, although it's chilly for early July. Funny how their method acting ceases abruptly when they're ordered to strip to their undies. "Do I have to? It's only an exercise . . ."

As part of my escape strategy, I've been trying to get in Dennis's line of sight as often as possible, so that he will remember me being here. That *was* the plan, anyhow, but today he doesn't seem to see me at all. Because I am neither important nor feigning injury, I don't count. I'm invisible.

I try one last time, as he strides towards the boffins. "Dennis," I whisper.

He stops, looks around him. Eventually he spots me. "Jo. What's the matter? Another death?" His eyes shine with excitement, though he must know how many casualties there'll be, as he was the one who planned the entire bloody thing.

"No, no. Nothing like that. I just wanted to say how well it seems to be going. You're in your element."

He frowns as he processes the information. "So no update then?"

"Well, no, I thought you might like some . . ." I try to find an important-sounding phrase. "Performance feedback."

Dennis tuts. "When I need feedback, do you think I'd want it from you?" He must register the shock in my face, because he adds, "I mean, no disrespect or anything, Jo, but you're not really an expert in this area, are you?"

"No," I mumble.

"Not that you aren't doing a fantastic job, I'm sure." He looks around him, at the dozens of people darting to and fro, and nods in satisfaction. "But it would really be best if you refrain from talking to me until the exercise is over, unless you have urgent data. We need to stay in our respective roles, and there is no chain of communication established between the head of operations and a . . . a . . . runner."

"Right."

"No offence. We'll celebrate later though, eh? Just the two of us." And he gives me such a leer that I realise faked death and destruction has done what I couldn't, and given Dennis his mojo back.

He resumes his journey towards the scientists, and I stand in the corner of the room, wanting to scream or sob or both.

But I don't. Instead I watch him as he interrupts two of the scientific advisers, snatching their papers and ticking them off for something, because he can.

My *soul mate*. The most reliable man I know. The one constant in my life.

I don't think I love him any more.

Oh God. I wait to feel something, a sharp pain or a blow to the head. But instead I feel a leaden certainty, like an indigestible meal sitting in my stomach.

He's moved over to Communications now, pushing that misbehaving kiss-curl off his forehead so he looks more weighty in interviews. But it isn't just Dennis, it's all of this, the pretence that you can prepare for the unthinkable, seems so *futile*. I can't think of a worse place for a scaredy-cat to work, dwelling on the worst that can happen, to the exclusion of the best. Don't let this happen, Jo. Focus on his good qualities, that confidence and certainty . . .

This feeling will pass, it must. I am not a wicked person. Loyal is my middle name. Dennis has nursed me and cared for me and stood by me. I *won't* let him down.

I'm tying myself in mental knots, so to stop myself, I go to look for Mikey. I find him sitting on a wall behind the school, rolling a joint.

"Talk about risky, with all these police around."

He shrugs. "They're a little preoccupied, don't you think? I needed to chill, mate. Whole things makes me feel sick."

"Yeah." I look back over my shoulder at the tents and ambulances and people and it reminds me of that awful bunker: I have to escape. Now. "Listen, I need to get going. Are you OK to take over?"

He abandons his rolling, and tucks the unlit joint back into his tobacco box. "Such sacrifices I make for you, Jo. Off you go to your octogenarian. Whatever he's got lined up, it's gotta be more fun than this."

CHAPTER
THIRTY-THREE

Pyrophobia — Fear of Fire

I power-walk to Frisky's villa, forcing myself to go faster and faster, to block out the confused thoughts that might derail me totally. I must stick to Plan A: stay loyal to Dennis. Count my blessings. Turn my back on Frisky and Luke before they get bored and reject me.

I can't meet Luke's eye when he answers the door, but fortunately he's equally cool with me. I've convinced myself that he can *tell* I imagined being kissed by him in Nathan's office.

Frisky's in the front of the Red Peril, giving Luke directions, and they're bickering like a pair of old women. But at least neither of them is checking their solemn, yet reassuring facial expression in the wing mirror of an ambulance, as I spotted Dennis doing earlier.

"Stop the car!"

We're in nowhere land, a big slice of 1960s' suburbia. The kind of place where wife-swapping and ouija-boarding flourishes, a place like Salzburg Avenue, where everything happens below the surface.

Luke's already opening the door, but Frisky puts his mottled hand out to stop him. "We're not there yet, but I wanted to say something important."

He turns around and those sharp brown eyes scrutinise me. Don't tell me he's guessed, too? About the snogging fantasy?

But he smiles and says, "I've asked a lot of you up till now, Joanna, and though it hasn't always been entirely painless, I like to think it's made a difference." He waits for me to say yes.

"Um. Yes. It has. I mean, I know I haven't become Wiltshire go-karting champion. Or set up my own decorating company. But you always make me think."

"Indeed. Well, today, I am going to ask you to do more than think. It means you must trust me like never before. But believe me when I say I have researched this thoroughly and it is *not* dangerous. And I did gain the permission of Dr Williams."

I blink. "Ri-ight." As if Nathan would dare to object to *anything* after what happened in his office. And the fact that Frisky's never bothered with this preamble before is worrying: the emergency planning exercise is suddenly looking a much safer place to be.

"As usual, of course, I will participate fully myself. Go first, in fact."

"Frisky, you know I trust you. But I can't absolutely promise I'll do whatever you want. I do need some discretion."

"A get-out clause, you mean?" Frisky frowns at me. "I would have hoped that by now you'd understand I have your best interests at heart."

410

He looks so vulnerable. So what if it's jumping out of a plane or diving into a reservoir in an aqualung? Surely I can do it, for him. Especially as it'll be the last time. "Sorry. I was being silly. If you're happy it's safe, then I'll try whatever you want."

He nods, unsmiling. "Now Luke, to be blunt, I know you regard spending time with me less desirable than facing a firing squad, but you've shown an admirable level of self-sacrifice for Joanna's sake. From which I conclude that you do want to help her?"

Luke shrugs. "You know I do." He does look adorable when he sulks. *Stop it, Jo.*

"And so when I tell you that today's challenge *may* cause a little initial alarm, and that what Joanna will need is a promise that both of us are willing to be at her side . . . you assent to this?"

"Jeez, can you not speak modern English? Yeah, I promise whatever it is. It's not like I have a choice."

"Good," Frisky says and taps the dashboard. "On we go then. Straight ahead. Don't spare the horses!"

I shiver in the back of the car, wondering what Luke and I have agreed to. I've always assumed that Frisky's accident is such ancient history that it no longer affects him, but what if all that Battle of Britain *bonhomie* has cunningly disguised the fact that he is flipped-lid, crazy-horse, full-on bonkers? That we're part of some plot to take over the world?

"Right, then immediate left, then pull up on the left."

The building doesn't look like World Domination HQ. It's a modern community hall, in bright yellow brick, far too cheery for this overcast day. There's a handwritten sign taped to the glass door: "Inner Strength Workshop, straight ahead in Citadel of Mental Powers (also known as the English Country Garden Seminar Room)".

"Inner strength?" I say, feeling reassured. "As in, bit of chanting, a few self-affirmations, and maybe some yogic breathing?"

"Something like that." Frisky coughs. "Though there may be some more *physical* activity required."

"Great," Luke says. "I've always wanted to know how to tear up a telephone directory."

"Shhh," Frisky says as we push open the door to the Citadel. Every surface has been Cath Kidstoned. Tea roses on the walls, the curtains, the tie-on chair cushions, and an air freshener in every corner, pumping out synthesised flower fragrance.

The man at the front glares at us. He's rather short for a guru, though he does have the prerequisite grey ponytail, held back by a thin piece of leather. "You've missed visualisation," he says, then checks himself. "But greetings, friends, and welcome to the journey."

We take seats behind everyone else, our bums sliding on the flowery cushions. There are about twenty delegates: New Agers, seeking the secrets of the universe; Trendy Old Dears looking for the secret of eternal youth; and balding Mid-Life Men, looking for meaning after redundancy or divorce.

No wonder the guru looked confused, we don't fit into any of his categories.

"So, once you've found your harnessing image, you can call on it any time you are feeling under pressure, or wish to reconnect with your life mission statement." Our guru wears loose linen clothes, and sandals. He has *horrible* feet, like a gorilla's, all gnarled, with rust-coloured nails that have begun to curl back into the tips of his toes. Can I really take advice from a man who neglects his soles?

"Time for refreshments," he says. "Though you three may like to join me for a catch-up before the walk."

The *walk*? Is this what Frisky's been making all the fuss about, an inspirational stroll round mystical Courtbridge?

The guru lets us queue for a herbal tea and take a millet flapjack, then we follow him into a corner. He begins to drone on about mind-power and sixth senses and inner cores.

". . . and I always find that the real proof of the visualisation is when people tell me they still feel their feet are being bathed in cool spring water, even in the midst of the fire-walk."

"Fire-walk?" The colour has drained from Luke's bronzed face.

"That's why we do it, really. I mean, the walking on hot coals thing is a bit of a cliché, can seem a bit city wanker, but it has *such* a positive effect on self-image and inner resources, that I had to reinstate it."

Now Frisky's warnings make sense. I feel terrified, but oddly curious. Could I do this? After all, I promised I'd try . . .

"You bastard," Luke says to Frisky, and marches out of the room.

413

The guru scowls. "I sense some tension here, guys. Can we talk out the issues?"

But Frisky's already followed Luke, and I am right behind him. I nearly collide with a woman walking her chihuahua before I spot the two of them next to the Red Peril.

". . . and all that bullshit about helping Jo, when this was about some weird, screwed-up mission to fuck with my head. You're unbelievable." Luke is rather magnificent in full flow.

Frisky seems calm. "You know, Luke, I wouldn't mind being on the receiving end of your anger, if I thought it was actually helping. But it's not helping, is it?"

"Cut the psychobabble. You know what this is about." Luke is fumbling with the car keys, trying to unlock the door, but his hands are shaking too much.

"So running away again is how you're going to deal with it, is it, Luke? Because it worked so well in the past, didn't it? Leaving America was *such* a bright new beginning." Sarcasm makes Frisky's voice sour.

"I didn't leave America because of that. I left it because of you."

"After four score years, I think I can look after myself."

Luke shakes his head. "Oh yeah. I remember. They wouldn't let you out of hospital on your own after the stroke, or have you conveniently forgotton that bit?"

Stroke? Frisky told me he'd had a "cerebral accident". I stare at him and his jaw goes slack, a

414

picture of defeat and shame, as if getting sick is the ultimate humiliation.

"They . . . they would have done. Fuss about nothing. And don't change the subject."

"You'd be in a care home if I hadn't come over," Luke says, then stops. "Not that I didn't want to help, Gramps, you know that I did. But I won't have you rewriting history." His voice is softer now.

Frisky notices me at last, and looks more embarrassed. "In case you've forgotten, Luke, you promised me you'd do this, for Joanna."

"It doesn't matter," I say, and Luke seems surprised to see me.

"I don't . . ." he begins. "Jo, I don't want you to get the wrong idea. I would do it, but . . ."

"Luke, it's fine." I don't know what's going on, but I know this isn't only about fire-walking.

"Yes, that's right, Luke," Frisky says. "Stay holed up in that caravan for the rest of your days. Never let anyone get close or see you're frightened. It's your life to throw away."

Finally, Luke manages to unlock the door to the Red Peril and, without meeting my eye, climbs inside and drives off. Frisky looks sheepish. "It's a long story."

Maybe if I was planning to stick around after today, I'd feel I had the right to hear it, but instead I nod. "Right."

"Oh, Joanna. I just wish I knew how to help him . . ." He sounds desperate, and I realise that our friendship isn't only about helping me, it's about rescuing all three of us.

"Sometimes people have to help themselves," I say. I try not to let myself dwell on how he's going to feel when I let him down.

"Yes. Yes, I have always had trouble realising that." He nods towards the community centre. "I'll understand if you don't want to . . ."

It's such a tempting no-fault get-out that I nearly accept, but I can't do this to him. I want him to see me as someone who can, just once, show some mettle.

Whatever that is.

"Let's go back inside. These feet were made for fire-walking, I reckon. So long as my nerve holds."

We endure sessions on incantations and the deity within, before our guru gets to the all-important science bit. Apparently we won't burn the soles of our feet because: number one, the skin there is much thicker than anywhere else on the body; number two, we barely make contact with the burning coals so, like putting your finger through a candle flame, there'll be no damage; and number three, when properly aligned, our chakras will protect us.

Somehow I find three reasons less convincing than one. He's protesting too much.

I keep drifting off, staring out of the window and wondering where Luke has gone, and why this particular activity had the effect it did. Intimacy is what most little boys are afraid of, isn't it? Only little girls are allowed to be afraid of pain and suffering. Luke stood up to the thugs at the fairground, and fell in love with earthquakes despite their dangers. Yet he wimps out now. It makes no sense.

The guru tells us how to approach the coals. It'll help if we're sweating, as most of us will be, because water is another barrier between us and the heat. "Ladies, think how you always wet your finger before testing the temperature of an iron. And finally, remember, this is essentially a spiritual experience, but even so it's as well not to dawdle."

Finally, we troop out to the back of the centre, past the children's playground and sandpit to an area that's already glowing like the barbecues Dennis opposes so fiercely on health and safety grounds.

I giggle at the thought of Dennis's reaction to the idea of walking over hot coals. "But *why*?" I imagine him saying. "What on earth would be the point?"

The doubts I have about the wisdom of the fire-walk drift away like smoke. Anything that Dennis would dismiss as madness seems instantly appealing.

The guru has a young male helper who has already prepared the trench: judging from the precise lines and concrete step up, the fire-walks are a regular event. Which must mean that it's safe. The trench itself is only ten feet long, but the heat the fire is generating is intense, primeval against the grey overcast sky. I think, suddenly, of the people at Hiroshima, of the choice between burning to death as the fires spread, or jumping into the boiling river.

"How do you feel?" Frisky asks, his face reflecting the red of the coals.

"Apprehensive. I heard what the guru said and I can believe it in my head. But when we stand here, I can't quite believe in my heart that we'll get across it unscathed."

He nods, back in the relentlessly positive mood I no longer quite believe. "Yes, but experience has shown me that whenever I'm afraid of something, it's almost always something worth doing."

The guru ushers us into line on the far side of the fire pit. "There'll be elderflower cordial and more flapjacks after the walk," he says.

So all that stands between me and an organic treat is ten feet of red-hot coals. I jostle with the others to get to the back of the queue. Not like Frisky, who steps confidently towards the front. We take off our shoes and socks, lining them up like children doing Tumbletots.

Frisky turns around, gives me an emphatic thumbs-up. "Here we go, then," he says, spitting on his hands as if he's about to wrestle the fire, rather than walk through it.

We all take a breath and hold it as Frisky's gnarled yet very patrician left foot lifts up to take the first step. "I'm tempted to misquote Neil Armstrong," he announces, "one small step for an old bugger and so on, but I do so hate to be predictable. Bottoms up!"

And he launches himself on to the coals, moving so fast that we barely have time to "ooh" and "aah" before he reaches the other side, grinning and laughing. "I couldn't feel a thing! Might have to do it again!"

The guru smiles a tight smile. "You'll have to go to the back of the queue. Right, who's next?"

418

I watch as the New Agers and the paunchy men and the right-on grans take their turn. Some whoop with joy afterwards, others are in tears — but not, our guru points out, due to injury. It's because they're ecstatic.

I *can* do this, can't I? I look ahead to the building only twenty feet away. My eye is drawn to the doorway where a tall figure, rendered wobbly by the heat haze, is standing quite still.

"Luke."

He walks slowly towards the fire and past it to me. "I shouldn't have run away," he says. "I don't break promises."

"I'm sure you had your reasons. But it's good you came back." As I speak, I realise it's more than *good*. "So are you going to watch me? Frisky's already done it."

He leans into me so close that I feel the warmth of his breath on my neck and it feels hotter than the fire pit. "Actually, I want to try it myself."

"But . . . is that a good idea? I mean, it's none of my business what happened but I know you must have your reasons."

"I want to tell you, Jo. Afterwards." And he turns to take a good look at the fire pit. "Sheesh. It looked a lot smaller from over there." His eyes glow in the firelight.

"You don't have anything to prove, Luke."

He shakes his head. "Really, I do. Maybe not to you or to my grandfather, but to myself."

Only an elderly woman is ahead of us now and she steps on to the coals, walking steadily across them as if she's on a sponsored hike. She turns when she gets to the other side, and waves across the heat haze, beckoning for me to follow.

"Do you want to go first?" I ask Luke. His hands are trembling as he takes off those dirty trainers, and fluffy sports socks.

"No. You'll give me something to cross the coals for."

I frown at him, trying to understand whether it's a joke, but before I can work it out, the guru calls across the smoke. "Right. Wish me luck, Luke."

"Good luck."

I approach the bed of coals and all I can smell is fuel. Surely it's not right to pour petrol on a fire we're about to walk on. I hold my foot above the pit and feel the heat, like a pulse, on my sole.

The guru wags his finger. "Heart over head, friend. You can't think about this too much."

Ah, thinking too much. My life would be so much simpler if I could break that habit.

Now's my chance.

I see Frisky at the other end of the pit. Ten feet. Five steps. Go, go, *go* . . .

I feel the heat on my legs, but not on my feet, as I take the first step on to the coals. They shift beneath my toes and all I can hear is crackling. Strangely, there's no sensation on my feet, and before I know it I'm on the other side, and the grass suddenly feels spikier than ever before and then Frisky takes me in his arms and gives me a huge, slobbery kiss. "Yes! Joanna! I knew you could do it."

I expected to feel euphoric or faint, but actually my main sensation now is of being grounded, balanced, capable of anything. No one else did that for me. I managed it on my own. I turn and there on the other side of the pit is Luke, still shaking. "It's easy," I shout across. "If I can do it, anyone can."

He bites his lip, and despite his height, he looks like a boy. Then, just like a boy, he plunges himself into the midst of the fire, taking great heavy steps that leave gaps between the coals.

He makes it to the other side, large drops of sweat running down his face.

"There! We all did it," I say, and even Frisky dares to get close.

"Well done, Luke. Never thought you'd manage it."

But then I look more closely at Luke's face and realise he isn't sweating. He's *crying*.

"It's the emotion," the guru says. "The harder they are, the harder they fall."

I feel a terrible sense of disappointment in Luke, and then a rush of guilt. I shouldn't judge a man because he's in touch with his sensitive side. That's what us girls want these days, isn't it? But I can't help it, I expected more of him.

He seems to be fighting for breath and I compose my face into an expression of sympathy, though I actually want to tell him to pull himself together.

Finally he manages to mumble. "It's not . . . it's not the emotion. It's my feet."

I peer down at his soles. They are blistering before my eyes, angry shapes like balloons inflating.

"Fuck," says the guru. "This has never happened . . . I mean, it's perfectly safe. It must have been the way you did it, yin and yang out of kilter. This is not my fault —"

Frisky pushes him out of the way. "Save it for the compensation claim. Now make yourself useful and help me lift him into the car. This boy doesn't need elderflower cordial. He needs a doctor."

CHAPTER
THIRTY-FOUR

Oneirophobia — Fear of Dreams

Somehow I manage to drive the rickety Red Peril to the hospital, abandoning it on the double yellows outside casualty. It didn't exactly make an ideal ambulance. The guru travelled with us, mumbling about public liability insurance, and now he holds Luke's head, while Frisky clutches his calves and I, rather embarrassingly, am allocated his . . . um, well, his bottom. Not that it's a bad bottom to have to support. On the contrary. It provides an extremely firm surface to grasp hold of.

He's been very stoical so far, the tears dried up within two minutes of leaving the centre and the only peep out of him has been an apology for weeping. He tried to insist on walking into the hospital but when Frisky touched his feet, ever so gently, with the tip of his finger, Luke began to retch, so instead we decided that we had to carry him.

It's not until the casualty nurse races forward with a wheelchair that we work out that might have been an easier way to bring him in. Perhaps fire-walking has singed our brain cells.

"Next of kin?" the nurse says, while Luke clenches his fists so he doesn't moan. They've propped his feet up on a plastic chair.

"Me," says Frisky.

Luke grunts. Then he says, "But if it's OK, I'd like *her* to stay with me."

The nurse stands up. "No skin off my nose. But you and your girlfriend could be in for a bit of a wait."

I blush again. The guru sees his chance to escape, mumbling about needing to realign the chakras of the other students, and Frisky looks from Luke, to me, and back again. "I can walk home," he says, "as you don't need me here."

"Don't go," I say, but Luke won't look at his grandfather.

"I think I should, Joanna. Now, next time, I'll pick something easy. Ballroom dancing or . . ." But his voice tails off as he understands that there can't possibly be a next time. In the worst way, this has taken the decision out of my hands. "Luke, I'm sorry. I know this is my fault. Playing God has become rather a habit of mine, hasn't it? Time to stop meddling now."

Before we can answer, he walks towards the sliding doors. I try to go after him, but Luke reaches out. "Leave him, Jo. I need you here."

"Do you?" I feel flattered and flustered. "Would you like a drink? Tea, coffee, water. Or I could go and see —"

"I said, I need you *here*, Jo. I'm feeling woozy. And my feet hurt like crazy."

424

I take a peep: the blisters are oozing yellow liquid that's crusting at the edges. And the ends of his toes are bright red. "Well, at least they haven't dropped off."

He manages a weak smile and then closes his eyes. I look around the department: it's full of fit young men, nursing sporting injuries, laughing and trying to outdo each other with Sunday afternoon war wounds.

"Everything OK, kid?" Luke asks.

"Yeah. Fine. I've just realised that this must have been where they brought me after my head injury."

"You don't remember?"

"No. My memory's a big black hole about some things, and totally hyperactive about others."

"What do you mean?"

I *wish* I hadn't said that. "Oh, it's nothing."

"Go on. Distract me from my agony."

"OK. But you have to promise me you won't think I'm mad." He nods. "Well, ever since the bang on my head, I get these weird flashbacks to things that happened to me years ago."

He stares at me and I realise he *does* think I'm mad. One of the football players switches on a portable radio, and "Bohemian Rhapsody" fills the waiting room. I'm trying to think of some witty comment about the karaoke evening to change the subject, perhaps a joke about my singing voice, when he says, "Thing is, I get flashbacks too, Jo."

"Right." Now it's my turn to look gob-smacked.

"What are yours of?" he asks.

"Um . . . school. Home. All kinds of different stuff that seemed really important when I was twelve. And yours?"

"The same thing, every single time." He winces.

I wait for him to explain. Freddie Mercury's voice fills the space as Luke takes his time.

"I've always been a heavy sleeper," he begins. "It was a joke at home. But in the flashbacks, the faintest crackling noises wake me up. And intense heat, like sunbathing at midday, but it's dark. The heat's coming from the corridor. I touch the hotel room door and it stings my hand and then I smell burning wood." His eyes are closed.

"You don't have to do this . . ."

He holds up his hand. "It kinda makes me choke so I go to the window and pull open the doors to the balcony and then when I step out the air feels so good but I see fire-tenders. Rows of 'em. And people on the sidewalk, in gowns and PJs."

"Go on."

"I lean against the front rail of the balcony and I crane my neck so I can see more of the building above me. The suite seven floors above me where my parents are, the room with one of the best views of Manhattan. We paid extra for it, for me to share with my grandfather because he'd flown all that way, a treat for his birthday. The big family reunion, like in the movies. But he insisted they take the suite. 'Suites are for couples,' he said. The suite that's leaking orange flames through broken windows."

"When was this, Luke?"

"Five years ago," he says, then opens his eyes. "Then nightly, seven days a week. With matinées on the weekend."

"They didn't make it, did they? My words sound too blunt. "Sorry. But Frisky told me your parents had died. He wouldn't give me the details."

He nods. "The fire started on the floor below them. My mom bust her ankle skiing at Whistler so we think that when they heard the alarm, they decided to stay where they were. Wait for help. Gramps woke same time as me, and we both tried to get to them. Ran down our corridor, up to the stairs, but the doors wouldn't budge. We pushed and pulled and we didn't notice the bars were red hot till much later." And he holds out his right hand, where the scar that matches Frisky's suddenly makes sense. "We gave up when the smoke got too much, Frisky dragged me downstairs. I wanted to stay. Keep trying." His eyes are dull now, and his voice resigned. "They said they were probably dead before we even left our room, from smoke."

I want to reach out and hug him. "Luke, I am so, so sorry. You tried. That was all you could do, wasn't it?"

"I guess I know that in here," he says, touching his head, "but I will never believe it in here." He holds his fist to his chest.

The song on the radio's changed to "Walking on Sunshine", until a nurse walks over and switches it off.

"And Frisky?"

Luke looks down. "Mom always said we were so alike but as we'd always lived in the States, and my grandmother died when Mom was twenty, I'd never

427

spent time with my British family. And that time was running out, you know. That's why he came over. Now what we have in common is watching that building burn."

"No wonder you two seem so spiky all the time."

"Yeah. We'd had two days to get to know each other, then the fire. He stayed a while, helped with all the funeral arrangements, then had a stroke six months after flying home. Maybe Mom dying brought it on, though the doctors won't say so for sure."

I wish I could hold him, tell him it'll be OK, but it seems too trite. Instead I say, "It was good of you to come to Britain, look after him. Give it all up."

He shrugs. "Had to get away from the States for a while anyhow, and I thought being in the house where Mom grew up might make me feel closer to her."

Three young lads come into casualty, the one in the middle supported by his friends. They're singing "Yesterday" with all the mournful enthusiasm of a pack of spaniels.

"It hasn't helped, though, has it?"

"Maybe a little."

I hesitate before saying more, wondering how far I ought to pry. Getting this right seems so important. "I suppose you've heard all the stuff about time healing?"

"Sure. One day maybe I might even be ready to quit the caravan."

A thought occurs to me. "That's why you live in the caravan. Because of the fire?"

"Yeah. I tried to sleep indoors but the nightmares . . . worse than the flashbacks. Always trapped

428

somewhere." He blinks hard, as if he's trying to banish the images. "Why, what did you think it was about?"

"Frisky told me you loved animals. That you were sleeping outside because local cats were being stolen."

"I'm allergic to cats." He begins to laugh, and I can't help joining in. The other patients give us wary glances. "I got to hand it to Frisky," Luke says, when he finally stops, "he's got one hell of an imagination. I guess he didn't want you to think I was a psycho."

I nod. "No, just a vigilante. But he did tell me about how you need to get away, sometimes. Where do you go?"

"Go?"

I feel embarrassed at my directness now. "Well, you know when Frisky and I decorated the parlour. He said you'd gone away."

"Yeah, sure. To Tokyo. I was giving a paper to a conference on how to earthquake-proof cities."

"Oh," I manage, after a while. "I didn't realise you were still working. I thought . . ."

"That I was a drop-out? No. Great thing about my job is I can work anywhere in the world. Laptop, modem, brain, that's all I need. Apart from anything, work helps me stop thinking. Jeez, he's really painted a great picture of me. Must be the world's worst matchmaker."

"Matchmaker?"

Luke looks down. "Well, yeah. That's what he's been trying to do, isn't it? Fix us up. Like any girl would go for a guy who has to sleep outdoors like a dog."

"Or any guy would go for a girl who is scared of her own shadow." We smile shyly at each other, united in self-deprecation. "He does care, though, Frisky does. Even this," I point at his poor feet, "was about wanting to help you, wasn't it?"

"Yeah. I worked that one out, in the car. I came back because I made my promise, but also because I don't *want* to be this way. No one would want to be this way. But this is part of me, now. I don't know if I can ever go home. Memories, you know."

We sit in silence and I can tell Luke's in a lot of pain. I keep talking to distract him. "Well, my flashbacks aren't quite like yours, but they're still scary. You know you said you were afraid of earthquakes, until you understood them? And I was scared of the A-bomb. Seems stupid now, doesn't it?"

"No, not stupid at all. Different times."

"But it's not just fear. In my flashbacks, I get so angry with the adults because they did nothing. I stop. "Sorry, I'm rambling. Shall I get you a drink? A chocolate bar?"

"No, keep talking. You're interesting."

"Me?" I blush. "Right, well, when you're a kid, you don't see why things have to stay the same. You fight. That's why I tried to protect us from the Bomb, though any idiot could see it was naïve. But then you grow up, you give in. That's what I did. Gave in to being afraid, so that the stuff I was scared of grew and grew, until it outnumbered the things I loved."

"And then came the accident, right?"

"Yes. Then came the accident and I understood that my self-imposed bunker had done me no good at all, made me make wrong decisions about my job and my . . ." I tail off. It's disloyal to mention Dennis. That fire-walk tricked me into feeling I'm invincible, when I should know better. "Anyhow, I'm not saying that's what you're doing, Luke, but if you leave it too long, well . . . I'm a warning, that's all."

"A warning, huh? Well, you're the nicest warning I've ever had, Jo."

"Oh." I don't know what to say. "Right. Thank you."

"And does your story have a happy ending?" he asks.

I sigh. "Um . . ." I think about my life ahead with Dennis, and my resolve falters. But I must be able to work things out. I'll invite the lesbians over for dinner, cultivate a friendship with the dope-grower. Encourage Dennis to be more outgoing, get over his resentment of nosy neighbours, forget the way his mother let him down, make him realise that, like John Lennon said, life is what happens when you're making other plans.

As if he'll ever accept that. My confidence in the future drains away faster than bathwater. Luke is staring at me. "So does it? Have a happy ending?"

"Well," I manage, "it's not an *unhappy* ending."

He blinks. "Right. Sure. Not unhappy. I guess I'd settle for that these days."

Well, that really was *terrific*, Jo, wasn't it? You're such a bloody inspiration.

Luke leans forward to touch his feet.

"Are they hurting again?" I ask and he nods, not looking at my face. I suddenly remember how I'd

431

pictured his feet when I was in bed with Dennis in Coventry. Even with singed edges, they're every bit as tanned and perfect as I'd imagined. I stand up, anxious to get away. "Let me see where you are in the queue for being seen."

I walk towards the reception area, and wait for the nurse to get off the phone. Against my better judgement, I look round at Luke. He seems so lonely, in the midst of the joking footballers. I can't turn my back on him now.

But I must. I pinch myself hard on the inside of my arm as I repeat in my head what Timmy told me, "sometimes selfish is good for everyone".

The middle-aged doctor, when we finally get to see him, is thorough but crotchety. As he examines Luke's feet, he mumbles under his breath, "bloody self-inflicted injuries".

"I beg your pardon?" I say. Luke is beyond speech.

"Every Sunday afternoon it's the same. Football injuries, rugby injuries, drinking in the pub injuries. At least your boyfriend's original."

"He's not my . . ."

"Though quite what makes anybody walk on coals is beyond me. Doesn't exactly help this afternoon that half my nurses are at some ludicrous emergency exercise. Great timing."

Shit. I look at the wall clock. Six thirty. The exercise must be nearly over by now, and Dennis will be wondering where I am. Or maybe not: he's probably cracked open the beers with the other bigwigs, backslapping away.

But I owe him my support. I need to work at loving him again, because he's the only person in the world who'll put up with me. "So how bad are the burns?"

"They look worse than they are. They haven't gone too deep, so we'll dress them and then your young man will have to keep his feet up for a week or so. Ever fancied yourself as a nurse?"

"I'm not his . . ." And then I stop. I'm making it worse.

While they dress Luke's feet, I order a taxi. Once he's been wheeled to the car, I chat inanely to the driver about the weather and the football results. Anything to stop Luke asking me for help that I can't give.

At the villa, the taxi parks near the front door, as I tell Frisky what the doctor said.

"We'll either kill each other or end up best buddies by the end of the week," he says, and I hover round the taxi, so he can't ask me to come and visit. I know I'm being horribly selfish, but I have to cut the ties.

By the time Frisky, the driver and I have manhandled Luke on to the chintzy chaise longue in the conservatory, we're all panting.

"Is it all right if I take the taxi on?" I say. "Only I have another appointment. I'm late as it is."

Luke and Frisky look at me, then each other, and their faces fall. "Can't you stay for a tea?" Frisky says.

"She's done enough already," Luke says. "Thank you, Jo. You kept me going."

Before I can stop myself, I kneel down and grab his hand. I whisper, "What I said. I didn't put it very well, but it matters, Luke. It really matters. Maybe it's a chance for you and Frisky to start over. Talk through the bad stuff. Get to know each other. *Please*."

He grips my hand back, hard. "Yeah. I know. Not easy, though. It'll be easier if you're around to remind me."

I take my hand back. "I . . . I don't know if . . ."

"I don't mean like a *girlfriend*. I just mean as a friend. I don't exactly have a whole posse of buddies about to show up with dirty movies and a crate of Miller Lite."

I stand up. "I'll try," I say, the guilt burning like the heat I can still feel from his hand in mine. "I need to go."

I turn to go but Frisky catches me for a hug. His body feels lighter than I expected, as though I could crush him in my arms.

"Thanks, Frisky. It was fun. Well, until . . ." and I wave towards Luke.

"Fun. Yes. Such a shame you can't stay. I had a special fishy treat arranged too, smoked salmon. Perhaps not the most tasteful, under the circumstances."

I wish I could tell him why I need to do this, but know I can't. I return to the taxi.

"Where to, love?"

"St Matthew's School? On the ring road? It's not far."

I stare through the back window as he accelerates away. The villa looks dark and reproachful, and I

434

imagine the days of bickering ahead. Maybe it was better to leave them to it, force them to settle their differences.

I turn to face forward again. This was only an interlude, a few strange months I'll forget as soon as I begin focusing on my old life again. And a *not unhappy ending* is still one hell of a lot better than most of us manage, after all. Look at my parents.

The playground is deserted, though judging from the soapy water still draining away from the decontamination shower tents, the exercise has only just finished.

I creep back into the hall, where Dennis has evidently finished his speech, and people are helping themselves to drinks from the free bar that's been set up on the scientific adviser's table. Rescuers dressed in chemical protection gear, and casualties with dog tags in paper smocks, sip from cans of Foster's and nibble on crisps. Having satisfied themselves they are invincible (though the scoreboard shows a total of eight fatalities, 200 hospitalised), Courtbridge can sleep easy.

Mikey emerges from the throng, carrying a beer. "Hey, Jo. You cut it fine." He offers me a drink and I take it, suddenly realising how thirsty I am.

"I was . . . delayed. Do you think he noticed?"

We both look over at command control, where Dennis and Mrs Fothergill are sharing a joke. "Nope. He's only had eyes for disaster."

"I suppose that's a good thing," I say.

"What's that smell? Like a bonfire?" Mikey says. "And you look a bit weird, Jo. Your face is all smudged, like a miner's. What exactly have you been up to?"

Before I have time to think up a convincing lie, Dennis finally spots me and works his way through the crowd, head held high, every inch the conquering hero. "Jo. *Jo*. It's gone *so* well, couldn't have been better." And he puts his arm around me. "Of course, it's not wholly down to me. It's also down to our little *foot soldiers*."

Mikey scowls. "Gee, thanks, mate. You're so generous with your praise." And he walks off in search of more alcohol.

"Yes, that's the secret of my success, motivating my staff," Dennis says. "And what about you, Jo? I've hardly seen you. Getting your hands dirty, eh? And your face by the look of it. My lovely Jo."

I get a sudden urge to tell him what I've really been doing but before I can speak, Dennis moves towards me for a triumphant beery kiss; when his mouth meets mine, the hoppy, yeasty bitterness is overpowering. I brace myself. I'm not going to spoil his day.

As I feel the tell-tale heaviness in my arms and legs, I wonder if I've ever been so glad of a flashback . . .

CHAPTER
THIRTY-FIVE

Athazagoraphobia — Fear of Being Forgotten

Beer-scented breath and sandalwood aftershave. My father's face, up close, inches from mine. His hand around my wrist.

"Come on, Jo. We need to get out of here. Now! Let me through . . . my daughter is finding it hard to breathe."

"Daddy." I don't think anyone hears me. I can't even tell if I said it out loud, because my lungs are empty.

He's pulling me through the crowd now. Dad releases my limbs from the jammed-together bodies, and I see Gillian, still wedged between angry people who can't seem to stop shouting. At least, I think they're shouting. Their mouths are opening and shutting, and the ones with free hands are pointing and prodding, but I can't hear anything. Once the crowd is no longer holding me up, it feels like my muscles have stopped working too, so he has to carry me, all the way across the road, and round the corner and into Savannah's salon.

Dad lifts me gently into one of the padded leather chairs at the back of the salon. In the mirror my face is blotchy, as if I've been crying, though I know I haven't.

I look up, and see Mum, with Timmy asleep on her lap, at the next chair along. "I'm sorry," she mouths. Gradually, my ears let in sounds again: the whirr of the hairdryers, the shoosh of the water in the basins, the low hum of speculation about the bedraggled arrivals. A huge poster of a woman with a Lady Diana flicked hairdo stares down at me.

"You came back for me." My voice is croaky, like an old woman's.

Dad looks hurt. "Of course I did."

"But I saw you with Mum and Timmy and I thought you'd forgotten."

"As if I would. I only got them first because they were nearer the front, where the angriest people were."

"Gillian! What about Gillian? Is she going to be OK?"

My parents exchange a look, then Mum stares at the ground. Finally my father says, "Gillian's a grown woman. She can take care of herself."

"Car's here," Savannah says, and Dad helps me up. Mum sits in the front and Dad lifts my brother back on to her lap without waking him. Then he joins me in the back. I smell the beer again and I wonder why he's been drinking at lunchtime, when he should be approving people's bank loans. But all that matters is that he didn't forget me.

The taxi's engine drowns out its radio, and I close my eyes. Then I hear my father's whispered voice.

438

"Bean, listen to me. This is between you and me. I *know*, OK? About your *collection*."

I open my eyes again, hoping he's talking about the gonk collection I bought from a girl at school, before I spent all my money on supplies.

"The tins and the packets," he says. He checks in the mirror to see whether Mum's listening, but she seems dazed, her mouth hanging open and her eyelids fluttering as if she's dreaming.

"And that leaflet, about bomb shelters. Under your bed. I knew something strange was going on when I found that bag after Timmy went missing, with the beans and the Dettol inside. At first I thought you had one of those eating disorders, like on TV. Or maybe you were shoplifting."

"I . . ." I imagine my father rifling through my painstakingly acquired stockpile. Tins of baked beans that I'd stacked carefully to take up less space, rolling all over the carpet. My lists inspected and laughed at. My sparse first-aid kit emptied on to my Holly Hobby rug. "Dad, I haven't stolen anything. It's for us. All of us. For when the Bomb comes."

He nods. "I know that now. It was almost a relief when I found that booklet."

I seize my chance. "The thing is, we really should move house, Dad. But if we can't do that straight away, we need a plan. Most people won't be prepared for nuclear attack, but if we are, then we'll have a hope of survival." He listens, and it's so rare that I keep talking, let it all out. "The booklet said the build-up to war might only last a fortnight. The shops will be emptied.

439

We can't rely on the government, we need to look after ourselves." I don't add *and this is your job, as head of the family, but as you haven't done it, I've had to.*

Finally, I run out of reasons. He puts his hand on mine. "Bean, it's going to be all right, you know."

"But they've got hundreds of bombs aimed at us. The Russians. SS20s. Hundreds of them."

"And we've got hundreds aimed at them. That's why it'll be all right. Trust me."

We're passing the common now, though none of us dares to look at the camp. I wonder if Gillian will be all right. I wish we'd made sure.

I want to tell Dad it's not up to him, he's not Brezhnev or Reagan, he's a bank manager, and what can he do? Instead I say, "Couldn't we move away, Daddy?"

"Oh, Bean. This isn't about nuclear war." He checks that Mum's still asleep. "Your mum and me have been bloody awful at noticing what's happening under our noses. I promise we'll try harder. Timmy's had the lion's share of attention lately, but that's going to change. We'll have fun. As a family. How does that sound?" He sounds as if he's trying to convince himself as much as me.

"Good, Daddy, but . . ." And then I understand that nothing I say will make him move, or persuade him to build a fall-out shelter in the back garden. He believes what he believes and that's that: adults can't change. They're set, like concrete. "It sounds good."

He smiles. "Fantastic. Just two things then. First, we don't tell your mother. She's got enough to worry

440

about and finding out about your stockpile . . . well, I don't think it would help her to know."

"OK," I say, knowing from experience that Dad always names the easiest thing first. "And the second thing?"

"You need to get rid of it, Bean. All of it. The tins. The first-aid kit. That bloody scary booklet with the pictures of bodies in bin-liners."

"But . . ."

"But nothing. It's all a reminder of . . . a bad time for the Morgans. Time for a new beginning, now."

I try a different tactic. "It's a terrible waste."

He nods, weighing up my point. "Fair enough. We give it away then. To an old folks' home or something. Though not the leaflet, obviously. Up to you to get shot of it . . . I'll give you seven days, Jo, no more than that, then I'll check up."

"All right."

"The sheltered housing near school, they'd be glad of the tinned stuff," he says.

But I've already decided where my precious stockpile is going.

To the peace camp. Lucky they're keen on tins.

The taxi pulls up in our road, and Dad gives the driver double the usual fare. He lifts Timmy from my mother's arms, and my brother wakes up now, rubbing his eyes and insisting on walking, rather than being carried. We could be any other nuclear family, on our way home from an August day trip. Tired but happy.

Except that as my father snakes his arm around my mother's sunken shoulders to lead her up the path, I hear him whisper, "It stops here, Lynda, the fun and games at Greenham. If you *ever* endanger my children's lives again, I will divorce you and take them with me. The courts won't grant custody to an unfit mother. Do you understand?"

Her lips twitch and her eyes open. And she nods, like a sleepy child.

"Good girl," he says in the voice he uses when Misty lies on her back, playing dead for the Queen. "Good girl."

CHAPTER
THIRTY-SIX

Tropophobia — Fear of Making Changes

By rights Dennis should be hanging a banner on the outside of our bungalow: "WELCOME HOME, JO MORGAN".

Yes, my fearless alter ego has done the decent thing, and quit town, with her: the tendency to feed squirrels, talk to cold-callers and send inappropriate emails. She's also packed off those peculiar ideas about taking risks or putting herself first.

I feel bad about the squirrels. They eyeball me through the patio doors, their flat-eared faces tight with annoyance. They try ever more impressive tricks to change my mind, and I wouldn't be surprised to look out one morning and see them juggling nuts, or playing a form of squirrel cricket with a magnolia leaf as the bat and berries as balls.

It's such a trivial thing, and I keep wondering what harm it would do to sneak out a few plates of sunflower seeds, where Dennis won't find them. But I'm not going to give in: there's more at stake here than a few hungry rodents. Turning myself back into the old Jo is going to be the hardest thing I've ever done. Like a method actor, I must adopt the mannerisms and behaviour of my former self, in the hope that eventually my performance will be so convincing that I'll fool myself.

But there's no banner yet, or streamers or party poppers. Dennis barely seems to have noticed the change. He ignored the bonfire I made of the brochures and junk mail. I watched alone as my possibilities of winning a Caribbean cruise or building up my own property empire went up in smoke.

The trouble is, the old Jo Morgan had a million things to think about, on behalf of the citizens of Courtbridge. AIDS, Bombs, Crashes, Disasters, Ebola, Flesh-eating Bugs, GM Crops, Hoodies, Ice Storms, Joyriders, Killer Clothing, Livestock Stampedes, Mobile Phone Masts, Nuclear War, Organised Crime, Plane Crashes, Quack Therapists, Rats, Spontaneity, Terrorism, UV Radiation, Volcanic Eruptions, Wasps, X-rays, Youth Crime and Zoonoses. Not necessarily in alphabetical order.

I've decided I can't face going back to my stupid job, but I'd give anything to be busy. Mum and Dad have down-graded their surveillance operation and Dennis is too distracted to pay me any attention. At first I thought it was because of this stupid stunt arranged by *Civil Protection Chronicle*, who convinced him to pose for a photograph eating a Victoria sandwich with a bunch of bakers, to prevent a diplomatic incident after my cake danger memo. I've seen the picture and he looks like that Tory minister who ate a hamburger at the height of the BSE crisis. But even since the photoshoot, he seems miles away.

So I have all the freedom I was longing for when I first came home from hospital, yet now I crave nature trails and duck-feeding expeditions. Anything to stop me thinking about Frisky and Luke. Every day I think it'll get easier, that this guilt will begin to be replaced by a fond nostalgia. That I won't wake up wondering how Luke's burns are healing, or whether he's exchanged two words with his grandfather, and whether those two words might be "stupid cow", or "scheming bitch".

I've started going for long walks, playing Russian roulette with my feet, which might misbehave and carry me to the villa, although I know it's the last place I should be. So far I've walked to St Matthew's School, where screaming infants have taken the place of fake casualties, and to the field next to the leisure centre, where the gondola ride is long gone and preparations are under way for the July carnival queen ceremony.

When the doorbell goes as I sit eating my organic lunch, I allow myself a moment of imagining it might be Frisky. But I'm not really surprised when it turns out to be my father.

"Bean! You sounded a bit fed up on the phone so I thought you might fancy a movie!" He pushes past me to the living room and begins to set up the DVD recorder.

I sigh, and go to make some tea. When I bring it in, I recognise the movie's opening sequence immediately:

445

a red sports car snaking round terrifying hairpin bends before exploding in a tunnel.

"Hey, is this meant to be a treat for me or for you, Dad?"

"Ah, I defy anyone to feel miserable after watching the finest British movie ever made."

We watch *The Italian Job* in reverential silence, except for gasps when the Minis do their stuff, giggles when the boys outsmart the Mafia, and the obligatory bit where we join in with Michael Caine when he says, "You were only supposed to blow the bloody doors off."

But I spend as much time watching Dad as the screen: with the cynicism gone from his face, he looks twenty years younger. Still just handsome enough to make heads turn.

As the credits roll, leaving Charlie Croker and his crew on the precipice, Dad sings along with the "Get a Bloomin' Move On" song, before remembering his tea, and drinking it down, cold, in one long gulp.

"Now, what are we going to do with you, Bean?"

"This wasn't a social call, then."

"I've been wanting to talk to you properly ever since you came out of hospital, but I knew I'd get in trouble with your mother if I said anything out of turn."

I open my mouth to protest that he's always been the one censoring her, but then I stop. Actually, he's the only person who hasn't been giving me unwanted advice since my accident. Even when he took me to the pub for those long nutritious lunches, he didn't seem his usual garrulous self. "So what did you want to tell me?"

"I just want my daughter to be happy. And I'm not convinced all this is doing the job." He waves vaguely around the room to indicate "all this".

I'd like to ask him what makes him the world expert on happiness. Instead I say, "What makes you think that, Dad?"

He must pick up on the sarcasm in my voice because he smiles. "I know what you're thinking, Bean. I've known you long enough to recognise *that* look, the one that says, 'Dad's 100 per cent wrong, but I can't be bothered to argue.' "

Now I'm smiling. "I'll give you the benefit of the doubt, just this once."

"Thing is, when you were in your coma, I felt so powerless, Bean. For the second time. I was useless when Timmy was ill and then he got better so it was all right, and then there I was again, nothing I could do to keep you alive, one of those times you wish you could convince yourself there's a God. I said to myself then, if she makes it, I'm going to tell her what I really think. Even if she hates me for it."

"Why would I hate you, Dad?" As I say it, I realise with a jolt that I *did* hate him, until that last flashback proved that he didn't abandon me, after all.

"Because I think Dennis is the wrong man for you." He flinches, anticipating a hostile reaction. When I say nothing, he continues warily. "Because he's . . . boring. That's not a crime in itself, Bean. I do realise that you're not exactly a wild-child yourself, and thank

447

goodness not everyone is like me. But the point of a partner is that they should make you *better* than the person you were alone. Not worse."

"Like you and Mum?" I say, sharper than I intended.

"Ah . . . Ah, well, I know you might not see it that way, but actually, yes. I'm a flawed person in so many ways, but if it wasn't for your mother . . . I've hurt her too often, Jo, but both of us had a lot to learn about how to treat someone you love. And I know this sounds arrogant, but I think she's better for having me around. She's always needed stability."

I think back to what Mum said at the barbecue, the way it sounded so clinical, more like an arranged marriage than the discovery of a soul mate, but maybe being unromantic isn't a crime. It's just a shame.

"Jo?"

"Thing is, Dad, if stability's a good thing, then aren't I lucky to have Dennis?"

He sighs. "Stability was what your mum needed, Jo. I think what you need is someone who will destabilise you, challenge all those neuroses. I was thrilled when you got home and started shouting at people, being a bit bonkers. At last you were standing up for yourself."

"I thought everyone hated the new me."

"Ah, but I've always been contrary, Bean. And maybe it's madly controlling of me, but I'd love to see you with a man who likes the new you too. Or at the very least, a man in possession of a sense of humour."

He's gone too far, now, sitting on Dennis's sofa, accusing him of being a humourless bore. *I'm* allowed to think it, but only because I appreciate his other

448

qualities. "Dennis looks after me, Dad. That's what I need. Not a stand-up comedian who subjects me to endless practical jokes. I'm feeling tired, now. I think you should go."

He nods. "Yes, you're probably right. Pushed my luck, maybe. But I thought it was worth the risk. Take care, Bean. You know where we are if you need us."

After he's gone, taking the precious DVD with him, I go to the understairs cupboard to look for photos of when Dennis and I first met, to remind myself of those qualities I'm trying so hard to appreciate.

But the first bag I pull out doesn't contain photo albums: it contains a rusty tin of tuna, a carved wooden fish, and an opened pack of Fisherman's Friends. I stick my nose in the carrier and breathe deeply, wondering if the strange cocktail of smells will take me back in time.

All that happens is my eyes begin to sting with tears. So I take the bag and push it to the back of the cupboard, behind the wellies and toolboxes. I ought to chuck it out, but I can't bring myself to do it, even though Frisky and Luke are my past. And Dennis is my future.

CHAPTER
THIRTY-SEVEN

Euphobia — Fear of Hearing Good News

When Dennis announced he was taking today off work (a Monday, too, the day Dennis says, "sets the tone for the working week!") for a "special trip", I thought it was touching and romantic. He'd finally noticed my efforts to change and was responding in kind. Once he hit the M40, with lots of meaningful looks in my direction, I managed not to groan at the prospect of another "inspiring" visit to Coventry.

But I wasn't expecting this.

"Would you mind repeating what you just said, Dennis? I think I must have misheard." *At least I hope I misheard.*

Dennis's smile falters for a fraction of a second and his hand gets halfway towards the lock of fringe he always pulls when he's nervous, before he brings himself back under control.

Oh please God, let me have misheard.

We're not back at the Warwickshire wife-swapping Plaza Hotel. Instead we're on a brand-new estate, with fake heraldic developers' flags at the entrance, and banners that promise "Your stamp duty paid!" and "Fab free furniture package! Ethically sourced!" Every road is named after a tree — Ash Rise, Oak Lane, and where we are now, Maple Drive. Though no one's bothered to plant so much as a sapling.

The brand-spanking-newness of everything is scary, as is the quiet: it makes Salzburg Avenue look like Soho on a Saturday night. But scariest of all is that Dennis appears to know his way round.

"It's ours," he says, very softly, with a fey, nervous wave at the large detached redbrick house behind him. It looks like it's built from Lego.

"Ours?" That's what I thought he said. "When? Why? How?" I sound like a Ladybird book.

"So many questions!" says Dennis, interpreting them as enthusiasm. "Which one shall I answer first?"

"Why?" I say, dully. There's a distinct whiff of *fait accompli* about this, though I can't possibly see how he . . .

"I've been offered a director's job."

A blow to the belly, as not so much the penny as an entire money-bag full of loose change drops. "Here? In Coventry?"

"In Coventry, yes," he says, looking slightly shamefaced. "You know I didn't want to be somebody's deputy for the rest of my life. And this is a big step up, a full *city* to look after. Population of a third of a million people to keep safe."

"Oh." I don't know how to react. "*Congratulations.*" The word comes out acid-dipped.

He doesn't hear the sarcasm. "It *is* a dream come true for me, Jo. But I wanted it to be special for you too, and I did my research, and this development is apparently the most popular —"

I interrupt him. "How long?"

"I only accepted a fortnight ago," he says. "I was itching to tell you, but with all that's happened . . . I didn't want to get you stressed so I waited till I'd made all the arrangements." He touches my arm lightly.

"You misunderstand me, Dennis," I say, brushing him off. "I meant, how long ago did you apply for the job?" As I speak, I realise he must done it before we went to Coventry for our "romantic" break. So much for accidentally booking into the wrong hotel.

His face flushes. "Well, um, I first saw the advert maybe . . . three months ago. And I couldn't discuss it with you then, could I? I mean you were just out of hospital, hardly in the right state of mind . . ."

"The right state of mind to discuss my entire future?"

He nods. "Yes, exactly. Exactly, Jo. I knew you'd understand. Your behaviour was so unpredictable, I wasn't sure there was a future to discuss."

I think through the implications of this: after my accident, Dennis either thought I didn't have a future *or* that we didn't have a future together.

I'm still digesting this, when a well-groomed middle-aged woman approaches us, brandishing keys.

"Mr Diffley, Mrs Diffley?"

"Miss Morgan," I say.

452

"Sorry. So, what do you think of it so far?" she says, her unfamiliar accent the only sign that we're in Coventry, rather than a thousand other identikit estates across the country. "I'm sure you'd like a look inside . . ."

I follow, dumbly, because I don't know what else to do. She regales us with a patter so rehearsed it could be playing from a tape in her handbag. "The Platinum is at the top of our range of executive homes, a uniquely generous, stylish and architect-designed space for the twenty-first-century family."

I'm tempted to ask her who usually designs new homes if it's not an architect, but there are more important things to devote my damaged neurons to right now.

"The mosaic-tiled hallway is the first gorgeous hint at the high specification and attention to detail of this luxury five-bedroomed property," she drones on, "from the Shaker kitchen, the two reception rooms, the rainforest-friendly west-facing sundeck and the double garage. All with full NHBC guarantee, of course."

Of course. It *is* a nice house, if you like somewhere with no history and no identity. Virgin appliances, unused baths, empty borders ready for your choice of tropical or traditional planting by Chelsea medal-winning horticulturalists.

We trail behind her, Dennis throwing me nervous glances which I refuse to return. Upstairs she keeps up the commentary as she shows us four perfect rectangular bedrooms — no awkward fireplaces or uneven walls — before we ascend to the master suite.

She opens the door to the en suite with a delighted flourish, like a parent unveiling a child's first bike on Christmas morning. "This is the same spa bath two former American presidents have chosen for their homes. *Ten* ozonic power jets. Perfect for relaxing after a stressful day."

I think she's finished now, but when I open my mouth, she adds, "You were so lucky to get this one. The last Platinum on the development. All the others went months ago."

"I'd like some time alone with my . . . partner, if that's OK?" I say, finally.

She nods. "Of course. I'll be waiting downstairs."

I listen to her heels on the Brazilian hardwood steps. "So you've bought the house, then, Dennis?"

"Yup," he says, sitting on the edge of the president-approved spa bath. "I knew it was the right one for us. What do you think?"

I ignore the question. "How, though? I mean, what about number 64?" I never thought I'd feel loyal towards Salzburg Avenue, but then I can't believe he'd toss the bungalow aside like a lover who's seen better days.

"I . . ." now he seems flustered, "I didn't want to put you through having people traipse round our home. So instead of putting it on the market the usual way, I had an open day."

"When?"

"When you went to that health place with Lorraine . . . worked a treat, actually. The market's so buoyant that I had three asking-price offers. It went to sealed bids."

There's a little trick Lorraine taught me years ago, when she first began her midwife training. Shallow breathing, used by women in labour, also comes in handy during moments of extreme stress. "You sold our home? Without asking me?"

He sighs now, as if I am deliberately spoiling his big surprise. "Well, it is in *my* name, Jo, and it's not like I can commute from Courtbridge, is it?"

"Dennis, have you considered at any point that I might not want to relocate?"

He adopts a serious face. "Of course I have. That's why I chose a place with five bedrooms, so your mum and dad can come to stay. And you and Lorraine can have girly week-ends."

"You're missing something. I don't have a job in Coventry."

"Well, we won't need two incomes when we move."

"It's not just about income," I say, the pitch of my voice rising with every word, "it's about the rest of my life. Unless you're expecting me to sit at home for ever like Elizabeth Barrett Browning."

"I could get you a dog, for company," he says.

"So long as it's one that doesn't need much exercise, with an invalid for an owner?" I suggest.

"Not a terrier, then," he says, apparently giving it serious thought. "But a Pekinese perhaps? Though you'd have to be willing to groom it every day."

"Well, according to you, I won't need to worry my pretty but dented little head about anything else, will I?"

He stands up, picks away at the tiny pieces of plastic still clinging to the new taps. "Oh. You were joking about the dog, then?"

"Yes, I was *joking about the dog*. But you're not joking about the *job*, are you?" I find myself raging in a whisper and he has to lean in to listen. "About dragging me off to a place I never wanted to visit, never mind live there. About seeing my job as so trivial and unimportant that I can happily abandon it to play housewife, without being consulted! Go on. I dare you. Tell me this is some elaborate, side-splitting, practical joke."

He shakes his head. "I was trying to look after you, Jo." He has collected a small ball of plastic, but with no bin to put it in, he rolls it between his hands. "After everything that's happened, I didn't want to make life any more stressful than it had to be."

"So you thought it'd be less stressful for me if you ran my life on my behalf?"

"The thing is, I . . ." he begins. "I mean, I didn't think you'd . . ." Now he shrugs apologetically at his complete failure to explain. "To tell you the truth, I didn't think it would make any difference to you one way or another. I mean, you always told me you had no ambition, except to be happy. You've never expressed any real preference about where you live or what you do."

I open my mouth to berate him for his arrogance, his cheek, his sheer chauvinist piggery, when I suddenly remember he's right. Until the accident, I didn't take decisions, or express an opinion, if there was any way of

456

avoiding it. My life was about self-preservation, the avoidance of risk, the careful balancing of one improbable danger over another equally unlikely hazard, paralysed by the unknown. I was all too willing to let other people take responsibility.

And Dennis was the perfect man for me, taking control of everything, from the most ethical electricity supplier, to the safest car. No wonder he thought it didn't matter to me where I ended up.

"Jo? I only wanted to take care of everything. A new life, for both of us. A blank slate."

I look around *our* bathroom suite. "It's that, all right." I go to the window and peer down at the identical decks at the back of each house. There are paddling pools and climbing frames all over the place. "This is a family house, Dennis."

And his cherubic face lights up, momentarily, and I understand this is part of the plan.

"A new start, Jo." For a moment, I feel terribly guilty; I know what it must mean to him to be able to contemplate children. It's taken him forty years to get over his mother's neglect, to be able to trust women. And here I am, about to destroy that trust for good.

I screw up my eyes, try to imagine myself here. Our own paddling pool, full of Maple Drive munchkins, the neighbours coming over for organic dinners, bringing bottles of the same wine that's on special offer at the same superstore where we all shop.

One hundred miles away from Frisky. One hundred miles away from Luke.

"Dennis . . . I don't think I can do this."

He frowns. "It's the shock, but I know that when you've had time to let it sink in, you'll see what an opportunity this is for me . . . I mean, for us."

I shake my head, knowing he won't believe me. I barely believe it myself. "Dennis. It's not about the house or the job. I can see what an opportunity it is for you and the house is . . ." I cast around for the right word, "incredible. Six months ago, it would have been perfect."

"Before the accident? As I've said before, Jo, you need to give yourself time to get back to normal."

I speak slowly, now, considering every word. "Dennis, you wouldn't believe how hard I've tried to get back to normal. With you, and Mum and Dad, and Lorraine, all on the sidelines, cheering me on. It's only very recently that I've admitted I will *never* be the same again."

"Oh God, Jo. Depression is very common among people who've suffered a life-threatening illness. I'm sure your doctor would prescribe one of the newer anti-depressants, just for a few months, to help you adjust. You *can* be your old self again."

"You don't understand, Dennis. I don't *want* to be my old self."

He's pulling frantically at his kiss-curl now, frustrated at my obstinacy. "That's not you talking, Jo. It's your illness."

"No. It is me. The illness has changed me for good, like . . ." I grasp for an analogy he might understand. "Imagine the bomb's dropped. And the chosen ones have been in the bunker, and after two weeks, they

458

come out again. They're still the same people, really, a bit pasty-faced, maybe, but everything's changed. Their job is to restore normality, but it can't *ever* be the same as it was."

"I don't see . . ."

"I've been in the bunker my whole life, Dennis. A bunker I built myself. The accident forced me out, and I don't want to go back in."

He nods, and his eyes look so hurt. "And that's what your life is like with me, is it? As if you're buried fifty feet underground?"

I shake my head, and reach for his hand. He won't touch me. "No. Dennis, you were the kindest, most caring man I've ever met."

"Were?"

I didn't even hear myself use the past tense. But he's right. "It really is me, not you. I am not the right person for you any more, Dennis. I will stop you leading the life you want."

"But this house. I've signed the contract, Jo."

"You mustn't change anything for me. You must take the job. It's what you're meant to do."

"And what are *you meant to do*?" He can't keep the coldness out of his voice, and I don't blame him.

"I haven't got a clue, Dennis. I think that's what I need to find out."

He stares at me, as if he's looking at a stranger. "Well, don't expect me to be waiting when you realise your mistake."

My once-upon-a-time soul mate turns and walks, with considered paces, out of the bathroom and back down the stairs. I know I'm doing the right thing, but the thought of how much I've hurt him makes me feel so wretched that I race for the unused toilet behind me, to throw up.

There's nothing there but bile, and as I stand up to flush it away — does vomit merit a full-power flush or a low-water eco-friendly one, it's the planet at stake, after all — the smell overwhelms me and I just have enough time to think, *oh no, not here* . . .

CHAPTER
THIRTY-EIGHT

Doxophobia — Fear of Expressing Opinions

"Now, you're sure you're feeling better, Timmy?"

My brother nods as Mum wipes the last yellowy smear of sick from his chin. She sighs at the wet stain that the vomit's made on his new pink tie. Dad protested that pink "makes him look like a little poof", but Timmy got his way, of course. As my mother said, "It is being held in his honour, so I think he should be allowed to wear what he likes."

We leave the loos and return to the foyer, where photographers and a cameraman pace the marble floor. Don't they realise that a child with a serious illness can't be relied upon to smile sweetly and be obediently tragic *all* the time? That they might occasionally sulk or scream or puke up in front of the cameras like a junior Johnny Rotten?

My mother now poses with her arms stretched across Timmy's chest, to cover the stain. Dad's nipped out from backstage in his MC outfit, black tie and shiny shoes. Mum and I are wearing dresses in the same shade of sky blue. Hers is made of silk and swirls when

461

she walks, it makes her look younger. Unfortunately so does mine: it has an irritating lace collar that I'll never live down if the girls from school see me. Though perhaps having a dying brother will get me off the hook.

Actually, I don't believe Timmy is going to die any more. He looks a little less like a ghost every day, and that must mean his blood is getting stronger, strong enough to put colour in his cheeks.

"So, Timmy, what are you looking forward to tonight?" the TV reporter asks.

"I'm looking forward to the ice cream in the interval," Timmy says.

"Nothing wrong with his appetite, then," the reporter says, and I recognise the posh bloke from the stones protest on Hiroshima Day. Dad never saw the report, but the whole thing escalated so much that Timmy ended up in the *Daily Mail*, with questions asked in Parliament and a charity appeal in the *Newbury Weekly News*. Dad stole back the thunder by setting up the fundraising concert to collect money for leukaemia research.

"If you're finished, guys," my father says, slipping into *Alfie* mode to charm the photographers, "we've gotta get our show on the road."

They pack up, and the doors are opened to let in the audience; smartly dressed people crowd around my brother, hungry for their share of our tragedy, cheap at the price of a £4 ticket for this one-off concert. They seem to need to touch him, as if he'll protect them and

462

their families from all the bad things that might happen in the late twentieth century.

As they move away to order their port and lemons for the interval, I hear fragments of conversation. "Bless him, what a cutie." "He had a twinkle in his eye, didn't he?" "But what about the mother? Do you think she was drunk?" "Ah, no, probably just a bit overwhelmed." "You know she was at the peace camp, I saw her on the telly." "No way! She doesn't look the type at all. Her hair's combed for a start."

The Timothy Morgan Birthday Benefit concert is like a present from my father to my mother, but you only need to look at her to know nothing in life is free. When Mum agreed to turn her back on Greenham, Dad began to pay her more attention. He brings home flowers and organises a babysitter so they can go to the Chinese for crispy duck and pancakes. He even went to the hospital when Timmy was having chemo, though he threw up more violently than my brother and the nurses suggested it might be better if he didn't go again.

In return, my mother has turned into the perfect wife. I know she's back on tablets, but the new ones seem different. She doesn't get so sleepy and she doesn't cry at all, but then again she doesn't do much apart from wander round with a vague smile on her face, cuddling Timmy at random.

She doesn't have to do much, anyway: Dad's hired a cleaner who comes in twice a week, leaving no carpet unturned. I'd never have got away with the stockpile under the new clean regime.

I took the tins to Greenham, late at night, and left them outside Gillian's tent. No note. I've started again, though it's slow going, because Dad keeps a list in each cupboard of how many tins, packets and sachets should be inside. So I buy a new can with my pocket money each week, and hide it in the garage. Sometimes I feel like giving up, because it's hopeless, but you can't, can you?

Someone rings a bell to let people know it's time to go into the auditorium, but we hold back. It's part of Dad's grand plan to have Timmy march in to a round of applause, "to remind everyone who this night is all about".

He means Timmy, not himself. You could have fooled me.

Through the glass I see three late arrivals. "Mum?"

"Oh God," she says. "Oh no."

She rushes to the door and the few stragglers who haven't yet taken their seats look round curiously.

"Hello, Lynda," Gillian says, holding out her arms to embrace my mother. Mum hesitates for several agonising seconds, then darts forward quickly to peck Gillian on the cheek. The women have made a special effort — even Mags has softened the spikes in her hair — but Mum's dress would show the tiniest speck of Greenham Common dirt.

"Gillian, Mags. Um . . ." She struggles with the last woman's name and so I whisper, "Claudette". "Claudette. What are you doing here?" Her voice is light, as if we've run into old friends on holiday.

464

Mags raises her eyebrows. "Well, what do you *think* we're doing here?"

"Ignore her, Lynda," Gillian says. "We're here for Timmy. For the concert. You supported us when it mattered and we wanted to do the same."

"Ri-ight," Mum says. I'm sure I can see her brain working as her eyes flicker from side to side. "It's very good of you to come." Timmy runs up to Gillian and jumps into her arms.

"Oof!" She clutches him as he wraps his legs around her waist. "He's putting weight on, Lynda. That must be a good thing."

Mum nods. "We think so. The doctors keep saying we have to be careful not to read too much into anything but it's so hard not to."

"Timmy, I'll have to let you get down now, or I'll fall over," Gillian pants. "We were worried, Lynda, after the demo. And then we saw the concert posters and we thought we'd come along."

Mum closes her eyes and I think she's going to faint, but as I step forward to take her weight, she opens them again. "I'm sorry," she says. "I'm so sorry to disappear like that, but . . ."

Mags interrupts. "We're used to it. Better to find out early on who can't cope, than invest our trust in people who aren't up to the job. It's going to get harder, too. There are rumours that bailiffs might be here next week. With bulldozers. No place for *cowards*."

My mother begins to cry, softly, like an abandoned animal. Gillian glares at Mags, then says to my mother, "We didn't come here to accuse you of letting the side

THE SELF-PRESERVATION SOCIETY

down. God knows, it must be hard enough to cope, without people wanting you to feel guilty."

"I wanted to come back, to say goodbye and *explain*, but I wasn't brave enough," my mother says.

The bell sounds again. "Time to find our seats," Mags says, pushing through the door.

"No!" Mum's voice is loud and panicky. "I mean, wait."

"Why?" Mags asks. "Oh, no, don't tell me. You're ashamed of us, aren't you?"

Mum peers down at her new blue shoes. "It isn't that. I admire you all. You're so much braver than I could ever be."

"I can hear a but coming," Mags says bitterly.

"If this was only about me, I'd sit in the front row with you," my mother says, each word slow and painful, "but I have to think of my family."

"Your husband, you mean."

Gillian looks as if she's about to slap Mags. "Let her speak, for pity's sake."

Mum hesitates. "At the camp, things seem so black and white. Peace or war. Love or hate. Life or death. But I'm not strong enough to forget the other choices I made, before I'd heard of a Cruise missile. I wish I was, but I'm not."

"Is that *hubby* talking or you, Lynda?"

"I know Ted isn't perfect. But then neither am I, and we've made a joint decision, to try to make things work. For the sake of Timmy and Jo." She takes my hand and I feel hers trembling.

466

"Look after your own and sod everyone else's kids, then? Very *Protect and Survive*," Mags sneers.

Mum stands up a little straighter, though she's crying again. "I won't stop you coming into the theatre. In another life, I'd want you here. But I don't have another life. I have this one."

Mags is frowning, Claudette is already turning round, but it's Gillian's face that makes me feel sad. Her eyes are narrowed with hurt and she's biting her lip. Finally, she nods to herself. "I understand, Lynda. Just remember, we are your friends, whatever happens. And you know where to find us. I have a feeling we won't be moving on for a while yet."

Gillian stoops down to kiss my brother's forehead and he pulls a face. Then she touches my arm. "Keep questioning things, Jo. Never feel you have to accept the status quo, because there's no such thing."

She leans forwards to kiss my mother on the cheek, but Mum moves back before she can help herself and Gillian smiles. "Take care of you and yours, Lynda. Stay happy." And she walks back through the door to join the other two. They don't look back.

The bell rings, as insistent as a siren, and I'm sure it's my dad's hand on the button. There's only the three of us in the foyer now, so I take Mum's hand and she takes Timmy's and we walk towards the stalls.

Mum stops. "I can't go on stage. I can't." She's crying properly now, tears running down her face in twin streams. "You take Timmy."

I leave her by the door and as the conductor sees Timmy and I walking up the red carpet between the aisle, the music begins.

The opening notes of Art Garfunkel's "Bright Eyes" fill the auditorium. My father designed the programme for tonight and he likes to lay it on thick. As I climb on to the stage with my brother, the footlights are dazzling, but I'm sure I can still see my mother at the back of the auditorium, one hand wiping away tears.

Dad winks at me from the wings. He couldn't be more pleased with himself. The concert, thousands already in the bag for leukaemia research, leading roles as Master of Ceremonies *and* head of the family, a platform for a little political posturing. Oh, and then there's the present he's bought for Mum, waiting at my grandparents' for the big handover.

"A kitten, Jo," he told me earlier. "Pedigree, the fluffiest one in the litter. They're a special breed, from Maine in America, and there's only one breeder in the whole of the UK. She'll love it, won't she?"

And all I keep thinking, as Dad fizzes on to the stage like a shaken-up can of Vimto, is that now I have to add Whiskas to my stockpile . . .

CHAPTER
THIRTY-NINE

Philophobia — Fear of Falling in Love

The view from the train is almost enough to make me forget the disaster zone my life has turned into.

Rows of cottages seem to sprout from Cotswold stone like square-topped mushrooms. Un-mad cows graze on what must be the greenest grass in the world. A blue Morris Minor with wooden window frames meanders along a narrow lane.

One of the Armageddon documentaries I watched as a teenager began with scenes like this. Dad must have been out at rehearsals, because I was normally banned from anything that might feed my obsession, yet I kept searching for bad news, like picking a scab. Predictably, within five minutes, the village in the programme was devastated by a blast wave that brought the church spire down on the boys' brigade.

No wonder I never worked out what I wanted from life: Mutually Assured Destruction focused my mind on basic survival, rather than the interesting stuff — careers, boyfriends, a home of my own.

Wrong call, Jo. The bomb never dropped, and while everyone else was filling in job applications and mortgage forms and wedding lists, I notice that the world had changed. Dennis and the job and Salzburg Avenue were my shelter from having to make a single decision of my own.

And now I've lost all three, and I can't think of a time I've felt more terrified — or more alive.

Lorraine will think I'm crazy. My parents will want to pack me off to hospital again. There's only one person I can think of who'll agree with me that my insanity is something to celebrate.

At Courtbridge, I step on to the platform and need to steady myself on another passenger.

"Sorry."

I'm laying the blame on nerves. My image of Frisky welcoming me into the conservatory, glass of wine and bowl of Greek olives at the ready, congratulating me for following my heart, sustained me on the journey, but now it seems ridiculous.

I walked out on him and Luke when they needed me most. I didn't even say goodbye. I wouldn't talk to me under the circumstances.

But I have to ignore my doubts — what else can I do with no home to go to? I begin the walk towards the villa. It's hotter here than in Coventry, and I tie my cardigan around my waist, like a schoolgirl. I feel light-headed, as I did the morning of the accident, and I remember that I haven't eaten since the motorway

470

service station breakfast Dennis treated me to on the M40.

I turn the corner into Frisky's road. The pavement is sticky with lime sap, and gravity-defying bees bumble around lush front gardens. I look for the Red Peril, but it's nowhere to be seen. Perhaps Luke is out. I'd prefer it if he was out.

Wouldn't I?

But he can't be out. His feet will only just have healed.

Come on, Jo. What's the worst that can happen?

I decide not to follow that particular train of thought and instead focus on putting one foot in front of the other, towards the villa. The stone façade looks perfect, the mellow sunshine bleaching out its many imperfections. I climb the steps and hesitate for a second before I ring the bell.

I hear it sound inside the house, and wait for footsteps. A woman with a pushchair passes the gate, singing "Ring a Ring o' Roses". I peer through the thick purple glass in the door. No sign of movement. I push my fingers through the letterbox but there's still nothing, and when I look down I see a pile of post on the doormat.

I feel sick. Why would both of them be out? I try ringing the bell again, pressing hard so it reverberates again and again.

What if Frisky's ill? He's eighty-five, and eighty-five-year-olds can go from fighting fit to terribly sick in days. And then there's the stroke. What if I broke his heart, triggered a terrible decline or a second stroke?

There's no other explanation. Even if Frisky's found himself another lost soul to rehabilitate in my place, then Luke would be confined to barracks because of his feet — and there's been enough time now for him to hobble to the door.

I imagine Frisky lying semi-conscious, mumbling my name.

I run down the steps and turn right, towards the hospital. I'm so out of condition that within a few yards I'm forced to take great gasping breaths, but I won't stop. I can't afford a wasted minute, because Frisky may not have that luxury.

My heart is hammering by the time I get to the hospital. I sprint over to the enquiry desk.

"You have to help me. I'm looking for my . . ." I hesitate, they may only be letting relatives in, "my godfather, I think he's here."

The woman nods. "Take a moment to get your breath back and tell me his name."

"He . . . his name is . . ." Oh shit. What is Frisky's real name? I try to remember that first meeting, outside that ugly clinic, the smoke clearing, the gnarled hand meeting mine, "Um. Roger. Roger Freeman Van Belle."

She frowns. "That's a mouthful." She types some letters into her keyboard, presses return. Waits. Then she tries again. And for a third time. "No. Nothing there. I've tried under Freeman, Van and Belle. No one as an in-patient or out-patient."

I start to cry. On one level, I know this has got to be *good* news, but I feel like I've failed. And without

Frisky to tell, how will I know if I've done the right thing?

The woman hands me a tissue. "There, there, love. Have you tried one of the other hospitals?"

I shake my head. "No, Frisky only lives round the corner."

Her face changes. "Frisky? As in, wrinkly old goat who can't stop talking?"

"Yes, that's him. Oh God, he is here." *Can't stop talking.* That has to be a good sign, surely?

"I didn't realise he was *really* posh, I thought he was putting on the airs and graces."

"So he is here?"

She nods. "I should think so. Frisky never misses the Monday Club."

I stare at her, as it sinks in. It's Monday. It's two o'clock. Of *course* he's here. "Thanks."

I run out of reception, past the car park, a fat man on crutches, the maternity unit, two nurses sneaking a cigarette, the wheelchair repair workshop, a teenager pushing a tea-urn on a trolley, and finally there is rehabilitation.

I am so puffed now that I feel faint. Have I been rehabilitated? Am I a fully functioning human being? Was I ever one in the first place?

There's laughter coming from the open window, and the loudest belongs to Frisky. Not only is he not at death's door, he's sounding very chirpy. I'm not sure that's allowed, shouldn't he be missing me?

No more dawdling, Miss Morgan. Time to face the music. I open the door, and smell the instant coffee. I

473

spot Frisky straight away: he has his back to me and his ice-cream curls bob as he laughs and laughs.

Familiar faces — Nathan, Monster, Falsie, the young chap who couldn't stop crying — peer back at me and the noise in the room fades away.

"Cat got our tongues or something?" Frisky says as he turns. He sees me and frowns. "Ah. Ah, right." He moves to one side and there, sitting on the squidgy sofa with his feet up, is Luke. Frisky clasps his hands together. "There, you see. I told you she'd come back!"

Nathan suggests the others accompany him on a tea and buns trip to the WRVS stall, which is good of him, as I'm sure he'd rather eavesdrop.

"I actually went to your place this morning, to try to talk you into coming to the club," Frisky says. "In a taxi, since my grandson here couldn't drive me. And some nice women over the road told me your house had been sold."

Trust the neighbours to know more than me. "Yes," I say. "Sorry. Bit of a shock to me too, actually."

Frisky takes out a cigar and lights it. "I was rather miffed. I always think of myself as rather a good judge of character."

Luke sits in silence on the sofa, his head turned away from me.

"Am I your first miscalculation then?"

Frisky's expression is obscured behind a cloud of blue-grey smoke. "Did I miscalculate? The jury is waiting for the case for the defence."

474

"Um." I know it has to be good. "It was Dennis's idea."

"For you to leave without saying goodbye? Or perhaps you were abducted?"

"No, not abducted. He's got a new job, you see, and expected me to go with him. Except he didn't tell me until it was a *fait accompli*. Today. I've just come from Coventry now."

Frisky's mouth hangs open. "Gosh. He didn't tell you he was selling the house? Um, forgive me if I'm speaking out of turn, but isn't that absolutely bloody outrageous. Unless you're happy to live someone else's life?"

Someone else's life. I think of that last flashback, of my mother wanting *another life*, where she could make decisions. But I saw what happened when she tried. "No, I'm not," I say, very quietly. "That's why I'm here."

"Ah . . ."

"I've left him, Frisky. Left Dennis."

Frisky's eyebrows shoot up. "Golly. And . . . well done. I know I never met the chap but he sounds like a fruitcake. And not in a nice way."

His certainty actually makes me question what I've done. "But he was the only man who ever thought I amounted to anything."

"Now that's not true at all, Joanna, and frankly I find it rather insulting. I'll forgive you, though, as you do look peaky. Are you hungry, by any chance?"

"Starving," I admit.

"Right. Decision made. I'm sure the Monday Club can get by without us. Time to celebrate your decision over tea and cake. Oh, and perhaps a tiny slug of my best vintage champagne."

Frisky goes to order a taxi to take us back, because Luke is still hobbling. "Entertain the invalid boy, will you, Joanna?" he tells me, before leaving the room.

There's an agonisingly long pause, while I try to think of something appropriate to say.

"I didn't know you came here. To the club."

Luke examines the backs of his hands. "First time. Got bored sitting on my ass."

"And do you like it?"

Finally he looks at me, his eyes cold. "What is it with the dumb questions? As if you care."

I feel my face heat up. "But I do want to know, Luke, honestly —"

"Yeah? That's why you ran off after I spilled my guts to you. You can charm Frisky, but I see what you are. A taker. He was too easy on you."

"Now hang on a minute. I know you've had a tough time, and I'm very sorry about what happened to your parents, but what about *your* behaviour? The last few months, whenever I tried to talk to you, you clammed up like a sulky child. And you're even ruder to your poor grandfather!"

Luke seems to shrink back into the sofa. "Yes, well, I admit I haven't always been too polite. But if you really want to know, Frisky and me, we've been getting along better lately."

476

I think of my last words to him, begging him to try harder. "Really? Why's that?"

"I couldn't exactly run away when he talked to me. Kinda *forced* us to make our peace."

"Oh. So it wasn't anything to do with what I said, then? I suppose it wouldn't have been, would it, seeing as how I am such a self-obsessed person."

He looks down at his hands again. "Maybe it did get me thinking."

"So if I apologise for going AWOL, will you apologise for being rude and childish?"

"You're calling me childish?"

I nod. Then I stick my tongue out for good measure. "Yep."

For a moment, his face is so serious that I think I've gone too far. Then he says, "Do you want to know the real reason I kept away from you?"

"Not really, but tell me if you must."

"Same reason I always got tongue-tied around a pretty girl at school."

"What?" I can't tell where the strange bubbly sensation begins, but it spreads like champagne.

"Yeah, only this time it's worse. Like, a hundred times worse. Number one, because no way am I the kinda guy to hit on a girl who's living with someone. And number two, because when I was at school, I wanted a girlfriend, and now I don't want a girlfriend *at all*."

"Oh." The bubbles go flat and I'm rather relieved. It didn't feel that different from indigestion. "Why not?"

He sighs. "Like I said before, what have I got to offer a girl? A rusty trailer? A phobia of sleeping indoors." He allows himself a shy smile. "Though, you know, I got that fixed. Frisky said he had no intention of coming out to the caravan in the middle of the night to help me take a piss."

"Bloody hell. And is it OK?"

"Didn't sleep for four long nights but, you know, in the end you can't stay awake any more. But if that's my biggest achievement in the last two years, is it any wonder I can't get a girl?"

"Hang on, though. A minute ago you said you didn't want a girl. Now you're saying you can't get one. Which I would dispute. Girls round these parts aren't *that* choosy. So which is it? Don't want or can't get?"

He frowns at me. "Have you taken an aggression pill? Only I never heard you talk like this before."

"Don't change the subject."

"All right. I guess if I was a girl *I* wouldn't go out with me so how could I expect anyone else to? I mean, would you go out with me?"

I gulp. "Hypothetically?"

"Uh-huh."

I scrutinise the overall package. Downsides, a screwed-up life story, no house, the Red Peril for a car (and that's not even his). Upsides, a sense of humour, a great singing voice, the strongest sense of right and wrong I've ever encountered, a wonderful body, a beautiful face.

And something else. How do I describe it, without sounding daft? I've never believed in auras, but there's

478

something about the man sitting opposite me that makes me realise I would trust him with my life.

Something I could no longer do . . . no, let's be honest, would never have done with my so-called soul mate.

"Don't keep me in suspense."

I look away. "Yeah. I'd consider it."

"Oh. Right. You'd *consider* it." He shrugs. "Well, that's *something*, I guess. I don't fall at the first hurdle."

"And what about me, Luke? Would you consider me?"

"Shit. That's direct." He blushes, so deeply that I'm sure every inch of him has turned pink. "Hypothetically, right?"

I should backtrack now, of course. Save us both the mortification. And anyway, what am I doing discussing dates when I'm only hours out of a long-term relationship?

So I think it comes as something of a surprise to both of us when I murmur. "No. Not hypothetically. *Really*. Here and now, live for today, for tomorrow we die, would you consider going out with me?"

He freezes and so do I. But it's OK. No harm done, I'll excuse myself from the glass of wine with Frisky, get the train to Newbury, move back home. It's good to follow your gut, sometimes, like Timmy says. Even if it ends in failure, humiliation, self-loathing . . .

"Jo . . ." Luke is trying to move himself out of his seat. There. I've embarrassed him *so* much that he can't

479

bear to be in the same room. He tries again. "This is hopeless. Help me up, please."

I reach for his hand and he grasps it. But instead of hoisting himself up, he pulls me down and it's only when I nearly lose my balance that I realise he's about to kiss me. Our mouths collide momentarily, before I bump my knee against the coffee table and leap back in pain.

"Oh shit," Luke says. "That didn't work out how I hoped."

"So does that mean that your answer is yes?"

"Remind me of the question," he says, and I groan. "No. Hang on. I remember. OK, Jo. Hypothetically, would you like me to try that again?"

"No," I say. "Not hypothetically. The word you're looking for is *definitely*."

And this time we're more synchronised. No bump. No clash of teeth. Just a feeling so good that champagne would seem flat in comparison . . .

From: Joanna Morgan
           [mailto:scaredycat@headbangers.net]
Sent: Monday 21 August
To: Courtbridge Accident Prevention, Public
           Protection and Civil Defence Team
Subject: Better to travel than arrive?

Dear ex-colleagues,
Imagine a life with the risks removed.

That's the one I've always led. OK, I could have gone even further: attached bicycle stabilisers to my ankles, worn a helmet and knee-pads to the pub, refused to leave the house without a chemical protection suit. But in every practical way, my life has been worthy of a British Standards Institute Kite Mark.

Not that I'd have dreamed of flying a kite. Think of the overhead power lines.

But my risk-assessed behaviour didn't actually keep me safe, did it? Wrong place, wrong time, and I was never the same again. Thank God.

There will be no more safety bulletins, my friends. I don't know what I want to do with my life right now, but I do know that twenty years of planning for disaster is enough for anyone. No disrespect: it's good to know you're there, doing it for me, but I don't want to be avoiding risk any more, I want to embrace it.

Yes, you never know when the Grim Reaper might come for you, but likewise you never know whether Cupid might get there first.

This is what I've learned about life. Statistics don't keep you safe. Earthquakes happen. Fires burn. Caring makes you vulnerable. People you love *can* leave you or die.

There's every reason to be afraid, but fear won't stop you hurting, though it can stop you living. Oh, and Prince Charming won't rescue you, because the person who loves you when you're scared will probably want you to stay that way.

So, for old time's sake, here are the most important statistics I will ever share:

Chances of dying: 100 per cent.

Chances of regretting things on your deathbed: 99 per cent.

Chances of living the life you want: one.

I'll miss you all, but it's time for me to make the most of my ninth life. Maybe you should get your skates on too . . .

Love,

Jo

Reformed Scaredy-cat

CHAPTER
FORTY

Ouranophobia — Fear of Heaven

Water laps sweetly against the black-painted wood of the gondola, and I hesitate before stepping in.

"Shouldn't there be a gangplank? It doesn't look very safe."

Luke laughs. I used to think that because Dennis never laughed at me, that made him my soul mate. But Luke's laugh is like my personal early warning system, alerting me to excessively wimpy behaviour. "And what would be the worst thing that would happen if you lost your footing?"

"I could fall in the canal."

"Would you drown?"

I remind myself that lagoons don't have dangerous eddies to drag me under. "No, because you or the gondolier would rescue me. But I might need my stomach pumped."

"Not if you kept your mouth shut." Then he smiles. "Unlikely, though."

"I might lose my handbag."

"We'd buy you another one, in the flea market. A souvenir."

I know I'm fighting a losing battle. "Our euros might get washed away . . ."

"Ever heard of cashpoints?"

And now that I can't think of any more dangers, I've no choice but to enjoy the ride.

It would be the fairytale ending, of course, if I'd been transformed from scaredy-cat to superhero when Luke kissed me. But in truth, it's a slower process. I'm ashamed to admit that even Luke's first properly romantic gesture brought out my killjoy tendencies. When he told me he was taking me to Venice for my birthday, I felt quite faint.

"Italy, in August? We'll melt. And it's number three in the international pick-pocketing league. Birmingham has as many canals, doesn't involve a flight and, as far as I know, is not in peril." I told him, before groaning. "Oh shit. That could have come straight out of Dennis's mouth."

"Well, it's too late anyhow. I already bought the tickets," he said, "and booked a place for you on the fear of flying course your dad told me about. Think of it as a dummy run for visiting the States with me — it's not like we can *walk* to San Francisco."

My next worry was that Venice could never live up to expectations, which distracted me on the plane (along with the visualisation I'd learned on the flying course).

But it'd take a hard, hard heart not to be melted by the city of Cornettos and *vaporetti*. The moment we stepped off the boat, I fell in love . . .

484

In love with overpriced pizzas; with bank account busting Bellinis at Harry's Bar (we did without dinner last night so we could afford them); with our hotel and its sliding floors and sliding doors that open right on to the canal three feet below (Luke's understandable fear of hotel fires is lessened by the ever-present water); and with the smell of drains and garlic (I wondered whether they might trigger a new set of flashbacks, but I haven't had a single one since leaving Dennis).

I'm in love with the Italian sun that's blasted through my factor twenty-five and turned my nose and shoulders bright pink. In love with the Italian men who whistle despite my sunburn. In love with the strappy, floaty dress Luke bought for me: the first red dress I've ever owned. It matches my hair — well, all but the white streak that I've allowed to grow, a precious reminder of the best thing that ever happened to me. I'm in love with the other couples, of every age and nationality, who float round the swarming city in their own bubble, insulated against the world.

And of course, I'm in love with Luke. It's not always straightforward, navigating his hang-ups and my own, but bloody hell, it's worth it. We spend twenty-four hours a day together, but that doesn't feel enough, even when we're arguing over rock versus pop, or American Budweiser versus European Stella Artois. And if he has the patience of a saint to put up with my daftness, then I like to think I'm good for him too. I arranged for two stars in Ursa Major to be named after his mum and dad, and even though we both know it's a bit barmy, he says he thinks of them every time we look up at the night sky.

I don't believe in soul mates any more (although, if I did, Luke would come pretty close). The whole idea suggests that the gods have matched us all up before we're born, that we never evolve or learn, and it's just not true. If Luke and I had met five years ago, we might never have known how happy we could be together.

That thought makes me feel quite sick . . .

And if that's not evidence enough of the strange nature of true love, there's Dennis and Lorraine, the world's unlikeliest couple. Or maybe not, now I think about it. All that time, she wanted a baby, and I think he secretly wanted someone who'd stand up to him. She took his side instead of mine, sent herself to Coventry to comfort him, and fell in love with Maple Drive. A baby hasn't materialised yet, as far as I know, but the last I heard she was enjoying her new life with the Director of Public Protection.

I bet the two of them are quite a hit in Warwickshire wife-swapping circles.

I'm happy for them, and though I've lost a best friend, I've also lost any residual guilt at walking away from Dennis. You can't stay with people because of what used to be. Look at my parents.

But even their relationship makes sense to me now that I've realised Dad isn't a dastardly villain and Mum isn't a helpless waif. They're bound by their history. Oh, and by Timmy and me: Mum told me when she came to see my new home at the villa that they bicker all the time about which of us makes them proudest. It made me well up. I never realised.

Life in the villa is certainly less comfortable than in Salzburg Avenue. Luke and I sleep in the same room as Frisky and Lucky the goldfish, while we finish the building work. Our relationship hasn't been forged over candlelit suppers and red roses, but over a plastering trowel and paintbrushes.

The villa is the most romantic place in the world . . . even Venice can't compete, though it comes a close second.

"You all right?"

The gondolier makes a sharp turn to avoid a water-taxi, and I wonder whether it's daft to feel seasick on a lagoon. "Fine."

Luke rummages in his back pocket for a tiny parcel. "Here."

"What's this?" I forget my giddiness as I unwrap the pink tissue paper. Nestling in the centre is a goldfish made of Murano glass.

"I took them a photograph of Lucky and they made it specially."

The fish's lips are curled in a smile, and no wonder: it has its own little eco-system. Slender glass tendrils of greenery rise from a sand-specked seabed. "It's gorgeous."

"Happy?" Luke asks. I think of that round the world funfair ride, on my very first danger date. Of wanting to see Venice, but never believing it could happen.

"Happy as Lucky the goldfish."

"I know which I'd rather cuddle up to," Luke says.

The gondolier slows as we approach a limestone bridge with barred windows. "Is Ponte dei Suspiri, the famous Bridge of Sighs," he says, pointing. "Is the final view criminals would see of Venice before going to their prison cells."

As Luke leans over to kiss me, I think of the snogging hoodies on Court Bridge on Valentine's night, the evening before my life changed for good. When his lips meet mine, I remember how they had to hold on to each other to keep their balance.

And at last I understand how they felt.